Conic Sections

straight line $ax + by = c$

parabola $\begin{cases} y = ax^2 + bx + c \\ x = ay^2 + by + c \end{cases}$

circle $\begin{cases} x^2 + y^2 = r^2 \\ (x - h)^2 + (y - k)^2 = r^2 \end{cases}$

ellipse $\dfrac{x^2}{a^2} + \dfrac{y^2}{b^2} = 1$

hyperbola $\begin{cases} \dfrac{x^2}{a^2} - \dfrac{y^2}{b^2} = 1 \\ \dfrac{y^2}{b^2} - \dfrac{x^2}{a^2} = 1 \end{cases}$

Variation

direct $y = kx$ for constant k

inverse $y = \dfrac{k}{x}$ for constant k

combined $y = \dfrac{kx}{z}$ for constant k

Logarithms

$\log_a N = L$ if and only if $N = a^L$

$\log_a(uv) = \log_a u + \log_a v$

$\log_a\left(\dfrac{u}{v}\right) = \log_a u - \log_a v$

$\log_a u^r = r \log_a u$

$\log_b N = \dfrac{\log_a N}{\log_a b}$

$\log_a u = \log_a v$ if and only if $u = v$

Binomial Expansion

$(a + b)^n = a^n + \left(\dbinom{n}{n-1}\right)a^{n-1}b^1 + \left(\dbinom{n}{n-2}\right)a^{n-2}b^2 + \cdots + \left(\dbinom{n}{n-r}\right)a^{n-r}b^r + \cdots + b^n$

$\dbinom{n}{r} = \dfrac{n!}{(n - r)!\, r!}$

Determinants

$\begin{vmatrix} a_1 & b_1 \\ a_2 & b_2 \end{vmatrix} = a_1 b_2 - a_2 b_1,$

$\begin{vmatrix} a_1 & b_1 & c_1 \\ a_2 & b_2 & c_2 \\ a_3 & b_3 & c_3 \end{vmatrix} = a_1 \begin{vmatrix} b_2 & c_2 \\ b_3 & c_3 \end{vmatrix} - a_2 \begin{vmatrix} b_1 & c_1 \\ b_3 & c_3 \end{vmatrix} + a_3 \begin{vmatrix} b_1 & c_1 \\ b_2 & c_2 \end{vmatrix}$

Arithmetic Progression

nth term $a_n = a_1 + (n - 1)d$

sum of n terms $\begin{cases} S_n = \dfrac{n}{2}(a_1 + a_n) \\ S_n = \dfrac{n}{2}[2a_1 + (n - 1)d] \end{cases}$

Geometric Progression

nth term $a_n = a_1 r^{n-1}$

sum of n terms $S_n = a_1 \dfrac{1 - r^n}{1 - r}, \quad r \neq 1$

Infinite Geometric Progression

sum $S_\infty = \begin{cases} \dfrac{a_1}{1 - r} & \text{if } |r| < 1 \\ \text{does not exist} & \text{if } |r| \geq 1 \end{cases}$

M000218433

Intermediate Algebra

Intermediate

LINDA GILBERT
JIMMIE GILBERT

Louisiana Tech University

Algebra

Prentice-Hall, Inc., Englewood Cliffs, New Jersey 07632

Library of Congress Cataloging in Publication Data

GILBERT, LINDA.
   Intermediate algebra.

   Includes index.
   1. Algebra.   I. Gilbert, Jimmie D.,
(date)   . II. Title.
QA154.2.G523 1983   512.9   82-12356
ISBN   0-13-469536-4

INTERMEDIATE ALGEBRA
Linda Gilbert
Jimmie Gilbert

Editorial/production supervision: Kathleen M. Lafferty and Paula Martinac
Manufacturing buyer: John B. Hall

Printed in the United States of America

10   9   8   7   6   5   4

ISBN 0-13-469536-4

Prentice-Hall International, Inc., London
Prentice-Hall of Australia Pty. Limited, Sydney
Editora Prentice-Hall do Brasil, Ltda., Rio de Janeiro
Prentice-Hall Canada Inc., Toronto
Prentice-Hall of India Private Limited, New Delhi
Prentice-Hall of Japan, Inc., Tokyo
Prentice-Hall of Southeast Asia Pte. Ltd., Singapore
Whitehall Books Limited, Wellington, New Zealand

To our children
Donna, Lisa, Martin, Dan, Beckie, and Matt

Contents

Applications

Linear Equations and Inequalities in Two Variables

Systems of Linear Equations and Inequalities

Polynomials

Factoring

Rational Expressions

Exponents, Radicals, and Complex Numbers

Quadratic Equations and Inequalities in One Variable

Quadratic Equations and Inequalities in Two Variables

Relations, Functions, and Their Graphs

Exponential and Logarithmic Functions

Sequences, Series, and the Binomial Expansion

Appendix: Cramer's Rule

Preface

Intermediate Algebra is designed for an introductory college course in algebra that will prepare the student for further study in mathematics. We have tried to present the material in a concise and natural manner, with abundant examples and exercises.

The first chapter provides a review of the real number system, with an optional section on sets. Classes with a stronger background may wish to omit the entire chapter.

It has been our experience that students find the topics of linear equations and inequalities to be fairly interesting and easy. For this reason, we have introduced these topics early, in Chapters 2 through 5. This is intended to get the course off to a good start.

Polynomials, factoring, and rational expressions follow in Chapters 6 through 8. The more difficult topics of radicals, complex numbers, quadratic equations and inequalities, and functions have been placed in Chapters 9 through 12. The last two chapters are devoted to the more advanced topics of exponential and logarithmic functions, sequences and series, and the binomial expansion. In a short course, the last two chapters and the optional sections in Chapters 4, 5, and 12 could be omitted.

We have included what we regard as a reasonable number of word problems and applications, with one early chapter devoted entirely to applications. Examples and practice problems with detailed solutions, totaling over 400, are included in each section. A practice test with answers is provided for each chapter.

There are over 4000 exercises in the text, with odd–even pairing, and arranged in order of increasing difficulty. Instructions for the exercises are keyed to the examples and practice problems. Answers, including graphs, are provided for all the odd-numbered problems. The most challenging problems are starred, and about 150 calculator problems are included and marked with *C*.

An instructor's manual with answers and graphs for the even-numbered problems is provided, and a student's study guide is available.

ACKNOWLEDGMENTS

For their helpful suggestions made in reviews, we wish to thank Terry Czerwinski, University of Illinois at Chicago Circle; Suzie Hessong, San Antonio College; Ed Huffman, Southwest Missouri State University; Eric Lubot, Bergen Community College; Jimmie McKim, University of Central Arkansas; Phyllis Meckstroth, San Diego State University; and Paul Pontius, Pan American University.

Our sincere thanks go also to Margaret Dunn for her expert typing of the entire manuscript; to Kathleen Lafferty for her guidance and cooperation in the production of the text; to Paula Martinac for her help in the final phases of production; and to Bob Sickles and Dennis Hogan for their editorial advice throughout the project.

We would also like to express our appreciation to the administration of Louisiana Tech University for its help and encouragement. We are indebted to our colleagues for their interest and encouragement, and we would like to give special thanks to Leamon Griffith for his assistance in checking the accuracy of the answers.

Linda Gilbert
Jimmie Gilbert

A Review of the Real Number System

1-1
Sets (Optional)

In our work in algebra, we deal with various types of sets of real numbers. For this reason, it is desirable to have available some of the language and notation that is commonly used in working with sets.

The word **set** is used to refer to a well-defined collection of objects. By "well-defined" we mean that it can be determined whether or not a particular object is in the set. The individual objects in the set are called **members** of the set, or **elements** of the set.

A set may be indicated either by listing its elements or by stating a qualification for membership. The set D of digits in the decimal system could be given by

$$D = \{0, 1, 2, 3, 4, 5, 6, 7, 8, 9\}$$

or by

$$D = \{x \mid x \text{ is a decimal digit}\}.$$

The vertical slash "$\mid$" is read as "such that," and the last notation for D is read as "D is the set of all x such that x is a decimal digit." The set

1

N of all counting numbers could be indicated by

$$N = \{1, 2, 3, 4, \ldots\}$$

or by

$$N = \{x \mid x \text{ is a counting number}\}.$$

The set D of decimal digits is an example of a finite set. A set S is called **finite** if it is possible to count the elements of S and come to a last element. A set that is not finite is called **infinite**. The set N of counting numbers is an infinite set.

In most of this book, our work is with sets of real numbers. In addition to the counting numbers, some other sets of real numbers are important enough to be designated with special names. The sets that are most important in our work are listed below. Some of them have more than one special name.

1. The set
$$N = \{1, 2, 3, \ldots\}$$
is called the set of **counting numbers,** or the set of **natural numbers,** or the set of **positive integers.**

2. The set
$$W = \{0, 1, 2, 3, \ldots\}$$
is the set of **whole numbers.**

3. The set
$$I = \{\ldots, -3, -2, -1, 0, 1, 2, 3, \ldots\}$$
is the set of **integers.**

4. The set
$$Q = \left\{ \frac{a}{b} \,\middle|\, a \text{ and } b \text{ are integers and } b \neq 0 \right\}$$
is the set of **rational numbers.** Every rational number has a decimal representation that either terminates (such as $\frac{3}{8} = 0.375$) or repeats (such as $\frac{14}{11} = 1.272727\ldots$).

5. The set I_r of **irrational numbers** is the set of all real numbers that are not rational numbers. Every irrational number has a decimal representation that does not repeat and does not terminate. The real numbers $\sqrt{3}$ and $\sqrt{5}$ are examples of irrational numbers. To five decimal places, $\sqrt{3}$ is given by
$$\sqrt{3} \approx 1.73205.$$

The symbol "$\approx$" is used for "approximately equals." The value 1.73205 is not exactly correct for $\sqrt{3}$, but it is closer to $\sqrt{3}$ than 1.73204 or 1.73206.

6. The set $\mathcal{R}$ of **real numbers** is formed by taking all of the rational numbers together with all of the irrational numbers. Any decimal number is a representation for a real number, and every real number has a decimal representation. Throughout this book, the symbol $\mathcal{R}$ is reserved to denote the set of all real numbers.

There are several shorthand notations that are useful in working with sets. The notation

$$x \in S$$

is read as "x is an element of S," or "x belongs to S," or "x is in S." Similarly,

$$x \notin S$$

is read as "x is not an element of S." The slash is used to indicate "not."

If A and B are sets such that every element of A is an element of B, then we say that A is a **subset** of B, and we write

$$A \subseteq B.$$

To indicate that A is not a subset of B, we write

$$A \nsubseteq B.$$

EXAMPLE 1   Let $D = \{0, 1, 2, 3, 4, 5, 6, 7, 8, 9\}$, $A = \{1, 3, 5, 7\}$, and $B = \{3, 7, 10\}$. Then each of the following statements is true.

(a) $5 \in D$, $5 \in A$, $5 \notin B$
(b) $A \subseteq D$, $B \nsubseteq D$, $D \nsubseteq A$
(c) $A \notin D$, $5 \nsubseteq A$, $\{5\} \subseteq A$

This example points out that "$\in$" is a symbol for individual membership in a set, whereas "$\subseteq$" is reserved for subset inclusion.

Two sets are declared to be **equal** if they contain precisely the same elements. In other words, $A = B$ if both $A \subseteq B$ and $B \subseteq A$ are true. If A and B are not equal sets, we write $A \neq B$.

There are two basic operations on sets. For sets A and B, the **union** of A and B is the set $A \cup B$ which consists of all those elements that are either an element of A, or an element of B, or an element of both A and B. In symbols,

$$A \cup B = \{x \mid x \in A \text{ or } x \in B\}.$$

The **intersection** of A and B is the set $A \cap B$ which consists of those elements that are in both A and B:

$$A \cap B = \{x \mid x \in A \text{ and } x \in B\}.$$

The operations of union and intersection can be performed in succession, and different orders of application are possible. It is necessary to use symbols of grouping (parentheses, brackets, braces) to indicate the order in which operations are to be performed in accordance with the following convention.

Any operation within a symbol of grouping is performed first, starting with the innermost symbol and working progressively to the outermost symbol.

This convention is illustrated in part (c) of Example 2.

EXAMPLE 2 Let the sets A, B, and C be given by

$$A = \{0, 2, 4, 5, 6, 8\},$$
$$B = \{1, 3, 5, 6, 7\},$$
$$C = \{6, 8, 10\}.$$

Find

(a) $A \cap B$
(b) $(A \cap B) \cup C$
(c) $B \cap [(A \cap B) \cup (A \cap C)]$

SOLUTION

(a) $A \cap B = \{5, 6\}$
(b) $(A \cap B) \cup C = \{5, 6\} \cup \{6, 8, 10\} = \{5, 6, 8, 10\}$
(c) $B \cap [(A \cap B) \cup (A \cap C)] = \{1, 3, 5, 6, 7\} \cap [\{5, 6\} \cup \{6, 8\}]$
$$= \{1, 3, 5, 6, 7\} \cap \{5, 6, 8\}$$
$$= \{5, 6\}$$

It may happen that two sets A and B have no elements in common. In that event, there are no elements at all in the intersection $A \cap B$. With this possibility in mind, it is natural to introduce the empty set. The **empty set** is denoted* by $\varnothing$, or by $\{ \ \}$. That is, $\varnothing$ is the set that has no elements, and $\varnothing$ is regarded as a subset of every set. Two sets are called **disjoint** if their intersection is $\varnothing$.

*The set $\{\varnothing\}$ is *not* the empty set. It is the set that has $\varnothing$ as its only element.

PRACTICE PROBLEM 1 (Solution on page 6) Determine

    (a) $W \cap I_r$,

    (b) $W \cup Q$

where W is the set of whole numbers, I_r is the set of irrational numbers, and Q is the set of rational numbers.

In expressions such as

$$D = \{x \mid x \text{ is a decimal digit}\},$$

the letter x is called a variable. More precisely, a **variable** is a letter or other symbol that represents an arbitrary or unspecified member of a given set with *more than one* element. The given set is called the **replacement set**, or the **domain**, of the variable. *Unless otherwise stated, the domain of a variable in this book is the set $\Re$ of all real numbers.* A letter representing a certain fixed number (a single number) is called a **constant**. The fundamental difference between arithmetic and algebra is that arithmetic deals with numbers only, whereas algebra deals with variables and constants.

EXAMPLE 3 If a circle has radius r meters, the circumference C in meters is given by the formula

$$C = 2\pi r.$$

The letters C and r are variables, each with domain the set of positive real numbers, while 2 and π are constants. (Recall that π is an irrational number that has the value $\pi \approx 3.14159$ to five decimal places.)

EXERCISES 1-1

Let $A = \{1, 2, 3, 4\}$, $B = \{4, 5, 6, 7, 8\}$, and $C = \{2, 4, 6, 8\}$. Label each of the following statements as true or false. (See Examples 1 and 2.)

1. $4 \in A$ 2. $\{4\} \subseteq B$

3. $\{4\} \in A$ 4. $4 \subseteq B$

5. $A \subseteq C$ 6. $B \nsubseteq C$

7. $(A \cap B) \subseteq C$ 8. $C \subseteq (A \cup B)$

9. $\varnothing \subseteq A$ 10. $\varnothing \in B$

Let W be the set of whole numbers, I the set of integers, Q the set of rational numbers, $\Re$ the set of real numbers, and I_r the set of irrational numbers. List all of the sets to which the given number belongs.

11. 0   12. 1

13. -2 14. $\frac{3}{4}$

15. 2.7   16. 0.25

17. 0.333 . . .   18. $-\frac{5}{7}$

19. $\sqrt{2}$ 20. $-\sqrt{7}$

Let A, B, and C be as given for problems 1–10. Find each of the following. (See Example 2.)

21. $A \cup B$ 22. $A \cup C$

23. $B \cap C$ 24. $A \cap B$

25. $(A \cup B) \cap C$ 26. $(A \cap B) \cup C$

27. $A \cup (B \cap C)$ 28. $A \cap (B \cup C)$

29. $(A \cup B) \cap (A \cup C)$ 30. $(A \cap B) \cup (A \cap C)$

31. $A \cup [(A \cup B) \cap (A \cup C)]$ 32. $A \cap [(A \cap B) \cup (A \cap C)]$

33. $A \cap [(A \cup B) \cap (A \cap C)]$ 34. $A \cup [(A \cap B) \cup (A \cup C)]$

Let $E = \{\ldots, -4, -2, 0, 2, 4, \ldots\}$ denote the set of **even integers** (the set of all multiples of 2), let $O = \{\ldots, -3, -1, 1, 3, \ldots\}$ denote the set of all **odd integers** (all integers not a multiple of 2), and let I denote the set of integers. Determine each of the following. (See Example 2 and Practice Problem 1.)

35. $E \cup O$ 36. $E \cap O$

37. $E \cup I$ 38. $O \cup I$

39. $O \cap I$ 40. $E \cap I$

41. List all of the subsets of $\{0, 1\}$.

42. List all of the subsets of $\{a, b, c\}$.

In problems 43 and 44, identify the variables in the given formula. (See Example 3.)

43. If a rectangle has length r meters and width s meters, the perimeter P in meters is given by the formula $P = 2r + 2s$.

44. If a circle has radius r meters, the area A in square meters is given by the formula $A = \pi r^2$.

SOLUTION FOR PRACTICE PROBLEM

1. (a) Since every element m of W is a rational number $m = m/1$, W has no elements in common with I_r and

$$W \cap I_r = \varnothing.$$

   (b) As in part (a), $W \subseteq Q$, so that

$$W \cup Q = Q.$$

In this section we review some of the relations on real numbers. The simplest relation on real numbers is that of **equality**. The familiar equality symbol "$=$" for real numbers is used to make a statement that two expressions designate the same real number. The relation of equality has the following basic properties, where a, b, and c represent arbitrary real numbers.

> 1. **Reflexive Property:** $a = a$.
> 2. **Symmetric Property:** If $a = b$, then $b = a$.
> 3. **Transitive Property:** If $a = b$ and $b = c$, then $a = c$.
> 4. **Substitution Property:** If $a = b$, then the value of any computation involving a is unchanged when a is replaced by b.

EXAMPLE 1   Each of the following statements illustrates the indicated property of equality.

(a) $2 = 2$. (*Reflexive Property*)
(b) If $3 = x$, then $x = 3$. (*Symmetric Property*)
(c) If $x = y$ and $y = 4$, then $x = 4$. (*Transitive Property*)
(d) If $x = y$, then $2x + 3 = 2y + 3$. (*Substitution Property*)

The other relations on real numbers that we shall consider in this section are the relations "less than" and "greater than." In working with these relations, it is helpful to have available the usual association between real numbers and points on a straight line. In this association, we start by selecting a point on a horizontal line and designating it as the **origin**. This point is labeled with the number 0. A point at a convenient distance to the right is labeled with 1. With the distance from 0 to 1 as a unit of measure, the points successively 1 unit farther to the right are labeled 2, 3, 4, and so on. Moving to the left from the origin with the same unit of measure, points successively 1 unit of measure farther to the left are labeled $-1, -2, -3, \ldots$ (see Figure 1.1).

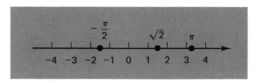

FIGURE 1.1

Rational numbers are located on the line by using distances corresponding to their representations as quotients a/b, and directions corresponding to their sign (positive to the right, negative to the left). Irrational numbers are located using their decimal approximations to any desired degree of accuracy. It is conventional to indicate the positive direction on the line by an arrowhead (see Figure 1.1).

The association described in the preceding paragraphs establishes a one-to-one correspondence between the real numbers and the points on the line. The point on the line that corresponds to a number is called the **graph** of the number, and the number that corresponds to a point on the line is called the **coordinate** of the point.

The one-to-one correspondence between real numbers and points on the number line provides a geometric setting for ordering the real numbers by using the relations of "less than" or "greater than" on the real numbers. The symbolic statement

$a < b$ is read as "a is less than b."

Geometrically, $a < b$ means that the point corresponding to a lies to the left of the point corresponding to b on the number line. This is shown in Figure 1.2. For conciseness, we simply say that a lies to the left of b on the number line.

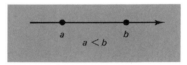

FIGURE 1.2

Similarly,

$a > b$ is read as "a is greater than b,"

and $a > b$ means that a lies to the right of b on the number line.

An algebraic formulation of each of these relations is given in Definition 1-1.

Definition 1-1   For real numbers a and b,

$a < b$ means that $b - a$ is positive, and
$a > b$ means that $a - b$ is positive.

In connection with this definition, the following remarks are worth noting.

> 1. $a > 0$ means that a is positive.
> 2. $a < 0$ means that a is negative.
> 3. $a > b$ means that $b < a$.

The last of these three remarks can be used to change any given inequality to an equivalent form with the **sense** (direction) of the inequality reversed.

EXAMPLE 2

(a) $3 > 0$ since 3 is a positive number.
(b) $-2 < 0$ since -2 is a negative number.
(c) If $3 > x$, then $x < 3$.

The inequality symbols "$<$" and "$>$" are frequently combined with possible equality in the following manners.

> $a \leq b$ means that a is less than or equal to b.
> $a \geq b$ means that a is greater than or equal to b.

Also, $a \nleq b$ means that a is not less than or equal to b, and similarly for $a \ngeq b$.

Two of the fundamental properties of order in the real numbers are stated below. These properties are intuitively clear from geometric considerations, and we assume their validity without proof.

> 1. **Transitive Property:** If $a < b$ and $b < c$, then $a < c$.
> 2. **Trichotomy Property:** Exactly one of the following is true:
> $$a < b, \qquad a = b, \qquad b < a.$$

As we indicated earlier, the *graph* of a real number a is the point on the number line which corresponds to that number. This term extends readily to a set of real numbers: The **graph** of a set of real numbers is the set of all points on the number line which correspond to numbers in the set.

EXAMPLE 3

The graph of the set $\{-2, 1, 4\}$ consists of three points, as indicated by the large dots in Figure 1.3.

FIGURE 1.3

EXAMPLE 4   The graph of the set of all real numbers x such that $x \leq 3$ is the set of all points at or to the left of 3 on the number line. This set is represented in Figure 1.4 by placing a large dot at 3 and drawing a bold arrow on the line extending to the left from 3.

FIGURE 1.4

The large dot at 3 in Figure 1.4 is used to indicate that the end point is included in the graph. If the end point is not to be included, this is indicated by an open circle at the end of the arrow instead of a large dot.

EXAMPLE 5   The graph of $x > 2$ is shown in Figure 1.5.

$x > 2$

FIGURE 1.5

More complicated graphs result when we consider compound statements made by combining inequalities with an "or" or an "and."

EXAMPLE 6   The graph of

$$x \leq 1 \qquad \text{or} \qquad x > 3$$

is shown in Figure 1.6.

FIGURE 1.6

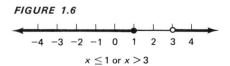

$x \leq 1$ or $x > 3$

EXAMPLE 7   The graph of

$$x > 0 \qquad \text{and} \qquad x < 2$$

is shown in Figure 1.7.

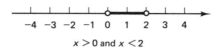

$$x > 0 \text{ and } x < 2$$

FIGURE 1.7

The compound statement

$$x > 0 \qquad \text{and} \qquad x < 2$$

in the last example could be rewritten so that the two inequalities would have the same sense. We could write

$$0 < x \qquad \text{and} \qquad x < 2$$

or

$$2 > x \qquad \text{and} \qquad x > 0.$$

These last statements can be written in the more compact forms

$$0 < x < 2$$

or

$$2 > x > 0.$$

Compact forms such as those preceding are useful, but some care must be used in employing them. They are subject to the following rules.

1. Compact forms such as $a < x < b$ are used only with compound statements involving "and."
2. The two inequality symbols used must have the same sense.

Graphs such as the one in Example 7 are called **intervals**. The graph of an inequality of the form $a \leq x \leq b$, where the end points are included, is called a **closed interval**. The graph of $a < x < b$, where neither end point is included, is called an **open interval**. An interval that includes one end point but not the other (such as $a \leq x < b$ or $a < x \leq b$) is neither open nor closed.

PRACTICE
PROBLEM 1 (Solution on page 14) Graph

$$-1 \leq x < 3.$$

EXAMPLE 8 Graph

$$-4 \leq x < 1 \quad \text{or} \quad x > 3.$$

SOLUTION The graph consists of the interval from -4 to 1, including -4, together with all points to the right of 3 (see Figure 1.8).

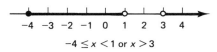

$$-4 \leq x < 1 \text{ or } x > 3$$

FIGURE 1.8

EXERCISES 1-2

Fill in the blank so as to make the given statement an application of the stated property. (See Example 1.)

1. $3 = $ ____.   (Reflexive Property)
2. $x = $ ____.   (Reflexive Property)
3. If $0 = x$, then $x = $ ____.   (Symmetric Property)
4. If $x = y$, then $y = $ ____.   (Symmetric Property)
5. If $4 = x$ and $x = y$, then ____ $= y$.   (Transitive Property)
6. If $a = x$ and $x = y$, then $a = $ ____.   (Transitive Property)
7. If $x = y$, then $2 \cdot x = 2 \cdot$ ____.   (Substitution Property)
8. If $x = y$, then $5 \cdot x + 3 = 5 \cdot$ ____ $+ 3$.   (Substitution Property)

Name the property that justifies the given statement.

9. If $y < x$ and $x < 3$, then $y < 3$.
10. If $3 < x$ and $x < y$, then $3 < y$.
11. Either $x < 3$, or $x = 3$, or $x > 3$.
12. Either $x < y$, or $x = y$, or $x > y$.

Fill in the blank with one of the symbols $<$ or $>$ so as to make a true statement. (See Example 2.)

13. -5 ____ 4 14. -3 ____ 2

12

15. 7 ____ 4

16. 8 ____ 3

17. −4 ____ −2

18. −6 ____ −2

19. 0 ____ −3

20. 0 ____ −6

Express each of the following relations by using the inequality symbols $<, >, \leq, \geq$. (See Example 2.)

21. 4 is less than 6

22. 2 is less than 5

23. −3 is greater than −5

24. −2 is greater than −4

25. 0 is greater than or equal to −1

26. 3 is greater than or equal to 0

27. 3 is between 1 and 4

28. −2 is between −3 and 0

29. x is between 3 and 1

30. x is between 1 and −2

Graph the given set of real numbers. (See Example 3.)

31. $\{-3, 0, 2\}$

32. $\{-1, 0, 3\}$

33. $\{-2, 4, 2\}$

34. $\{5, -3, 1\}$

If it is possible, write the following compound statements in compact form. (See Example 7.)

35. $x > 2$ and $5 > x$

36. $x > -1$ and $2 > x$

37. $x < 0$ and $-2 < x$

38. $x < 4$ and $1 < x$

39. $x > -1$ and $x < 2$

40. $x > 0$ and $x < 3$

41. $x < 0$ and $x > -3$

42. $x < 2$ and $x > -4$

43. $x > 1$ or $x < -2$

44. $x > 2$ or $x < -3$

45. $x < 0$ or $x > 4$

46. $x < -1$ or $x > 1$

In problems 47–62, draw the graph of the given statement. (See Examples 4–8 and Practice Problem 1.)

47. $x < 2$

48. $x < -1$

49. $x \geq -3$

50. $x \geq 0$

51. $x > 1$ or $x \leq -2$

52. $x > 2$ or $x \leq 1$

53. $x \geq 0$ or $x \leq -3$

54. $x \geq 2$ or $x \leq -1$

55. $x > -1$ and $x \leq 4$

56. $x > 2$ and $x < 5$

57. $x \geq -3$ and $x < 0$

58. $x \geq -1$ and $x < 1$

59. $-3 \leq x < 1$

60. $-2 < x \leq 4$

61. $-2 < x \leq -1$ or $x \geq 0$

62. $-3 \leq x < 2$ or $x > 4$

*63. $x < 1$ or $x \geq 0$

*64. $x \leq 2$ or $x > -2$

*65. $x \leq 0$ and $x > 2$

*66. $x < 1$ and $x \geq 3$

*67. Graph the inequality $-3 < x \leq 2$ for x an *integer*.

*68. Graph the inequality $-2 \leq x < 4$ for x an *integer*.

1. The graph of $-1 \leq x < 3$ consists of -1 and all points between -1 and 3. The end point 3 is not included. This is shown in Figure 1.9.

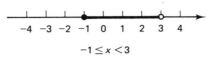

$$-1 \leq x < 3$$

FIGURE 1.9

1-3
Properties of the
Real Numbers

The operations of addition, subtraction, multiplication, and division are performed on real numbers in the study of arithmetic. All of the computations done there are based on a set of basic properties which is sometimes called the **field properties**. This set of properties is given in the following list.

Basic Properties for the Real Numbers

1. **Addition Properties.** The operation of addition of real numbers has the following properties.†

    (a) **Closure Property.** $a + b \in \mathfrak{R}$ for all $a \in \mathfrak{R}$ and $b \in \mathfrak{R}$.

    (b) **Associative Property.** $a + (b + c) = (a + b) + c$ for all $a, b, c \in \mathfrak{R}$.

    (c) **Additive Identity.** There is a unique real number 0 such that $a + 0 = 0 + a = a$ for all $a \in \mathfrak{R}$.

    (d) **Additive Inverses.** For each $a \in \mathfrak{R}$, there is a unique real number $-a$ such that $a + (-a) = (-a) + a = 0$.

    (e) **Commutative Property.** $a + b = b + a$ for all $a \in \mathfrak{R}$ and $b \in \mathfrak{R}$.

2. **Multiplication Properties.** The operation of multiplication of real numbers has the following properties.

    (a) **Closure Property.** $a \cdot b \in \mathfrak{R}$ for all $a \in \mathfrak{R}$ and $b \in \mathfrak{R}$.

    (b) **Associative Property.** $a \cdot (b \cdot c) = (a \cdot b) \cdot c$ for all $a, b, c \in \mathfrak{R}$.

    (c) **Multiplicative Identity.** There is a unique real number 1 such that $1 \neq 0$ and $a \cdot 1 = 1 \cdot a = a$ for all $a \in \mathfrak{R}$.

    (d) **Multiplicative Inverses.** For each *nonzero* $a \in \mathfrak{R}$, there is a unique real number $\frac{1}{a} \in \mathfrak{R}$ such that $a\left(\frac{1}{a}\right) = \left(\frac{1}{a}\right)a = 1$.

    (e) **Commutative Property.** $a \cdot b = b \cdot a$ for all $a \in \mathfrak{R}$ and $b \in \mathfrak{R}$.

3. **Distributive Property.** $a(b + c) = ab + ac$ and $(b + c)a = ba + ca$ for all $a, b, c \in \mathfrak{R}$.

---

†Recall that $\mathfrak{R}$ denotes the set of all real numbers.

The substitution property of equality implies the following properties of equality in connection with addition and multiplication. The variables a, b, and c represent real numbers.

Addition Property of Equality

If $a = b$, then $a + c = b + c$.

Multiplication Property of Equality

If $a = b$, then $ac = bc$.

EXAMPLE 1   The following statements illustrate the addition and multiplication properties of equality.

(a) If $x = 3$, then $x + 2 = 3 + 2$ or $x + 2 = 5$, by the addition property of equality.

(b) If $x = 4$, then $3x = 12$, by the multiplication property of equality.

The additive identity property 1(c) in the list "Basic Properties for the Real Numbers" states the fundamental property of 0 in the real numbers: $a + 0 = 0 + a = a$, for all real numbers a. The real number 0 also has the following special property with regard to multiplication.

Multiplication Property of Zero

$a \cdot 0 = 0$ for any real number a.

To many students, the inverse properties 1(d) and 2(d) are the most troublesome of all the basic properties. For one thing, they are sometimes designated by different names.

For $a \neq 0$, the number $1/a$ is called the **multiplicative inverse** of a, or the **reciprocal** of a.

EXAMPLE 2   (a) $\frac{1}{3}$ is the reciprocal of 3.

(b) 3 is the reciprocal of $\frac{1}{3}$.

(c) $\frac{3}{2}$ is the reciprocal of $\frac{2}{3}$.

(d) 1 is the reciprocal of 1.

(e) 0 does not have a reciprocal.

The number $-a$ which has the property that

$$a + (-a) = (-a) + a = 0$$

is called the **additive inverse** of a, or the **opposite** of a. For example,

$$\text{if } a = -5, \text{ then } -a = 5$$

since

$$(-5) + 5 = 5 + (-5) = 0.$$

This could also be stated in the form

$$-(-5) = 5.$$

The two symbols "$-$" in this equation have entirely different meanings. The first indicates an additive inverse, and the second indicates a negative number.

$$-(-5) = 5$$
additive inverse$\overset{\uparrow}{\rule{0pt}{0pt}}$ $\overset{\uparrow}{\rule{0pt}{0pt}}$negative number

This illustrates the following:

> **Double Negative Property**
> $-(-a) = a$ for any real number a.

On the number line, a real number and its additive inverse are located at the same distance from 0. This is depicted in Figure 1.10, where

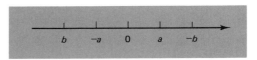

FIGURE 1.10

a is a positive number and b is a negative number: a and $-a$ are the same distance from 0, and b and $-b$ are the same distance from 0. Note that $-b$ is a positive number in this figure. This situation leads to the geometric definition of absolute value:

> $|a|$ is the distance between a and 0.

It follows from the geometric definition that $|a| = 0$ if and only if $a = 0$. If $a \neq 0$, $|a|$ is a positive number that is the distance from 0.

EXAMPLE 3   Each of the following statements evaluates an absolute value.

(a) $|0| = 0$.

(b) $|4| = 4$ since 4 is located 4 units from 0.

(c) $|-5| = 5$ since -5 is located 5 units from 0.

(d) $|-\sqrt{2}| = \sqrt{2}$ since $-\sqrt{2}$ is located $\sqrt{2}$ units from 0.

(e) If $a > 0$, then $|a| = a$.

(f) If $a < 0$, then $-a > 0$ and $|a| = -a$.

The last part of Example 3 leads to the algebraic definition of absolute value stated in Definition 1-2.

Definition 1-2 For any real number a,

$$|a| = \begin{cases} a & \text{if } a \geq 0 \\ -a & \text{if } a < 0. \end{cases}$$

EXAMPLE 4 From the algebraic definition of absolute value, we have

(a) $|9| = 9$

(b) $|-9| = -(-9) = 9$

The facts listed in the next theorem are not hard to visualize on the number line.

Theorem 1-3 Let d be a *positive* real number, and let x represent an arbitrary real number. Then

(a) $|x| < d$ if and only if $-d < x < d$

(b) $|x| > d$ if and only if $x > d$ or $x < -d$

(c) $-|x| \leq x \leq |x|$

Geometrically, part (a) of Theorem 1-3 states that the distance between x and 0 is less than d if and only if x is somewhere between $-d$ and d. This is pictured in Figure 1.11.

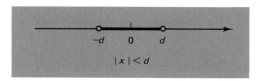

FIGURE 1.11

EXAMPLE 5 Graph

$$|x| < 3.$$

SOLUTION The graph of $|x| < 3$ is the set of all points between -3 and 3 on the number line, not including -3 and 3 (see Figure 1.12).

$|x| < 3$

FIGURE 1.12

***PRACTICE
PROBLEM 1***

(Solution on page 20) Graph

$$|x| \leq 2.$$

The statement in part (b) of Theorem 1-3 states that the distance between 0 and x is greater than d if and only if x is either to the right of d on the number line or the left of $-d$ on the number line. This is shown graphically in Figure 1.13.

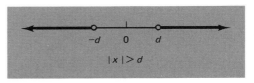

FIGURE 1.13

EXAMPLE 6 Graph

$$|x| > 1.$$

SOLUTION From the preceding discussion, $|x| > 1$ represents all numbers to the right of 1 or to the left of -1. The graph is drawn in Figure 1.14.

$|x| > 1$

FIGURE 1.14

***PRACTICE
PROBLEM 2***

(Solution on page 20) Graph

$$|x| \geq 4.$$

EXERCISES 1-3

Fill in the blank so as to make the given statement an application of the stated property. Variables represent real numbers. (See Example 1.)

1. $a + b =$ ____ (Commutative Property, Addition)

2. $a \cdot (b \cdot c) = $ _____   (Associative Property, Multiplication)

3. $(a + b) + c = $ _____   (Associative Property, Addition)

4. $b \cdot a = $ _____   (Commutative Property, Multiplication)

5. _____ $\cdot a = a$ (Multiplicative Identity)

6. _____ $\cdot a = 0$ (Multiplication Property of Zero)

7. _____ $+ a = 0$ (Additive Inverse)

8. $a(\underline{\quad}) = 1$ (Multiplicative Inverse)

9. If $a = x$, then $ab = $ _____.   (Multiplication Property of Equality)

10. If $a = x$, then _____ $= x + b$.   (Addition Property of Equality)

Name the property that justifies the given statement. Variables represent real numbers.

11. If $x = 2$, then $5x = 10$.

12. If $x = 3$, then $x + 4 = 7$.

13. $1 \cdot 5 = 5$

14. $5 + 0 = 5$

15. $a \cdot b$ is a real number

16. $a + b$ is a real number

17. $a(1/a) = 1$

18. $a + (-a) = 0$

19. $c(a + b) = ca + cb$

20. $(a + b)c = ac + bc$

21. $-(-2) = 2$

22. $3 + (4 + 5) = (3 + 4) + 5$

Fill in the blank so as to make a true statement. (See Examples 2 and 3.)

23. _____ is the reciprocal of $-\frac{3}{4}$.

24. $\frac{8}{5}$ is the reciprocal of _____.

25. 5 is the opposite of _____.

26. _____ is the opposite of -3.

27. _____ is the multiplicative identity.

28. _____ is the additive identity.

29. _____ is the distance between x and 0.

30. $|a| = -a$ if _____

31. $x(y + z) = xy + $ _____

32. $(y + z)x = $ _____ $+ zx$

Evaluate each of the following quantities. (See Examples 3 and 4.)

33. $|7|$

34. $|6|$

35. $|-4|$

36. $|-2|$

37. $|\sqrt{3}|$

38. $|\sqrt{5}|$

39. $|-\sqrt{5}|$

40. $|-\sqrt{3}|$

41. $|-0|$

42. $-|0|$

43. $-|3|$

44. $-|5|$

45. $-|-9|$

46. $-|-8|$

C47. $|\sqrt{817} - 29.13|$

C48. $|31.04 - \sqrt{923}|$

C49. $|\sqrt{72.8} - 8.52|$

C50. $|\sqrt{8.53} - 2.91|$

*51. $|x - 2|$, if $x > 2$

*52. $|x - 3|$, if $x > 3$

*53. $|x - 2|$, if $x < 2$

*54. $|x - 3|$, if $x < 3$

Identify the part of Theorem 1-3 that justifies each statement.

55. $|x| > 3$ if $x < -3$

56. $|x| > 2$ if $x > 2$

57. $|x| < 5$ if $-5 < x < 5$

58. $|x| < 4$ if $-4 < x < 4$

59. $-|3| \leq 3 \leq |3|$

60. $-|-4| \leq -4 \leq |-4|$

Draw the graph of the given statement. (See Examples 5 and 6 and Practice Problems 1 and 2.)

61. $|x| < 4$

62. $|x| < 1$

63. $|x| \leq 1$

64. $|x| \leq 5$

65. $|x| > 3$

66. $|x| > 4$

67. $|x| \geq 2$

68. $|x| \geq 3$

SOLUTIONS FOR PRACTICE PROBLEMS

1. The graph of $|x| \leq 2$ consists of the line segment joining -2 and 2, together with the end points (see Figure 1.15).

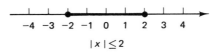

$|x| \leq 2$

FIGURE 1.15

2. The graph of $|x| \geq 4$ consists of all points either to the right of 4 or to the left of -4, together with 4 and -4 (see Figure 1.16).

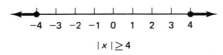

$|x| \geq 4$

FIGURE 1.16

1-4
Addition and
Subtraction

The chances of success in the study of algebra are severely diminished by inadequate skill in arithmetic. For this reason, we review the four fundamental operations (addition, subtraction, multiplication, and division) on real numbers in this and the following section. Even if one has mastered arithmetic, it is usually worthwhile to review the formal statements of the definitions and properties of these operations near the beginning of the study of intermediate algebra. As a starting point in our review, **we assume that addition and subtraction of nonnegative numbers are thoroughly familiar.**

The most fundamental propety of addition of real numbers is the closure property for positive numbers under addition: *The sum of two positive numbers is a positive number*. This property can be stated briefly and symbolically as follows.

Additive Closure Property of Positive Numbers

If $a > 0$ and $b > 0$, then $a + b > 0$.

Since the absolute value of a real number is never negative, we have assumed in the first paragraph of this section that addition and subtraction of absolute values is familiar. Addition of any two real numbers can then be described in terms of their absolute values and their signs. A number is said to be of **positive sign** if it is a positive number, and of **negative sign** if it is a negative number. Two numbers are said to be of **like sign** if they are either both positive numbers or both negative numbers. Two numbers are of **opposite** (or **different**) **sign** if one is a positive number and the other is a negative number.

Rule for Addition

1. To add two numbers of **like sign**, add their absolute values and give the result their common sign.

2. To add two numbers of **opposite sign**, subtract the smaller absolute value from the larger, and give the result the sign of the number that has the larger absolute value.

EXAMPLE 1 The various possibilities in the Rule for Addition are illustrated in the following computations.

(a) $6 + 3 = |6| + |3|$
$\qquad = 9$

(b) $(-5) + (-2) = -(|5| + |2|)$
$\qquad\qquad = -7$

(c) $(-3) + 7 = (|7| - |-3|)$
$\qquad\qquad = 7 - 3$
$\qquad\qquad = 4$

(d) $(-8) + 5 = -(|-8| - |5|)$
$$= -(8 - 5)$$
$$= -3$$

It is possible to present the second part of the Rule for Addition in the following more formal and algebraic way.

Theorem 1-4 If a is a negative number and b is a positive number, then

$$a + b = \begin{cases} -(|a| - |b|) & \text{if } |a| \geq |b| \\ |b| - |a| & \text{if } |a| < |b|. \end{cases}$$

Parts (c) and (d) in Example 1 provide illustrations of the statement in Theorem 1-4.

The numbers involved in an addition are called **terms**, and the result is called the **sum** of the numbers.

EXAMPLE 2 In

$$-5 + 3 = -2,$$

the *terms* are -5 and 3, and -2 is the *sum* of the terms.

The operation of subtraction is defined in terms of addition.

Definition 1-5 For any real numbers a and b, the **difference** of a and b is the number $a - b$ defined by

$$a - b = a + (-b).$$

The operation that combines a and b to yield $a - b$ is called **subtraction** of b from a.

Subtraction of b from a can be described in words as follows.

To subtract b from a, add the opposite of b to a.

In other words, change the sign of b and add.

In connection with the Additive Inverse Property in Section 1-3, it was noted that the symbol "$-$" could have two different meanings: It could denote a negative number, or it could denote an additive inverse. We have now added a third possibility: It can also denote the operation of subtraction.

EXAMPLE 3   (a) $3 - 7 = 3 + (-7)$
$$= -4$$
(b) $-5 - (-8) = -5 + 8$
$$= 3$$

When symbols of grouping are used with the operations of addition and subtraction, we follow the same convention as in Section 1-1 with set unions and intersection.

> Any operation within a symbol of grouping is performed first, starting with the innermost symbol and working progressively to the outermost symbol.

EXAMPLE 4   Each of the following computations illustrates the removal of symbols of grouping.

(a) $6 - [3 - (-2 + 7)] = 6 - [3 - 5]$
$$= 6 - [-2]$$
$$= 8$$

(b) $[6 - 3] - [-2 + 7] = 3 - 5$
$$= -2$$

(c) $[(6 - 3) - (-2)] + 7 = [3 - (-2)] + 7$
$$= 5 + 7$$
$$= 12$$

(d) $-8 + \{5 - [4 - (-9 + 2)]\} = -8 + \{5 - [4 - (-7)]\}$
$$= -8 + \{5 - 11\}$$
$$= -8 + (-6)$$
$$= -14$$

PRACTICE PROBLEM 1   (Solution on page 26) Perform the indicated operations:
$$|-5| - \{-|-9| - [3 - (-5 + 4)]\}.$$

EXAMPLE 5   If $x = -3$, $y = 2$, and $z = -4$, find the value of

(a) $x - y + z$
(b) $x - (y + z)$
(c) $|x| - |y| + |z|$

SOLUTION   (a) $x - y + z = -3 - 2 + (-4)$
$$= -9$$

(b) $x - (y + z) = -3 - [2 + (-4)]$
$$= -3 - [-2]$$
$$= -3 + 2$$
$$= -1$$

(c) $|x| - |y| + |z| = 3 - 2 + 4$
$$= 7 - 2$$
$$= 5$$

PRACTICE (Solution on page 26) If $x = 4$, $y = -6$, and $z = -7$, find the value of
PROBLEM 2 $$-x - \{y - [z - (y - x)]\}.$$

There is an important property of additive inverses that should be mentioned in connection with our work with signed numbers in this section. This property is sometimes used to describe addition of negative numbers. It states that, for all real numbers a and b,

$$-(a + b) = (-a) + (-b).$$

To see why this is true, we recall from the basic properties that each real number has a unique (one and only one) additive inverse. In particular, $-(a + b)$ is that unique number which yields 0 when added to $a + b$. To show that $-(a + b) = (-a) + (-b)$, we need only show that the sum of $(-a) + (-b)$ and $a + b$ is 0.

$[(-a) + (-b)] + [a + b]$

$\qquad = [(-a) + a] + [(-b) + b]$ (Associative and Commutative Properties)

$\qquad = 0 + 0$ (Definition of Additive Inverses)

$\qquad = 0$

EXERCISES 1-4

Perform the following additions. (See Example 1.)

1. $6 + (-8)$ 2. $-9 + 4$

3. $-5 + (-12)$ 4. $0 + (-8)$

5. $-21 + 13$ 6. $-18 + (-8)$

7. $7 + (-11)$ 8. $-3 + 15$

9. $-6 + (-18)$ 10. $0 + (-19)$

11. $-37 + 23$ 12. $-29 + (-8)$

Perform the following subtractions. (See Example 3.)

13. $3 - 8$

14. $4 - 9$

15. $-3 - 9$

16. $-6 - 5$

17. $-5 - (-11)$

18. $-6 - (-10)$

19. $7 - (-5)$

20. $7 - (-6)$

21. $-14 - (-8)$

22. $-16 - (-7)$

C23. $-71.42 - (-185.3)$

C24. $-21.17 - (-920.6)$

Perform the indicated operations. (See Example 4 and Practice Problem 1.)

25. $7 - 11 - (-4)$

26. $8 - 13 - (-5)$

27. $-3 - 14 - (-17)$

28. $-6 - 17 - (-23)$

29. $-3 + 9 - (-4)$

30. $-7 + 11 - (-6)$

31. $5 - (-3) - (-12)$

32. $9 - (-7) - (-17)$

33. $-8 - 7 - 22$

34. $-9 - 3 - 18$

35. $-5 + (-9) - 13$

36. $-7 + (-6) - 21$

37. $11 - 7 - (-23)$

38. $16 - 12 - (-15)$

39. $7 - 4 + 8 - 5 - (-9)$

40. $9 - 7 + 6 - 11 - (-8)$

41. $(-11 + 9 - 6) + (9 - 5 - 8)$

42. $(-13 + 22 - 16) + (-17 + 11 - 3)$

43. $14 - [7 - (-8 + 6)]$

44. $9 - [3 - (8 - 12)]$

45. $-4 - \{5 - [-4 - (-7 + 1)]\}$

46. $-2 - \{9 - [-9 - (-3 + 10)]\}$

47. $-|-2| + |-5| - |9| + |-7| - |8|$

48. $-|-7| + |-9| - |3| + |-1| - |8|$

If $x = -4$, $y = -2$, and $z = -7$, find the value of each of the following.
(See Example 5 and Practice Problem 2.)

49. $x - y - z$

50. $x - (y - z)$

51. $(x - y) - z$

52. $x - (y + z)$

53. $|x| - (|y| - |z|)$

54. $|x| - |y| - |z|$

If $x = 4.738$, $y = -6.195$, and $z = -7.286$, find the value of each of the
following.

C55. $x + y + z$

C56. $x - y - z$

C57. $x - y + z$

C58. $x + y - z$

C59. $x - (y + z)$

C60. $x - (y - z)$

1. $|-5| - \{-|-9| - [3 - (-5 + 4)]\} = |-5| - \{-|-9| - [3 - (-1)]\}$
$= |-5| - \{-|-9| - [4]\}$
$= 5 - \{-9 - 4\}$
$= 5 - \{-13\}$
$= 18$

2. $-x - \{y - [z - (y - x)]\} = -4 - \{-6 - [-7 - (-6 - 4)]\}$
$= -4 - \{-6 - [-7 - (-10)]\}$
$= -4 - (-6 - 3)$
$= -4 - (-9)$
$= 5$

1-5
Multiplication
and Division

In this section we conclude our review of the four fundamental operations on real numbers. As our starting point here, we assume proficiency in multiplication and division of positive numbers.

The positive numbers are closed under multiplication: *The product of two positive numbers is a positive number*. This can be stated in symbols as follows.

Multiplicative Closure Property of Positive Numbers
If $a > 0$ and $b > 0$, then $ab > 0$.

It can be shown that there is only one way to extend the definition of multiplication from the set of positive numbers to the set of all real numbers and be consistent with the Basic Properties listed in Section 1-3. For example, the following steps show that the product of 2 and -5 must be -10.

$$2(-5) = (1 + 1)(-5) \qquad \text{(Since } 2 = 1 + 1\text{)}$$
$$= (1)(-5) + (1)(-5) \qquad \text{(Distributive Property)}$$
$$= (-5) + (-5) \qquad \text{(Multiplicative Identity)}$$
$$= -10 \qquad \text{(By addition)}$$

Without going into any general explanation, we state the following rule for multiplication.

Rule for Multiplication

1. The product of two numbers of **like sign** is **positive**, and is equal to the product of their absolute values.

2. The product of two numbers of **opposite sign** is **negative**, and is equal to the negative of the product of their absolute values.

In connection with this rule, we recall the

> **Multiplication Property of Zero**
>
> $a \cdot 0 = 0$ for any real number a.

EXAMPLE 1

(a) $(3)(5) = 15$
(b) $(-3)(-5) = (3)(5) = 15$
(c) $(-3)(5) = -[(3)(5)] = -15$
(d) $(3)(-5) = -[(3)(5)] = -15$
(e) $(3)(0) = 0$

The numbers involved in a multiplication are called **factors**, and the **product** is the result of the multiplication.

EXAMPLE 2 In

$$(-3)(5) = -15,$$

the *factors* are -3 and 5, and -15 is the *product* of the factors.

The relationship between additive inverses and multiplication comes up here, in much the same way as it did with addition. Part of this relationship is described by the following property. It states that, for any real numbers a and b,

$$a(-b) = -(ab).$$

In words, the product of a and the additive inverse of b is equal to the additive inverse of the product of a and b.

To see that this is true, we recall that $-(ab)$ is the unique real number such that $-(ab) + ab = 0$. To show that $a(-b) = -(ab)$, we need only show that the sum of $a(-b)$ and ab is 0.

$$a(-b) + ab = a[(-b) + b] \qquad \text{(Distributive Property)}$$
$$= a \cdot 0 \qquad \text{(Additive Inverse)}$$
$$= 0 \qquad \text{(Multiplication Property of Zero)}$$

This property is sometimes used to describe multiplication of numbers with opposite signs.

There are several other equations similar to $a(-b) = -(ab)$ that can be deduced by the same sort of reasoning as that used in the preceding paragraph. These are collected in the following list, where $-ab$ denotes $-(ab)$.

$$a(-b) = -ab$$
$$(-a)b = -ab$$
$$(-a)(-b) = ab$$
$$(-1)(a) = -a$$

The operation of division is defined in terms of multiplication, in a manner similar to the way in which subtraction is defined in terms of addition.

Definition 1-6 Let a and b be real numbers with $b \neq 0$. The **quotient** of a by b is the number $\frac{a}{b}$ defined by

$$\frac{a}{b} = a \cdot \left(\frac{1}{b}\right), \qquad \text{where } b \neq 0.$$

The operation that combines a and b to yield $\frac{a}{b}$ when $b \neq 0$ is called **division** of a by b.

Besides the fractional form $\frac{a}{b}$, the quotient of a by b is also denoted by $a \div b$, or by a/b:

$$a \div b = a/b = \frac{a}{b} = a\left(\frac{1}{b}\right), \qquad \text{where } b \neq 0.$$

For $b \neq 0$, the Multiplication Property of Zero gives the result

$$\frac{0}{b} = 0\left(\frac{1}{b}\right) = 0 \qquad \text{for } b \neq 0.$$

The complete role of zero in division is described by

$$\frac{0}{b} = 0 \qquad \text{if } b \neq 0;$$

$$\frac{a}{0} \text{ is undefined for } all \ a.$$

EXAMPLE 3 (a) $\dfrac{-8}{4} = (-8)\left(\dfrac{1}{4}\right) = -2$

(b) $\dfrac{\frac{3}{4}}{\frac{6}{5}} = \left(\dfrac{3}{4}\right)\left(\dfrac{1}{\frac{6}{5}}\right) = \left(\dfrac{3}{4}\right)\left(\dfrac{5}{6}\right) = \dfrac{5}{8}$

(c) $\dfrac{5}{0}$ is undefined.

Because division is defined in terms of multiplication, the relationship between division and additive inverses is determined by the relationship between multiplication and additive inverses. Stated in fractional form, this relationship is given by

$$-\dfrac{a}{-b} = -\dfrac{-a}{b} = \dfrac{-a}{-b} = \dfrac{a}{b}$$

and

$$\dfrac{a}{-b} = \dfrac{-a}{b} = -\dfrac{-a}{-b} = -\dfrac{a}{b},$$

where $-\dfrac{a}{b}$ denotes $-\left(\dfrac{a}{b}\right)$. As an example,

$$\dfrac{15}{-3} = (15)\left(\dfrac{1}{-3}\right) = (15)\left(-\dfrac{1}{3}\right) = -5.$$

It is considered bad taste to leave a fraction with a negative number or a "$-$" symbol in the denominator.‡ The other forms are called the **standard forms** for a fraction.

EXAMPLE 4 Write each of the following fractions in one of the standard forms.

(a) $\dfrac{3}{-5}$

(b) $\dfrac{-4}{-7}$

(c) $-\dfrac{2}{-3}$

(d) $-\dfrac{-8}{-9}$

‡In a/b, a is called the *dividend* or the *numerator*, and b is called the *divisor* or *denominator*.

(a) Either $\dfrac{-3}{5}$ or $-\dfrac{3}{5}$ is acceptable.

(b) Either $\dfrac{4}{7}$ or $-\dfrac{-4}{7}$ fits the condition, but $\dfrac{4}{7}$ is preferred since it has fewer "$-$" symbols.

(c) Either $-\dfrac{-2}{3}$ or $\dfrac{2}{3}$, with $\dfrac{2}{3}$ preferred.

(d) Either $\dfrac{-8}{9}$ or $-\dfrac{8}{9}$.

Computations involving several of the four fundamental operations could lead to confusing expressions. For instance,

$$2 \cdot 3 + 7$$

could mean $(2)(10) = 20$ if addition is performed first, or it could mean $6 + 7 = 13$ if multiplication is performed first. Situations like this are clarified by the use of symbols of grouping and by rules that have been established to govern the order in which operations are to be performed. These rules are stated below.

Symbols of Grouping and Hierarchy of Operations

1. If symbols of grouping are present, any operation within a symbol of grouping is performed first, starting with the innermost symbol and working progressively to the outermost symbol.

2. With no symbols of grouping present, all multiplications and divisions are performed from left to right.

3. In the last step, all additions and subtractions are performed from left to right.

A special case of the second rule on the order of operations is worth noting. The dividing bar in a fraction has the effect of a grouping symbol, and this means that the numerator and denominator should be evaluated first, with the division held for last. Thus

$$10 - \frac{4 + 6}{2} = 10 - \frac{10}{2} = 10 - 5 = 5.$$

With regard to the question concerning $2 \cdot 3 + 7$, we see from Rule 2 that the correct computation is

$$2 \cdot 3 + 7 = 6 + 7 = 13.$$

As a slightly more general example, $2x + 7$ indicates the number obtained by first multiplying x by 2, and then adding 7 to the product. Later, we shall work with many expressions of the same form as $2x + 7$.

EXAMPLE 5   Perform the following operations, if possible.

(a) $6 \div 2 + 4$

(b) $6 \div (2 + 4)$

(c) $54 + (18 \div 9) - (3 \cdot 3)$

(d) $(54 + 18) \div (9 - 3 \cdot 3)$

(e) $\{[(54 + 18) \div 9] - 3\} \cdot 3$

(f) $\dfrac{\left(\dfrac{2}{5} \cdot 15\right) + 4}{6 - 17 + \left(8 \div \dfrac{4}{3}\right)}$

SOLUTION

(a) $6 \div 2 + 4 = 3 + 4 = 7$

(b) $6 \div (2 + 4) = 6 \div 6 = 1$

(c) $54 + (18 \div 9) - (3 \cdot 3) = 54 + 2 - 9 = 47$

(d) $(54 + 18) \div (9 - 3 \cdot 3) = 72 \div (9 - 9)$
$$= 72 \div 0, \quad \text{which is undefined}$$

(e) $\{[(54 + 18) \div 9] - 3\} \cdot 3 = \{[72 \div 9] - 3\} \cdot 3$
$$= (8 - 3) \cdot 3$$
$$= 5 \cdot 3$$
$$= 15$$

(f) $\dfrac{\left(\dfrac{2}{5} \cdot 15\right) + 4}{6 - 17 + \left(8 \div \dfrac{4}{3}\right)} = \dfrac{6 + 4}{6 - 17 + 6} = \dfrac{10}{-5} = -2$

PRACTICE PROBLEM 1   (Solution on page 35) Perform the following operations, if possible.
$$\{[(44 + 12) \div 4] - 2\} \div 3$$

We conclude our review of the real number system with a summary of the basic formulas for working with fractions, or quotients. These are all familiar properties of the rational numbers, and they hold for real numbers as well as rational numbers. In more advanced courses, Definition 1-6 and the Basic Properties of the Real Numbers are used to establish these formulas by formal proofs.

Basic Formulas for Fractions

Let a, b, c, and d be real numbers with $b \neq 0$ and $d \neq 0$.

1. $\dfrac{a}{b} = \dfrac{c}{d}$ if and only if $ad = bc$.

2. $\dfrac{ad}{bd} = \dfrac{a}{b}$

3. $\dfrac{a}{b} + \dfrac{c}{b} = \dfrac{a + c}{b}$

4. $\dfrac{a}{b} + \dfrac{c}{d} = \dfrac{ad + bc}{bd}$

5. $\dfrac{a}{b} \cdot \dfrac{c}{d} = \dfrac{ac}{bd}$

6. If b, c, and d are all nonzero,

$$\dfrac{\dfrac{a}{b}}{\dfrac{c}{d}} = \dfrac{a}{b} \div \dfrac{c}{d} = \dfrac{a}{b} \cdot \dfrac{d}{c} = \dfrac{ad}{bc}$$

The second formula in this list is the one that is used to reduce a quotient of integers to lowest terms when working with rational numbers. We recall that a quotient of two integers is in **lowest terms** if the only common factors in the numerator and denominator are 1 and -1, and a fraction is reduced to lowest terms by dividing out all common factors different from 1 and -1.

EXAMPLE 6 Perform the indicated operations, and leave the result in lowest terms.

(a) $\dfrac{3}{8} + \dfrac{1}{8}$

(b) $\dfrac{1}{2} - \dfrac{1}{3}$

(c) $\dfrac{3}{10} \cdot \dfrac{25}{-6}$

(d) $\dfrac{\dfrac{9}{8}}{-\dfrac{3}{4}}$

SOLUTION (a) $\dfrac{3}{8} + \dfrac{1}{8} = \dfrac{3 + 1}{8} = \dfrac{4}{8} = \dfrac{1}{2}$

(b) $\dfrac{1}{2} - \dfrac{1}{3} = \dfrac{1}{2} + \dfrac{-1}{3}$

$\qquad = \dfrac{(1)(3) + (2)(-1)}{(2)(3)}$

$\qquad = \dfrac{1}{6}$

(c) $\dfrac{3}{10} \cdot \dfrac{25}{-6} = \dfrac{(3)(25)}{(10)(-6)}$

$\qquad = \dfrac{\overset{1}{\cancel{(3)}}(5)\overset{1}{\cancel{(5)}}}{(2)\cancel{(5)}(-2)\underset{1}{\cancel{(3)}}}$

$\qquad = \dfrac{5}{-4}$

$\qquad = -\dfrac{5}{4}$

(d) $\dfrac{\dfrac{9}{8}}{-\dfrac{3}{4}} = \dfrac{9}{8} \cdot \dfrac{4}{-3}$

$\qquad = \dfrac{\overset{3}{\cancel{(9)}}\overset{1}{\cancel{(4)}}}{-(8)\cancel{(3)}}$

$\qquad = -\dfrac{3}{2}$

EXERCISES 1-5

Perform the following multiplications. (See Example 1.)

1. $(-6)(7)$ 　　　　　　　　 2. $(-5)(9)$

3. $(4)(-13)$ 　　　　　　　　 4. $(7)(-12)$

5. $(-5)(-8)$ 　　　　　　　　 6. $(-6)(-9)$

7. $(-14)(0)$ 　　　　　　　　 8. $(-3)(0)$

C9. $(-43.2)(-16.7)$ 　　　　 C10. $(-6.51)(0.0373)$

Perform the following divisions, if possible. (See Example 3.)

11. $\dfrac{-24}{3}$ 　　　　　　　　 12. $\dfrac{-15}{5}$

13. $\dfrac{16}{-4}$ 　　　　　　　　 14. $\dfrac{18}{-3}$

15. $\dfrac{-52}{-4}$ 　　　　　　　　 16. $\dfrac{-42}{-3}$

17. $\dfrac{0}{-3}$ 18. $\dfrac{0}{-5}$

19. $\dfrac{-3}{0}$ 20. $\dfrac{-5}{0}$

Write each of the following fractions in a standard form with as few "$-$" symbols as possible. (See Example 4.)

21. $\dfrac{2}{-7}$ 22. $\dfrac{3}{-8}$

23. $-\dfrac{9}{-5}$ 24. $-\dfrac{8}{-7}$

25. $-\dfrac{-5}{6}$ 26. $-\dfrac{-4}{9}$

27. $\dfrac{-4}{-9}$ 28. $\dfrac{-5}{-7}$

29. $-\dfrac{-5}{-2}$ 30. $-\dfrac{-7}{-6}$

Perform the indicated operations, and leave the result in lowest terms. (See Example 6.)

31. $\dfrac{2}{17} + \dfrac{3}{17}$ 32. $\dfrac{4}{7} + \dfrac{2}{7}$

33. $\dfrac{4}{9} + \dfrac{2}{9}$ 34. $\dfrac{5}{8} + \dfrac{1}{8}$

35. $\dfrac{3}{4} - \dfrac{5}{6}$ 36. $\dfrac{5}{6} - \dfrac{7}{8}$

37. $\dfrac{1}{9} - \dfrac{7}{2}$ 38. $\dfrac{2}{3} - \dfrac{3}{4}$

39. $\dfrac{3}{14} \cdot \dfrac{7}{-6}$ 40. $\dfrac{5}{9} \cdot \dfrac{3}{-10}$

41. $\dfrac{-4}{7} \cdot \dfrac{-21}{20}$ 42. $\dfrac{2}{3} \cdot \dfrac{27}{40}$

43. $\dfrac{\frac{3}{4}}{\frac{5}{6}}$ 44. $\dfrac{\frac{5}{6}}{\frac{7}{8}}$

45. $\dfrac{\frac{2}{3}}{\frac{-3}{7}}$ 46. $\dfrac{\frac{-4}{9}}{\frac{-8}{11}}$

Perform the indicated operations, if possible. (See Example 5 and Practice Problem 1.)

47. $3 \cdot 4 + 5$ 48. $2 \cdot 6 + 4$

49. $15 \div 3 + 2$ 50. $14 \div 2 + 5$

51. $(15 \div 3) + 2$

52. $(14 \div 2) + 5$

53. $15 \div (3 + 2)$

54. $14 \div (2 + 5)$

55. $54 + (18 \div 6) - (3 \cdot 2)$

56. $24 + (8 \div 4) - (2 \cdot 2)$

57. $(54 + 18) \div (6 - 3 \cdot 2)$

58. $(24 + 8) \div (4 - 2 \cdot 2)$

59. $[(54 + 18) \div 6] - 3 \cdot 2$

60. $[(24 + 8) \div 4] - 2 \cdot 2$

61. $\{[(54 + 18) \div 6] - 3\} \cdot 2$

62. $\{[(24 + 8) \div 4] - 2\} \cdot 2$

63. $\dfrac{7(-3 - 5)}{-8}$

64. $\dfrac{8(-3 - 4)}{2(-3) - 1}$

65. $\dfrac{(7)(-8) - 3(-2) + (5)(3)}{9 - 2 - 7}$

66. $\dfrac{(6)(-3) - 7(-2) + (4)(1)}{11 - 4(3) + 1}$

67. $\dfrac{(-3)(-7) - 4(-5) - 2(8)}{(-4)(3) + 7}$

68. $\dfrac{(-8)(-3) - 6(-2) - 6(8)}{(-5)(-2) - 7(2)}$

69. $\left(\dfrac{8 - 3}{4 - 9}\right)\left(\dfrac{5 - 7}{6 - (-4)}\right)$

70. $\dfrac{4 - 3\left(\dfrac{11 - 18}{7 + (-6)}\right)}{3 + 2\left(\dfrac{-8 - 5}{-7 + 6}\right)}$

71. $\left[6 - 3\left(\dfrac{1 - \dfrac{5 - 3}{7 - 5}}{5 - 11}\right)\right] - 4$

72. $\dfrac{-5\left(\dfrac{3 - 8}{8 - (-17)}\right) - 4\left(\dfrac{2 - 7}{7 - (-3)}\right) + 3(-2)}{9 - 6\left(\dfrac{18 - 8}{-3 - 2}\right) + \dfrac{11 - 7}{4 - 6}}$

73. $\dfrac{2 \cdot 8 - \left[2\left(\dfrac{14 + 8}{-4 - 7}\right) - 3\left(\dfrac{27 - 3}{-3 - 3}\right)\right]}{4 \cdot 5 - \left[3\left(\dfrac{16 + 10}{-8 - 5}\right) + 2\left(\dfrac{25 - 3}{8 - (-3)}\right)\right]}$

74. $\dfrac{\left[6(-3) - 7\left(\dfrac{-2 + 4}{11 - 4(3)}\right)\right] + 2\left(\dfrac{7 - 8}{-3 - (-2)}\right)}{\left[9(-2) - 4\left(\dfrac{-6 + 2 - 4}{5 - 7 + (-2)}\right)\right] - 2\left(\dfrac{3 - 11 + 2}{5 - 3 - 5}\right)}$

In problems 75–78, round the answer to the nearest hundredth.

C75. $\dfrac{436.1 - 1130}{(6.281)(-5.772)}$

C76. $\dfrac{(-14.38)(-7.203)}{-14.38 - (-7.203)}$

C77. $\dfrac{(831.6)(4.047) - (-237.4)(-3.892)}{1.621 - (-31.05)}$

C78. $\dfrac{(3.476)(-180.3) - (7.104)(-6.431)}{729.3 - 7(108.9)}$

SOLUTION FOR PRACTICE PROBLEM

1. $\{[(44 + 12) \div 4] - 2\} \div 3 = \{[56 \div 4] - 2\} \div 3$
$= (14 - 2) \div 3$
$= 12 \div 3$
$= 4$

PRACTICE TEST for Chapter 1

1. Let $A = \{1, 2, 3\}$, $B = \{3, 4, 5, 6\}$, and $C = \{2, 4, 6, 8\}$. Find each of the following.
   (a) $A \cap (B \cup C)$
   (b) $(A \cap B) \cup C$
   (c) $A \cup (B \cap C)$
   (d) $(A \cup B) \cap C$
   (e) $(A \cup B) \cap (A \cup C)$

2. List all of the subsets of $\{1, 2, 3\}$.

3. If it is possible, write the following compound statements in compact form.
   (a) $x > 1$ and $x < 4$
   (b) $x < 2$ or $x > 3$

4. Draw the graph of
$$-2 \leq x < 1 \qquad \text{or} \qquad x > 3.$$

5. Evaluate each of the following quantities.
   (a) $|-3|$
   (b) $-|-5|$
   (c) $|0|$
   (d) $-|6|$
   (e) $|\sqrt{2} - 2|$

6. Draw the graph of $|x| > 2$.

7. Perform the indicated operations.
   (a) $-5 + (-2)$
   (b) $-8 + 6$
   (c) $-7 - 4$
   (d) $-9 - (-5)$
   (e) $-3 - \{8 - [-7 - (-2 + 6)]\}$

8. If $x = -4$, $y = 5$, and $z = -6$, find the value of each of the following expressions.
   (a) $x - y - z$
   (b) $x - (y - z)$
   (c) $(x - y) - z$
   (d) $x - (y + z)$
   (e) $|x| - (|y| - |z|)$

In problems 9 and 10, perform the indicated operations, if possible.

9. (a) $(-3)(-4)(-5)$
   (b) $\dfrac{-56}{-4}$
   (c) $\dfrac{0}{3}$
   (d) $\dfrac{3}{0}$
   (e) $\dfrac{-\dfrac{2}{3}}{-\dfrac{5}{6}}$

10. (a) $(12 \div 4) + 2$
    (b) $12 \div (4 + 2)$
    (c) $12 \div 4 + 2$
    (d) $\{[(27 + 9) \div 6] - 2\} \cdot 3$
    (e) $(27 + 9) \div (6 - 2 \cdot 3)$

Linear Equations and Inequalities in One Variable

2-1
Linear Equations

One of the most basic tools used in mathematics and science is an equation. An **equation** is a statement of the equality of two mathematical expressions For example,

$$3x + 4 = -x, \qquad a = -a, \qquad |2y - 1| = 3,$$

are equations. In the equation $3x + 4 = -x$, the letter "x" is called the **variable**. The "$3x$," "4," and "$-x$" are the **terms** of the equation. Any term that does not contain a variable is called a *constant term*, or simply a **constant**. Hence "4" is a constant. In the terms "$3x$" and "$-x$," the "x" is the *variable part* of each term, and the "3" and "$-$" (or "-1")* are the *constant parts* of the terms. The constant part of a term involving a variable is called the **coefficient** of the term. Thus "3" and "-1" are the coefficients in "$3x$" and "$-x$," respectively. Variable terms containing

*Recall: $-x = -1 \cdot x$.

exactly the same variable part are called **like terms** and can be added or subtracted by using the distributive property.

EXAMPLE 1
(a) The terms $5x$ and $3x$ are like terms and hence can be added or subtracted by using the distributive property.

$$5x + 3x = (5 + 3)x = 8x$$

$$5x - 3x = (5 - 3)x = 2x$$

(b) The terms $2x$ and $3y$ are not like terms since the variable part in $2x$ is x and the variable part in $3y$ is y. Hence the sum of $2x$ and $3y$ is $2x + 3y$ and cannot be simplified using the distributive property.

(c) The terms $-4a$ and 1 are not like terms since $-4a$ contains the variable a and 1 is a constant. Thus the sum $-4a + 1$ cannot be simplified using the distributive property.

PRACTICE PROBLEM 1
(Solution on page 44) Simplify, if possible, by using the distributive property.

(a) $3x - 2x$ (b) $-x + 3y$

(c) $9 - 2z$ (d) $-2(x + 7) + 3(-2x + 8) - (-x)$

In the equation

$$3x + 4 = -x$$

the expression "$3x + 4$" is called the *left side*, or *left member*, of the equation, while the term "$-x$" is called the *right side*, or *right member*, of the equation. This equation leads to either a true or false statement, depending on the value that the variable assumes. For example, whenever x is replaced by the number 2, the resulting statement is false since

$$3x + 4 = -x \quad \text{becomes} \quad 3(2) + 4 = -2,$$

and

$$6 + 4 = -2$$

is not a true statement. We write $6 + 4 \neq 2$. The symbol "$\neq$" is read "is not equal to." But when x assumes the value -1, this equation leads to a true statement since

$$3x + 4 = -x \quad \text{becomes} \quad 3(-1) + 4 = -(-1),$$

and

$$-3 + 4 = 1$$

is true. This discussion leads to the following definition.

Definition 2-1 The set of all values that the variable in an equation can assume is the **replacement set** for the equation. The set of all values from the replacement set that makes the equation a true statement is the **solution set** of the equation. Those elements in the solution set are called **solutions** for the equation.

Unless otherwise specified, the replacement set for all equations under consideration in this text is the set of real numbers.

EXAMPLE 2 Whenever y is replaced by 2, the equation

$$4y - 1 = 5 + y \qquad \text{becomes} \qquad 4(2) - 1 = 5 + 2$$
$$\text{or} \qquad 8 - 1 = 7,$$

which is a true statement. Thus 2 is in the solution set. After replacing y by several other real numbers, it appears that no other real number will "work." We shall soon see that this is indeed the case. Thus the solution set is $\{2\}$, and we say that "2 is the solution of the equation."

In this section we study a special type of equation called the **linear equation** in one variable. Since linear equations are also called **first-degree equations** (the reason for this will become clear in Chapter 4), we use the names interchangeably here.

Definition 2-2 A **linear (first-degree) equation** in one variable is any equation that can be put in the form

$$\boxed{ax + b = 0,}$$

where a and b are constants with $a \neq 0$.

Our chief concern is to determine the solution set of any linear equation. The next definition proves to be useful.

Definition 2-3 **Equivalent equations** are equations that have the same solution sets.

EXAMPLE 3 The following equations are equivalent since each has $\{3\}$ as its solution set:

$$2x = 6, \qquad 4 - 5x = -11, \qquad x = 3.$$

EXAMPLE 4 The following equations are not equivalent since their solution sets are different.

EQUATION	$x = -2$	$|x| = 2$
SOLUTION SET	$\{-2\}$	$\{-2, 2\}$

Up to this point, the trial-and-error method is the only method we have available for determining solutions to equations. That is:

1. Choose a number from the replacement set.
2. Replace the variable by that number in the equation.
3. Determine whether the resulting statement is true or false.

A more sophisticated and more direct technique for solving equations is desirable. The following theorem supplies the necessary tools for solving linear equations.

Theorem 2-4 Let R, S, and T be algebraic expressions.† Then the equation

$$R = S$$

is equivalent to

(a) $R + T = S + T$,

and

(b) $TR = TS, T \neq 0$.

In words, an equivalent equation is obtained if the same quantity is added to both sides of an equation or if both sides of an equation are multiplied by the same nonzero quantity.

The next two examples illustrate the use of this very important theorem.

EXAMPLE 5 Solve

$$1 + 2x = -3.$$

SOLUTION We use Theorem 2-4(a) to "isolate" the variable terms on one side of the equation and the constant terms on the other side. The equation

$$1 + 2x = -3$$

†An *algebraic expression* is a symbolism that uses constants, variables, and any mathematical operations to represent a real number.

is equivalent to the equation obtained by adding -1 to both sides:
$$1 + 2x + (-1) = -3 + (-1).$$
Combining like terms yields
$$2x = -4,$$
and the variable terms and constant terms have been isolated. Next we use Theorem 2-4(b) to force the coefficient of the variable term to be 1. This is accomplished by multiplying both sides of
$$2x = -4$$
by $\frac{1}{2}$,
$$\tfrac{1}{2}(2x) = \tfrac{1}{2}(-4),$$
yielding
$$x = -2.$$
This equation is equivalent to the original equation. The solution set of this last equation (and hence of the original equation) is $\{-2\}$. We can check this value in the original equation.
$$1 + 2(-2) = 1 - 4 = -3$$

EXAMPLE 6 Solve
$$7 + 3y = 5y - 2.$$

SOLUTION Isolate the variable terms on one side of the equation.

$$7 + 3y - 5y = 5y - 2 - 5y \qquad \text{(Adding } -5y \text{ to both sides)}$$
$$7 - 2y = -2 \qquad \text{(Combining like terms)}$$

Isolate the constant terms on the other side.

$$7 - 2y - 7 = -2 - 7 \qquad \text{(Adding } -7 \text{ to both sides)}$$
$$-2y = -9 \qquad \text{(Combining like terms)}$$

Force the coefficient of y to be 1.

$$-\tfrac{1}{2}(-2y) = -\tfrac{1}{2}(-9) \qquad \text{(Multiplying both sides by } -\tfrac{1}{2})$$
$$y = \tfrac{9}{2}$$

This value checks in the original equation. Thus the solution set is $\{\tfrac{9}{2}\}$.

PRACTICE PROBLEM 2 (Solution on page 44) Solve

(a) $9y + 7 = 4y - 3$

(b) $3(x + 2) - 1 = x - 2(1 - 3x)$

EXAMPLE 7 Solve

$$\tfrac{4}{3}x = \tfrac{1}{12} + \tfrac{1}{2}x.$$

SOLUTION We first eliminate the denominators by multiplying both sides of the equation by 12, which is the least common denominator of the three fractions $\tfrac{4}{3}, \tfrac{1}{12},$ and $\tfrac{1}{2}$.

$$12(\tfrac{4}{3}x) = 12(\tfrac{1}{12} + \tfrac{1}{2}x)$$
$$16x = 12(\tfrac{1}{12}) + 12(\tfrac{1}{2}x)$$
$$16x = 1 + 6x$$
$$10x = 1$$
$$x = \tfrac{1}{10}$$

EXERCISES 2-1

Simplify by using the distributive property, if possible. (See Example 1 and Practice Problem 1.)

1. $7x - 4x$
2. $-4y + 3y$
3. $3x - 2y$
4. $10a - b$
5. $-2x + 1$
6. $3 - 5y$
7. $5y + 7y$
8. $-11a - 2a$
9. $14a - 1 - 2a + 3$
10. $3x + 4 - 2x - 7$
11. $6x + 3y - 8x + 3y$
12. $-11r + 3s + 3r - 3s$
13. $4(x + 2) - 8(2 - x)$
14. $7(x - 2) + 3(2x - 1)$
15. $9(5 - 2y) + 7(1 + y)$
16. $5(2y + 3) - 4(y - 8)$
17. $-2(3 - x) - 4(2x - 1)$
18. $-2(-2x + 7) - 5(x - 6)$
19. $-(-3a - 2b + 1) - 2(a - b)$
20. $-(-4b - 3a - 5) - (-b + a + 3)$
21. $-[-2(z - 1) - 3] + 2(5z - 4)$
22. $-[-(1 - 3z) - 2] - 3(2 - 4z)$
23. $3 - 2[-(4 - a) - (-a + 1)] - (a + 7) - 1$
24. $1 - 3[-(-2a + 4) - 5(-a)] - 2(a + 6) - a$

Determine whether the given number(s) is a solution for the given equation. (See Example 2.)

25. $5, -x = -5$
26. $4, 3y = 12$
27. $0, x = 5$
28. $-2, x = 2$
29. $3, 3a - 1 = -10$
30. $-1, 5 = a + 4$

31. $-4, 4y + 3 = 3y - 1$

32. $3, 7y - 3 + y = 7y$

*33. $1, 3; |x - 2| = 1$

*34. $2, -2; |5x| = 10$

*35. $1, -1; |2x - 1| = 1$

*36. $3, -2; |x + 4| = 2$

Solve the following equations using the techniques illustrated in Examples 5–7 and Practice Problem 2.

37. $3x - 5 = 7$

38. $4y + 2 = -6$

39. $4z + 7 = 6z + 2$

40. $11a - 3 = 9 - 4a$

41. $2x + 1 = 16 - 3x$

42. $5x - 4 = -5x + 6$

43. $3b + 12 = 4b + 16$

44. $1 - 2d = 3d + 26$

45. $3t + 2 - 4t = 9 - 2t + 3$

46. $4w + 5 - 10w = 8 - 13w - 3$

47. $-2 + 6x - 5 = 15 + 30x - 2x$

48. $9 - 9x + 11 + 2x = 15 + 9x - 3$

49. $1 - 3x + 2 = 12 + 4x - 9 - 5x$

50. $5 - 3x + 7 = 9x - 24$

51. $4p + 4 - 7p + 1 = 9 + 3p - 7$

52. $5 + 3r - 3 + 20r = -4 - 7r$

53. $2(x - 3) + 3x = 1 - (x + 1)$

54. $4(2x - 1) + 3 = 5x - 4(1 - x)$

55. $11(x - 3) + 2(x + 4) = 4x$

56. $-19x - 3(4 - x) = 4$

57. $2(z - 5) + 3 = -3(2 - z) - 12$

58. $3(4n - 3) - 2(n + 1) - 13 = 3(n - 7) + 2(3n - 1)$

59. $[2 - (x + 3) - 3x] - 1 = 3 - 2[x + 3(1 - x)] - 15$

60. $2[4 - 3(1 + x)] + 5x = -\{[2(2 - x) + 7] - 22\}$

61. $\dfrac{3x}{4} - \dfrac{7}{4} = -\dfrac{1}{4}$

62. $\dfrac{4x}{3} + 4 = -\dfrac{8}{3}$

63. $\dfrac{2a}{3} + \dfrac{1}{3} = \dfrac{4a}{3} - \dfrac{1}{3}$

64. $\dfrac{c}{4} + \dfrac{3}{2} = \dfrac{-5c}{2} + \dfrac{1}{4}$

65. $3x - \dfrac{1}{2} = \dfrac{5}{4} - \dfrac{x}{2}$

66. $3x + \dfrac{5}{2} = \dfrac{17}{2} - 6x$

67. $\dfrac{7x}{9} + \dfrac{1}{9} = \dfrac{-11x}{9} + \dfrac{1}{3}$

68. $\dfrac{x}{8} - \dfrac{1}{12} = \dfrac{x}{4} + \dfrac{1}{2}$

69. $\dfrac{2k}{9} - \dfrac{5}{6} = \dfrac{4k - 1}{6}$

70. $\dfrac{v}{4} - \dfrac{5v}{6} = \dfrac{5 - 4v}{6}$

*71. $3 - 2x = 4x - 6(x - 1) - 3$

*72. $4(y + 1) - 1 = 3(y + 1) + y$

*73. $t - 7(t + 2) - 5 = -6(t + 3) - 1$

*74. $8y - 15(3 - y) = 20(y - 2) - 3(2 - y) + 1$

*75. $2z - 9 - (3z - 7) = 4(z - 1) - 5z$

*76. $x - (3 - x) + 7 = 9x - (8 + 7x) + 5$

*77. $7(x + 1) - 3(1 - 2x) = 5x + 4(2x - 3)$

*78. $8 - 9y + 2(3y - 1) = 10(y - 4) + 12(3 - y) - y$

In problems 79–82, round the answer to the nearest tenth.

C79. $1.1p + 4.2 = 9.7 - 1.0p$ C80. $1.4q + 3.2 - 3.8q = 0$

C81. $-11.3x + 22.1(x - 10.2) = 0$ C82. $2.71(x - 98.2) + 11.6 = 9.33x$

SOLUTIONS FOR PRACTICE PROBLEMS

1. (a) $3x - 2x = (3 - 2)x = 1x = x$
   (b) The expression $-x + 3y$ cannot be simplified since $-x$ and $3y$ are not like terms.
   (c) The expression $9 - 2z$ cannot be simplified since 9 and $2z$ are not like terms.
   (d) $-2(x + 7) + 3(-2x + 8) - (-x) = -2x - 14 - 6x + 24 + x$
   $$= (-2 - 6 + 1)x + (-14 + 24)$$
   $$= -7x + 10$$

2. (a)
$$9y + 7 = 4y - 3$$
$$9y + 7 - 7 = 4y - 3 - 7$$
$$9y = 4y - 10$$
$$9y - 4y = 4y - 10 - 4y$$
$$5y = -10$$
$$\tfrac{1}{5}(5y) = \tfrac{1}{5}(-10)$$
$$y = -2$$

(b)
$$3(x + 2) - 1 = x - 2(1 - 3x)$$
$$3x + 6 - 1 = x - 2 + 6x$$
$$3x + 5 = 7x - 2$$
$$3x + 5 + 2 = 7x - 2 + 2$$
$$3x + 7 = 7x$$
$$3x + 7 - 3x = 7x - 3x$$
$$7 = 4x$$
$$\tfrac{1}{4}(7) = \tfrac{1}{4}(4x)$$
$$\tfrac{7}{4} = x$$

2-2
Formulas and
Literal Equations

The ability to manipulate formulas is essential in work done in disciplines ranging from homemaking to the most technical sciences. In working with formulas the value of any single variable can be determined if the values of all the other variables are known.

EXAMPLE 1
The area, A, of a triangle (see Figure 2.1) is the product of one-half the length of the base, b, times the height, h. Find the length of the base of a triangle whose area is 12 square inches and height is 4 inches.

FIGURE 2.1

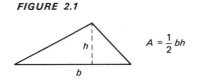

$A = \dfrac{1}{2} bh$

SOLUTION In the formula for the area of a triangle,

$$A = \tfrac{1}{2}bh,$$

we have $A = 12$ and $h = 4$. Substituting these values into the formula leads to a linear equation in the variable b.

$$12 = \tfrac{1}{2}b(4)$$
$$12 = 2b$$

Solving for b yields

$$b = 6.$$

PRACTICE (Solution on page 48) Fahrenheit temperature, F, and Celsius tempera-
PROBLEM 1 ture, C, are related by the formula

$$F = \tfrac{9}{5}C + 32.$$

Find the Celsius temperature equivalent to the Fahrenheit temperature 212° (boiling point of water).

Equations involving more than one variable are sometimes called **literal equations.** A literal equation can be solved for any specified variable in terms of the others by treating all other variables as if they are constants.

EXAMPLE 2 Solve for w in the literal equation

$$P = 2l + 2w.$$

SOLUTION We isolate w on one side of the equation.

$$P = 2l + 2w$$
$$P - 2l = 2w$$
$$\frac{P - 2l}{2} = w$$

PRACTICE (Solution on page 48) Solve for t in
PROBLEM 2

$$P = \frac{A}{1 - rt}$$

EXERCISES 2-2

The area, A, of a rhombus (see Figure 2.2) with diagonals p and q is given by one half the product of p and q. Use this information to solve for the unknown quantities in problems 1–4. (See Example 1.)

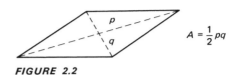

$$A = \frac{1}{2}pq$$

FIGURE 2.2

1. $A = 14$ square inches, $p = 4$ inches
2. $A = 20$ square centimeters, $q = 5$ centimeters
3. $A = 4$ square miles, $p = \frac{1}{2}$ mile
C4. $A = 2.09$ square yards, $p = 1.1$ yards

Fahrenheit temperature, F, and Celsius temperature, C, are related by the formula

$$F = \tfrac{9}{5}C + 32.$$

(See Figure 2.3.) Use this formula to solve for the unknown quantities in problems 5–8. (See Practice Problem 1.)

FIGURE 2.3

5. $C = 0°$
6. $C = 50°$
7. $F = 36°$
8. $F = 63°$

The area, A, of a trapezoid (see Figure 2.4) with bases of lengths a and b and height h is one-half the product of the height times the sum of the bases. Use this information to solve for the unknown quantities in problems 9–12.

FIGURE 2.4

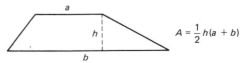

$$A = \frac{1}{2}h(a + b)$$

9. $A = 10$ square inches, $a = 3$ inches, $h = 2$ inches

10. $A = 70$ square meters, $h = 5$ meters, $b = 13$ meters

11. $A = 420$ square centimeters, $a = 12$ centimeters, $b = 8$ centimeters

C12. $A = 9.4850$ square feet, $h = 2.71$ feet, $a = 5.62$ feet.

The cost, C, of an item and the retail price, R, are related by the formula

$$R = C + rC,$$

where r is the percent markup. Use this formula to find the unknown quantities in problems 13–16.

13. $R = \$35.64$, $r = 32\%$ 14. $R = \$234.30$, $r = 20\%$

15. $R = \$638.22$, $C = \$483.50$ 16. $R = \$23.79$, $C = \$19.50$

The proceeds, P, of a discount note with maturity value, A, discounted at r percent per year for n years is given by

$$P = A(1 - rn).$$

Use this formula to find the unknown quantities in problems 17–20.

17. $P = \$760$, $r = 12\%$, $n = 2$ years

18. $P = \$1095$, $r = 18\%$, $n = 1.5$ years

19. $P = \$980$, $A = \$2000$, $n = 3$ years

20. $P = \$3000$, $A = \$4000$, $r = 10\%$

Solve each of the following literal equations for the variable indicated. (See Example 2 and Practice Problem 2.)

21. $D = rt$, for t (Distance formula)

22. $P = RB$, for R (Percentage)

23. $I = prt$, for r (Simple interest)

24. $V = \dfrac{KT}{P}$, for T (Volume of a gas)

25. $ax + by = c$, for y (Straight line)

26. $y = mx + b$, for m (Straight line)

27. $S = 2\pi Rh$, for h (Surface area of a right circular cylinder)

28. $V = \frac{1}{3}Bh$, for B (Volume of a pyramid)

29. $P = \frac{1}{2}A + 110$, for A (Normal blood pressure)

30. $D = L - N$, for N (Trade discount)

31. $R = \dfrac{C - S}{n}$, for S (Depreciation, straight line method)

32. $p = \dfrac{S}{S + F}$, for F (Probability of a success)

33. $d = \dfrac{i}{1 + ni}$, for n (Discount rate)

34. $P = A(1 - rn)$, for r (Proceeds of discounted note)

35. $D = ad - bc$, for d (Determinant of a matrix)

36. $I = \dfrac{Pti}{365}$, for t (Exact simple interest)

37. $A = P + PRT$, for P (Amount of a simple interest loan)

38. $A = \dfrac{h}{2}(b + c)$, for c (Area of a trapezoid)

39. $V = \frac{1}{6}h(b + 4M + B)$, for M (Volume of a prismatoid)

40. $S = \pi(r + R)S$, for r (Surface area of a frustrum of a cone)

41. $S = \dfrac{n}{2}[2a + (n - 1)d]$, for d (Sum of the terms in an arithmetic progression)

42. $S = \dfrac{a - rl}{1 - r}$, for r (Sum of the terms in a geometric progression)

43. $m = \dfrac{C(100 - p)}{100 - d}$, for d (Marked price of an item)

44. $D = 7130 + 195(C - 160)$, for C (Demand function)

SOLUTIONS FOR PRACTICE PROBLEMS

1. Substituting $F = 212°$ into

$$F = \tfrac{9}{5}C + 32$$

yields

$$212 = \tfrac{9}{5}C + 32.$$

Solving for C gives

$$212 - 32 = \tfrac{9}{5}C$$
$$180 = \tfrac{9}{5}C$$
$$\tfrac{5}{9}(180) = C$$
$$100° = C.$$

2.
$$P = \dfrac{A}{1 - rt}$$
$$(1 - rt)P = A$$
$$P - Prt = A$$
$$-Prt = A - P$$
$$t = \dfrac{A - P}{-Pr}$$
$$t = \dfrac{P - A}{Pr}$$

2-3
Linear
Inequalities

In Chapter 1 we considered inequalities of the form

$$a > b, \qquad a < b, \qquad a \geq b, \qquad a \leq b,$$

where a and b are real numbers.

Definition 2-5 Any inequality that can be expressed in one of the forms

$$(1)\ ax + b < 0$$
$$(2)\ ax + b \le 0$$

where a and b are real numbers with $a \ne 0$, is called a **linear inequality** in one variable.

Examples of linear inequalities are

$$3x - 5 < 0, \qquad 3(x - 2) + 5 \ge -2x + 4, \qquad \frac{x + 3}{6} \le \frac{2x - 6}{4}.$$

Notice that only one of the inequalities above is actually expressed in one of the forms described in Definition 2-5. The following theorem can be used to express any linear inequality in one of those forms. More important, it can be used to *solve* an inequality, that is, to find the values of the variables for which the inequality is true. This set of values is called the **solution set** and two inequalities are said to be **equivalent** if they have the same solution set.

Theorem 2-6 Let R, S, and T be algebraic expressions with $T \ne 0$. Then the inequality

$R < S$

is equivalent to

(a) $R + T < S + T$,

(b) $RT < ST$ if $T > 0$,

(c) $RT > ST$ if $T < 0$.

Analogous theorems can be stated where the inequality "$<$" in $R < S$ is replaced by "$>$" or "$\ge$" or "$\le$" and corresponding changes are made in statements (a), (b), and (c). Notice that
Part (a) states:
A quantity can be added to (or subtracted from) both sides of an inequality.
Part (b) states:
Both sides of an inequality can be multiplied (or divided) by the same *positive* quantity.
Part (c) states:
If both sides of an inequality are multiplied (or divided) by a *negative* quantity, the sense of the inequality *reverses*.

The procedure to follow to solve an inequality is:

> 1. Use Theorem 2-6(a) to isolate the variable terms on one side of the inequality and the constant terms on the other side.
> 2. Use either part (b) or part (c) to force the coefficient of the variable to 1.

This procedure is illustrated in the following examples.

EXAMPLE 1   Solve

$$3x - 5 < -2.$$

SOLUTION

> **Step 1.**   Isolate the variable terms on one side and the constants on the other.

$$3x - 5 + 5 < -2 + 5 \qquad \text{(Adding 5 to both sides)}$$
$$3x < 3 \qquad \text{(Combining like terms)}$$

> **Step 2.**   Force the coefficient of x to 1.

$$\frac{3x}{3} < \frac{3}{3} \qquad \text{(Dividing‡ by the } \textit{positive} \text{ number 3)}$$
$$x < 1 \qquad \text{(Simplifying)}$$

Thus the solution set for the inequality is

$$\{x \mid x < 1\},$$

which is represented graphically in Figure 2.5.

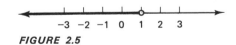

FIGURE 2.5

EXAMPLE 2   Solve and graph the solution set of

$$-4x + 5 \geq 2x + 7.$$

‡We could also have multiplied both sides by $\frac{1}{3}$.

Step 1. Isolate the variable terms on one side and the constant terms on the other.

$$-4x + 5 - 2x \geq 2x + 7 - 2x \qquad \text{(Subtracting } 2x \text{ from both sides)}$$

$$-6x + 5 \geq 7 \qquad \text{(Combining like terms)}$$

$$-6x + 5 - 5 \geq 7 - 5 \qquad \text{(Subtracting 5 from both sides)}$$

$$-6x \geq 2 \qquad \text{(Combining like terms)}$$

Step 2. Force the coefficient of the variable term to 1.

$$\frac{-6x}{-6} \leq \frac{2}{-6} \qquad \text{(Dividing both sides by the } \textit{negative} \text{ quantity } -6 \textit{ reverses} \text{ the inequality)}$$

$$x \leq -\frac{1}{3} \qquad \text{(Simplifying)}$$

The solution set is

$$\{x \mid x \leq -\tfrac{1}{3}\},$$

and its graph is given in Figure 2.6.

FIGURE 2.6

It may sometimes be necessary to simplify the expressions in the inequality before applying Theorem 2-6. This is illustrated in the next two examples.

EXAMPLE 3 Solve and graph

$$3(y - 2) + 5 \geq -2y + 4.$$

SOLUTION

$$3(y - 2) + 5 \geq -2y + 4$$

$$3y - 6 + 5 \geq -2y + 4 \qquad \text{(Removing parentheses)}$$

$$3y - 1 \geq -2y + 4 \qquad \text{(Combining like terms)}$$

$$3y - 1 + 2y + 1 \geq -2y + 4 + 2y + 1 \qquad \text{(Adding } 2y + 1)$$

$$5y \geq 5 \qquad \text{(Combining like terms)}$$

$$y \geq 1 \qquad \text{(Dividing by 5, which is } \textit{positive})$$

The graph of the solution set

$$\{y \mid y \geq 1\}$$

is given in Figure 2.7.

FIGURE 2.7

PRACTICE PROBLEM 1 (Solution on page 56) Solve and graph
$$4(x - 3) + 2 < 5(x - 1).$$

EXAMPLE 4 Solve and graph
$$\frac{x + 3}{6} \leq \frac{2x - 6}{4}.$$

SOLUTION

$$12\left(\frac{x + 3}{6}\right) \leq 12\left(\frac{2x - 6}{4}\right) \qquad \text{(Multiplying by the least common denominator 12, which is } \textit{positive})$$

$$2(x + 3) \leq 3(2x - 6) \qquad \text{(Simplifying)}$$

$$2x + 6 \leq 6x - 18 \qquad \text{(Removing parentheses)}$$

$$2x + 6 - 6x - 6 \leq 6x - 18 - 6x - 6 \qquad \text{(Subtracting } 6x \text{ and subtracting 6)}$$

$$-4x \leq -24 \qquad \text{(Combining like terms)}$$

$$x \geq 6 \qquad \text{(Dividing both sides by the } \textit{negative} \text{ quantity } -4 \textit{ reverses} \text{ the inequality)}$$

The graph of the solution set

$$\{x \mid x \geq 6\}$$

is given in Figure 2.8.

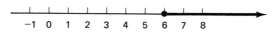

FIGURE 2.8

We conclude this section with the next two examples, illustrating the techniques for solving compound inequalities.

EXAMPLE 5   Solve and graph
$$-3 < 5 - 2x \le 7.$$

SOLUTION   In solving compound inequalities as we have here, we need to isolate the variable term in the middle and then force its coefficient to 1, using Theorem 2.6.

$$-3 < 5 - 2x \le 7$$

$$-3 - 5 < -2x \le 7 - 5 \qquad \text{(Subtracting 5 from all three members)}$$

$$-8 < -2x \le 2 \qquad \text{(Combining like terms)}$$

$$\frac{-8}{-2} > \frac{-2x}{-2} \ge \frac{2}{-2} \qquad \text{(Dividing by the } \textit{negative} \text{ quantity } -2 \textit{ reverses} \text{ the inequalities)}$$

$$4 > x \ge -1 \qquad \text{(Simplifying)}$$

$$-1 \le x < 4 \qquad \text{(Rewriting in natural order)}$$

The graph of the solution set
$$\{x \mid -1 \le x < 4\}$$
is given in Figure 2.9.

FIGURE 2.9

EXAMPLE 6   Solve and graph the compound inequality
$$2x - 5 \ge -1 \qquad \text{or} \qquad 2 - 5x > -3.$$

SOLUTION   We solve each of the two inequalities individually and then form the union of their solution sets.

$$
\begin{array}{ll}
2x - 5 \ge -1 & \qquad 2 - 5x > -3 \\
2x \ge 4 & \qquad -5x > -5 \\
x \ge 2 & \qquad x < 1
\end{array}
$$

The solution set for the compound inequality is

$$\{x \mid x \geq 2\} \cup \{x \mid x < 1\},$$

and the graph is given in Figure 2.10.

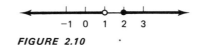

FIGURE 2.10

PRACTICE PROBLEM 2

(Solution on page 56) Solve and graph

$$-3r > 6 \quad \text{and} \quad r - 1 < 2.$$

EXERCISES 2-3

Use Theorem 2-6 to fill in the blank so that the second inequality is equivalent to the first inequality.

1. $x + 5 < -2$, $x < \underline{\quad}$
2. $4x - 3 < 0$, $4x < \underline{\quad}$
3. $3y \geq 6$, $y \geq \underline{\quad}$
4. $4y \leq -8$, $y \leq \underline{\quad}$
5. $-2z < 4$, $z \underline{\quad} -2$
6. $-3z \geq -9$, $z \underline{\quad} 3$
7. $-10 > 5x$, $x \underline{\quad} -2$
8. $4 > 2x$, $x \underline{\quad} 2$

Solve and graph the following inequalities. (See Examples 1–4 and Practice Problem 1.)

9. $2x - 5 \geq 3$
10. $5x + 7 > -23$
11. $-3x + 4 > 1$
12. $-4x + 8 \leq 12$
13. $2a - 5 \geq 4a - 9$
14. $11b + 7 < 3 - b$
15. $5 - 4x + 11 \leq 5x - 2$
16. $17 - 2x - x < 2$
17. $\dfrac{z - 2}{5} \geq \dfrac{4 - z}{5}$
18. $\dfrac{2z - 7}{3} > \dfrac{z - 14}{3}$
19. $\dfrac{2s - 3}{2} < \dfrac{s - 7}{3}$
20. $\dfrac{5t - 2}{3} \leq \dfrac{2t - 5}{4}$
21. $3(x - 4) + 1 \geq -2(1 - x) + 4x$
22. $5(x - 2) - 3x > 3 - (x - 2)$
23. $-2(r + 3) + r < -3$
24. $4(1 - 2r) + 10 \leq -(2 - r)$

In problems 25–28, round the answer to the nearest hundredth.

C25. $2.7x - 1.9 \geq 0.013$
C26. $0.886 - 2.31x > 11.7$
C27. $11x - 0.021 < 3.2 - 8.8x$
C28. $0.27x - 0.35 \leq 0.54 - 0.83x$

Solve and graph the following compound inequalities. (See Examples 5 and 6 and Practice Problem 2.)

29. $3 < y + 2 < 7$

30. $-5 \le y - 2 \le 0$

31. $0 \le 2x \le 10$

32. $-3 \le 3x \le 6$

33. $-4 \le -x < 2$

34. $-3 < -x \le 0$

35. $-5 < 2 - a < 7$

36. $-4 < 3 - a < 2$

37. $1 \le 4x - 3 < 5$

38. $-6 < 5x + 4 \le -1$

39. $-2 \le 1 - 3t \le 7$

40. $-5 < -3 - 2t < 7$

*41. $-1 < \dfrac{x + 7}{2} < 3$

*42. $-3 < \dfrac{1 - x}{3} \le 4$

*43. $-\dfrac{1}{3} \le \dfrac{2 - x}{3} < \dfrac{1}{6}$

*44. $-\dfrac{3}{2} < \dfrac{5 - 2x}{4} < \dfrac{1}{2}$

45. $x - 5 > 0$ or $2x - 1 \le -3$ 46. $3x > 4 - x$ or $1 < 1 - x$

47. $-2 > 1 - c$ or $4c - 2 \ge 1 - 7c$

48. $2 - 3d > -1$ or $d - 7 \le -5$

49. $2y - 3 \le y - 7$ or $5y - 2 > 2y - 5$

50. $8 + 3z \le 5z$ or $7 + z > 1 - z$

51. $6x - 3 \ge 9$ or $4 + x \ge 2x$

52. $x + 3 < 0$ or $6 - 7x \le x - 2$

53. $2x - 1 \le 5$ and $7 - 4x \le -1$

54. $3x - 8 < -2$ and $1 < 3 + 2x$

55. $4x - 3 < x - 6$ and $2x - 5 \ge 3x - 1$

56. $5n - 2(n + 3) \le 2 - n$ and $4n + 2(1 - n) > n - 3$

57. $5(s + 3) - 1 > s + 2$ and $3s - 4 \ge s - 2$

58. $8x - (10 - x) < 10 - x$ and $5x - 7 \le 2(x + 3) - 1$

59. $5(x + 3) - 1 < x + 2$ and $3x - 4 \ge x - 2$

60. $8v - (10 - v) < 10 - v$ and $5v - 7 > 2(v + 3) - 1$

61. $x - (2x - 1) > x - 5$ or $5 + x - (2x + 3) > 9 - 2x$

62. $1 - 2(x + 2) - x > -(1 + x)$
    or $2(x + 2) - (1 - x) > 3(1 - 3x) + 10x$

63. $5(x - 1) < 4x - (x + 3)$ or $3(x + 1) - 1 > 1 - (x - 2) + 3x$

64. $4(x - 1) + 1 < 2(1 - x) + 2(x + 1) - 7$
    or $8(x + 2) - (9x + 7) < 4(3 - x) - 3(1 - x) + x$

65. $5(z + 2) + 3 - 2z \le 3(4 + z) + 5(2 - z) + 1$
    and $2(2z + 7) - 1 \le 5(z + 3) - 4$

66. $2(2z - 3) - 3(z - 5) - 8 \le 0$
    and $3(2z + 5) - 7 \ge 2(2z - 3) - (z + 1) + 12$

67. $4(x - 3) + 11 - x < -(x + 1)$ or $-1 < x - 2 < 3$

68. $-5 < 3x - 2 < 7$ or $2(x - 1) \ge 2 + x$

69. $4 \leq 1 - a < 6$ or $2(2a + 3) - 5 > 1 + 2a$

70. $-2 \leq 3a - 8 < 1$ or $6a + 1 \leq 4(2 - a) + 2a + 1$

SOLUTIONS FOR PRACTICE PROBLEMS

1. $4(x - 3) + 2 < 5(x - 1)$
$$4x - 12 + 2 < 5x - 5$$
$$4x - 10 < 5x - 5$$
$$4x < 5x + 5$$
$$-x < 5$$
$$x > -5$$

The graph is shown in Figure 2.11.

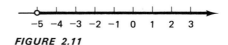

FIGURE 2.11

2. $-3r > 6$ and $r - 1 < 2$
   $r < -2$ and $r < 3$
   Solution set $= \{r \mid r < -2\} \cap \{r \mid r < 3\}$
   $= \{r \mid r < -2\}$

The graph is shown in Figure 2.12.

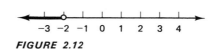

FIGURE 2.12

2-4
Equations
Involving
Absolute Value

Recall, from Chapter 1, the definition of absolute value:

$$|a| = \begin{cases} a, & a \geq 0 \\ -a, & a < 0. \end{cases}$$

In this section we study equations involving absolute value. Consider, for example,

$$|x| = 3.$$

This means that the distance between 0 and x is 3 units, as pictured in Figure 2.13. Thus $x = 3$ or $x = -3$, which can be expressed compactly

FIGURE 2.13

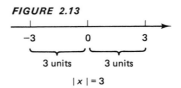

as $x = \pm 3$. The "$\pm$" is read "plus or minus." This discussion leads to the following theorem.

Theorem 2-7   Suppose that $a \geq 0$. Then

$$|x| = a \text{ is equivalent to } x = \pm a.$$

This theorem is used to solve equations involving absolute value, as illustrated in the next example.

EXAMPLE 1   Solve

$$|2x - 3| = 7.$$

SOLUTION   Using Theorem 2-7, we have

$$|2x - 3| = 7 \text{ is equivalent to } 2x - 3 = \pm 7.$$

Solving the two linear equations gives

$$2x - 3 = 7 \quad \text{or} \quad 2x - 3 = -7$$
$$2x = 10 \qquad\qquad 2x = -4$$
$$x = 5 \qquad\qquad x = -2.$$

It is easy to check that these values for x make $|2x - 3| = 7$ a true statement, and the solution set is $\{5, -2\}$.

PRACTICE PROBLEM 1   (Solution on page 60) Solve

$$|1 - 4x| = 5.$$

Not every equation involving absolute value has a solution. This is illustrated in the next example.

EXAMPLE 2   Solve

$$|9x - 5| = -3.$$

SOLUTION   There is no solution since $|9x - 5|$ is either positive or zero and cannot be negative. In other words,

$$|9x - 5| \neq -3.$$

for any value of x, and the solution set is $\varnothing$.

Often, an equation involving absolute value must be rewritten before applying Theorem 2-7.

EXAMPLE 3   Solve

$$|1 - 2x| + 3 = 6.$$

SOLUTION   Before applying Theorem 2-7, we isolate the term involving absolute value on one side of the equation. Hence

$$|1 - 2x| + 3 = 6 \quad \text{becomes} \quad |1 - 2x| = 3$$

which is equivalent to

$$1 - 2x = \pm 3.$$

Solving the two linear equations, we have

$$
\begin{array}{ll}
1 - 2x = 3 \quad \text{or} & 1 - 2x = -3 \\
-2x = 2 & -2x = -4 \\
x = -1 & x = 2.
\end{array}
$$

Thus the solution set is $\{-1, 2\}$.

In equations of the form

$$|a| = |b|,$$

we use the following fact: Since $|a|$ represents the distance between a and 0, and $|b|$ represents the distance between b and 0, then $|a| = |b|$ means that a and b are equally distant from 0. Thus they must either be equal or opposite in sign. Hence

$$\boxed{|a| = |b| \text{ is equivalent to } a = \pm b.}$$

We use this property in the next example.

EXAMPLE 4   Solve

$$|4 - 3x| = |x|.$$

SOLUTION   The expressions within the absolute value symbols are either equal or opposite in sign. Hence we have

$$4 - 3x = x \quad \text{or} \quad 4 - 3x = -x$$
$$4 = 4x \qquad\qquad 4 = 2x$$
$$1 = x \qquad\qquad 2 = x.$$

Thus the solutions to $|4 - 3x| = |x|$ are $x = 1, 2$.

**PRACTICE
PROBLEM 2**

(Solution on page 60) Solve

$$|5x - 2| = |4x - 7|.$$

EXERCISES 2-4

Use Theorem 2-7, when possible, to solve the equations. (See Examples 1 and 2 and Practice Problem 1.)

1. $|x| = 4$
2. $|x| = 2$
3. $|5 - x| = 4$
4. $|2x - 3| = 11$
5. $|7 + 5y| = 2$
6. $|4y + 1| = 15$
7. $|6 - 2z| = 0$
8. $|4 + z| = 0$
9. $|\frac{4}{3}x| = -3$
10. $|x - 2| = -4$
11. $|9x - 5| = 13$
12. $|2x - 10| = 8$

Solve the following equations by rewriting before applying Theorem 2-7. (See Example 3.)

13. $|a| - 2 = 0$
14. $|5a| - 10 = 0$
15. $|1 - 3b| + 3 = 0$
16. $|2 - 9b| + 2 = 0$
17. $|5x + 3| + 2 = 15$
18. $|-3x - 4| + 2 = 8$
19. $4 - |9x - 8| = 4$
20. $2 + |2x - 3| = 2$

Solve the following equations involving absolute value. (See Example 4 and Practice Problem 2.)

21. $|3x - 8| = |2x|$
22. $|2x| = |4 - x|$
23. $|1 - w| = |2w + 1|$
24. $|4r - 3| = |3r - 4|$
25. $|x| - |2x - 1| = 0$
26. $|10 - 3x| - |x - 2| = 0$
*27. $|5x - 7| + |3x| = 0$
*28. $|4 - 2x| + |2x| = 0$
*29. $|t| + 2t = 3$
*30. $|3 - t| + 2t = 2$

In problems 31–34, round the answer to the nearest tenth.

C31. $|3.1x - 2.7| = 9.8$
C32. $|0.571x + 3.09| = 11.3$
C33. $|2.8x - 5.6| = |2.8 - 1.8x|$
C34. $|0.32x + 0.43| = |0.67 - 0.72x|$

1. $|1 - 4x| = 5$

$$1 - 4x = 5 \quad \text{or} \quad 1 - 4x = -5$$
$$-4x = 4 \qquad\qquad -4x = -6$$
$$x = -1 \qquad\qquad x = \tfrac{6}{4} = \tfrac{3}{2}$$

Solutions: $x = -1, \tfrac{3}{2}$

2. $|5x - 2| = |4x - 7|$

$$5x - 2 = 4x - 7 \quad \text{or} \quad 5x - 2 = -(4x - 7)$$
$$5x = 4x - 5 \qquad\qquad 5x - 2 = -4x + 7$$
$$x = -5 \qquad\qquad\qquad 5x = -4x + 9$$
$$9x = 9$$
$$x = 1$$

Solutions: $x = -5, 1$

2-5
*Linear Inequalities
Involving
Absolute Value*

In Chapter 1 we saw that for $a > 0$,

> (a) $|x| < a$ is equivalent to $-a < x < a$, and
>
> (b) $|x| > a$ is equivalent to $x > a$ or $x < -a$.

These results, together with the techniques described in Section 2-3 for solving compound inequalities, are used to solve inequalities involving absolute value.

EXAMPLE 1   Solve and graph

$$|1 - x| < 4.$$

SOLUTION   We transform this inequality involving absolute value to a compound inequality:

$$|1 - x| < 4 \qquad \text{becomes} \qquad -4 < 1 - x < 4.$$

We then use the techniques from Section 2-3 to solve the compound inequality

$$-4 < 1 - x < 4.$$
$$-5 < -x < 3 \qquad \text{(Subtracting 1 from all three members)}$$
$$5 > x > -3 \qquad \text{(Multiplying by } -1 \text{ \textit{reverses} the inequalities)}$$
$$-3 < x < 5 \qquad \text{(Rewriting in natural order)}$$

The solution is

$$-3 < x < 5,$$

and its graph is shown in Figure 2.14.

$$-3 < x < 5$$

FIGURE 2.14

PRACTICE PROBLEM 1 (Solution on page 63) Solve and graph

$$|2x - 1| \leq 3.$$

EXAMPLE 2 Solve and graph

$$|3x - 1| \geq 2.$$

SOLUTION We write an equivalent compound inequality, and then solve the inequality. Thus

$$|3x - 1| \geq 2$$

is equivalent to

$$3x - 1 \geq 2 \qquad \text{or} \qquad 3x - 1 \leq -2$$
$$3x \geq 3 \qquad\qquad 3x \leq -1$$
$$x \geq 1 \qquad\qquad x \leq -\tfrac{1}{3}.$$

The solution for $|3x - 1| \geq 2$ is

$$x \geq 1 \qquad \text{or} \qquad x \leq -\tfrac{1}{3},$$

and its graph is given in Figure 2.15.

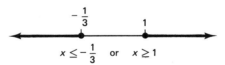

$$x \leq -\tfrac{1}{3} \quad \text{or} \quad x \geq 1$$

FIGURE 2.15

PRACTICE PROBLEM 2 (Solution on page 64) Solve and graph

$$|x - 3| > 2.$$

We must rely on the definition of absolute value to solve the special cases of absolute value inequalities which occur when a is positive or zero in $|x| > -a, |x| \geq -a, |x| < -a$ or $|x| \leq -a$. Three of these special cases are illustrated in the next examples.

*EXAMPLE 3 Solve

$$|4x - 3| \leq -2.$$

SOLUTION Since $|4x - 3|$ can never be negative, it certainly cannot be smaller than -2. Thus there is *no solution* to $|4x - 3| \leq -2$.

EXAMPLE 4   Solve
$$|3 - x| > 0.$$

SOLUTION   Since $|3 - x|$ is always positive except when $3 - x = 0$, then
$$|3 - x| > 0$$
is satisfied for all x except $x = 3$. The solution set is
$$\{x \mid x \neq 3\},$$
and its graph is given in Figure 2.16.

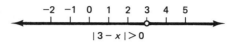

FIGURE 2.16

EXAMPLE 5   Solve
$$|x + 5| \geq -3.$$

SOLUTION   Since $|x + 5|$ is always positive or zero, $|x + 5|$ is always greater than any negative number. Thus any real x is a solution, and $\mathcal{R}$, the set of real numbers, is the solution set.

PRACTICE PROBLEM 3   (Solution on page 64) Solve
$$|2x + 5| \leq 0.$$

SUMMARY OF SPECIAL CASES (c is positive number)	
Linear Inequality	**Solution**
$\|ax + b\| < -c$ $\|ax + b\| \leq -c$ $\|ax + b\| < 0$	no solution
$\|ax + b\| > -c$ $\|ax + b\| \geq -c$ $\|ax + b\| \geq 0$	any real number
$\|ax + b\| \leq 0$	$x = -b/a$
$\|ax + b\| > 0$	any real number except $x = -b/a$

Solve and graph the following absolute value inequalities. (See Examples 1 and 2 and Practice Problems 1 and 2.)

1. $|x| < 3$

2. $|2x| \leq 4$

3. $|1 - x| \leq 2$

4. $|2 - x| < 1$

5. $|5x - 2| < 3$

6. $|2x + 7| \leq 1$

7. $\left|\dfrac{4x - 1}{2}\right| \leq 3$

8. $\left|\dfrac{2x + 1}{3}\right| < 1$

9. $|3x - 4| < 7$

10. $|5x - 2| < 7$

11. $|6x - 1| \leq 11$

12. $|4x - 9| \leq 1$

13. $|9 - 2x| \leq 1$

14. $|7 - 3x| \leq 2$

15. $|1 - x| > 1$

16. $|2 - x| > 3$

17. $|3x - 1| > 2$

18. $|2x - 1| \geq 3$

19. $|5x + 6| \geq 1$

20. $|3x + 4| > 2$

21. $|4x - 5| > 7$

22. $|2x + 2| \geq 8$

23. $\left|\dfrac{5x - 3}{3}\right| \geq 1$

24. $\left|\dfrac{x + 4}{2}\right| \geq 3$

In problems 25–28, round the answer to the nearest tenth.

C25. $|0.17x - 0.11| < 0.37$

C26. $|37.2 + 5.31x| \leq 92.6$

C27. $|0.857x + 27.2| \geq 43.0$

C28. $|2.1x - 7.4| > 4.8$

Solve the following special cases of absolute value inequalities. (See Examples 3–5 and Practice Problem 3.)

*29. $|x + 7| > 0$

*30. $|5x - 7| > 0$

*31. $|4x - 1| \leq -2$

*32. $|3 - x| \leq -10$

*33. $|x + 3| \geq -5$

*34. $|3x - 8| \geq -5$

*35. $|4x + 8| \leq 0$

*36. $|2x - 1| \leq 0$

*37. $|5 - 3x| < 0$

*38. $|6 + 5x| < 0$

*39. $|x + 2| > -2$

*40. $|x + 2| < -2$

SOLUTIONS FOR PRACTICE PROBLEMS

1. $\quad |2x - 1| \leq 3$
   $-3 \leq 2x - 1 \leq 3$
   $\quad -2 \leq 2x \leq 4$
   $\quad\quad -1 \leq x \leq 2$

The graph is shown in Figure 2.17.

FIGURE 2.17

2. $|x - 3| > 2$

$x - 3 > 2$ or $x - 3 < -2$

$x > 5$ or $x < 1$

The graph is shown in Figure 2.18.

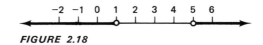

FIGURE 2.18

3. Since $|2x + 5|$ is never negative, $|2x + 5| \leq 0$ only when $2x + 5 = 0$. Hence the only solution is $x = -\frac{5}{2}$.

PRACTICE TEST for Chapter 2

1. Simplify, if possible, by using the distributive property.
   (a) $4x - 5x$ (b) $3y + 2$
   (c) $2a - 6(b - a) + 2(-a - 3b)$ (d) $4r - [-2(s + 5) - 6] + r$

2. Solve the linear equations.
   (a) $5x - 3 = 3x + 5$
   (b) $3y + 7 - y = 5 - 4y$
   (c) $7(s - 1) + 4[3 - 2(s - 1)] = 4 + s$
   (d) $\dfrac{10x}{3} - \dfrac{x}{2} = \dfrac{3x}{4} - \dfrac{5}{4}$

3. Solve each literal equation for the variable indicated.
   (a) $S = \frac{1}{3}(a + b + c)$, for c (b) $x = \dfrac{yz}{y + z}$, for z

Solve and graph the solution set of each inequality in problems 4 and 5.

4. (a) $5(x - 1) + 3 < x - 6$ (b) $-4 \leq 3y - 4 < 11$
5. (a) $x + 3 \leq 2$ or $2x - 5 > 1$
   (b) $2z - 7 < 3(1 - z)$ and $-5(z + 3) \geq z + 3$

Solve the absolute value equations in problems 6–8.

6. (a) $|2 - x| = 5$ (b) $|3x - 8| = 2$
7. (a) $|9 + 2b| = -2$ (b) $|10 - a| = 0$
8. (a) $|8 + 2x| = |1 + x|$ (b) $|3x - 2| - |6 - x| = 0$

Solve and graph the solution set of each absolute value inequality in problems 9 and 10.

9. (a) $|3 - x| < 5$ (b) $|3x - 8| \leq 5$
10. (a) $|4x + 2| \geq 10$ (b) $|4x - 1| > 3$

3-1
Introduction to
Word Problems

Problems arise in various situations which can be expressed mathematically, and hence can be solved using mathematical techniques. In this chapter we examine several types of "stated" or "word" problems which lead to linear equations or inequalities in one variable.

There are five basic steps involved in working a word problem. They are:

1. Decide what the unknown is, that is, what we must solve for.

2. Write down expressions involving that unknown and piece together an equation (or inequality) using the expressions.

3. Solve the equation (or inequality) using the techniques presented in Chapter 2.

4. Write out results for all parts of the problem requested.

5. Check these results in the original problem.

Step 2 is probably the most difficult step to accomplish successfully. The student must be able to translate English phrases into mathematical expressions. Consider the next example.

EXAMPLE 1 Translate the following English phrases into mathematical expressions.

English Phrase	Unknown	Mathematical Expression
1 more than a number	x	$x + 1$
3 times an integer	n	$3n$
5 less than twice a number	y	$2y - 5$
the sum of two consecutive integers	n	$n + (n + 1)$
10% of the principal	P	$0.10P$
3 less than twice Dan's age	D	$2D - 3$
5 more than half the length	l	$5 + \frac{1}{2}l$

In each part of this example we chose a letter to represent the unknown. Any letter could be used. It is left up to the student to make the choice of letters for the variable and then write the mathematical expression in terms of that variable.

PRACTICE PROBLEM 1 (Solution on page 70) Choose a letter to represent the unknown and translate the English phrase into a mathematical expression.

(a) twice the contents
(b) 40 miles per hour faster than the car
(c) 1 less than 3 times as many dimes
(d) the product of two consecutive odd integers

Next, the mathematical expressions must be pieced together to form an equation or inequality.

EXAMPLE 2 Suppose that fourteen more than twice a number is one less than seven times the number. Find the number.

SOLUTION   Let *n* represent the number. Then translate the English phrases into mathematical expressions and piece together the equation:

$$\underbrace{\text{14 more than twice } n}_{2n + 14} \quad \underbrace{\text{is}}_{=} \quad \underbrace{\text{1 less than 7 times } n}_{7n - 1}$$

Solve the equation:

$$2n + 14 = 7n - 1$$
$$14 = 5n - 1$$
$$15 = 5n$$
$$3 = n.$$

Write out the solution:

$$n = 3.$$

Check the solution:

Fourteen more than twice 3 is $14 + 2 \cdot 3 = 14 + 6 = 20$.
One less than seven times 3 is $7(3) - 1 = 21 - 1 = 20$.

PRACTICE PROBLEM 2   (Solution on page 70) The sum of two consecutive integers is 27. Find the integers.

Sometimes a diagram or chart is helpful in setting up the equation. This is particularly true in problems involving ages.

EXAMPLE 3   Suppose that a mother is sixteen times as old as her daughter. In eight years the mother will be four times as old as her daughter will be then. Find the present ages of each.

SOLUTION   Let *d* be the daughter's present age. Write out the mathematical expressions described in the problem:

	Present Age	*Age 8 Years from Now*
Daughter	*d*	*d* + 8
Mother	16*d*	16*d* + 8 = present age plus 8 4(*d* + 8) = four times as old as the daughter will be then

68

Notice that there are two ways of writing the mother's age 8 years from now. Hence these expressions must be equal. Thus

$$16d + 8 = 4(d + 8)$$
$$16d + 8 = 4d + 32$$
$$12d = 24$$
$$d = 2.$$

The daughter's current age is 2 and the mother's current age is 16(2), or 32.

Check: Eight years from now the daughter will be $2 + 8 = 10$. Eight years from now the mother will be $32 + 8 = 40$, which is 4 times as old as the daughter will be then.

PRACTICE PROBLEM 3 (Solution on page 71) The length of a rectangle is four centimeters longer than the width. If each dimension is increased by ten centimeters, the perimeter is doubled. Find the dimensions of the original rectangle.

EXERCISES 3-1

In problems 1–8, choose a letter to represent the unknown and translate the English phrase into a mathematical expression. (See Example 1 and Practice Problem 1.)

1. half the rate

2. twice the cost

3. ten more freckles

4. three less than one-third the base

5. three percent of the freshmen students

6. Lisa's age four years ago

7. all the students except five

8. four more than twice the number of cans

In problems 9–24, solve the word problems. (See Examples 2 and 3 and Practice Problems 2 and 3.)

9. Five more than twice a number is ten less than three times the number. Find the number.

10. Nine less than four times a number is fifteen more than the number. Determine the number.

11. The sum of two consecutive integers is ninety-three. Find the integers.

12. Seven times an integer is three more than twice the next integer. Find the two integers.

13. One side of a rectangle is three feet more than half as long as the other side, and the perimeter is twenty-one feet. Find the dimensions of the rectangle.

14. The perimeter of a square is tripled when the lengths of its sides are increased by ten. Find the dimensions of the original square.

15. The sides of one square are five centimeters shorter than the sides of a second square. If the sum of their perimeters is 140 centimeters, find the lengths of the sides of each square.

16. In a rectangular garden the length is twice the width. If each dimension is increased by twenty-one meters, the perimeter is tripled. Find the dimensions of the original garden.

17. In five years, Pam will be twice as old as she was seven years ago. What is her present age?

18. Three years from now James will be half as old as he will be twenty-three years from now. What is James's present age?

19. Donna is six years older than Martin. Thirteen years ago Donna was twice as old as Martin. Find their present ages.

20. A grandmother is five times as old as her grandson. Eight years ago she was two more than eleven times as old as her grandson. Find the current ages of each.

21. Twice as many adult tickets for a basketball game were sold as children's tickets. The attendance was 8322. How many tickets of each type were sold?

22. A child shook twenty-nine coins out of her piggy bank. There were three more dimes than nickels and four more nickels than pennies. How many coins of each type did she find?

*23. Suppose that a student scored 95, 78, 87, and 92 on the first four math tests. What is the minimum score that he can make on the fifth test so that his average grade on all five tests is at least 90?

*24. A child saves 15¢ a week. How many weeks will it take for him to save at least $2.49?

SOLUTIONS FOR PRACTICE PROBLEMS

1. (a) $2c$, where $c =$ contents
   (b) $40 + r$, where $r =$ rate of the car
   (c) $3d - 1$, where $d =$ number of dimes
   (d) $n(n + 2)$, where $n =$ first odd integer

2. Let $n =$ first integer
   $n + 1 =$ second integer

   Equation:
   $$n + n + 1 = 27$$
   $$2n + 1 = 27$$
   $$2n = 26$$
   $$n = 13$$

Solution: 13, 14.
Check: 13 + 14 = 27.

3. Let w = width of original rectangle.

	Original Rectangle	*New Rectangle*
Width = w	w	$w + 10$
Length = l	$w + 4$	$w + 4 + 10 = w + 14$
Perimeter = $2(w + l)$	$2[(w) + (w + 4)]$	$2[(w + 10) + (w + 14)]$ $2 \cdot 2[(w) + (w + 4)]$ = twice the perimeter of original rectangle

Equation: $2[(w + 10) + (w + 14)] = 2 \cdot 2[(w) + (w + 4)]$
$$2(2w + 24) = 4(2w + 4)$$
$$4w + 48 = 8w + 16$$
$$32 = 4w$$
$$8 = w$$

Solution: width = 8 centimeters, length = 12 centimeters.
Check: perimeter of original rectangle is $2 \cdot (8 + 12) = 40$.
dimensions of new rectangle are 18×22.
perimeter of new rectangle is $2(18 + 22) = 80$, which is twice the perimeter of the original rectangle.

**3-2
Mixture Problems**

There are two types of mixture problems which we study in this section. The first involves mixing together substances or articles of different monetary values. The linear equation associated with this type of mixture problem is based on the following fact:

> The value of the mixture must equal the sum of the values of the ingredients in the mixture.

EXAMPLE 1 A popular snack consists of candied popcorn and candied peanuts. If the popcorn is valued at $0.50 a pound and the peanuts are valued at $3.25 a pound, determine the mixture of a 1-pound box that sells for $1.82.

SOLUTION Let x represent the number of pounds of peanuts used in the mixture. The amounts and values of the ingredients and mixture are described in the following table.

	Amount	Value = $\left(\begin{array}{c}\textbf{\textit{Price per}}\\\textbf{\textit{Pound}}\end{array}\right) \times \left(\begin{array}{c}\textbf{\textit{Number of}}\\\textbf{\textit{Pounds}}\end{array}\right)$
Peanuts	x pounds	$3.25x
Popcorn	$1 - x$ pounds	$0.50(1 - x)$ } value of ingredients
Mixture	1 pound	$1.82(1)

Since the sum of the values of the ingredients must equal the value of the mixture, we solve the following equation.

$$3.25x + 0.50(1 - x) = 1.82$$
$$3.25x + 0.50 - 0.50x = 1.82$$
$$2.75x = 1.32$$
$$x = \frac{1.32}{2.75} = 0.48 \text{ pound}$$
$$1 - x = 1 - 0.48 = 0.52 \text{ pound}$$

Thus a 1-pound box worth $1.82 contains 0.48 pound of peanuts and 0.52 pound of popcorn.

We leave it to the student to check these results in the original problem, as well as the answers to the examples and practice problems in the remainder of this chapter.

PRACTICE (Solution on page 75) Suppose that 23 dimes and nickels amount to **PROBLEM 1** $1.55. How many coins of each type are there?

The second type of mixture problem deals with mixing together substances of different concentrations. The linear equation associated with this type is based on the next fact:

> The amount of pure substance in the mixture is equal to the sums of the amounts of the pure substance in the ingredients of the mixture.

EXAMPLE 2 Suppose that a marine biologist wishes to prepare a 40,000-liter tank for studying saltwater fish. How much salt water that is 2.4% salt should she mix with a second solution that is 0.8% salt to obtain 40,000 liters of a 1.8% solution?

SOLUTION Let x represent the number of liters of the 2.4% salt water to be used. The following table is helpful in setting up the necessary linear equation.

	Percent Salt	Quantity of Solution	Amount of Pure Salt
Ingredients	2.4% = 0.024	x	$0.024x$
	0.8% = 0.008	$40,000 - x$	$0.008(40,000 - x)$
Mixture	1.8% = 0.018	40,000	$0.018(40,000)$

Since the sum of the amounts of pure salt in the ingredients must equal the amount of pure salt in the mixture, we solve the following equation.

$$0.024x + 0.008(40,000 - x) = 0.018(40,000)$$
$$0.024x + 320 - 0.008x = 720$$
$$0.016x = 400$$
$$x = \frac{400}{0.016} = 25,000 \text{ liters}$$
$$40,000 - x = 15,000 \text{ liters}$$

Hence 25,000 liters of the 2.4% solution of salt water should be mixed with 15,000 liters of the 0.8% solution of salt water.

PRACTICE PROBLEM 2 (Solution on page 75) How much water must be added to 8 liters of a solution that is 30% acid to obtain a new solution that is 12% acid?

EXERCISES 3-2

1. An auditorium seats 500 people. If tickets for a concert sold for $7.00 per adult and $4.00 per child, determine the number of each type of ticket sold if proceeds were $3149.00 and all 500 seats were filled.

2. Suppose that admission to a museum is $2.25 per adult and $1.00 per child. How many children and adults visited the museum on a certain

day if the total receipts were $511.50 and twice as many adults visited the museum as did children?

3. Ten pounds of a mixture of two types of nuts cost $23.20. If one type of nut is worth $3.10 per pound and the second type is worth $1.80 per pound, how many pounds of each type are used in the mixture?

4. How many pounds of candy worth $3.20 a pound should be mixed with 3 pounds of candy worth $2.00 a pound to obtain a mixture worth $2.75 per pound?

5. Frances found 9 dimes and nickels worth 55¢ in her purse. How many coins of each type were there?

6. The waitresses at Cookie's Coffee Shop put all their tips in a jar and divide the money evenly at the end of their shift. How many coins of each type were in the jar if there were 3 less than twice as many nickels as dimes and 4 more than 3 times as many quarters as dimes, all of which amounted to $22.70?

7. Waldo sells corned beef for $3.85 a pound and peppered beef for $4.90 a pound. How many pounds of each did he sell to Maria for $19.95 if Maria bought $\frac{1}{2}$ pound more of the peppered beef than of the corned beef?

8. Maria hired Waldo to cater her party. She decided to serve ham, salami, and pastrami totaling 20 pounds. She asked for twice as much pastrami as ham and the rest in salami. How many pounds of each did Maria receive if Waldo charged $82.00 with ham costing $2.85 per pound, salami costing $2.75 per pound, and pastrami costing $4.95 per pound?

9. How much orange juice must be added to 10 liters of a punch that is 10% fruit juice to obtain a punch that is 25% fruit juice?

10. How much vinegar (rounded to the nearest tenth of an ounce) should be added to 8 ounces of a solution that is 20% vinegar to increase the concentration of vinegar to 45%?

11. What percent (to the nearest percent) butterfat does a 14-ounce malt contain if it is made from 5 ounces of milk containing 3% butterfat and 9 ounces of ice cream containing 18% butterfat?

12. What percent butterfat does 100 gallons of milk contain if it is a mixture of 25 gallons of milk that is 5% butterfat and 75 gallons of milk that is 3% butterfat?

13. How much pure acid must be added to 12 liters of a 10% acidic solution to increase the acidity to a 46% level?

14. How much cream containing 30% butterfat should be mixed with 4 liters of milk containing 2% butterfat to obtain a mixture containing 5% butterfat?

15. The Do-Em-Right Popcorn Company claims that its customers can expect 95% of the kernels to pop. Tests made on this year's bumper crop showed that 98% of the popcorn popped. How much of last year's old crop of popcorn testing at 82% can be mixed with this year's popcorn so that the company's claim of 95% popping is upheld on a batch totaling 40,000 pounds of popcorn?

16. Mr. Morales prepared a solution to kill ticks by mixing 45 gallons of water with 5 gallons of insecticide. He used all he needed on the ticks and had one-fourth of the mixture left. Next he decided to use the remaining solution to spray pine trees for pine beetle infestation. Since pine beetles are harder to kill than ticks, he must increase the amount of insecticide in his solution to 18%. How much insecticide (rounded to the nearest tenth of a gallon) must he add?

SOLUTIONS FOR PRACTICE PROBLEMS

1.

	Number of Coins	*Value of Coins*
Dimes	d	$0.10d$
Nickels	$23 - d$	$0.05(23 - d)$
Mixture	23	$1.55

$$0.10d + 0.05(23 - d) = 1.55$$
$$0.10d + 1.15 - 0.05d = 1.55$$
$$0.05d = 0.40$$
$$d = 8$$
$$23 - d = 15$$

Solution: 8 dimes, 15 nickels

2.

	Percent Acid	*Quantity of Solution*	*Amount of Pure Acid*
Ingredients { Water	0% = 0.00	x	$0 \cdot x = 0$
30% solution	30% = 0.30	8	0.30(8)
Mixture	12% = 0.12	$x + 8$	$0.12(x + 8)$

$$0 \cdot x + 0.30(8) = 0.12(x + 8)$$
$$2.40 = 0.12x + 0.96$$
$$1.44 = 0.12x$$
$$12 = x$$

Solution: 12 liters of water

3-3
Uniform Motion Problems

The distance, d, traveled by an object moving at a uniform rate of speed, r, for a time, t, is given by the following equation, known as the *distance formula*.

$$\boxed{\begin{array}{c} \text{distance} = \text{rate} \cdot \text{time} \\ d = r \cdot t \end{array}}$$

Care must be taken in using this formula since the units in which the quantities are expressed must be in agreement. The following table gives some common units of measure used in the distance formula.

Distance	Rate	Time
kilometers	kilometers per hour	hours
miles	miles per hour	hours
feet	feet per second	seconds
meters	meters per minute	minutes

EXAMPLE 1

Suppose that two cars leave Dallas at the same time traveling in opposite directions. If one travels 40 miles per hour and the other travels 55 miles per hour, how long will it take them to be 380 miles apart?

SOLUTION

Let t represent the time traveled by both cars. The sum of the distances traveled by each car is 380 miles (see Figure 3.1). Thus we solve the following equation:

$$\left\{\begin{array}{c} \text{distance traveled} \\ \text{by car 1} \end{array}\right\} + \left\{\begin{array}{c} \text{distance traveled} \\ \text{by car 2} \end{array}\right\} = 380$$

$$40t \quad + \quad 55t \quad = 380$$
$$95t = 380$$
$$t = 4.$$

After 4 hours the cars will be 380 miles apart.

FIGURE 3.1

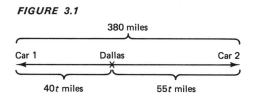

PRACTICE PROBLEM 1 (Solution on page 81) A boat traveling at the rate of 20 miles per hour takes 3 hours to travel upstream and 2 hours to travel the same distance downstream. Find the rate of the current.

Uniform motion problems can be generalized to include other types of problems involving rate and time. Suppose that a machine works at a uniform rate of speed, r, for a time, t. The output or work, w, done by the machine is given by the following *work formula*:

$$\boxed{\begin{array}{c} \text{work} = \text{rate} \cdot \text{time} \\ w = r \cdot t \end{array}}$$

For example, suppose that a card reader on a computer reads cards at a constant or uniform rate of 350 cards per minute. After 4 minutes the number of cards read is the amount of work done and

$$w = (350 \text{ cards per minute}) \cdot (4 \text{ minutes})$$
$$= 1400 \text{ cards.}$$

EXAMPLE 2 Suppose that Beckie can shell a sack of pecans by hand in 20 minutes and Wanda can shell a sack of the same size using a pecan sheller in 6 minutes. How long does it take the two girls to shell a sack of pecans if they work together?

SOLUTION Let x represent the number of minutes the girls work together. The work done, rates, and times are given in the following table.

	Time	Rate	Work = Rate · Time
Beckie	20 minutes	$\frac{1}{20}$ sack per minute	1 sack = $\frac{1}{20} \cdot 20$
	x minutes	$\frac{1}{20}$ sack per minute	$\frac{x}{20}$ sacks = $\frac{1}{20} \cdot x$
Wanda	6 minutes	$\frac{1}{6}$ sack per minute	1 sack = $\frac{1}{6} \cdot 6$
	x minutes	$\frac{1}{6}$ sack per minute	$\frac{x}{6}$ sacks = $\frac{1}{6} \cdot x$
Together	x minutes	$\frac{1}{x}$ sacks per minute	1 sack = $\frac{1}{x} \cdot x$

The sum of the amount of work done by Beckie in x minutes and the amount of work done by Wanda in x minutes must be equal to the amount of work done together in x minutes. Thus we solve the following equation:

$$\frac{x}{20} + \frac{x}{6} = 1$$

$$60 \cdot \left(\frac{x}{20} + \frac{x}{6} \right) = 60 \cdot 1$$

$$60\left(\frac{x}{20}\right) + 60\left(\frac{x}{6}\right) = 60$$

$$3x + 10x = 60$$

$$13x = 60$$

$$x = \frac{60}{13} = 4\frac{8}{13} \text{ minutes.}$$

Since

$$\frac{8}{13} \text{ minutes} = \frac{8}{13} \text{ (60 seconds)} \approx 36 \text{ seconds,}$$

it takes approximately 4 minutes 36 seconds for the girls to do the job together.

PRACTICE (Solution on page 81) Suppose that water can be pumped out of a 1000-
PROBLEM 2 liter tank at the rate of 20 liters per minute. The same tank can be completely filled by a hose in 10 minutes. If the pump and the hose are turned on simultaneously when the tank is empty, how long does it take to fill the empty tank?

EXERCISES 3-3

In problems 1–6, use the distance formula to find the unknown quantity.

1. Find d if $r = 40$ miles per hour and $t = 3$ hours.
2. Find d if $r = 20$ feet per second and $t = 9$ seconds.
3. Find r if $d = 105$ kilometers and $t = 3.5$ hours.
4. Find r if $d = 440$ yards and $t = 40$ seconds.
5. Find t if $d = 90$ meters and $r = 2.5$ meters per minute.
C6. Find t if $d = 440.3$ kilometers and $r = 62.9$ kilometers per hour.

Use the formula for work to find the unknown quantity in problems 7–12.

7. A paper machine produces 20 tons of paper per week. How much paper is produced during a 12-week summer?

8. A computer printer can print 670 lines per minute. If it runs continuously for 1 hour, how many lines will be printed?

9. Granny shells peas at the rate of 1 bushel in 40 minutes. How long will it take her to shell 2.5 bushels of peas?

10. Nick can mow his yard in 3 hours. At what rate per hour is he working?

11. An assembly line worker twists 9600 wires during her 8-hour shift. At what rate per hour is she working?

C12. A card sorter can sort 1225 computer cards per minute. How long will it take to sort 37,975 cards?

UNIFORM MOTION PROBLEMS

(See Example 1 and Practice Problem 1.)

13. Beth left Houston driving 45 miles per hour. At the same time James left Houston driving 50 miles per hour. They stopped driving at the same time but James had gone 40 miles farther than Beth. How far had each traveled?

14. Lisa and David each drive at the same rate of speed. During 4 hours Lisa drives 50 miles farther than David did in 3 hours. How far did each travel?

15. Two trains leave the railroad station at the same time traveling in opposite directions. If one is traveling 12 miles per hour faster than the other and after 4 hours they are 448 miles apart, find the rate of each.

16. Two businessmen whose offices are 342 miles apart agree to meet in Atlanta, located between the two offices, for a noon conference. Each leaves his office at 9:00 A.M., with one traveling 10 miles per hour faster than the other. How fast did each travel if they both reached Atlanta at noon?

17. A canoeist can row at the rate of 4 miles per hour in still water. If he can row upstream in 2 hours and the same distance downstream in 1.5 hours, what is the rate of the current?

18. Anxious Angelo flies his private plane from Gulfport to Hattiesburg in 33 minutes to pick up his bride. His return trip takes 42 minutes. There is a steady breeze blowing in the direction from Gulfport to Hattiesburg during both flights. What is the rate of the breeze if the rate of his plane is 125 miles per hour in still air?

19. Jason had been riding his bike for 8 miles at 30 miles per hour when he had a flat tire. In order not to be any later than possible for his date with Julie, he left his bike at that point and ran at 10 miles per hour until he reached Julie. If he made the entire trip in 28 minutes, how far did he have to run?

20. Suppose that Angie, Angelo's bride, was in Jackson shopping for her trousseau when she found out that Angelo was on his way to Hattiesburg to pick her up. She hurriedly finished her shopping and patiently drove 55 miles per hour for the first 33 miles on the way back to Hattiesburg. Then she foolishly increased her speed to the dangerous 72 miles per

hour so as to return to Hattiesburg 1 hour 11 minutes after she left Jackson. How far is it from Jackson to Hattiesburg?

21. Suppose that a boy leaves for school at 7:30 A.M. riding his bicycle at the rate of 16 miles per hour. At 7:45 his father leaves for work in his car traveling at 40 miles per hour along the same path as the boy. When does the father overtake his son?

22. When the 3:30 dismissal bell rings at school, it takes Johnny 2 minutes to get to his motorcycle. He heads for home 3.5 miles away traveling 25 miles per hour. At home when the mantel clock chimes 3:30, Johnny's dog, Bowzer, begins running 8 miles per hour to meet him. At what time do they meet?

WORK PROBLEMS   (See Example 2 and Practice Problem 2.)

23. Juan can keypunch data cards at the rate of 250 cards per hour, while Juanita can punch cards at the rate of 300 per hour. How long does it take them working together to punch a batch of 165,000 cards?

24. Kenneth and Caroline work at Fatso's Fast Food Factory. Their job is to assemble Fatso's Fabulous Super Submarine Sandwiches. Caroline can assemble 80 in one hour and the more meticulous Kenneth can assemble 64 in one hour. During the noon rush, how long would it take Kenneth and Caroline to assemble 126 of Fatso's Fabulous Super Submarine Sandwiches?

25. If Mildred can wax the gym floor in 10 hours and Scotty can wax the gym floor in 7 hours, how long does it take for them to wax the gym floor if they work together?

26. Midnight can consume a 50-pound sack of dogfood in 45 days. Snowball can consume a 50-pound sack of dogfood in 30 days. If both dogs are fed out of the same 50-pound sack, in how many days will they consume an entire sack of dogfood?

27. A washing machine fills up with cold water in 120 seconds. The same washing machine fills up with hot water in 90 seconds. If both faucets are open, how long does it take to fill the machine?

28. Suppose that the washing machine in problem 27 develops a hole in the tub and all the water leaks out of the full tub in 1080 seconds. Starting with an empty tub, how long does it take both faucets to fill the leaky tub?

29. Pepe, a painter, can paint an office in 20 minutes and Andy, his apprentice, can paint the same size office in 32 minutes. How long would it take them working together to paint 39 offices all of the same size?

30. How long (rounded to the nearest minute) would it take Pepe and Andy (in the problem above) to paint a classroom that is three times as large as an office?

1. Let r represent the rate of the current.

	Rate	Time	Distance
Upstream	$20 - r$	3	$3(20 - r)$
Downstream	$20 + r$	2	$2(20 + r)$

Since the distance traveling upstream is the same as the distance traveling downstream,

$$3(20 - r) = 2(20 + r)$$
$$60 - 3r = 40 + 2r$$
$$20 = 5r$$
$$4 = r.$$

The rate of the current is 4 miles per hour.

2. Let t represent the number of minutes necessary to fill the tank when the hose and pump are both used.

	Time	Rate	Work
Pump	1 minute	20 liters per minute	20 liters
	t minutes	20 liters per minute	$20t$ liters
Hose	10 minutes	100 liters per minute	1000 liters
	t minutes	100 liters per minute	$100t$ liters
Together	t minutes	$\dfrac{1000}{t}$ liters per minute	1000 liters

The amount of work done to fill the tank is the amount of work done by the hose minus the work done by the pump. Thus

$$100t - 20t = 1000$$
$$80t = 1000$$
$$t = 12.5 \text{ minutes.}$$

3-4
Consumer Applications

Applications of linear equations arise frequently in commonplace business transactions. We consider a few such applications in the remainder of this chapter.

EXAMPLE 1 (Tax)

Suppose that the room rates for hotels in San Francisco are subject to a 9.75% city hotel tax. Determine the cost of a one-night stay in a hotel that lists its rate for a "double" room as $64.00.

SOLUTION

The total cost of the room includes the room rate plus the tax. To determine the amount of tax, we multiply the room rate by the tax rate:

$$\text{amount of tax} = (\text{room rate}) \times (\text{tax rate})$$
$$= \$64.00 \, (0.0975)$$
$$= \$6.24.$$

Adding the tax to the room rate gives

$$\text{total cost of room} = (\text{room rate}) + (\text{tax})$$
$$= \$64.00 + \$6.24$$
$$= \$70.24.$$

EXAMPLE 2 (Pricing)

An advertisement in the local newspaper states that all items in Handyman's Hardware Haven are on sale for 20% off. What is the sale price of a $45.00 drill?

SOLUTION

The sale price is the retail price less the markdown, where the markdown is a certain percent of the retail price:

$$\text{markdown} = (\text{markdown percent}) \times (\text{retail price})$$
$$\text{sale price} = \text{retail price} - \text{markdown}.$$

Thus for the $45.00 drill on sale for 20% off, we have

$$\text{markdown} = 0.20(\$45.00) = \$9.00$$
$$\text{sale price} = \$45.00 - \$9.00 = \$36.00,$$

and the drill is on sale for $36.00.

PRACTICE PROBLEM 1

(Solution on page 87) What is the markdown percent if a $20.00 shirt is on sale for $17.60?

**EXAMPLE 3
(Commission)**

Sales personnel often receive an incentive to sell in the form of a commission, which is computed as a percent of their sales. If Sally is entitled to a commission of 8% of her monthly sales in addition to her monthly salary of $930, what is her pay for the month in which her sales amount to $1400?

SOLUTION

Since

$$\text{amount of commission} = (\text{rate of commission}) \times (\text{amount of sales})$$

then Sally's amount of commission is computed as

$$\text{amount of commission} = 0.08(\$1400) = \$112.$$

Thus Sally's pay at the end of the month is given by

$$\text{pay} = (\text{amount of commission}) + (\text{salary})$$
$$= \$112 + \$930$$
$$= \$1042.$$

A successful financier once said: "The fastest way to make money is with money." One way that money makes money is through investment. Individuals or businesses are sometimes willing to pay rent for the use of someone else's money. The rent that is paid is called **interest**. The amount of interest depends on four things:

> 1. The amount of money being loaned or invested, called the **principal**.
> 2. The rate at which the interest is computed, called the **interest rate**.
> 3. The length of time for which the money is loaned or invested.
> 4. The type of loan or investment that is being made.

We consider only one type of interest problem here, the **simple-interest problem**. In the simple-interest problem, interest is computed as

$$I = PRT,$$

where I represents the amount of interest earned by a principal, P, at an interest rate per time period, R, for T time periods. At the end of T time periods we say that the principal has grown to an **amount**, A, given by

$$\boxed{A = P + I.}$$

Since $I = PRT$, we have

$$A = P + PRT$$

or

$$\boxed{A = P(1 + RT).}$$

Unless otherwise specified, the interest rate in the simple-interest problems is an annual rate.

EXAMPLE 4 What will $400 amount to in 3 years if it is placed in a savings account that pays simple interest at the rate of 2% per quarter?

SOLUTION Since 1 year represents 4 quarters, we have

$$P = \$400$$
$$T = 3(4) = 12 \text{ time periods}$$
$$R = 0.02.$$

Hence

$$A = P(1 + RT) = 400(1 + 0.02 \cdot 12) = 400(1.24) = \$496.00.$$

Note that $400 earned $96 in interest during the 3 years.

EXAMPLE 5 If $1000 is invested at a simple-interest rate of 8% per year, what amount must be invested at a simple-interest rate of 12% per year in order for the total investment to earn $242 of interest in 1 year?

SOLUTION Let P represent the amount invested at 12%. The following table describes the situation.

Principal	Interest Rate	Time	Interest Earned
$1000	0.08	1	0.08($1000)
P	0.12	1	0.12P
$1000 + P$	—	1	$242

Since the income from the total investment must equal the sum of the incomes on the individual investments, we have

$$0.08(1000) + 0.12P = 242$$

$$80 + 0.12P = 242$$

$$0.12P = 162$$

$$P = \frac{162}{0.12} = 1350.$$

Hence $1350 must be invested at 12%.

PRACTICE
PROBLEM 2

(Solution on page 87) Suppose that a widow has $10,000, part of which she is going to invest at a simple interest rate of 8% per year and the remainder at 10% per year. How much should she invest at each rate so that her total annual income is $950?

EXERCISES 3-4

TAX PROBLEMS

(See Example 1.)

1. Compute the amount of tax and the total cost of a $15.75 fan if the tax rate is 4%.

2. Compute the amount of tax and the total cost of a room in San Francisco if the room rate is $58 and the city hotel tax rate is 10.25%.

In problems 3 and 4, determine the total cost of all the items together whose marked prices are listed, where grocery items are subject to a 1% sales tax and nongrocery items are subject to a 6.5% sales tax.

3.

	Marked Prices				
Grocery	$ .33	$ .97	$1.05	$ .29	$2.36
Nongrocery	$1.29	$3.27	$1.18		

4.

	Marked Prices				
Grocery	$ 1.89	$2.17	$ .43	$6.09	
Nongrocery	$11.24	$5.23	$12.19	$1.01	$5.95

(See Example 2 and Practice Problem 1.)

5. Find the sale price of a $36.90 hair dryer marked down 30%.

6. Find the sale price of a $67.75 clock radio marked down 12%.

7. Find the total cost of a $250.00 watch on sale for 42% off if the sales tax rate is 6.2%.

8. Margaret wanted a $4800 fur coat for Christmas, but could not afford to buy it. After Christmas the coat was put on sale for 25% off. Find the sale price of the coat. What was the total cost of the coat on sale if the sales tax rate was 14%?

9. Find the markdown percent if a $1500 lawn mower is marked down $180.

10. Find the markdown percent if a $26.50 flannel shirt is marked down $6.89.

11. Find the markdown percent if a $4800 coat is put on sale for $3456.

12. Find the markdown percent if a $343.00 clock is put on sale for $264.11.

13. What is the presale price of a toy marked down 15% to a sale price of $16.98?

14. What is the presale price of a tape player marked down 18% to $75.85?

15. What is the presale price of a sweater marked down 30% to a sale price of $31.50?

16. What is the presale price of a dishwasher marked down 15% to a sale price of $352.95?

(See Example 3.)

17. A salesclerk makes a commission of 7% on all her sales. If her monthly sales amount to $2500, what is her commission that month?

18. Mac, the merciless mechanic, makes a daily salary of $125 plus a commission of 5% of the price of the parts he installs. If he spends 1 day installing $275 worth of parts on a car, what is his pay for that day?

19. A sales manager makes a commission of 10% of her monthly sales in addition to 3% of the monthly sales of 3 salesclerks working in her department. If total sales for 1 month are $6700, of which $1200 are the manager's sales, what is the amount of her commission?

20. A salesperson makes a commission of 8% on the first $3000 worth of monthly sales, and 12% on all sales beyond the first $3000. Compute the amount of commission on monthly sales amounting to (a) $2523; (b) $7352.

(See Examples 4 and 5 and Practice Problem 2.)

Compute the simple interest and amount when the principal, rate, and time of a loan are as given in problems 21–24.

21. $P = \$1500$, $r = 18\%$ per year, $t = 5$ years

22. $P = \$500$, $r = 2\%$ per month, $t = 9$ months

23. $P = \$1100$, $r = 8\%$ per quarter, $t = 2$ years

24. $P = \$100$, $r = 9.5\%$ per year, $t = 20$ years

25. Suppose that part of $10,000 is to be invested at 5% and the remainder at 8.75%. Determine how much should be invested at each rate to yield an annual income of $830.

26. Suppose that part of $15,000 is to be invested at 8% and the remainder at 10.2%. How much should be invested at each rate to yield an annual income of $1431?

27. If $900 is invested at the rate of 10%, how much additional money needs to be invested at 5% so that the annual income from the two investments together is $150?

28. If $4000 is invested at 13%, how much additional money needs to be invested at 15% so that the annual income from the two investments together is $970?

29. Jessie has twice as much money invested in bonds paying 6% as she has in stocks paying 12%. If her total annual income is $3600, how much does she have invested in each?

30. Fernando has 4 times as much money invested in bonds paying 9% as he has in stocks paying 21%. If his total annual income is $511.50, how much does he have invested in each?

31. If $4000 is invested at 2% and $5500 is invested at 9%, at what rate should $3000 be invested so that the total annual income from the three investments is $800?

32. If $3000 is invested at 8% and $4500 is invested at 18%, at what rate should $10,000 be invested so that the total annual income from the three investments is $2550?

SOLUTIONS FOR PRACTICE PROBLEMS

1. Amount of markdown = retail price − sale price

$$= \$20.00 - \$17.60$$

$$= \$2.40$$

$$\text{Markdown percent} = \frac{\text{amount of markdown}}{\text{retail price}}$$

$$= \frac{2.40}{20.00}$$

$$= 0.12 = 12\%$$

2. Let P be the principal invested at 8%.

Principal	Rate	Time	Interest
P	0.08	1	0.08P
$10,000 - P$	0.10	1	0.10($10,000 - P$)
$10,000	—	1	$950

$$0.08P + 0.10(10{,}000 - P) = 950$$
$$0.08P + 1{,}000 - 0.10P = 950$$
$$-0.02P = -50$$
$$P = \frac{50}{0.02} = \$2500$$

PRACTICE TEST for Chapter 3

1. The sum of three consecutive integers is 282. Find the integers.

2. Margie is one year less than three times as old as her son Barry. In ten years Margie will be twice as old as Barry will be then. Find their present ages.

3. A car salesperson sold one more than twice as many compacts as midsize cars and six more pickups as he did compacts. If he sold a total of 28 vehicles, how many of each type did he sell?

4. Suppose that 52 dimes, nickels, and quarters are worth $7.90. If there is one more nickel than dimes, how many of each type coin are there?

5. How many grams of an alloy containing 60% nickel must be mixed with 400 grams of an alloy containing 36% nickel if the resulting alloy is to contain 50% nickel?

6. At 9:00 A.M. Mike began walking at the rate of 3 miles per hour toward the playground. Fifteen minutes later his little sister Sue discovered that Mike had left without her, so she began running 8 miles per hour to catch up with him. At what time did Sue catch up with Mike?

7. An ice crusher can crush enough ice to fill an ice chest in 20 minutes. A full ice chest can melt and drain in 90 minutes. How long does it take to fill the ice chest if while the ice crusher is working, some of the ice melts and the water drains out of the chest?

8. If a $200.00 suit is put on sale for 25% off, what is the total cost of the suit if the sales tax rate is 7.4%?

9. A car salesperson receives a 14% commission on new-car sales and a 3% commission on used-car sales. What is the amount of her commission if her total sales amount to $52,000, where $11,500 are used-car sales?

10. An investor invests a sum of money at 12% and twice that amount at 10%. What is his total amount invested if his total annual income from both investments is $1600?

Linear Equations and Inequalities in Two Variables

4-1
Straight Lines

In Section 1-2 it was shown how a one-to-one correspondence can be set up between the set of all real numbers and the set of all points on a line. Points are located on the line by their corresponding numbers, and the result is called a number line. The correspondence between the points and the numbers is sometimes referred to as a **coordinate system** for the line, and the number that corresponds to a point is called the **coordinate** of the point on the line. The **Cartesian** (or **rectangular**) **coordinate system** furnishes a similar method for locating points in the plane.

To set up a Cartesian coordinate system for the plane, we begin with a horizontal number line and a vertical number line which intersect at their zero points. (It is customary to use the same scale, or unit of length, on the two lines, but this is not required.) The horizontal line is called the *x*-**axis**, the vertical line is called the *y*-**axis**, and they are labeled as shown in Figure 4.1. Normally, the axes are positioned so that the positive directions are to the right on the *x*-axis, and upward on the *y*-axis.

With the coordinate axes drawn, points in the plane are made to correspond to ordered pairs (x, y) of real numbers x and y by the following rule: The first number, x, is the distance from the *y*-axis to the point, measured positive to the right, negative to the left; the second number, y, is the distance from the x-axis to the point, measured positive upward and negative downward. The ordered pair (x, y) is called the **coordinates** of the point. This is illustrated in Figure 4.1.

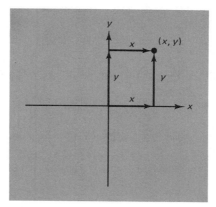

FIGURE 4.1

The first number, or x-value, in an ordered pair (x, y) is called the **x-coordinate**, or the **abscissa**, of the point with coordinates (x, y). The second number, or y-value, is called the **y-coordinate**, or the **ordinate**, of the point with coordinates (x, y). It is common practice to shorten the phrase "the point with coordinates (x, y)" to "the point (x, y)." In Figure 4.2 we have located the points $(4, 2)$, $(-4, 2)$, $(-4, -2)$, $(4, -2)$, and $(0, 0)$. The point $(0, 0)$ where the axes cross is called the **origin**.

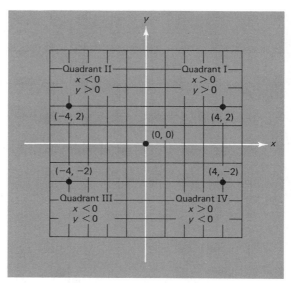

FIGURE 4.2

The point located by the coordinates (x, y) is sometimes called the **graph** of the ordered pair (x, y). The process of locating the point with given coordinates is referred to as **plotting** the point, or **graphing** the point.

The two coordinate axes separate the plane into four regions, which are called **quadrants**. The quadrants are numbered as indicated in Figure 4.2, and the corresponding conditions on the coordinates are indicated there. The points along the coordinate axes are not in any quadrant.

EXAMPLE 1   Graph (plot) the points A, B, C, D, and E which have the indicated coordinates:

$$A(3, 4); \quad B(-4, 0); \quad C(2, -3); \quad D(0, 5); \quad E(-3, 2).$$

SOLUTION   The points are plotted as shown in Figure 4.3.

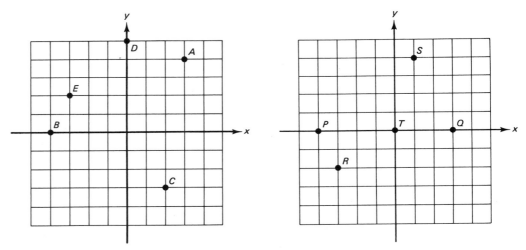

FIGURE 4.3   **FIGURE 4.4**

EXAMPLE 2   Points P, Q, R, S, and T are located on a Cartesian coordinate system in Figure 4.4. Find the coordinates of each of these points.

SOLUTION   The coordinates are given by

$$P(-4, 0); \quad Q(3, 0); \quad R(-3, -2); \quad S(1, 4); \quad T(0, 0).$$

One of the simplest uses of a Cartesian coordinate system is to provide a picture of the solution sets to equations in two variables. We have seen in Chapter 2 that the solution set for an equation in one variable is the set of all values of the variable that make the equation a true statement. The solution set for an equation in two variables is defined in a similar way.

Definition 4-1 The **solution set** for an equation in two variables x and y is the set of ordered pairs (x, y) of real numbers x and y which make the equation a true statement. The **graph of the solution set** of an equation in x and y is the set of all points with coordinates (x, y) that satisfy the equation (that is, make the equation a true statement). This graph is usually referred to as the **graph of the equation**.

In this section we are interested in the graphs of equations in x and y which are equivalent to an equation in the special form

$$ax + by = c,$$

where not both a and b are zero. Equations of this type are called **linear equations** because of the fact that the graph of such an equation is always a **straight line** (a fact that we shall not prove here).

Definition 4-2 The special form

$$\boxed{ax + by = c}$$

is called the **standard form** for an equation of a line.

As an illustration, consider the graph of the equation

$$y = x + 3.$$

This equation can be put in standard form $ax + by = c$ by subtracting x from each side:

$$(-1)x + y = 3.$$

However, it is easier to graph by using the form $y = x + 3$ and assigning values to x. In this form, x is called the **independent variable**, and y is called the **dependent variable**. For example, if we assign the value -4 to x, we easily obtain

$$y = -4 + 3$$
$$= -1.$$

This illustrates how the value of y *depends* on the value of x. The point $(-4, -1)$ is in the graph of $y = x + 2$. To obtain some other points in the graph, we can use $-3, -1, 0, 2, 3$ as values of x in succession and obtain

$$(-3, 0), \quad (-1, 2), \quad (0, 3), \quad (2, 5), \quad (3, 6).$$

These points are plotted in Figure 4.5, and the straight-line graph is drawn through the points. The graph of the equation $y = x + 3$ consists of *all* of the points in the line: Every point that lies in the line has coordinates that satisfy the equation, and every point which has coordinates that satisfy the equation lies in the line. It is convenient to record points of the graph in a table such as we have in Figure 4.5.

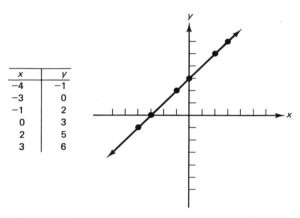

x	y
−4	−1
−3	0
−1	2
0	3
2	5
3	6

FIGURE 4.5

Actually, only two points are needed to determine a straight line, so more work was done in Figure 4.5 than was necessary to graph the equation $y = x + 3$. It is a good idea to plot three points, though, so that the third point will provide a check on the other two.

The easiest points to use in graphing a line are the points where the line crosses one of the coordinate axes. The values of the variables at these points have special names: If there is a point where the graph crosses the x-axis, the x-coordinate of that point is called an **x-intercept**, and if there is a point where the graph crosses the y-axis, the y-coordinate of that point is called a **y-intercept**. If there is an x-intercept, it is found by solving for x after setting $y = 0$ in the equation. Similarly, setting $x = 0$ and solving for y will yield the y-intercept, if there is one.

EXAMPLE 3   Graph the equation

$$3x + 4y = 12$$

and find the x-intercept and y-intercept, if they exist.

SOLUTION   To find the x-intercept, we set $y = 0$ and obtain

$$3x + 4(0) = 12$$
$$3x = 12$$
$$x = 4.$$

Thus the x-intercept is 4. To find the y-intercept, we set $x = 0$ and obtain

$$3(0) + 4y = 12$$
$$4y = 12$$
$$y = 3,$$

so the y-intercept is 3. To get a third point, we let $x = 8$ (there is no particular reason for this choice):

$$3(8) + 4y = 12$$
$$4y = -12$$
$$y = -3.$$

Figure 4.6 shows the points that we have found and the graph of the equation $3x + 4y = 12$.

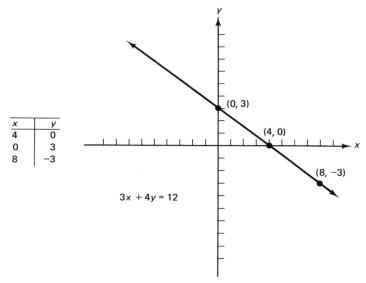

x	y
4	0
0	3
8	-3

$3x + 4y = 12$

FIGURE 4.6

PRACTICE PROBLEM 1   (Solution on page 101) Graph

$$2x - 3y = 6$$

and find the x-intercept and y-intercept, if they exist.

EXAMPLE 4   Graph the equation

$$y = 4$$

and find the *x*-intercept and *y*-intercept, if they exist.

SOLUTION   It is worth noting that the standard form for this equation is

$$0(x) + 1(y) = 4,$$

because this emphasizes that, for *every* value of *x*, the corresponding value of *y* is 4. That is, the graph consists of all points that have coordinates (*x*, 4). These points all lie on the horizontal line 4 units above the *x*-axis, as shown in Figure 4.7. The *y*-intercept is 4, and an *x*-intercept does not exist since the graph does not cross the *x*-axis.

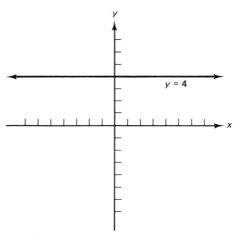

FIGURE 4.7

EXAMPLE 5   Graph

$$x = -3.$$

SOLUTION   Without going into as much detail as in Example 4, it is clear that the graph consists of all points that have coordinates (−3, *y*), and consequently is a vertical line 3 units to the left of the *y*-axis. The *x*-intercept is −3, and there is no *y*-intercept. The graph is shown in Figure 4.8.

Examples 4 and 5 illustrate the general facts that the graph of an equation of the form

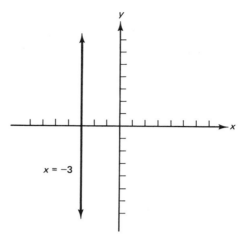

FIGURE 4.8

$$y = c, \quad \text{where } c \text{ is a constant,}$$

is always a **horizontal line**, and the graph of an equation of the form

$$x = c, \quad \text{where } c \text{ is a constant,}$$

is always a **vertical line**.

In applications, physical considerations sometimes place restrictions on one or both of the variables in a linear equation. (For example, if x represents the number of automobiles manufactured by a factory, then x cannot be negative.) For this reason, it is appropriate to consider an example of this type.

EXAMPLE 6 Graph

$$y = 2x + 1 \quad (x \geq -1).$$

SOLUTION The restriction is that x must be equal to or greater than -1. Since this is our first example of this type, we solve the problem in two steps:

(a) We graph the entire line that has the equation $y = 2x + 1$.
(b) We retain only that part of the line where $x \geq -1$.

It is easily found that the x-intercept for the line is $-\frac{1}{2}$, and the y-intercept is 1. Since -1 is the cutoff point for the x-values, we include $x = -1$ in our values, and graph the whole line as shown in part (a) of Figure 4.9.

The graph of $y = 2x + 1$ $(x \geq -1)$ is then obtained by deleting all the points for which $x < -1$. This resulting *half-line* is shown in part (b) of Figure 4.9.

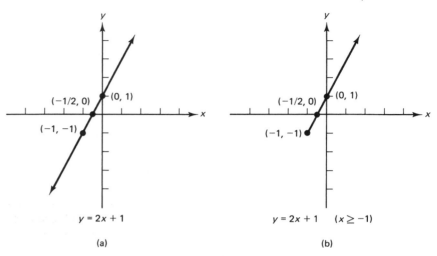

FIGURE 4.9

In graphing equations that involve an absolute value, half-lines arise in a very natural way.

EXAMPLE 7 Graph

$$y = |x - 2|.$$

SOLUTION From the definition of absolute value, $y = |x - 2|$ is equivalent to

$$y = x - 2 \qquad \text{if } x - 2 \geq 0;$$
$$y = -(x - 2) \qquad \text{if } x - 2 < 0.$$

We note that $x - 2 \geq 0$ is equivalent to $x \geq 2$, and $x - 2 < 0$ is equivalent to $x < 2$. All we need to do, then, is to graph the two half-lines

$$y = x - 2 \qquad \text{if } x \geq 2;$$
$$y = -x + 2 \qquad \text{if } x < 2.$$

This is done by the method used in Example 6. The tables and graph are shown in Figure 4.10.

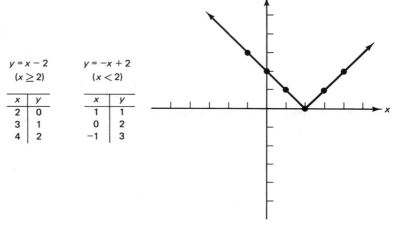

$y = x - 2$ $(x \geq 2)$			$y = -x + 2$ $(x < 2)$	
x	y		x	y
2	0		1	1
3	1		0	2
4	2		−1	3

FIGURE 4.10

***PRACTICE
PROBLEM 2**   (Solution on page 101) Graph $y = |x + 1|$.

EXERCISES 4-1

Graph the following points. (See Example 1.)

1. (4, 1)   2. (1, 3)

3. (−2, 3)   4. (−3, 1)

5. (0, −4)   6. (0, −2)

7. (−3, −2)   8. (−2, −5)

Graph the straight lines that are determined by the following pairs of points.

9. (−2, 0), (1, 4)   10. (0, 3), (2, 1)

11. (−2, −1), (1, 2)   12. (−1, −2), (2, 1)

13. (2, 3), (−2, 3)   14. (3, 2), (−1, 2)

Graph each equation, and find the x-intercepts and y-intercepts, if they exist. (See Examples 3–5 and Practice Problem 1.)

15. $y = 2x - 4$ 16. $y = 3x - 12$

17. $y + 8 = 3x + 2$ 18. $y - 5 = 3x + 7$

19. $3x + 2y = 12$ 20. $2x + 5y = 10$

21. $3x - 2y = 6$

22. $5x - 2y = 10$

23. $4x + y + 8 = 0$

24. $5x + 4y + 20 = 0$

25. $x = -4$

26. $x = 2$

27. $y = 5$

28. $y = -3$

29. $2x + y = 0$

30. $x + 2y = 0$

In problems 31–34, round the intercepts to the nearest tenth.

C31. $1.13x + 2.37y = 24.8$

C32. $2.53x + 3.14y = 32.4$

C33. $21.3x + 14.6y = 356$

C34. $19.2x - 24.8y = 255$

Graph the following half-lines. (See Example 6.)

35. $y = x + 1 \ (x \geq 0)$

36. $y = x - 2 \ (x \geq 0)$

37. $y = x - 3 \ (x \geq -1)$

38. $y = x + 4 \ (x \geq -2)$

39. $y = 2x - 4 \ (x < 1)$

40. $y = 3x - 6 \ (x < 3)$

41. $y = -x + 1 \ (x > 0)$

42. $y = -x + 2 \ (x > 0)$

Graph each equation. (See Example 7 and Practice Problem 2.)

*43. $y = |x|$

*44. $y = |x + 3|$

*45. $y = |x - 3|$

*46. $y = |x - 2|$

*47. $y = |x| - 3$

*48. $y = |x| - 2$

*49. $|y| = x - 3$

*50. $|y| = x - 2$

51. On a loan of $1000, a certain bank charges a $10 credit investigation fee and interest on the $1000 at the rate of 2% per month. The total cost of such a loan after x months is

$$y = 10 + (0.02)(1000)x$$
$$= 10 + 20x.$$

Find the total cost after (a) 3 months; (b) 6 months.

52. Graph the equation in problem 51, using appropriate restrictions on x to reflect the meaning of that variable.

53. The approximate population P of the United States between 1880 and 1950 is given by the formula

$$P = 50 + 1.5x,$$

where P is the population in millions of people and x is the number of years since 1880. (Thus $x = 0$ in 1880, $x = 30$ in 1910, etc.) Find the population P for each of the following years: (a) 1890; (b) 1900; (c) 1930; (d) 1950.

54. Graph the equation in problem 53, using appropriate restrictions on x to reflect the meaning of that variable.

1. Setting $y = 0$ in $2x - 3y = 6$ and solving for x, we find that the x-intercept is 3. Setting $x = 0$ gives -2 as the y-intercept. The graph is shown in Figure 4.11.

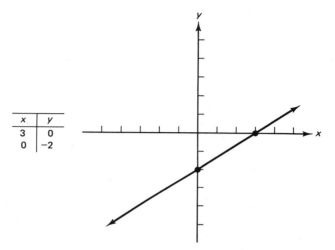

x	y
3	0
0	-2

FIGURE 4.11

*2. The equation $y = |x + 1|$ is equivalent to

$$y = \begin{cases} x + 1 & \text{if } x \geq -1 \\ -x - 1 & \text{if } x < -1. \end{cases}$$

The graph is shown in Figure 4.12.

FIGURE 4.12

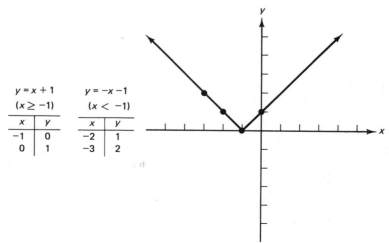

$y = x + 1$		$y = -x - 1$	
$(x \geq -1)$		$(x < -1)$	
x	y	x	y
-1	0	-2	1
0	1	-3	2

It was noted in the preceding section that two distinct points determine a straight line. A line is also determined by one of its points and its direction. One way to describe the direction of a line is to give its *slope*. The definition of slope is as follows.

Definition 4-3 The **slope** m of the line that passes through two distinct points (x_1, y_1) and (x_2, y_2) is

$$m = \frac{y_2 - y_1}{x_2 - x_1}.$$

In Figure 4.13 a line is drawn through the points (x_1, y_1) and (x_2, y_2). As indicated in the figure, the slope of a line is the ratio of the change in y to the change in x, or the ratio of the *rise* to the *run*:

$$m = \frac{y_2 - y_1}{x_2 - x_1} = \frac{\text{change in } y}{\text{change in } x} = \frac{\text{rise}}{\text{run}}.$$

In Figure 4.13(a), a line is drawn that slants upward to the right. For such a line, the value of y increases as x increases along the line, and the slope is *positive* since the rise and the run are numbers of like sign. On the other hand, if a line slants downward to the right as in Figure 4.13(b), the value of y decreases as x increases along the line, and the slope is *negative* since the rise and the run are numbers of opposite sign.

FIGURE 4.13

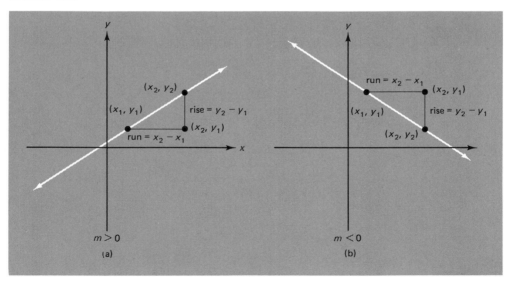

In summary, a line with *positive* slope *rises* from left to right, and a line with *negative* slope *falls* from left to right.

The special cases where a line is horizontal or vertical are pictured in Figure 4.14. In Figure 4.14(a), a horizontal line is drawn through two points where $y_1 = y_2$ and $m = 0$. In Figure 4.14(b), a vertical line is drawn through two points where $x_1 = x_2$ and the slope is undefined since

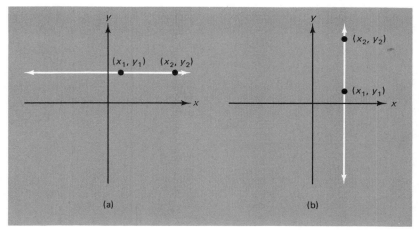

FIGURE 4.14

$x_2 - x_1 = 0$ in the denominator of the formula for m. These drawings illustrate the following important facts:

> 1. Any horizontal line has slope 0.
> 2. Any vertical line has an undefined slope.

One more remark is in order about the formula in Definition 4-3. Since the ratios of corresponding sides in similar triangles are equal, the slope of a line is independent of the choice of the two distinct points (x_1, y_1) and (x_2, y_2) on the line (see Figure 4.15).

EXAMPLE 1   Find the slope of the line that contains the points $(3, -1)$ and $(-2, 9)$.

SOLUTION   If we choose $(3, -1)$ to be (x_1, y_1) and $(-2, 9)$ to be (x_2, y_2), the slope formula gives

$$m = \frac{y_2 - y_1}{x_2 - x_1} = \frac{9 - (-1)}{-2 - 3} = \frac{10}{-5} = -2.$$

Since the slope of a line is independent of the choice of the two points

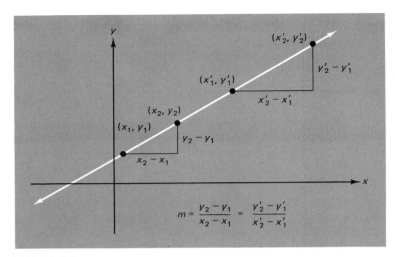

FIGURE 4.15

on the line, we could just as well choose $(-2, 9)$ to be (x_1, y_1) and $(3, -1)$ to be (x_2, y_2). With this choice, the computation appears as

$$m = \frac{y_2 - y_1}{x_2 - x_1} = \frac{-1 - 9}{3 - (-2)} = \frac{-10}{5} = -2,$$

the same answer as obtained before.

EXAMPLE 2 Find the slope of the line through $(2, -1)$ and $(2, 4)$.

SOLUTION With $(2, -1)$ as (x_1, y_1) and $(2, 4)$ as (x_2, y_2), we have

$$m = \frac{y_2 - y_1}{x_2 - x_1} = \frac{4 - (-1)}{2 - 2} = \frac{5}{0}.$$

But division by zero is impossible, so the slope of this line is *undefined*.

EXAMPLE 3 Find the slope of the line that has the equation
$$5x + 3y = 30.$$

SOLUTION Any two points on the line can be used to find the slope. The easiest ones to use are those where the line crosses the coordinate axes:

when $y = 0$, $5x = 30$ and $x = 6$;

when $x = 0$, $3y = 30$ and $y = 10$.

Thus $(6, 0)$ and $(0, 10)$ are the points where the line crosses the axes, and

$$m = \frac{y_2 - y_1}{x_2 - x_1} = \frac{10 - 0}{0 - 6} = -\frac{5}{3}.$$

The next example shows how the slope of a line can be used in drawing the graph of the line.

EXAMPLE 4 Graph the line through (1, 2) that has slope $-\frac{3}{4}$.

SOLUTION To draw the line, we need only find another point on the line besides the point (1, 2). The information that we have to work with is that

$$m = \frac{\text{change in } y}{\text{change in } x} = -\frac{3}{4}.$$

One easy way to find another point on the line is to take -3 as the change in y and 4 as the change in x, beginning at (1, 2). This gives a new y-value of

$$y = 2 + (-3) = -1,$$

and a new x-value of

$$x = 1 + 4 = 5.$$

That is, $(5, -1)$ is a second point on the line. Using this point, the line is drawn in Figure 4.16. We could have found a second point on the line by moving 3 units in the y-direction and -4 units in the x-direction, or by any other choice of changes in y and x which had a ratio of $-\frac{3}{4}$.

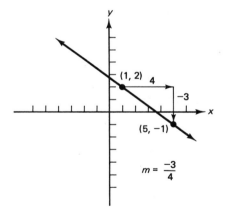

FIGURE 4.16

PRACTICE PROBLEM 1 (Solution on page 108) Graph the line that has x-intercept -2 and slope 3.

Although we do not go into the details here, it can be shown that:

Two lines with slope m_1 and m_2 are

1. **Parallel** if and only if $m_1 = m_2$, and

2. **Perpendicular** if and only if $m_1 m_2 = -1$, or $m_2 = -\dfrac{1}{m_1}$.

EXAMPLE 5 Determine if the following pair of lines are parallel or perpendicular lines:

$$4x - 3y = 12 \quad \text{and} \quad 15x + 20y = -60.$$

SOLUTION We need to find the slope of each line so that they can be compared. These slopes can be found easily by using the points where the lines cross the coordinate axes. The line

$$4x - 3y = 12 \text{ crosses at } (3, 0) \text{ and } (0, -4),$$

so it has slope

$$m_1 = \frac{0 - (-4)}{3 - 0} = \frac{4}{3}.$$

The line

$$15x + 20y = -60 \text{ crosses at } (-4, 0) \text{ and } (0, -3)$$

so it has slope

$$m_2 = \frac{0 - (-3)}{-4 - 0} = -\frac{3}{4}.$$

The lines are not parallel since they have unequal slopes, and they are *perpendicular* since $m_1 = \frac{4}{3}$ and $m_2 = -\frac{3}{4}$ are negative reciprocals of each other (that is, $m_2 = -1/m_1$).

PRACTICE PROBLEM 2 (Solution on page 108) Determine if the following pair of lines are parallel or perpendicular lines.

$$y - 3x = -6 \quad \text{and} \quad 5x + 15y = 6$$

EXERCISES 4-2

If it exists, find the slope of the line through the given pair of points. (See Examples 1 and 2.)

1. $(1, -2)$ and $(-3, 1)$ 2. $(4, 0)$ and $(7, 3)$

3. $(0, 2)$ and $(3, 5)$ 4. $(0, 0)$ and $(2, 3)$

5. $(1, 3)$ and $(-3, 3)$ 6. $(-2, 5)$ and $(5, 5)$

7. $(7, -2)$ and $(7, 7)$ 8. $(3, 5)$ and $(3, 1)$

In problems 9 and 10, round the answer to the nearest hundredth.

C9. $(1.37, -25.1)$ and $(-4.33, -72.9)$

C10. $(4.79, 3.55)$ and $(2.61, -7.73)$

Graph the line that has the given equation, and find the slope of the line, if it exists. (See Example 3.)

11. $2x + 5y = 10$ 12. $4x + 3y = 12$

13. $x - 2y = 4$ 14. $x - 3y = 6$

15. $2x - y = 4$ 16. $3x - 2y = 6$

17. $y = 2x - 3$ 18. $y = 3x - 4$

19. $x = 1 - 2y$ 20. $x = 7 - 2y$

21. $4x = 5y + 7$ 22. $3x = 4y + 5$

23. $x = -3$ 24. $x = \frac{1}{2}$

25. $y = 1$ 26. $y = -2$

Graph the line that satisfies the given conditions. (See Example 4 and Practice Problem 1.)

27. through $(1, -2)$, slope 3   28. through $(-3, -1)$, slope 2

29. through $(-1, 2)$, slope -2 30. through $(1, 4)$, slope -3

31. through $(2, 3)$, slope $-\frac{2}{3}$ 32. through $(-1, 3)$, slope $-\frac{3}{2}$

33. y-intercept 2, slope $-\frac{1}{2}$ 34. y-intercept -1, slope $\frac{1}{2}$

35. x-intercept 2, slope 1   36. x-intercept 1, slope 2

37. y-intercept -2, slope 0

38. x-intercept -3, slope does not exist

Determine if the following pairs of lines are parallel or perpendicular lines. (See Example 5 and Practice Problem 2.)

39. The line through $(1, -2)$ and $(4, 3)$, and the line through $(2, 4)$ and $(-3, 7)$.

40. The line through $(5, 2)$ and $(1, -5)$, and the line through $(-2, 1)$ and $(2, 8)$.

41. $x = 3$ and $y = 2$

42. $x = -2$ and $x = 4$

43. $4x = 2y + 5$ and $y = 2x$

44. $6x = 2y + 9$ and $y = 3x$

45. $2x - 5y = 10$ and $15x + 6y = 30$

46. $5x - 3y = 15$ and $6x + 10y = 15$

47. $2x + 3y = 6$ and $3x + 2y = 6$

48. $3x + 5y = 15$ and $5x + 3y = 15$

*49. The line through $(2, 6)$ and $(-3, y)$ is parallel to a line that has slope 2. Find the value of y.

*50. The line through $(-4, 9)$ and $(x, 3)$ is perpendicular to a line that has slope 3. Find the value of x.

*51. A parallelogram is a four-sided figure which has opposite sides that are parallel. Show that the points $(-3, -2)$, $(2, 4)$, $(4, 7)$, and $(-1, 1)$ are vertices of a parallelogram.

*52. Show that the points $(-2, 4)$, $(0, 8)$, and $(2, 2)$ are vertices of a right triangle.

SOLUTIONS FOR PRACTICE PROBLEMS

1. The point $(-2, 0)$ is on the line, and

$$m = \frac{\text{change in } y}{\text{change in } x} = 3 = \frac{3}{1}.$$

With 3 as the change in y and 1 as the change in x, we get new values of

$$y = 0 + 3 = 3 \quad \text{and} \quad x = -2 + 1 = -1.$$

This gives $(-1, 3)$ as another point on the line. The graph is drawn in Figure 4.17.

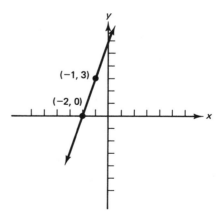

FIGURE 4.17

2. The line $y - 3x = -6$ crosses the coordinate axes at $(2, 0)$ and $(0, -6)$. Thus it has slope

$$m = \frac{-6 - 0}{0 - 2} = 3.$$

The line $5x + 15y = 6$ crosses the axes at $(\frac{6}{5}, 0)$ and $(0, \frac{2}{5})$, so it has slope

$$m = \frac{\frac{2}{5} - 0}{0 - \frac{6}{5}} = -\frac{1}{3}.$$

Since $m_2 = -1/m_1$, the two lines are perpendicular to each other.

The special form

$$ax + by = c,$$

where not both a and b are zero, was designated in Definition 4-2 as the *standard form* for an equation of a line. In this section we study two other special forms for equations of lines which are very useful in certain situations. These are known as the *slope–intercept form* and the *point–slope form*.

Consider a line that has slope m and y-intercept b; see Figure 4.18. Since b is the y-intercept, the point $(0, b)$ is on the line. Let (x, y) be any other point on the line. Using $(0, b)$ and (x, y) in the slope formula, we have

$$\frac{y - b}{x - 0} = m,$$

$$y - b = mx,$$

and

$$y = mx + b.$$

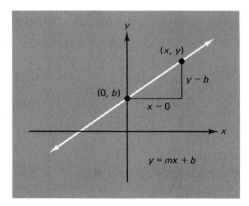

FIGURE 4.18

This last equation is satisfied by every point (x, y) on the line, including $(0, b)$. Thus we have established the following theorem.

Theorem 4-4 The line with slope m and y-intercept b has an equation of the form

$$\boxed{y = mx + b.} \tag{1}$$

This particular form for the equation of the line is called the **slope–intercept form**.

EXAMPLE 1   Write an equation of the line with slope 4 and *y*-intercept 2.

SOLUTION   Simple substitution of $m = 4$ and $b = 2$ into the slope–intercept form gives

$$y = 4x + 2.$$

It is easy to see that if the equation of a line is written in the form of equation (1), the slope of the line is equal to the coefficient of x and the y-intercept of the line is equal to the constant b. For example, the line with equation

$$y = -3x + 8$$

has slope -3 and y-intercept 8. This observation provides a much easier way to find the slope than by using two points on the line as we did in Section 4-2. We can simply solve the equation for y, and the slope is then the coefficient of x.

EXAMPLE 2   Find the slope and *y*-intercept of the line with equation
$$3x - 7y = 14.$$

SOLUTION   Solving the equation for y, we have
$$-7y = -3x + 14$$
$$y = \tfrac{3}{7}x - 2.$$
Thus the slope is $m = \tfrac{3}{7}$, and the y-intercept is -2.

In more advanced work in mathematics, one often needs to write an equation for a line that contains a specified point and has a specified slope. To obtain an equation for such a line, let (x_1, y_1) represent the specified point and let m be the specified slope. For any other point (x, y) on the line, the slope formula gives

$$\frac{y - y_1}{x - x_1} = m,$$

and
$$y - y_1 = m(x - x_1).$$

The last equation is also satisfied by the coordinates (x_1, y_1), so it is an equation for *all* the points on the line. This important result is recorded in Theorem 4-5.

Theorem 4-5   The line through (x_1, y_1) with slope m has an equation of the form

$$y - y_1 = m(x - x_1). \tag{2}$$

This form for the equation of the line is called the **point–slope form**.

EXAMPLE 3   Write an equation, in slope–intercept form, of the line which passes through $(3, -7)$ and has slope -2.

SOLUTION   Using $m = -2$ and $(3, -7)$ as (x_1, y_1) in the point–slope form, we get
$$y - (-7) = -2(x - 3),$$
or
$$y + 7 = -2(x - 3).$$
To obtain the slope–intercept form, we solve for y:
$$y + 7 = -2x + 6,$$
$$y = -2x - 1.$$

PRACTICE PROBLEM 1   (Solution on page 115) Write an equation, in slope–intercept form, of the line through the points $(-3, 2)$ and $(5, -2)$.

The next example illustrates that the slope of a line need not always be given explicitly.

EXAMPLE 4   Write an equation, in slope–intercept form, for the line that passes through $(2, -1)$ and is perpendicular to the line $2x - 3y = 6$.

SOLUTION   To obtain the slope of the required line, we must first find the slope of $2x - 3y = 6$. Solving for y in this equation, we have

$$-3y = -2x + 6,$$
$$y = \tfrac{2}{3}x - 2.$$

Thus $2x - 3y = 6$ has slope

$$m_1 = \tfrac{2}{3},$$

and the required line has slope

$$m_2 = -\frac{1}{m_1} = -\tfrac{3}{2}$$

since the two lines are perpendicular. Using the slope $-\tfrac{3}{2}$ and the point $(2, -1)$ in the point–slope form, the desired equation is obtained as follows:

$$y - (-1) = -\tfrac{3}{2}(x - 2),$$
$$y + 1 = -\tfrac{3}{2}x + 3,$$
$$y = -\tfrac{3}{2}x + 2.$$

PRACTICE PROBLEM 2 (Solution on page 115) Write an equation, in standard form, for the line that passes through $(-1, 3)$ and is parallel to the line $4x + 2y = 9$.

In practical situations, lines may be encountered that do not have the nice appearance of our "textbook examples." One of the most common difficulties that occurs is the problem of scale: One of the variables in a linear equation may have great magnitude in comparison with the other variable. In such cases, we make an appropriate adjustment of scale on the axes, and use approximate locations of points. This is illustrated in the following example.

EXAMPLE 5 Sketch the graph of the line that has the equation

$$601x - 1.87y = -203,$$

and find the slope and y-intercept.

SOLUTION Solving for y, we have

$$-1.87y = -601x - 203,$$
$$y = \frac{601}{1.87}x + \frac{203}{1.87}.$$

The slope is $m = 601/1.87$, and the y-intercept is $b = 203/1.87$. To locate another point on the graph, we find the x-intercept:

$$601x = -203,$$
$$x = -\tfrac{203}{601}.$$

We have a slope near 300 (more accurately, 321.39), a y-intercept near 100 (more accurately, 108.56), and an x-intercept near $-\frac{1}{3}$ (more accurately, -0.338). To make a reasonable picture, we use approximate locations on a large scale on the x-axis, marked off in units, and a very small scale on the y-axis, marked off in hundreds. This is shown in Figure 4.19. Notice that the slope is badly distorted by the scaling, so that it appears to be nowhere near 300.

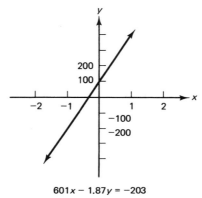

$601x - 1.87y = -203$

FIGURE 4.19

EXERCISES 4-3

Graph the line that has the given equation, and find the slope and y-intercept, if they exist. (See Example 2.)

1. $2x - y = 6$ 2. $3x + y = 6$
3. $3x - 4y = 12$ 4. $4x - 5y = 20$
5. $2x + 5y = 0$ 6. $3x - 5y = 0$
7. $x = -4$ 8. $y = 3$

Find an equation of the straight line that satisfies the given conditions, and write the equation in slope–intercept form. (See Examples 1 and 3 and Practice Problem 1.)

9. slope 5, y-intercept -3 10. slope -2, y-intercept 4
11. slope -3, through $(2, -1)$ 12. slope 4, through $(-1, 1)$
13. horizontal, through $(3, 4)$ 14. vertical, through $(-2, 4)$
15. through $(-1, 2)$ and $(2, -4)$ 16. through $(-2, 3)$ and $(1, -1)$
17. x-intercept -2, y-intercept 3   18. x-intercept -2, y-intercept 4
19. x-intercept 0, slope 3   20. x-intercept 0, slope 2
21. slope -3, y-intercept 2   22. slope 4, y-intercept -8

23. x-intercept 4, slope does not exist

24. x-intercept 2, slope does not exist

25. y-intercept -1, through $(2, 1)$

26. x-intercept 2, through $(-1, -3)$

27. x-intercept 4, y-intercept does not exist

28. y-intercept -2, x-intercept does not exist

Find an equation of the straight line that satisfies the given conditions, and write the equation in standard form. (See Example 4 and Practice Problem 2.)

29. through $(-1, 2)$, parallel to $y = 3x - 6$

30. through $(2, -3)$, parallel to $y = 2x + 4$

31. through $(-2, 0)$, parallel to $6x + 10y = 15$

32. through $(0, 4)$, parallel to $3x - 2y = 5$

33. through $(0, 0)$, perpendicular to $y = 3x - 6$

34. through $(0, 0)$, perpendicular to $y = 2x + 4$

35. through $(-2, 0)$, perpendicular to $6x + 10y = 15$

36. through $(0, 4)$, perpendicular to $3x - 2y = 5$

37. Do the points $(-3, -2)$, $(0, 4)$, and $(1, 6)$ lie in the same straight line? Justify your answer.

38. Do the points $(-7, 5)$, $(-2, 2)$, and $(3, -1)$ lie in the same straight line? Justify your answer.

39. Charmelle bought a used Harley for \$550 and sold it 22 months later for \$220. During the time she owned the bike, it depreciated (lost value) at the same rate every month. The value y of the bike after x months is given by the linear equation

$$y = 550 - 15x.$$

This type of depreciation is known as *linear depreciation*.
(a) Find the monthly decrease in value of the bike.
(b) Compare the monthly decrease with the slope of the line with equation $y = 550 - 15x$.

40. Ms. Coblentz bought a washing machine for \$500 and sold it 15 months later for \$230. Assume that the machine, like the bike in problem 39, depreciated linearly at the same rate every month.
(a) How much value did the machine lose each month?
(b) Find a linear equation $y = mx + b$ that gives the value y of the machine after x months.

41. In producing a new book entitled *Algebra for Everybody*, the publisher finds that the number x of copies produced and the cost C, in dollars, of

producing these copies are related by a linear equation in x and C. Given that it costs \$90,000 to produce 2000 copies and \$102,000 to produce 4000 copies, find a linear equation in x and C.

42. The publisher of the book in problem 41 finds that the number x of copies produced and the profit P, in dollars, from producing and selling these copies are related by a linear equation in x and P. If profits are \$2000 when 20,000 copies are produced and sold, and profits are \$42,000 when 30,000 copies are sold, find a linear equation in x and P.

Graph the line that has the given equation, and find the slope and y-intercept. (See Example 5.)

C43. $41.6x + 1.08y = 207$ C44. $1.96x - 40.1y = 806$

*45. Find a formula for the slope of $ax + by = c$, if $b \neq 0$.

*46. Show that the line which passes through (x_1, y_1) and (x_2, y_2) has an equation of the form

$$y - y_1 = \frac{y_2 - y_1}{x_2 - x_1}(x - x_1). \text{ if } x_1 \neq x_2$$

SOLUTIONS FOR PRACTICE PROBLEMS

1. The slope of the line through $(-3, 2)$ and $(5, -2)$ is given by

$$m = \frac{y_2 - y_1}{x_2 - x_1} = \frac{-2 - 2}{5 - (-3)} = \frac{-4}{8} = -\frac{1}{2}.$$

Using the point–slope form for the equation of the line through $(-3, 2)$ with slope $m = -\frac{1}{2}$, we get

$$y - 2 = -\tfrac{1}{2}(x + 3).$$

To get the equation in slope-intercept form, we solve for y:

$$y - 2 = -\tfrac{1}{2}x - \tfrac{3}{2},$$
$$y = -\tfrac{1}{2}x + \tfrac{1}{2}.$$

2. Since the required line is parallel to $4x + 2y = 9$, it will have the same slope. To find the slope of $4x + 2y = 9$, we solve for y:

$$2y = -4x + 9,$$
$$y = -2x + \tfrac{9}{2}.$$

Thus $m = -2$, and an equation for the required line is

$$y - 3 = -2(x + 1).$$

To get the standard form $ax + by = c$, we collect the variable terms on the left, and the constant on the right:

$$y - 3 = -2x - 2,$$
$$2x + y = 1.$$

A **linear inequality** in x and y is a statement that is obtained from a linear equation such as $ax + by = c$ by replacing the equality symbol "$=$" by one of the inequality symbols "$<$," "$>$," "$\leq$," or "$\geq$." Some examples of linear inequalities are

$$2x + 3y < 12,$$
$$5x > 2y - 10,$$
$$y \leq 3x - 2,$$
$$7x - 2y + 14 \geq 0.$$

The definitions of solution set and graph of an equation in two variables extend readily to inequalities.

Definition 4-6 The **solution set** of an inequality in two variables x and y is the set of ordered pairs (x, y) of real numbers x and y that make the inequality a true statement. The **graph of the solution set** of an inequality in x and y is the set of all points in the plane with coordinates that satisfy the inequality. This graph is called the **graph of the inequality**.

In contrast to the graphs of linear equations, the graphs of linear inequalities are *regions* in the plane rather than straight lines. For instance, consider the graph of the inequality

$$y < x + 3.$$

To determine the graph of the inequality, we first consider the equality

$$y = x + 3.$$

The graph of this equality is drawn as a dashed line in Figure 4.20. Consider a particular point (x_0, y_0) on this line. Since this point is on the line, the coordinates satisfy the equation of the line:

$$y_0 = x_0 + 3.$$

Now a displacement from (x_0, y_0) to a point straight below (x_0, y_0) produces a point that has coordinates (x_0, y), where $y < y_0$; see Figure 4.20. But $y_0 = x_0 + 3$, so this means that

$$y < x_0 + 3.$$

In other words, (x_0, y) is a solution to $y < x + 3$. Similar reasoning applies to any point below the line $y = x + 3$, and we see that *all the points below the line represent solutions* to the inequality $y < x + 3$.

Similarly, any point above the line $y = x + 3$ has a y-coordinate which is greater than $x + 3$, because a displacement in the upward direction increases the y-coordinate. We therefore conclude that the graph of the inequality

$$y < x + 3$$

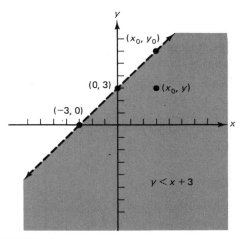

FIGURE 4.20

is the *half-plane* that consists of all points below the line $y = x + 3$. This is indicated by shading in Figure 4.20. The line $y = x + 3$ is drawn as a dashed line to indicate that the points on the line are not part of the graph.

Figure 4.20 is typical of the graphs of linear inequalities: They always consist of half-planes. A line with equation $ax + by = c$ separates the plane into three subsets:

1. The points (x, y) on the line, where $ax + by = c$.
2. The points (x, y), where $ax + by > c$.
3. The points (x, y), where $ax + by < c$.

The points where $ax + by > c$ always lie in a half-plane on one side of the line, and the points where $ax + by < c$ lie in a half-plane on the other side of the line. The line is called the **boundary** of each of the half-planes.

The graphs of some linear inequalities include the boundary. This is illustrated in the following example.

EXAMPLE 1   Graph the inequality

$$2x + 3y \geq 6.$$

SOLUTION   We first graph the boundary line $2x + 3y = 6$. The x-intercept is 3, and the y-intercept is 2. Since possible equality is included in the statement $2x + 3y \geq 6$, the boundary is part of the graph, and the line is drawn solid in Figure 4.21 to indicate this fact. To determine the half-plane which represents the solution set, we simply test a point on one side of the line. The origin $(0, 0)$ is a convenient point to use when it is not on the line. Since

$$2(0) + 3(0) \geq 6$$

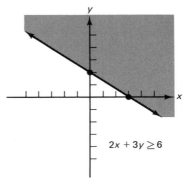

FIGURE 4.21

is equivalent to
$$0 \geq 6,$$
and this is *not true*, the points on the same side of the line as the origin *do not represent solutions*. The graph of
$$2x + 3y \geq 6$$
consists of those points on the opposite side of the line from the origin, together with those points on the line. This set,
$$\{(x, y) \mid 2x + 3y \geq 6\} = \{(x, y) \mid 2x + 3y > 6\} \cup \{(x, y) \mid 2x + 3y = 6\},$$
is shown shaded in Figure 4.21.

PRACTICE PROBLEM 1 (Solution on page 120) Graph
$$2x - 3y \leq 12.$$

Inequalities that involve absolute values of linear expressions can be handled by the same technique used in Section 4-1 for equations.

*EXAMPLE 2 Graph
$$y < |x - 2|.$$

SOLUTION Using the same approach as we did in Example 1, we first graph the equality
$$y = |x - 2|.$$
As in Example 7 of Section 4-1, this is equivalent to
$$y = \begin{cases} x - 2 & \text{if } x \geq 2 \\ -x + 2 & \text{if } x < 2. \end{cases}$$

The graph of $y = |x - 2|$ is drawn as two dashed half-lines in Figure 4.22 since these points are not part of the graph of $y < |x - 2|$. Using the same kind of reasoning as in the introductory example in this section, the points below the dashed half-lines form the graph of $y < |x - 2|$.

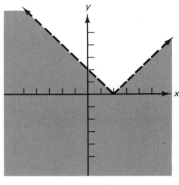

$$y < |x - 2|$$

FIGURE 4.22

PRACTICE PROBLEM 2 (Solution on page 120) Graph

$$x \geq |y + 3|.$$

EXERCISES 4-4

Graph the following linear inequalities. (See Example 1 and Practice Problem 1.)

1. $x \geq 1$ 2. $y \geq -1$
3. $y < -2$ 4. $x < 3$
5. $x + y < 3$ 6. $x - y < 2$
7. $2x + 3y > 12$ 8. $5x + 2y > 10$
9. $6x - 3y \leq 6$ 10. $x - 4y \leq 8$
11. $4x \geq 3y + 24$ 12. $3x \geq 8y + 24$
13. $5x + 7y - 15 < 0$ 14. $6x + 7y - 12 < 0$
15. $y \leq -2x$ 16. $y \geq -x$
17. $5y < 3x + 12$ 18. $4y < 8 - 3x$

In problems 19–22, round the coordinates to the nearest hundredth.

C19. $2.71x + 3.15y < 8.77$ C20. $4.11x - 8.91y \leq -9.21$
C21. $2.45y \geq 1.93x + 6.55$ C22. $43.5y > 51.9 - 37.1x$

Graph the solution sets of the following statements. (See Example 2 and Practice Problem 2.)

*23. $|x| > 2$ *24. $|x| \leq 4$

*25. $|y| \geq 1$ *26. $|y| > 3$

*27. $|x + 1| \leq 3$ *28. $|y - 2| > 1$

*29. $y \leq |x + 2|$ *30. $x > |y - 4|$

*31. $|y| = |x|$ *32. $|y| \leq |x|$

SOLUTIONS FOR PRACTICE PROBLEMS

1. We first draw the graph of $2x - 3y = 12$ as a solid line (see Figure 4.23), since the points on the line are a part of the graph of $2x - 3y \leq 12$. The x-intercept is 6, and the y-intercept is -4. Testing the origin, we have

$$2(0) - 3(0) \leq 12,$$

so $(0, 0)$ is a solution. This tells us that the graph consists of those points on the same side of the line as the origin. This set is shaded in Figure 4.23.

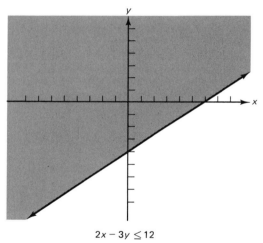

$2x - 3y \leq 12$

FIGURE 4.23

*2. We first graph $x = |y + 3|$. This equation is equivalent to

$$x = \begin{cases} y + 3 & \text{if } y \geq -3 \\ -y - 3 & \text{if } y < -3. \end{cases}$$

The graph is drawn as two solid half-lines in Figure 4.24, since these points represent solutions to $x \geq |y + 3|$. Testing the origin,

$$0 \geq |0 + 3| \text{ is not true,}$$

and (0, 0) is not a solution. Therefore, the points on the other side of the boundary are solutions, and this region is shaded in Figure 4.24.

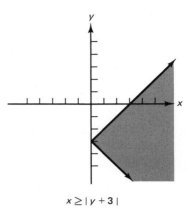

$$x \geq |y + 3|$$

FIGURE 4.2

PRACTICE TEST for Chapter 4

1. Graph each equation, and find the x-intercepts and y-intercepts, if they exist.
   (a) $2x - 6y = 6$ (b) $x = -3$

2. Graph $y = 3x - 2$ $(x \geq 0)$.

3. Graph the line $y - 2x = 3$, and find the slope of the line, if it exists.

4. Graph the line that passes through $(2, 4)$ and has slope $-\frac{3}{2}$.

5. Determine if the following pair of lines are parallel or perpendicular lines.

$$3x = 6y - 10 \quad \text{and} \quad 4x + 8y = 9$$

6. Find the slope and y-intercept of the line that has equation $3x - 2y = 12$.

7. Find an equation of the straight line that passes through $(-2, -3)$ and $(4, 2)$, and write the equation in slope–intercept form.

8. Find an equation of the straight line that passes through $(3, -1)$ and is perpendicular to $y = 2x + 4$, and write the equation in standard form.

In problems 9 and 10, graph the given linear inequalities.

9. $x < -1$

10. $3x - 5y \geq 15$

Systems of Linear Equations and Inequalities

5-1
Systems of Linear Equations in Two Variables

In working with graphs of equations or inequalities, it is sometimes desirable to find the **points of intersection** of two or more graphs, that is, to find the points that are common to the graphs. The simplest form of this problem is to find the point of intersection of two straight lines, and the simplest method of solution is the **graphical method.**

In using the graphical method, the points of intersection are estimated, or guessed, from carefully drawn graphs. The method works reasonably well in finding the point of intersection of two straight lines that cross at a point which has nice integral coordinates.

EXAMPLE 1

Use the graphical method to find the point of intersection of the lines $2x + y = 4$ and $2x - 3y = 12$.

SOLUTION

The two lines are drawn in Figure 5.1. It appears from the graphs that the lines intersect at $(3, -2)$. Checking $x = 3$ and $y = -2$ in both equa-

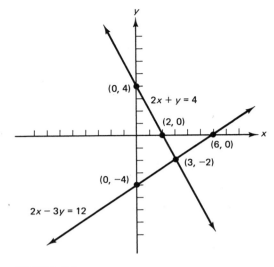

FIGURE 5.1

tions, we find that

$$2(3) + (-2) = 6 - 2$$
$$= 4$$

and

$$2(3) - 3(-2) = 6 + 6$$
$$= 12.$$

The point $(3, -2)$ is indeed on both lines, and we have found the point of intersection.

The graphical method is not very practical, especially if the point of intersection has messy coordinates. For this reason, we shall soon consider some algebraic approaches that are manipulative in nature.

In working problems which require that more than one statement be satisfied, the set of statements involved is called a *system* (a system of equations, perhaps, or a system of inequalities). We are concerned here with systems of equations in two variables. The ordered pairs that satisfy all the equations are called the **simultaneous solutions** of the system, or simply the **solutions** of the system. The solution set of a system is thus the intersection of the solution sets of the individual equations. To **solve** a system is to find its solution set. In Example 1 we have solved the system

$$2x + y = 4$$
$$2x - 3y = 12.$$

The solution set for the system is

$$\{(x, y) \mid 2x + y = 4\} \cap \{(x, y) \mid 2x - 3y = 12\} = \{(3, -2)\}.$$

In this section we confine our attention to systems of two linear equations in two variables:

$$a_1x + b_1y = c_1$$
$$a_2x + b_2y = c_2,$$

where, in each equation, the coefficients of x and y are not both zero. Such systems are called **linear systems**.

Before developing our manipulative techniques for solution, it is in order to consider the types of solution sets that are possible for a linear system. There are three types of solution sets that may occur, depending on the graphs of the two equations involved.

(a) If the two equations represent nonparallel lines, there is one ordered pair in the solution set, corresponding to the point of intersection [see Figure 5.2(a)]. A system of this type is called **independent**.

(b) If the two equations represent distinct parallel lines, the solution set is empty, corresponding to the fact that the two lines have no points in common [see Figure 5.2(b)]. A system of this type is called **inconsistent**.

(c) If the two equations represent the same line, there is an infinite number of solutions, corresponding to all of the points on the line [see Figure 5.2(c)]. A system of this type is called **dependent**.

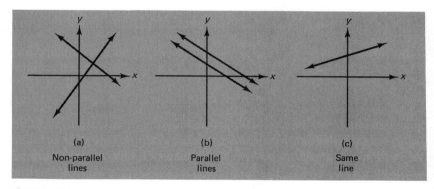

| (a) | (b) | (c) |
| Non-parallel lines | Parallel lines | Same line |

FIGURE 5.2

In addition to the graphical method, we consider the method of solution by **substitution**, and the method of solution by **elimination** in this section.* The substitution method is the simpler one of these methods.

*Another method, called *Cramer's Rule*, is presented in Appendix A-1.

In the **substitution method**, one solves for one of the variables in one of the equations, and then substitutes this value in the other equation. This results in an equation involving only one variable, and the value of this variable is then readily obtained. To clarify the procedure, we shall solve the system in Example 1 by this method.

EXAMPLE 2   Solve the following system by the substitution method.

$$2x + y = 4 \tag{1}$$
$$2x - 3y = 12 \tag{2}$$

SOLUTION   It is easy to solve for y in the first equation:

$$y = -2x + 4. \tag{3}$$

Substituting this value for y in the second equation, we have

$$2x - 3(-2x + 4) = 12.$$

Solving for x in this equation, we get

$$2x + 6x - 12 = 12$$
$$8x = 24$$
$$x = 3.$$

To obtain the corresponding value for y, we go back to equation (3) and use the value $x = 3$:

$$y = -2(3) + 4$$
$$= -2.$$

Thus $\{(3, -2)\}$ is the solution set for the system, and this agrees with the result of Example 1.

PRACTICE PROBLEM 1   (Solution on page 132) Solve by the substitution method:

$$2x - 3y = 5$$
$$x + 3y = 7.$$

The substitution method sometimes leads to the use of fractions, and these fractions can be messy to work with. In such cases, the elimination method is usually better. The **elimination method** is based on the following theorem.

Theorem 5-1   Let m_1 and m_2 be any two real numbers. If (x, y) is a solution to the system

$$a_1 x + b_1 y = c_1 \qquad (4)$$
$$a_2 x + b_2 y = c_2, \qquad (5)$$

then (x, y) is also a solution to the equation

$$m_1(a_1 x + b_1 y) + m_2(a_2 x + b_2 y) = m_1 c_1 + m_2 c_2. \qquad (6)$$

Notice that equation (6) can be obtained by multiplying both members of equation (4) by m_1, multiplying both members of equation (5) by m_2, and adding the corresponding sides of these equations:

$$m_1(a_1 x + b_1 y) = m_1 c_1$$
$$m_2(a_2 x + b_2 y) = m_2 c_2$$
$$\overline{m_1(a_1 x + b_1 y) + m_2(a_2 x + b_2 y) = m_1 c_1 + m_2 c_2.}$$

The key to success in the elimination method is to choose the multipliers m_1 and m_2 so that one of the variables is eliminated when the sum is formed.†

EXAMPLE 3 Solve the following system by the elimination method.

$$5x - 2y = -16 \qquad (7)$$
$$3x = 15 - 7y \qquad (8)$$

SOLUTION We first replace the second equation by an equivalent equation in standard form. This is accomplished by adding $7y$ to both sides.

$$5x - 2y = -16$$
$$3x + 7y = 15$$

The multipliers can be chosen so as to eliminate the variable of our choice. We decide to eliminate the variable y. This can be done by using the multiplier 7 on the first equation and the multiplier 2 on the second equation.

$$35x - 14y = -112$$
$$6x + 14y = 30$$
$$\overline{41x = - 82}$$
$$x = -2$$

We can find the value of y by substituting $x = -2$ in either equation (7) or equation (8). Using equation (7), we have

---

†The equation (6) can be regarded as the sum of m_1 times the first equation and m_2 times the second equation. For this reason, it is sometimes called a *linear combination* of equations (4) and (5).

$$5(-2) - 2y = -16$$
$$-10 - 2y = -16$$
$$-2y = -6$$
$$y = 3.$$

Thus $\{(-2, 3)\}$ is the solution set for the system.

Two systems are **equivalent** if they have the same solution set. The work in Example 3 illustrates the following theorem.

Theorem 5-2 An equivalent system of equations is obtained whenever one of the equations in the system is replaced by

(a) an equivalent equation, or
(b) the sum of m_1 times that equation and m_2 times another equation of the system, where m_1 and m_2 are both *nonzero* numbers.

PRACTICE PROBLEM 2 (Solution on page 132) Solve by the elimination method:

$$3x + 5y = 12$$
$$2x - 3y = 8.$$

The next two examples show how the elimination method works with inconsistent or dependent systems.

EXAMPLE 4 Solve by the elimination method:

$$6x - 3y = 4$$
$$-2x + y = 1.$$

SOLUTION We decide to eliminate x. Multiplying the second equation by 3 and adding, we have

$$6x - 3y = 4$$
$$\underline{-6x + 3y = 3}$$
$$0 = 7.$$

We find that y was automatically eliminated along with x, and the equation $0 = 7$ is impossible. The system is inconsistent, and the solution set is $\varnothing$.

EXAMPLE 5 Solve by the elimination method:

$$3x + y = 4$$

$$6x + 2y = 8.$$

SOLUTION We decide to eliminate y by multiplying the first equation by -2 and adding.

$$-6x - 2y = -8$$
$$\underline{6x + 2y = 8}$$
$$0 = 0.$$

We find that x was automatically eliminated along with y, and the resulting equation, $0 = 0$, is a true statement. This is our signal that the system is dependent, and the solution set is

$$\{(x, y) \mid 3x + y = 4\}.$$

We note that the second equation can be obtained from the first by multiplying by 2.

Examples 4 and 5 of this section suggest that the ratios of the coefficients and the ratio of the constants in a linear system

$$a_1 x + b_1 y = c_1$$

$$a_2 x + b_2 y = c_2$$

determine whether or not a system is inconsistent or dependent. This is the situation:

---

1. If $\dfrac{a_1}{a_2} = \dfrac{b_1}{b_2} \neq \dfrac{c_1}{c_2}$, the system is **inconsistent**.

2. If $\dfrac{a_1}{a_2} = \dfrac{b_1}{b_2} = \dfrac{c_1}{c_2}$, the system is **dependent**.

EXERCISES 5-1

Use the graphical method to solve the following systems. (See Example 1.)

1. $2x + 3y = 12$
   $x + y = 5$

2. $x + y = 3$
   $x - y = -1$

3. $x + 4y = 8$
   $x - 4y = 0$

4. $2x + y = 6$
   $x - y = 0$

5. $2x + y = 3$
   $x - 2y = -1$

6. $x + 2y = -1$
   $2x - y = 3$

Solve the following systems by the substitution method. (See Example 2 and Practice Problem 1.)

7. $x + y = 3$
   $3x + 2y = 7$

8. $x + 4y = 7$
   $x - y = -3$

9. $5x - 2y = 7$
   $y - 4 = 0$

10. $4x + 3y = 1$
    $x + 5 = 0$

11. $3y = 9 - x$
    $3x = 11 - y$

12. $2y = x - 4$
    $2x = y - 1$

13. $6x + 4y = 8$
    $9x + 6y = 12$

14. $2x + 6y = 8$
    $3x + 9y = 12$

15. $5x + 6y = 15$
    $6x - 3y = 1$

16. $2x + 5y = 2$
    $8x - 7y = -1$

Solve by using the elimination method. (See Examples 3–5 and Practice Problem 2.)

17. $2x - 3y - 8 = 0$
    $5x + 2y - 1 = 0$

18. $5x + 4y - 2 = 0$
    $3x + 2y - 1 = 0$

19. $x + 2y = 4$
    $3x - 2y = -12$

20. $2x + 9y = 3$
    $5x + 7y = -8$

21. $2x - 3y - 18 = 0$
    $3x = 2y + 22$

22. $2x = 5y + 20$
    $3x + 4y - 7 = 0$

23. $4x + 6y = 1$
    $6x + 9y = 4$

24. $9x + 6y = 4$
    $6x + 4y = 1$

Solve the following systems by any method.

25. $4x - 3y = 9$
    $2x + y = 12$

26. $9x + y = 9$
    $x + 3y = 14$

27. $3x = 2y + 8$
    $2x = 3y + 7$

28. $3y = 1 - 4x$
    $5y = 2x + 19$

29. $6x + 5y = 39$
    $3x - 2y = 6$

30. $4x + 3y = 4$
    $3x + 2y = 2$

31. $x - 3y = 4$
    $2x = 6y + 5$

32. $3x = 2y + 5$
    $6y = 9x + 15$

33. $\frac{3}{2}x - \frac{1}{3}y = 1$
    $x + \frac{2}{3}y = 10$

34. $\frac{1}{3}x + \frac{2}{7}y = 1$
    $\frac{7}{6}x - 2y = 2$

C35. $1.02x - 4.23y = 5.25$
     $2.81x + 1.73y = 1.08$

C36. $6.13x + 2.72y = 9.54$
     $1.13x + 9.81y = -7.55$

C37. $43.8x + 23.6y = 16.8$
     $21.5x - 14.2y = 85.6$

C38. $3.74x - 8.68y = 21.1$
     $5.16x - 3.17y = 11.5$

39. Martin can row a boat 12 miles downstream in 2 hours, and he can row the boat 9 miles upstream in 3 hours. Find the rate that Martin can row in still water and the rate of the current in the stream.

40. Dan's motorboat takes 3 hours to travel upstream 84 miles to Vicksburg, and makes the return trip in 2 hours. Find the rate of the current and the rate of the boat in still water.

41. Georgia has an annual income of $6600 from two investments, one at 8% annual interest and the other at 9% annual interest. She has $11,000 more invested at 9% than she has at 8%. How much is invested at each rate?

42. Ella has invested $10,000, part at 6% annual interest and the rest at 8% annual interest. If her total return from both investments amounts to $650 per year, how much is invested at 6%?

43. A rock concert is to be held in Bull Frog Stadium (BFS). The "reserved seat" tickets are to cost three times as much as the "cheap seat" tickets. There are 1000 reserved seats and a total capacity of 10,000 in BFS. Assuming a capacity crowd, what price can be charged for each ticket so that the ticket sales will be $42,000?

44. Work problem 43 if the "reserved seat" tickets are to cost $3 more than three times as much as the "cheap seat" tickets, and all other information is unchanged.

45. The Maranto Peanut Farm (MPF) grows two kinds of peanuts: Spanish peanuts and goobers. The selling price for both kinds is $2 per pound. The profit margin is 15% on Spanish peanuts and 25% on goobers. If MPF sells 80,000 pounds of peanuts next year, and if the profit must be $25,000, how many pounds of Spanish peanuts should be grown?

46. Work problem 45 if the profit margin on goobers is 20%, and all other information is unchanged.

47. The demand for a new book entitled *Algebra for Everybody* is given by

$$D = -\tfrac{3}{2}x + 40,$$

where D is the number of people (in thousands) who want to buy the book, and x is the selling price of the book in dollars. The supply S of books is given by

$$S = 3x - 50,$$

where S is in thousands. Find the price x for which supply equals demand. (This is called the *equilibrium price*.)

48. The demand D for Pedalex subcompact cars, in thousands of cars, is given by

$$D = 49 - 5x,$$

where x is the price in thousands of dollars. The supply S, in thousands of cars, is given by

$$S = 7x - 35.$$

Find the equilibrium price of Pedalex cars. (See problem 47.)

49. Terri has two copper–nickel alloys. The first alloy is 30% copper and 70% nickel, while the second is 60% copper and 40% nickel. What amounts of each alloy should be used to obtain 330 kilograms of an alloy that is 55% copper and 45% nickel?

50. Jeffrey Breaux needs to make an alloy that will contain 65% copper and weigh 170 kilograms. He has two alloys available, one containing 42% copper and the other containing 76% copper. What amounts of each of these should be used?

*51. Last week, Anna and Roberto worked with two mowers and mowed their lawn in 2 hours. Yesterday morning, Roberto mowed alone for 4 hours, and Anna finished the job in 1 hour that afternoon. How long would it take Roberto to mow all of the lawn by himself?

*52. Martin Goldsworth has two backhoes that can make an excavation for a basement in 15 hours if they are operated together. The larger machine was operated alone on the excavation for 9 hours and broke down. Operated alone, the smaller machine finished digging for the basement in 25 hours. How long would it take the larger machine operated alone to dig the excavation?

SOLUTIONS FOR PRACTICE PROBLEMS

1. Solving for x in the second equation yields

$$x = 7 - 3y.$$

Substituting this value for x in the first equation, we obtain

$$2(7 - 3y) - 3y = 5$$
$$14 - 6y - 3y = 5$$
$$-9y = -9$$
$$y = 1.$$

Using $y = 1$ in $x = 7 - 3y$, we obtain

$$x = 7 - 3(1)$$
$$x = 4.$$

Thus $\{(4, 1)\}$ is the solution set for the system.

2. We can eliminate y by using the multiplier 3 on the first equation and the multiplier 5 on the second equation.

$$9x + 15y = 36$$
$$\underline{10x - 15y = 40}$$
$$19x = 76$$
$$x = 4$$

Substituting $x = 4$ in the first equation of the original system, we get

$$3(4) + 5y = 12$$
$$y = 0.$$

Thus $\{(4, 0)\}$ is the solution set for the system.

It is a natural extension of the preceding section to consider systems of equations of the same type which have more equations and more variables. This kind of system is an extremely important topic in mathematics, and many sophisticated treatments of such systems have been devised. In our development here, we limit ourselves to the study of **linear systems** of three equations in three variables. These are systems of the form

$$a_1x + b_1y + c_1z = d_1$$
$$a_2x + b_2y + c_2z = d_2$$
$$a_3x + b_3y + c_3z = d_3,$$

where, in each equation, not all of the coefficients of the variables x, y, and z are zero.

The **solution set** of such a system is naturally the set of ordered triples (x, y, z) of real numbers which have values of the variables that make all the equations in the system true statements. That is, it is the *intersection* of the solution sets of the individual equations. To **solve** a system is to find its solution set.

There is a three-dimensional geometric interpretation of systems like this and their solutions. In this interpretation, planes represent the individual equations and the solution set is represented by a plane, a straight line, or a point. The usefulness of this interpretation in our development does not justify the effort required to formulate it, and we do not go into it for that reason.

There are many techniques for solving a linear system of three equations in three variables. We consider only one method in this section,‡ one that is a variation of the elimination method presented in Section 5-1. The idea behind this method is to obtain an equivalent system in which one of the variables has been eliminated from two of the equations, to solve the resulting subsystem in two variables, and then obtain the value of the third variable by substitution. This routine is illustrated in the following example.

EXAMPLE 1 Solve the following system.

$$x - 2y + z = 8 \tag{1}$$
$$3x + y - 2z = 5 \tag{2}$$
$$2x - y + 3z = 11 \tag{3}$$

SOLUTION Any of the three variables can be chosen as the one to be eliminated. We choose x to be eliminated. With the first two equations we proceed as follows.

‡Another method, known as *Cramer's Rule*, is presented in Appendix A-2.

$$x - 2y + z = 8 \xrightarrow{\text{multiply by } -3} -3x + 6y - 3z = -24$$
$$3x + y - 2z = 5 \xrightarrow{\hspace{3cm}} \underline{3x + y - 2z = 5}$$
$$\text{(by adding)} \qquad 7y - 5z = -19 \qquad (4)$$

This gives one of the desired equations in two variables. To obtain another equation without an x-term, we may use the first and third equations in the following manner.

$$x - 2y + z = 8 \xrightarrow{\text{multiply by } -2} -2x + 4y - 2z = -16$$
$$2x - y + 3z = 11 \xrightarrow{\hspace{3cm}} \underline{2x - y + 3z = 11}$$
$$\text{(by adding)} \qquad 3y + z = -5 \qquad (5)$$

By Theorem 5-2, the original system is equivalent to

$$x - 2y + z = 8 \qquad (1)$$
$$7y - 5z = -19 \qquad (4)$$
$$3y + z = -5. \qquad (5)$$

We now solve the subsystem in y and z by the methods of Section 5-1:

$$7y - 5z = -19 \xrightarrow{\hspace{3cm}} 7y - 5z = -19$$
$$3y + z = -5 \xrightarrow{\text{multiply by } 5} \underline{15y + 5z = -25}$$
$$\text{(by adding)} \quad 22y = -44$$
$$y = -2.$$

The value of z may be found by substituting $y = -2$ in any of the y, z equations. Choosing $3y + z = -5$, we have

$$3(-2) + z = -5$$
$$-6 + z = -5$$
$$z = 1.$$

The value of x may now be found by using $y = -2$ and $z = 1$ in equation (1):

$$x - 2(-2) + 1 = 8$$
$$x + 5 = 8$$
$$x = 3.$$

Thus the solution set to the system is

$$\{(3, -2, 1)\}.$$

The general procedure for solving a linear system of three equations in three variables by the elimination method is as follows.

Step 1. Select one of the variables as the one to be eliminated. Use appropriate multipliers to eliminate this variable from a pair of the equations.

Step 2. Use appropriate multipliers with a *different* pair of the equations to eliminate the *same* variable.

Step 3. Solve the subsystem of two equations in two variables which is obtained from steps 1 and 2.

Step 4. Substitute the values obtained in step 3 into one of the equations in the original system, and then solve for the remaining variable.

PRACTICE PROBLEM 1   (Solution on page 138) Solve the system

$$x - 3y + z = 6$$
$$x - 2y - z = 3$$
$$4x - 3y = 11.$$

Just as it happens with linear systems in two variables, a linear system in three variables may be *inconsistent* (no solution) or *dependent* (many solutions). In these cases, the elimination procedure will yield results of the same type that were obtained in corresponding situations in Section 5-1. If the system is inconsistent, we will obtain an impossible equation, such as $0 = 7$. If the system is dependent, we will obtain one or more true equations of the form $0 = 0$.

EXAMPLE 2   Solve the system

$$2x - 3y - 2z = 1$$
$$x + 2y + 4z = 2$$
$$6x - 9y - 6z = 2.$$

SOLUTION   We choose x as the variable to be eliminated. Using the first and second equations, we have

$$
\begin{array}{llll}
2x - 3y - 2z = 1 & \xrightarrow{} & 2x - 3y - 2z = 1 \\
x + 2y + 4z = 2 & \xrightarrow{\text{multiply by } -2} & \underline{-2x - 4y - 8z = -4} \\
& & -7y - 10z = -3.
\end{array}
$$

Using the second and third equations to obtain another equation in y and z, we have

$$x + 2y + 4z = 2 \xrightarrow{\text{multiply by} -6} -6x - 12y - 24z = -12$$
$$6x - 9y - 6z = 2 \longrightarrow \underline{6x - 9y - 6z = 2}$$
$$-21y - 30z = -10.$$

Solving the subsystem in y and z we obtain

$$-7y - 10z = -3 \xrightarrow{\text{multiply by} -3} 21y + 30z = 9$$
$$-21y - 30z = -10 \longrightarrow \underline{-21y - 30z = -10}$$
$$0 = -1.$$

The impossible equation $0 = -1$ indicates that the system is inconsistent and has no solutions.

EXAMPLE 3 Solve the following system if it has a unique solution. Otherwise, state if the system is dependent or inconsistent.

$$4x + y + 5z = 2$$
$$x - y + 3z = 1$$
$$9x + y + 13z = 5$$

SOLUTION It is easier to eliminate y in this system. Adding the first two equations, we get

$$5x + 8z = 3.$$

Adding the second and third equations, we obtain

$$10x + 16z = 6.$$

Solving the subsystem, we have

$$5x + 8z = 3 \xrightarrow{\text{multiply by} -2} -10x - 16z = -6$$
$$10x + 16z = 6 \longrightarrow \underline{10x + 16z = 6}$$
$$0 = 0.$$

This indicates that the original system is dependent, and there are infinitely many solutions.

EXERCISES 5-2

Solve those of the following systems that have a unique solution. Otherwise, state if the system is dependent or inconsistent.

1. $x + 3y + 2z = 3$ 2. $x + 2y + 2z = 8$
    $3x - 2y + z = 3$ $2x + y + z = 7$
    $x - 4y - 3z = 1$ $3x + y + 2z = 13$

3. $x - 2y + 2z = -1$
   $3x + y - z = 4$
   $2x - y + 3z = 5$

4. $x - 4y - 2z = -10$
   $3x + 2y - z = 12$
   $2x + 2y + z = 10$

5. $x + y + 3z = 10$
   $2x + 2y - z = -1$
   $3x + y - 2z = -3$

6. $x + 3y + 4z = 0$
   $x + y + z = 1$
   $2x - y + 2z = 8$

7. $x + 6y - 5z = 24$
   $5x + 3y - z = 21$
   $2x - 7y + 3z = -10$

8. $x + 2y + 3z = -8$
   $x - 3y + z = -10$
   $2x + y + 2z = -6$

9. $x - 5y + 3z = 0$
   $3x + y + 2z = 2$
   $2x - y + 2z = 1$

10. $x + 2y + 3z = 3$
    $3x + y - 2z = 15$
    $x - 3y - 4z = 5$

11. $2x - 2y - z = 3$
    $x - 3y - 5z = -9$
    $x - 5y + 2z = -8$

12. $2x + 5y + 3z = 3$
    $x + 2y - 3z = -2$
    $3x + 4y - z = 6$

13. $x + y = 3$
    $x + 2y + 2z = 1$
    $y - z = 1$

14. $4x + 2z = 10$
    $y + 5z = 6$
    $x + 2y + z = 5$

15. $3x + y = 16$
    $2x + z = 15$
    $x - 2y + 2z = 16$

16. $x + z = 6$
    $2x + y + z = 11$
    $3x + y + 3z = 19$

17. $2x - y + 3z = 9$
    $5x - 2y + 4z = 2$
    $3x + 3y - z = -15$

18. $5x + 3y - z = 6$
    $2x - 7y + 3z = 27$
    $3x - y - 2z = 12$

19. $3x + y + 7z = 8$
    $x - 2y + 7z = 5$
    $2x + 4y - 2z = 2$

20. $2x + y + z = 4$
    $2x - y - 5z = 0$
    $3x - 2y - 9z = 5$

21. $2x + y = 3$
    $x - y - 3z = -3$
    $x - 2y - 5z = -6$

22. $4x + y + 5z = 2$
    $x - y + 5z = 3$
    $2x + y + z = 0$

23. Find $a, b,$ and c so that each of $(3, 1, 1)$, $(1, 1, 4)$, and $(1, -1, 2)$ is a solution (x, y, z) to $ax + by + cz = 9$.

24. The sum of three numbers is 22. The first number is equal to the sum of the other two, and the second is five more than the third. Find the three numbers.

25. Rodger has \$5.65 in nickels, dimes, and quarters. There are twice as many dimes as there are quarters, and 47 coins in all. How many coins of each kind does Rodger have?

26. The sum of three perfect squares is 49, which is another perfect square. The first perfect square is equal to 4 times the second, and it is also equal to 9 times the third. Find the three perfect squares.

27. The angles A, B, and C in a triangle have a sum of 180°. Angle A is 40° more than B, and angle A is 20° more than C. Find each angle.

28. The containers A, B, and C hold acid solutions of strengths 30%, 40%, and 60%, respectively. It is desired to mix proper amounts of the three solutions so as to make up 1400 cubic centimeters of a 50% solution. Because of a large volume in C, it is decided to use four times as much solution from C as from A. Find the amount to be taken from each container.

29. Jaime has a contract to supply toasted nuts to a chain of variety stores. He must fill an order for 46 pounds of mixed peanuts, cashews, and pecans at a price of $180, and the order specifies that the mixture must contain half as many cashews as it does peanuts. If prices are $3 per pound for peanuts, $4 per pound for cashews, and $6 per pound for pecans, how many pounds of each should he put in the mixture?

*30. A tank can be filled by three pumps, A, B, and C, as follows: A and B together in 3 days; A and C together in 4 days; all three together in 2 days. Find the time required for each pump to fill the tank alone.

SOLUTION FOR PRACTICE PROBLEM

1. Since the third equation does not have a z-term, it is easier to eliminate z. Adding the first two equations, we have

$$\begin{array}{r} x - 3y + z = 6 \\ x - 2y - z = 3 \\ \hline 2x - 5y \quad\; = 9. \end{array}$$

This equation and the third in the original system form a subsystem in x and y, which we solve as follows.

$$2x - 5y = \;\;9 \xrightarrow{\text{multiply by } -3} -6x + 15y = -27$$

$$4x - 3y = 11 \xrightarrow{\text{multiply by } 5} \underline{\;20x - 15y = \quad 55\;}$$

$$\begin{array}{r} 14x \quad\quad = 28 \\ x = 2 \end{array}$$

Substituting $x = 2$ in $4x - 3y = 11$, we get

$$4(2) - 3y = 11$$
$$-3y = 3$$
$$y = -1.$$

Using $x = 2$ and $y = -1$ in the first equation of the original system, we get

$$2 - 3(-1) + z = 6$$
$$z = 1.$$

The solution set is $\{(2, -1, 1)\}$.

5-3
Systems of Linear
Inequalities in
Two Variables
(Optional)

The basic ideas that we have used in working with systems of linear equations carry over in a natural way to systems of linear inequalities in two variables. The **solution set** of a system of statements (equalities or inequalities) in x and y is the set of all ordered pairs (x, y) that make all the statements in the system true. That is, the solution set of a system is the intersection of the solution sets of the individual statements. The **graph** of the solution set of a system consists of all the points with coordinates (x, y) that belong to the solution set of the system. This set of points is the same as the *intersection of the graphs of the individual statements*. The phrase "the graph of the solution set of the system" is frequently abbreviated to "the graph of the system."

EXAMPLE 1   Graph the following system.

$$3x + y > 7$$
$$x - y \le 1$$
$$y < 4$$

SOLUTION   We first locate the points of intersection of the boundaries:

$$3x + y = 7 \text{ and } x - y = 1 \text{ intersect at } (2, 1);$$
$$3x + y = 7 \text{ and } y = 4 \text{ intersect at } (1, 4);$$
$$x - y = 1 \text{ and } y = 4 \text{ intersect at } (5, 4).$$

These points are graphed in Figure 5.3, where the lines $3x + y = 7$ and

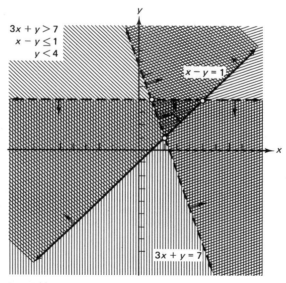

FIGURE 5.3

139

$y = 4$ are drawn as dashed lines to indicate that the boundaries are not part of the graph. Testing $(0, 0)$ in each inequality, we find that

$(0, 0)$ is not a solution to $3x + y > 7$;

$(0, 0)$ is a solution to $x - y \leq 1$;

$(0, 0)$ is a solution to $y < 4$.

The half-planes of solutions for each inequality are indicated in Figure 5.3 by arrows based on the boundaries. The intersection of the three half-planes is shaded in the figure, and this is the graph of the solution set of the system.

PRACTICE PROBLEM 1

(Solution on page 141) Graph the following system.

$$2x + y < -2$$
$$4x - 3y \geq -24$$
$$y \geq -4$$

EXERCISES 5-3

Graph the following systems.

1. $x + 2y \geq 8$
   $x - y \geq 2$

2. $x - y \leq 2$
   $-x + 4y \leq 10$

3. $x - y \leq 1$
   $x + 2y \geq 4$

4. $x + y \leq 8$
   $x - y \geq -5$

5. $x + y \geq 2$
   $x - y < 2$

6. $x + y < 4$
   $x - y \leq 2$

7. $x + y < 6$
   $x + 2y \leq 10$

8. $x + 2y \leq 2$
   $-2x + y < 2$

9. $x + 2y < 2$
   $3x - 2y < 8$

10. $x + 2y > 4$
    $2x + 3y < 17$

11. $2x + 3y < 17$
    $-2x + 3y < 13$

12. $3x - 2y < 8$
    $2x - y > -2$

13. $-2x + y \geq -10$
    $2x - y < 20$

14. $2x - 6y < 9$
    $x - 3y \geq -3$

15. $x - 2y < 2$
    $2x - 4y \geq 7$

16. $x + y \leq 3$
    $2x + 2y > 11$

17. $2x + 5y \geq 10$
    $-3x + 5y < 20$
    $x \geq 1$

18. $3x - 5y \geq -20$
    $x - 5y > -30$
    $x \geq 1$

19. $x - y > 1$
    $x + y \leq 3$
    $y > 3$

20. $2x - y < 10$
    $2x + y \leq -2$
    $x > 4$

1. The points of intersection of the boundaries are as follows:

$2x + y = -2$ and $4x - 3y = -24$ intersect at $(-3, 4)$;

$2x + y = -2$ and $y = -4$ intersect at $(1, -4)$;

$4x - 3y = -24$ and $y = -4$ intersect at $(-9, -4)$.

Testing $(0, 0)$ in each inequality:

$(0, 0)$ is not a solution to $2x + y < -2$;

$(0, 0)$ is a solution to $4x - 3y \geq -24$;

$(0, 0)$ is a solution to $y \geq -4$.

The half-planes of solutions for each inequality are indicated in Figure 5.4 by arrows drawn from the boundaries. The intersection of the three half-planes, which is the graph of the system, is shown shaded in the figure.

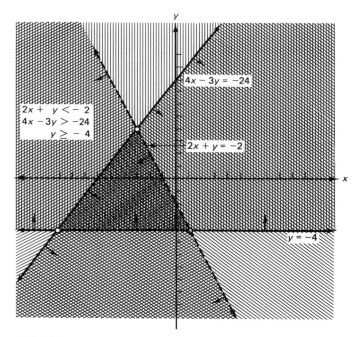

FIGURE 5.4

PRACTICE TEST for Chapter 5

1. Solve the following system by the substitution method.

$$2x - 5y = 3$$
$$3x - y = -2$$

2. Solve the following system by the elimination method.

$$4x - 3y = 5$$
$$3x + y = 7$$

Solve the following systems by any method. If a system is dependent or inconsistent, so state.

3. $x - 2y = -3$
   $-2x + 4y = 6$

4. $x - 3y = 4$
   $-2x + 6y = 7$

5. $x - 2y + 3z = -5$
   $2x - y + z = 2$
   $8x + 3y + 2z = 7$

6. $3x - 2y + 9z = 1$
   $2x + y + 6z = 3$
   $2x - 4y + 6z = 2$

Graph the following systems.

7. $x - 2y < 2$
   $2x - 3y \geq 3$

8. $2x + 3y < -6$
   $4x + 6y > 12$

9. $x - 2y \leq 2$
   $3x + 4y < 16$
   $x > 2$

10. $2x + 3y \leq 12$
    $2x - y > 4$
    $y \geq 4$

6

Polynomials

A product such as $x \cdot x \cdot x \cdot x \cdot x$ in which all the factors are the same can be written in a shortened form. We write x^5 for $x \cdot x \cdot x \cdot x \cdot x$. The general definition is as follows.

Definition 6-1 If x represents a real number and n a positive integer, then

$$x^n = \underbrace{x \cdot x \cdot x \cdots x.}_{n \text{ factors}}$$

The expression x^n is called an **exponential**, where x is the **base** and n is the **exponent** (or **power**) of x.

In other words, the exponential x^n is a product of n factors of the base x. If no exponent is written, the exponent is understood to be 1. That is, $x = x^1$.

143

EXAMPLE 1 Write each exponential as a product and identify the base and the exponent.

(a) x^4 (b) $(-y)^3$ (c) $(2a)^5$ (d) $(x-y)^2$

SOLUTION

	Base	Exponent
(a) $x^4 = x \cdot x \cdot x \cdot x$	x	4
(b) $(-y)^3 = (-y)(-y)(-y)$	$-y$	3
(c) $(2a)^5 = 2a \cdot 2a \cdot 2a \cdot 2a \cdot 2a$	$2a$	5
(d) $(x-y)^2 = (x-y)(x-y)$	$x-y$	2

EXAMPLE 2 Write each product as an exponential and identify the base and exponent.

(a) $a \cdot a$

(b) $4y \cdot 4y \cdot 4y$

(c) $(-2)(-2)(-2)(-2)$

SOLUTION

	Base	Exponent
(a) $a \cdot a = a^2$	a	2
(b) $4y \cdot 4y \cdot 4y = (4y)^3$	$4y$	3
(c) $(-2)(-2)(-2)(-2) = (-2)^4$	-2	4

We note that $-2^4 = -(2)(2)(2)(2) = -16$ and $(-2)^4 \neq -2^4$.

Next, we consider a product in which the factors themselves are exponentials. Since, for x any real number,

$$x^m \cdot x^n = \underbrace{\underbrace{x \cdot x \cdot x \cdots x}_{m \text{ factors}} \cdot \underbrace{x \cdot x \cdot x \cdots x}_{n \text{ factors}}}_{m + n \text{ factors}} = x^{m+n}$$

is true for all positive integers m and n, we have the first law of exponents (sometimes called the **product rule** for exponents).

$$x^m \cdot x^n = x^{m+n}$$

The next example illustrates the use of the product rule for exponents to simplify exponentials.

EXAMPLE 3

(a) $x \cdot x^9 = x^{1+9} = x^{10}$

(b) $(-2)^5(-2)^4 = (-2)^{5+4} = (-2)^9$

(c) $(x - y)^{10}(x - y)^2 = (x - y)^{10+2} = (x - y)^{12}$

(d) $5^3x^2 \cdot 5^2x^5 = (5^3 \cdot 5^2)(x^2 \cdot x^5) = 5^{3+2}x^{2+5} = 5^5x^7$

Consider now a product consisting of n factors of the exponential x^m:

$$(x^m)^n = \underbrace{x^m \cdot x^m \cdot x^m \cdots x^m}_{n \text{ factors of } x^m}$$

$$= \underbrace{\underbrace{x \cdot x \cdot x \cdots x}_{m \text{ factors}} \cdot \underbrace{x \cdot x \cdot x \cdots x}_{m \text{ factors}} \cdots \underbrace{x \cdot x \cdot x \cdots x}_{m \text{ factors}}}_{n \text{ factors of } \underbrace{x \cdot x \cdot x \cdots x}_{m \text{ factors}}}$$

$$= \underbrace{x \cdot x \cdot x \cdots x}_{m \cdot n \text{ factors of } x}$$

$$= x^{mn}.$$

This result is the **power rule** of exponents. For x a real number and m and n positive integers,

$$\boxed{(x^m)^n = x^{mn}.}$$

EXAMPLE 4

(a) $(x^2)^5 = x^{2 \cdot 5} = x^{10}$

(b) $(y^3)^2 = y^{3 \cdot 2} = y^6$

(c) $[(x - y)^2]^9 = (x - y)^{2 \cdot 9} = (x - y)^{18}$

(d) $(x^4)^3(y^3)^6 = x^{4 \cdot 3}y^{3 \cdot 6} = x^{12}y^{18}$

Quotients of exponentials with the same base can also be simplified. Consider, for example, where $x \neq 0$,

$$\frac{x^7}{x^2} = \frac{x \cdot x \cdot x \cdot x \cdot x \cdot x \cdot x}{x \cdot x} = \frac{x \cdot x \cdot x \cdot x \cdot x}{1} = x^5.$$

Two factors of x have been divided out of numerator and denominator of $\frac{x^7}{x^2}$, leaving five factors of x in the numerator. Hence we have

$$\frac{x^7}{x^2} = x^{7-2} = x^5.$$

The general **quotient law** of exponents is: For x a nonzero real number and m and n positive integers,

$$\frac{x^m}{x^n} = \begin{cases} x^{m-n}, & x \neq 0, \quad m > n, \\ \dfrac{1}{x^{n-m}}, & x \neq 0, \quad n > m, \end{cases}$$

and its use is illustrated in the next example. We shall assume that all denominators are nonzero throughout the remainder of this chapter.

EXAMPLE 5

(a) $\dfrac{x^9}{x} = x^{9-1} = x^8$

(b) $\dfrac{5^{10}x^{12}}{5^8 x^{40}} = \dfrac{5^{10-8}}{x^{40-12}} = \dfrac{5^2}{x^{28}} = \dfrac{25}{x^{28}}$

(c) $\dfrac{3^3(1-a)^5}{3(1-a)^4} = 3^{3-1}(1-a)^{5-4} = 3^2(1-a)^1 = 9(1-a)$

It would be satisfying if the quotient law of exponents were true for $m = n$, which is indeed the case and leads to an important definition. For $x \neq 0$,

$$1 = \frac{x^n}{x^n} = x^{n-n} = x^0.$$
$$\text{\small by the quotient law of exponents}$$

We now allow zero exponents in any of the laws of exponents.

Definition 6-2 If x is any real number, then

$$\boxed{\begin{array}{l} x^0 = 1 \quad \text{if } x \neq 0; \\ 0^0 \text{ is undefined.} \end{array}}$$

EXAMPLE 6

(a) $2x^0 = \begin{cases} 2(1) = 2 & \text{if } x \neq 0 \\ \text{undefined} & \text{if } x = 0 \end{cases}$

(b) $(2x)^0 = \begin{cases} 1 & \text{if } x \neq 0 \\ \text{undefined} & \text{if } x = 0 \end{cases}$

(c) $(5 - 2)^0 = 3^0 = 1$

(d) $5^0 - 2^0 = 1 - 1 = 0$

(e) $(3 - 3)^0 = 0^0$, which is undefined.

(Solution on page 150) Simplify the following.

(a) $3^2x^4 \cdot 3^4x^3$

(b) $(y^2)^5$

(c) $\dfrac{x^2y^5}{xy^3}$

(d) $(x - y)^0$

The next two laws of exponents involve exponentials whose base contains two variables. First consider an exponential whose base is a product.

$$(xy)^n = \underbrace{(xy)(xy)(xy) \cdots (xy)}_{n \text{ factors of } (xy)}$$

$$= \underbrace{(x \cdot x \cdot x \cdots x)}_{n \text{ factors}} \cdot \underbrace{(y \cdot y \cdot y \cdots y)}_{n \text{ factors}}$$ (Since multiplication is commutative and associative)

$$= x^n \cdot y^n$$

Thus we have

$$(xy)^n = x^ny^n.$$

A similar result holds for quotients. For $y \neq 0$,

$$\left(\frac{x}{y}\right)^n = \underbrace{\left(\frac{x}{y}\right)\left(\frac{x}{y}\right)\left(\frac{x}{y}\right) \cdots \left(\frac{x}{y}\right)}_{n \text{ factors of } \left(\frac{x}{y}\right)}$$

$$= \frac{\overbrace{x \cdot x \cdot x \cdots x}^{n \text{ factors}}}{\underbrace{y \cdot y \cdot y \cdots y}_{n \text{ factors}}}$$

$$= \frac{x^n}{y^n}.$$

Thus

$$\left(\frac{x}{y}\right)^n = \frac{x^n}{y^n}, \qquad y \neq 0.$$

These two laws of exponents are illustrated in the next example.

EXAMPLE 7

(a) $(3x)^2 = 3^2x^2 = 9x^2$

(b) $(a^2b)^3 = (a^2)^3b^3 = a^6b^3$

(c) $\left(\dfrac{x^2}{4}\right)^3 = \dfrac{(x^2)^3}{4^3} = \dfrac{x^6}{64}$

(d) $\left(\dfrac{ab}{a-b}\right)^5 = \dfrac{(ab)^5}{(a-b)^5} = \dfrac{a^5b^5}{(a-b)^5}, \quad a \neq b$

We summarize the laws of exponents in the form of a theorem.

Theorem 6-3 (Laws of Exponents) Let m, n be nonnegative integers and x, y be real numbers so that x^m, x^n, and y^n are defined. Then

(a) $x^m \cdot x^n = x^{m+n}$ **(product rule)**

(b) $(x^m)^n = x^{mn}$ **(power rule)**

(c) $\dfrac{x^m}{x^n} = \begin{cases} x^{m-n}, & x \neq 0 \quad m \geq n \\ \dfrac{1}{x^{n-m}}, & x \neq 0 \quad n > m \end{cases}$ **(quotient rule)**

(d) $(xy)^n = x^ny^n$

(e) $\left(\dfrac{x}{y}\right)^n = \dfrac{x^n}{y^n}, \quad y \neq 0$

PRACTICE PROBLEM 2

(Solution on page 150) Simplify each of the following.

(a) $(-2a^3b)^5$

(b) $[x(x-y)]^2$

(c) $\left(\dfrac{3a}{2b}\right)^2$

(d) $\left(\dfrac{x^6y^3}{x^4y^2}\right)^5$

EXERCISES 6-1

Write each exponential as a product and identify the base and exponent. (See Example 1.)

1. 2^5

2. $(-2)^5$

3. x^4

4. y^3

5. $(5a)^8$

6. $(-3xy)^4$

7. $(x-y)^5$

8. $(2x+3y)^3$

148

Write each product as an exponential and identify the base and exponent. (See Example 2.)

9. $(2z)(2z)(2z)(2z)$

10. $(-3xy)(-3xy)(-3xy)$

11. $(x + 3)(x + 3)$

12. $(\frac{5}{2}x)(\frac{5}{2}x)(\frac{5}{2}x)(\frac{5}{2}x)(\frac{5}{2}x)$

Find the value of each of the following.

13. $(-3)^4$

14. -3^4

15. $(-1)^3$

16. -1^3

17. -1^6

18. $(-1)^6$

19. $[(-3)^2]^3$

20. $(-3^2)^3$

21. $(-5^2)^2$

22. $-(5^2)^2$

23. $(-2^3)2^3$

24. $(-2)^3 2^3$

25. $\left(\frac{3^2}{-2^3}\right)^2$

26. $\left[\frac{(-3)^2}{(-2)^3}\right]^2$

27. $\left(\frac{-5^2}{4^3}\right)^1$

28. $\left[\frac{(-5)^2}{4^3}\right]^1$

29. $\left[\frac{(-7)^2}{12^4}\right]^0$

30. $\left(\frac{-7^2}{12^4}\right)^0$

31. $[2^2(-7)]^2$

32. $[(-4)(-3)^2]^3$

33. $(3 - 7)^2$

34. $(1 + 11)^3$

35. $(4 - 4)^9$

36. $(4 + 4)^3$

Simplify; that is, use the laws of exponents to rewrite each of the following so that each variable occurs only once in the result. Assume that all denominators are nonzero.

(See Example 3.)

37. $x^5 x^7$

38. $y^3(-y^2)$

39. $-3x^2 \cdot 4x^2$

40. $2^3 xy^3 \cdot 2x^3 y^5$

41. $-5x^3 y^2 \cdot 12x^4 y$

42. $(-4a^3 b)(-2a^2 b^3)$

43. $(3a - 2)^3(3a - 2)^2$

44. $(x - 9)^{17}(x - 9)^{43}$

(See Example 4.)

45. $(x^5)^2$

46. $(y^3)^{40}$

47. $(a^2)^3 \cdot (a^4)^2$

48. $r^4 \cdot (r^2)^6$

49. $[(z + y)^4]^9$

50. $[(2x - 1)^2]^3$

(See Example 5.)

51. $\frac{-x^4}{2x^2}$

52. $\frac{27y^5}{-3y}$

53. $\dfrac{5xy^3}{xy^5}$

54. $\dfrac{24a^2b^4}{30a^6b^3}$

55. $\dfrac{-2(x-7)^5}{-(x-7)^2}$

56. $\dfrac{x^8y^3(z-1)^2}{x^4y(z-1)}$

(See Example 6.)

57. $(-9)^0$

58. -9^0

59. $a^0 + b^0$

60. $a^0 - b^0$

61. $(a-b)^0,\ a \neq b$

62. $(a-b)^0,\ a = b$

(See Example 7 and Practice Problems 1 and 2.)

63. $(2x^3y)^2$

64. $(5x^2z^5)^2$

65. $(-3a^2b^5)^4(-a^3b)^3$

66. $(-rs^2)^3(r^3s)^2$

67. $\left(\dfrac{4}{x^2}\right)^3$

68. $\left(-\dfrac{2y^3}{z}\right)^4$

69. $\left[\dfrac{(-x^2)^6y}{3x^{15}}\right]^2$

70. $\left[\dfrac{(a^2b)^2c^3}{a(bc)^4}\right]^3$

71. $\left[\dfrac{(x-y)^3z^2}{((x-y)z)^3}\right]^2$

72. $\left[\dfrac{-(a+2b)^9}{(c(a+2b)^2)^3}\right]^2$

*73. $\left[\dfrac{z^7(2x-y)^7}{3w^2(2x-y)^2}\right]^3\left[\dfrac{w^5(2x-y)}{z^3}\right]^4$

*74. $\left[\dfrac{a^2b^3(4a)^4}{a^5(8b)^2}\right]^9\left[\dfrac{(8a^3b)^{15}}{2ab^4a^9}\right]^0$

Evaluate each of the following, rounding each answer to the nearest tenth.

C75. $(2.31)^3$

C76. $(-1.71)^7$

C77. $\dfrac{(-249)^4}{(-41.1)^5}$

C78. $\dfrac{(21.1)^3(1.31)^3}{(43.1)^2}$

C79. $[(20.3)^3(0.0301)^2]^2$

C80. $[(1.73)^2(1.21)^3]^2$

SOLUTIONS FOR PRACTICE PROBLEMS

1. (a) $3^2x^4 \cdot 3^4x^3 = 3^{2+4}x^{4+3} = 3^6x^7 = 729x^7$
   (b) $(y^2)^5 = y^{2\cdot5} = y^{10}$
   (c) $\dfrac{x^2y^5}{xy^3} = x^{2-1}y^{5-3} = xy^2$
   (d) $(x-y)^0 = \begin{cases} 1 & \text{if } x \neq y \\ \text{undefined} & \text{if } x = y \end{cases}$

2. (a) $(-2a^3b)^5 = (-2)^5(a^3)^5b^5 = -32a^{15}b^5$
   (b) $[x(x-y)]^2 = x^2(x-y)^2$
   (c) $\left(\dfrac{3a}{2b}\right)^2 = \dfrac{3^2a^2}{2^2b^2} = \dfrac{9a^2}{4b^2}$
   (d) $\left(\dfrac{x^6y^3}{x^4y^2}\right)^5 = (x^2y)^5 = (x^2)^5y^5 = x^{10}y^5$

6-2 *Addition and Subtraction of Polynomials*

A **polynomial** is a sum of terms where the variable part of each term is an exponential containing only positive or zero exponents and no variable in the denominator. Some examples of polynomials are given in Figure 6.1.

Polynomial	*Type*	*Degree*
$3x^2 - 4x + 1$	Trinomial	2 (quadratic)
$5a^3 - 2a + 7$	Trinomial	3 (cubic)
$y^{93} - 27y$ (monic)	Binomial	93
$2x - 1$	Binomial	1 (linear)
-3	Monomial	0 (constant)
x^4 (monic)	Monomial	4 (quartic)
$3x^3y^2 - 5x^2y + 7y - 3x$	Multinomial	5
$2xy - 2$	Binomial	2 (quadratic)
$-x^5 + x^4 + x^3 - x^2 + 3x - 1$	Multinomial	5

FIGURE 6.1

One characteristic of a polynomial is the number of terms it contains. Polynomials are given special names depending on the number of terms they contain. A polynomial containing one term is called a **monomial**; two terms, a **binomial**; three terms, a **trinomial.** A polynomial that contains more than three terms is sometimes called a **multinomial.**

Another characteristic of polynomials is called their **degree.** The *degree of a nonzero term* of a polynomial is the sum of the exponents of the variables involved in the term. The real number 0 has no degree. Some terms and their degrees are listed below.

Term	x^3	$-9x^2$	$14y^9$	$-8a^2b$	$-2x^3y^8$	$2 = 2x^0$	0
Degree	3	2	9	3	11	0	no degree

The *degree of a polynomial* is said to be the largest degree of the terms making up the polynomial. Some special names are also given to polynomials depending on their degree.

Degree	0	1	2	3	4
Special Name	Constant	Linear	Quadratic	Cubic	Quartic

Figure 6.1 also lists the degree, and special name when applicable, of the polynomials appearing there.

A polynomial is called a **monic** polynomial if the coefficient of the term of largest degree is 1. Thus $x^2 - 3x + 1$ is a monic quadratic trinomial.

It is common to use the notation

$$P(x)$$

to indicate a polynomial P in the variable x. The notation $P(x)$ is read "P of x" or "P evaluated at x." It does *not* indicate the product of P and x.

EXAMPLE 1 Suppose that $P(x) = 3x^4 + 2x^3 + x - 1$. Evaluate:

(a) $P(1)$ (b) $P(0)$ (c) $P(-2)$ (d) $P(a)$ (e) $P(a - 1)$

SOLUTION (a) The notation $P(1)$ indicates that the variable x assumes the value 1. Hence

$$P(1) = 3(1)^4 + 2(1)^3 + 1 - 1 = 3 + 2 + 1 - 1 = 5$$

and the value of the polynomial P is 5 when the variable x is 1.

(b) We replace x by 0 and obtain

$$P(0) = 3 \cdot 0^4 + 2 \cdot 0^3 + 0 - 1 = -1.$$

The value of the polynomial P is -1 when x is 0.

(c) Since

$$P(-2) = 3(-2)^4 + 2(-2)^3 + (-2) - 1$$
$$= 3(16) + 2(-8) - 2 - 1$$
$$= 48 - 16 - 2 - 1$$
$$= 29,$$

the value of the polynomial is 29 when x is -2.

(d) $P(a) = 3a^4 + 2a^3 + a - 1$

(e) $P(a - 1) = 3(a - 1)^4 + 2(a - 1)^3 + (a - 1) - 1$

(Solution on page 157) If $P(x) = x^2 - 2x - 3$, find

(a) $P(0)$ (b) $P(-1)$ (c) $P(h)$

Polynomials are usually written in order of decreasing degree of their terms. For example, the terms of the polynomial

$$P(y) = 3y - 4y^3 + 2y^2 - 3$$

can be commuted so that the polynomial will appear as

$$P(y) = -4y^3 + 2y^2 + 3y - 3.$$

Recall from Chapter 2 that *like terms* are terms that contain the same variable parts. A polynomial is said to be expressed in **simplest form** if all the like terms have been combined using the distributive property and written either in decreasing powers of x or in increasing powers of x. For example, the terms of the polynomial

$$P(x) = 3x^4 - 2x^3 + x^4 + 5x^4 + x^3$$

can be rearranged and combined using the distributive property:

$$P(x) = 3x^4 + x^4 + 5x^4 - 2x^3 + x^3$$
$$= (3 + 1 + 5)x^4 + (-2 + 1)x^3$$
$$= 9x^4 - x^3.$$

The resulting form is a simplest form of the polynomial.

Addition of polynomials is achieved by combining like terms of the polynomials being added and writing the result in simplest form.

EXAMPLE 2 Write the sum $P(x) + Q(x)$ in simplest form where $P(x) = 9x^3 + 4x^2 - 3x + 2$ and $Q(x) = 5x^3 + 2x - 9$.

SOLUTION

$$P(x) + Q(x) = (9x^3 + 4x^2 - 3x + 2) + (5x^3 + 2x - 9)$$
$$= 9x^3 + 5x^3 + 4x^2 - 3x + 2x + 2 - 9$$
$$= (9 + 5)x^3 + 4x^2 + (-3 + 2)x + (2 - 9)$$
$$= 14x^3 + 4x^2 - x - 7$$

ALTERNATIVE SOLUTION

The polynomials can be lined up vertically and arranged so that the like terms are one under another.

$$9x^3 + 4x^2 - 3x + 2 \longleftarrow P(x)$$
$$5x^3 \qquad + 2x - 9 \longleftarrow Q(x)$$

Combining like terms $\quad 14x^3 + 4x^2 - x - 7 \longleftarrow P(x) + Q(x)$

PRACTICE (Solution on page 158) Write the sum $R(x) + S(x)$ in simplest form,
PROBLEM 2 where $R(x) = 5x^4 - x^3 + 2x - 3$ and $S(x) = 3x^3 + x^2 + 1$.

The product of a constant and a polynomial is also computed using the distributive property.

$$a(b + c) = ab + ac.$$

EXAMPLE 3 Given $P(x) = 5x^2 - 2x + 3$ and $Q(x) = x - 3$, write each of the following in simplest form.

(a) $2P(x)$ (b) $(-1)P(x)$ (c) $P(x) + 2Q(x)$

SOLUTION (a) $2P(x) = 2(5x^2 - 2x + 3)$
$= 2(5x^2) + 2(-2x) + 2(3)$ (By the Distributive Property)

$= 10x^2 - 4x + 6$
(b) $(-1)P(x) = (-1)(5x^2 - 2x + 3)$
$= (-1)(5x^2) + (-1)(-2x) + (-1)(3)$ (By the Distributive Property)

$= -5x^2 + 2x - 3$
(c) $P(x) + 2Q(x) = (5x^2 - 2x + 3) + 2(x - 3)$
$= 5x^2 - 2x + 3 + 2x - 6$ (Removing parentheses)
$= 5x^2 - 3$ (Combining like terms)

Recall from Chapter 1 that for any real number a,

$$-a = -1 \cdot a.$$

This same result holds for polynomials, $P(x)$:

$$\boxed{-P(x) = (-1)P(x).}$$

Similarly, we saw in Chapter 1 that subtraction can be expressed in terms of addition. That is, for all real numbers a and b,

$$a - b = a + (-b).$$

For polynomials $P(x)$ and $Q(x)$, we have

$$P(x) - Q(x) = P(x) + (-Q(x)) = P(x) + (-1)Q(x).$$

EXAMPLE 4   Given $P(x) = -3x^2 + 2x + 7$ and $Q(x) = 4x^2 + 3$, write the following in simplest form.

(a) $P(x) - Q(x)$
(b) $Q(x) - 2P(x)$

SOLUTION

$$
\begin{aligned}
\text{(a) } P(x) - Q(x) &= P(x) + (-1)Q(x) \\
&= (-3x^2 + 2x + 7) + (-1)(4x^2 + 3) \\
&= (-3x^2 + 2x + 7) + (-4x^2 - 3) \\
&= -3x^2 + 2x + 7 - 4x^2 - 3 \\
&= -7x^2 + 2x + 4 \\
\text{(b) } Q(x) - 2P(x) &= (4x^2 + 3) - 2(-3x^2 + 2x + 7) \\
&= (4x^2 + 3) - (-6x^2 + 4x + 14) \\
&= 4x^2 + 3 + 6x^2 - 4x - 14 \\
&= 10x^2 - 4x - 11
\end{aligned}
$$

PRACTICE PROBLEM 3   (Solution on page 158) Write $4(-2x^2 - 3) - 2(x^3 - x + 4)$ in simplest form.

EXERCISES 6-2

Classify the following polynomials as to the number of terms and the degree, using the special names when appropriate. Also state which, if any, are monic. (See Figure 6.1.)

1. $x^2 - 2x$

2. $x^3 - 8$

3. $6x^2 + x + 1$

4. $8x^9 + 7x^6 - 1$

5. $15x$

6. -7

7. $xy - y$

8. $xyz + 1$

9. $3x^2y + 7xy^2 + 14x$

10. $x^{80} - x^{40} + x^{20} - 1$

11. $a - 2$

12. x^4

Given $P(x) = x^2 + 2x + 1$ and $Q(x) = 5x^3 - x + 2$, evaluate each of the following. (See Example 1 and Practice Problem 1.)

13. $P(1)$

14. $P(0)$

15. $Q(-1)$

16. $P(-2)$

17. $Q(0)$

18. $P(-\frac{1}{2})$

19. $P(2) - Q(-1)$

20. $Q(1) - 2P(2)$

21. $Q(a)$

22. $P(2a)$

*23. $P(Q(0))$

*24. $Q(P(0))$

*25. $P(P(2))$

*26. $Q(Q(-1))$

*27. $P(Q(1))$

*28. $Q(P(2))$

C29. $P(1.32)$

C30. $Q(-2.17)$

Perform the indicated operations and write the resulting polynomial in simplest form.

ADDITION

(See Example 2 and Practice Problem 2.)

31. $(5x + 7) + (3x + 2)$

32. $(9x^2 + 3x + 1) + (2x^2 + x + 5)$

33. $(x^2 + 3x - 1) + (2x^2 - x - 2)$

34. $(x^2 + 4x - 8) + (3x^2 - 7x - 3)$

35. $(8x^3 + 4x^2 + 2x - 6) + (1 - x + x^2 - x^3)$

36. $(5x^4 + 3x^3 - 2x^2 + x - 1) + (-x + 2x^4 - 3x^2 - 3x^3 + 4)$

37. $(-x^5 + x^3 + 4x - 1) + (x^4 + 2x^3)$

38. $(4x^3 - 5x + 3) + (x^2 + 3x - 1)$

SUBTRACTION

(See Example 4.)

39. $(3x - 2) - (7x + 1)$

40. $(4x^2 + 1) - (2x^2 - 11)$

41. $(-x^2 + x - 4) - (3x^2 + 5x - 8)$

42. $(-3x^2 + x - 9) - (x^2 + 7x - 2)$

43. $(15x^3 + 7x^2 - 11x + 2) - (14x^3 - 2x^2 + 10x + 8)$

44. $(7x^4 - 2x^5 + 3) - (x^2 - x^5 + x^4)$

45. $(x^4 + 3x^2 - 8x^3 + 5) - (1 - x^2 + x - 5x^4)$

46. $(-1 + 3x + 4x^3) - (-2x^2 + 3x^3 - 11)$

GENERAL

(See Examples 3 and 4 and Practice Problem 3.)

47. $2(x - 3) + 3(x + 2)$

48. $5(2x - 7) + 4(-3x + 2)$

49. $-2(2x^2 + 3x - 1) + 5(-x^2 + x - 1)$

50. $-3(5x^3 + 4x - 9) + (-2)(x^2 + 3x + 12)$

51. $-(x^5 + 3x^4 - 2x + 3) + (-5)(-x^2 + 3x - 7)$

52. $-(4x^{10} + 7x^5 + 3) + (-2)(-2x^{10} + 3x^5 - 1)$

53. $3(8x - 3) - (7x + 2)$

54. $2(4x^2 - 1) - (-2x^2 + 3x - 11)$

55. $-3(7x - 4) - 2(4x - 3)$

56. $4(3x^3 - 7x + 2) - 5(2x^2 + 11x + 1)$

57. $-2(4x^5 + 6x^3 - x) - (-3)(x^5 + 2x^3 - 4)$

58. $(-4)(-5x^9 + 7x^6 - 3x^3 + 4) - (-1)(x^9 + x^6 - x^3 - 1)$

59. $-\{2(x - 3) - [x^2 + 3(x - 2)]\}$

60. $-\{x - 2[5 - 3x^3 - (x + 3)] + 3x\}$

61. $-[-x - (x^2 - x^3)] + [x^3 - (x - x^2)]$

62. $-3\{x^3 - [x^2 - 2x - (x + 3)]\} + 4(x - 1)$

63. $5[x - (x^2 + 3x - 1) - x^2] - 2[x^2 - 2(x - 3) + 1]$

64. $2[x^3 - 3(x - x^2) + x - 1] - 4[2x^2 + x - (5 - x)]$

65. $-\{-[-(x - 1)] - [-2(x + 3)]\}$

66. $-3\{-[-2(1 - x)] - 3[2 - (1 - x)]\}$

Given $R(x) = x^3 - 2x + 1$, $S(x) = 2x^2 + x - 1$, and $T(x) = -x^3 + 3x^2 + x - 3$, write each of the following in simplest form.

67. $R(x) + S(x)$

68. $S(x) + R(x)$

69. $R(x) - S(x)$

70. $S(x) - R(x)$

71. $[R(x) + S(x)] + T(x)$

72. $R(x) + [S(x) + T(x)]$

73. $3R(x) - 2S(x)$

74. $5T(x) - [R(x) + 2S(x)]$

A polynomial $P(x)$ is called **even** if $P(-x) = P(x)$. A polynomial $P(x)$ is called **odd** if $P(-x) = -P(x)$. Classify each of the following polynomials as either even or odd or neither even nor odd.

*75. $P(x) = 2x - 1$

*76. $P(x) = 4x + 2$

*77. $P(x) = 5x$

*78. $P(x) = -4x$

*79. $P(x) = 2x^2 - 1$

*80. $P(x) = 5x^4 + x^2 - 2$

*81. $P(x) = 3x^2 + 2x - 1$

*82. $P(x) = 2x^3 + 1$

*83. $P(x) = x^3 - x$

*84. $P(x) = 15$

SOLUTIONS FOR PRACTICE PROBLEMS

1. $P(x) = x^2 - 2x - 3$
   (a) $P(0) = 0^2 - 2 \cdot 0 - 3 = -3$
   (b) $P(-1) = (-1)^2 - 2(-1) - 3 = 1 + 2 - 3 = 0$
   (c) $P(h) = h^2 - 2h - 3$

2. $R(x) + S(x) = (5x^4 - x^3 + 2x - 3) + (3x^3 + x^2 + 1)$
$\qquad\qquad\quad = 5x^4 + (-x^3 + 3x^3) + x^2 + 2x + (-3 + 1)$
$\qquad\qquad\quad = 5x^4 + 2x^3 + x^2 + 2x - 2$

3. $4(-2x^2 - 3) - 2(x^3 - x + 4) = -8x^2 - 12 - 2x^3 + 2x - 8$
$\qquad\qquad\qquad\qquad\qquad\quad = -2x^3 - 8x^2 + 2x - 20$

6-3

Multiplication of Polynomials

In Section 6-2 we formed a product $cP(x)$ of a polynomial $P(x)$ and a constant c by using the distributive property. We rely on the distributive property heavily in the general multiplication of two polynomials $P(x)$ and $Q(x)$. First, we consider an example where $P(x)$ is a monomial and $Q(x)$ is not a monomial.

EXAMPLE 1 Let $P(x) = 3x^2$ and $Q(x) = x^2 + 4x - 3$. Write the product $P(x) \cdot Q(x)$ in simplest form.

SOLUTION $P(x) \cdot Q(x) = (3x^2)(x^2 + 4x - 3)$

$\qquad\qquad\qquad = 3x^2 \cdot x^2 + 3x^2 \cdot 4x + 3x^2 \cdot (-3)$ (By the Distributive Property)

$\qquad\qquad\qquad = 3x^4 + 12x^3 - 9x^2$ (By the Laws of Exponents)

Next suppose that both $P(x)$ and $Q(x)$ are binomials.

EXAMPLE 2 Multiply $P(x) \cdot Q(x)$, where $P(x) = x - 3$ and $Q(x) = 2x + 1$.

SOLUTION **HORIZONTAL METHOD** We apply the distributive property twice.

$P(x) \cdot Q(x) = (x - 3)(2x + 1)$

$\qquad\qquad = (x - 3)(2x) + (x - 3)(1)$ (By the Distributive Property)

$\qquad\qquad = x(2x) + (-3)(2x) + x(1) + (-3)(1)$ (By the Distributive Property)

$\qquad\qquad = 2x^2 - 6x + x - 3$

$\qquad\qquad = 2x^2 - 5x - 3$ (Combining like terms)

FOIL METHOD Since the product of two binomials occurs so frequently in mathematics a method has been devised especially for the product of two binomials. In

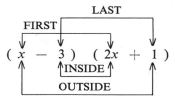

the pair x and $2x$ are the first terms in each bonomial; the pair x and 1 are the outside terms; the pair -3 and $2x$ are the inside terms; and the pair -3 and 1 are the last terms. The product of the two binomials consists of the sum of the products of the four pairs of terms just described. Hence the multiplication appears as

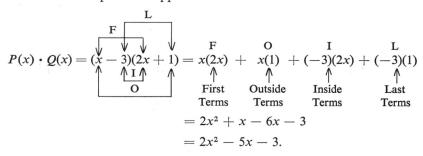

$$= 2x^2 + x - 6x - 3$$
$$= 2x^2 - 5x - 3.$$

VERTICAL METHOD The distributive property can be applied twice using a vertical setup.

Write one polynomial under the other. $P(x) \longrightarrow x - 3$
$Q(x) \longrightarrow 2x + 1$

Arrange like terms   Multiply $(x - 3)(2x) \longrightarrow 2x^2 - 6x$
one under the other.   Multiply $(x - 3)(1) \longrightarrow \quad\quad x - 3$
Combine like terms. $P(x) \cdot Q(x) \longrightarrow 2x^2 - 5x - 3$

**PRACTICE
PROBLEM 1**

(Solution on page 163) Multiply $(4x - 3)(-x + 5)$.

The vertical method of multiplying two binomials extends readily to multiplying polynomials with more than two terms.

EXAMPLE 3   Write the product $P(x) \cdot Q(x)$ in simplest form where $P(x) = x^2 + 2x - 3$ and $Q(x) = x^3 - 2x + 4$.

159

SOLUTION

$$P(x) \longrightarrow x^2 + 2x - 3$$
$$Q(x) \longrightarrow x^3 - 2x + 4$$

$$(x^2 + 2x - 3)(x^3) \longrightarrow x^5 + 2x^4 - 3x^3$$
$$(x^2 + 2x - 3)(-2x) \longrightarrow \qquad - 2x^3 - 4x^2 + 6x$$
$$(x^2 + 2x - 3)(4) \longrightarrow \qquad\qquad\qquad 4x^2 + 8x - 12$$

Arrange like terms one under the other.

$$P(x)Q(x) \longrightarrow x^5 + 2x^4 - 5x^3 + 0x^2 + 14x - 12$$

Thus $P(x)Q(x) = x^5 + 2x^4 - 5x^3 + 14x - 12$.

PRACTICE PROBLEM 2 (Solution on page 163) Multiply $(2x^4 - 3x^2 + x)(-x^2 + 1)$.

There are several special products which deserve special attention. Each can be verified by direct multiplication.

The first is called the *product of the sum and difference of two quantities* yielding the **difference of two squares.**

$$(x + y)(x - y) = x^2 - y^2$$

Notice that x is the first term of each factor and y is the second term. The product can be described as: (first term squared) — (second term squared).

$$(x + y)(x - y) = \qquad x^2 \qquad - \qquad y^2$$

first term   second term   first term squared   second term squared

EXAMPLE 4
(a) $(x + 2)(x - 2) = x^2 - 2^2 = x^2 - 4$
(b) $(1 + 3a)(1 - 3a) = 1^2 - (3a)^2 = 1 - 9a^2$

PRACTICE PROBLEM 3 (Solution on page 163) Use the special product formula to find
$$(4x + y)(4x - y).$$

Two other special products are in the form of the **square of a binomial**, whose product is *always* a *trinomial*.

$$(x + y)^2 = x^2 + 2xy + y^2$$
and
$$(x - y)^2 = x^2 - 2xy + y^2$$

160

The result of squaring a binomial can be described as

$$\left(\begin{matrix}\text{first term}\\\text{squared}\end{matrix}\right) \pm \left(\begin{matrix}\text{twice the product}\\\text{of the two terms}\end{matrix}\right) + \left(\begin{matrix}\text{last term}\\\text{squared}\end{matrix}\right).$$

The "$\pm$" indicates that the "$+$" is used if the binomial is a sum and the "$-$" is used if the binomial is a difference.

$$(x \pm y)^2 = \underset{\substack{\uparrow \\ \text{first term} \\ \text{squared}}}{x^2} \pm \underset{\substack{\uparrow \\ \text{twice the} \\ \text{product}}}{2xy} + \underset{\substack{\uparrow \\ \text{last term} \\ \text{squared}}}{y^2}$$

EXAMPLE 5

(a) $(x + 3y)^2 = x^2 + 2(x)(3y) + (3y)^2 = x^2 + 6xy + 9y^2$

(b) $(4a - 5b)^2 = (4a)^2 - 2(4a)(5b) + (5b)^2 = 16a^2 - 40ab + 25b^2$

PRACTICE PROBLEM 4

(Solution on page 163) Use the special product formulas to find

(a) $(3x + 2y)^2$ and (b) $(5 - y)^2$.

These special product formulas can be used even when the factors appear to be more complicated than those in the preceding examples. Consider the next example.

*EXAMPLE 6

Use the special product formulas to find $(a + b + c)(a + b - c)$.

SOLUTION

We first use the formula for the difference of two squares, and then the formula for the square of a binomial.

$$(a + b + c)(a + b - c) = [(a + b) + c][(a + b) - c] \quad \text{(By grouping)}$$
$$= (a + b)^2 - c^2 \quad \text{(Difference of two squares)}$$
$$= a^2 + 2ab + b^2 - c^2 \quad \text{(Square of a binomial)}$$

*PRACTICE PROBLEM 5

(Solution on page 163) Use the special product formulas to find $(x - y + z)^2$.

Write the result of the multiplication in simplest form.
(See Example 1.)

1. $4y^2(8y - 3)$
2. $-y^3(2y^2 - 1)$
3. $-2ab(a^2b - 3ab)$
4. $5ac^2(-a + c^2)$
5. $x^2(4 - x^3 + x^9)$
6. $-3y^3(-1 + 2y^2 + 4y^4)$
7. $-3r^5s^2(3 - r^5 - s^2)$
8. $-9r(4r^2 + 2r - 3)$

(See Example 2 and Practice Problem 1.)

9. $(x + 2)(x + 3)$
10. $(x + 5)(x + 4)$
11. $(2x - 1)(x + 5)$
12. $(4x - 9)(x + 8)$
13. $(5x - 1)(3x - 2)$
14. $(10x - 7)(2x - 3)$
15. $(4x + 11)(x - 7)$
16. $(8x - 3)(5x + 3)$

(See Example 3 and Practice Problem 2.)

17. $(x - 3)(2x^2 + x - 1)$
18. $(x + 4)(x^3 + 2x^2 + 1)$
19. $(2y - 1)(4y^3 + y)$
20. $(4y - 3)(9y^3 - 2y)$
21. $(x^2 + x - 2)(4x^2 + 3x - 1)$
22. $(2x^2 + x - 3)(5x^2 - 2x - 9)$
23. $(x^3 + x - 1)(2x^2 + 7x - 3)$
24. $(x^4 + 3x^2 - 2)(x^3 + 5x - 4)$

(See Example 4 and Practice Problem 3.)

25. $(x + 3)(x - 3)$
26. $(y + 5)(y - 5)$
27. $(2a + b)(2a - b)$
28. $(3a + 4)(3a - 4)$
29. $(9r + 2s)(9r - 2s)$
30. $(7r + 8)(7r - 8)$
31. $(1 + ab)(1 - ab)$
32. $(x + yz)(x - yz)$

(See Example 5 and Practice Problem 4.)

33. $(x + 4)^2$
34. $(x + 8)^2$
35. $(2y - 1)^2$
36. $(3y - 1)^2$
37. $(5x - 2)^2$
38. $(4x + 3)^2$
39. $(2y + 7z)^2$
40. $(3y - 8z)^2$

Perform the following multiplications using the special product formulas when applicable.

41. $3a^2b(4a - 2b)$
42. $-5xy(x^2 + 2xy + y^2)$
43. $(a - b)(a^2 - 2ab + b^2)$
44. $(x + y)(x^2 + 2xy + y^2)$
45. $(a + b)^3$
46. $(x - y)^3$

47. $(3a - b)(3a + b)^2$

48. $(2 - a)^2(1 + 2a)$

49. $y(y + 7)(y - 3)$

50. $(x - 1)(x + 2)(x - 3)$

51. $(1 + a)(3 - b)$

52. $(3a - 2)(b + 3)$

53. $(a - b)(c - d)$

54. $(x + y)(z + w)$

55. $(4 - xy)^2$

56. $(ab - 3)^2$

57. $(2x - 7)(2x + 7)$

58. $(1 - a)(1 + a)$

59. $(3 - ab^2)(3 + ab^2)$

60. $(y^3 - x^2)(y^3 + x^2)$

61. $(x - 1)(x^2 + x + 1)$

62. $(y + 1)(y^2 - y + 1)$

63. $(a + b)(a^2 - ab + b^2)$

64. $(a - b)(a^2 + ab + b^2)$

65. $(1 - x)[1 - x(x^2 - 1)]$

66. $1 - x[1 - x(x^2 - 1)]$

67. $x(3 - x) - [x - 4(x - 1)(x - 2)]$

68. $x^3(x^2 - x)(1 - x) + 2[1 - x(2 - x)]$

69. $3x - (x^2 - 1)\{-[x - 3x(1 - x)] + 2\}$

70. $(3x - x^2 - 1)\{-[(x - 3)x(1 - x)] + 2\}$

71. $x^3 - x\{x - (1 - x)(1 + x) - 3x[2(x - 5) + 1]\}$

72. $(1 - x)(1 + x)[(x - 1) - 2x(-4x)]$

(See Example 6 and Practice Problem 5.)

*73. $(x + y + 2)(x + y - 2)$

*74. $(1 - 2a + b)(1 + 2a - b)$

*75. $(a - 2b - c)^2$

*76. $(x + 2y + 1)^2$

*77. $(a + b + c + d)^2$

*78. $(x + y - z - w)^2$

SOLUTIONS FOR PRACTICE PROBLEMS

1. $(4x - 3)(-x + 5) = (4x - 3)(-x) + (4x - 3)5$
$$= 4x(-x) + (-3)(-x) + 4x(5) + (-3)(5)$$
$$= -4x^2 + 3x + 20x - 15$$
$$= -4x^2 + 23x - 15$$

2.
$$\begin{array}{r} 2x^4 - 3x^2 + x \\ -x^2 + 1 \\ \hline -2x^6 + 3x^4 - x^3 \\ 2x^4 \qquad - 3x^2 + x \\ \hline -2x^6 + 5x^4 - x^3 - 3x^2 + x \end{array}$$

3. $(4x + y)(4x - y) = (4x)^2 - y^2$
$$= 16x^2 - y^2$$

4. (a) $(3x + 2y)^2 = (3x)^2 + 2(3x)(2y) + (2y)^2 = 9x^2 + 12xy + 4y^2$
   (b) $(5 - y)^2 = 5^2 - 2(5)(y) + y^2 = 25 - 10y + y^2$

5. $(x - y + z)^2 = [(x - y) + z]^2$
$$= (x - y)^2 + 2(x - y)z + z^2$$
$$= x^2 - 2xy + y^2 + 2xz - 2yz + z^2$$
$$= x^2 + y^2 + z^2 - 2xy + 2xz - 2yz$$

A polynomial $P(x)$ assumes real values: When x is replaced by a real number, the value of the polynomial $P(x)$ is a real number. In the study of division (or quotients) of polynomials it is important to note that we must restrict the variable from assuming a value that leads to the polynomial in the denominator assuming the value zero, since division by zero is undefined. Hence if $P(x) = 3x^4 - 2x^3 + x^2$ and $D(x) = x - 2$, then the quotient

$$\frac{P(x)}{D(x)} = \frac{3x^4 - 2x^3 + x^2}{x - 2}$$

is not defined for $x = 2$ [since $D(2) = 2 - 2 = 0$]. Thus we might write

$$\frac{P(x)}{D(x)} = \frac{3x^4 - 2x^3 + x^2}{x - 2}, \qquad x \neq 2.$$

EXAMPLE 1   Restrict the value of the variable so that the quotient is defined.

(a) $\dfrac{9y^3 + 2y - 11}{y - 3}$

(b) $\dfrac{4x^{10} - 11x^3 + x}{(x - 2)(2x + 3)}$

(c) $\dfrac{11a^3b + 4a^2b^2}{3ab}$

SOLUTION   (a) The denominator $y - 3$ is zero when $y = 3$. Thus the restriction is: $y \neq 3$.

(b) If $x = 2$ or if $x = -\frac{3}{2}$, the denominator $(x - 2)(2x + 3)$ is zero. Hence the restriction must be: $x \neq 2$, $x \neq -\frac{3}{2}$.

(c) If $a = 0$ or $b = 0$, the denominator is zero. Thus the restriction is: $a \neq 0$, $b \neq 0$.

**PRACTICE
PROBLEM 1**   (Solution on page 169) Restrict the value of the variable so that the quotient is defined.

(a) $\dfrac{90x^3y + 40x^2y^2 + 10xy^3}{x - y}$

(b) $\dfrac{(x - 5)(x - 4)}{(x - 1)(x - 2)(x - 3)}$

Throughout the remainder of this chapter we shall assume, without so stating, that the necessary restrictions are made so that all quotients are defined.

Just as with multiplication of polynomials we begin with the simplest type of polynomial division, in which a polynomial $P(x)$ is divided by a monomial $D(x)$ to form the quotient

$$\frac{P(x)}{D(x)}.$$

We use the property of fractions which states that

$$\frac{a + c}{b} = \frac{a}{b} + \frac{c}{b}.$$

Consider the next example.

EXAMPLE 2   Write the quotient as a polynomial in simplest form.

$$\frac{9x^6 - 12x^4 + 27x^2}{3x^2}$$

SOLUTION   We apply the property of fractions stated above and then simplify using the laws of exponents.

$$\frac{9x^6 - 12x^4 + 27x^2}{3x^2} = \frac{9x^6}{3x^2} - \frac{12x^4}{3x^2} + \frac{27x^2}{3x^2}$$

$$= 3x^4 - 4x^2 + 9$$

Sometimes division of a polynomial by a monomial does not yield a result that is a polynomial. Consider the next example.

EXAMPLE 3   Write the quotient as a sum and simplify.

$$\frac{8x^3y^2 + 5x^2y - 20x}{4xy}$$

SOLUTION

$$\frac{8x^3y^2 + 5x^2y - 20x}{4xy} = \frac{8x^3y^2}{4xy} + \frac{5x^2y}{4xy} - \frac{20x}{4xy}$$

$$= 2x^2y + \frac{5x}{4} - \frac{5}{y}$$

$$= 2x^2y + \frac{5}{4}x - \frac{5}{y}$$

This result, $2x^2y + \frac{5}{4}x - \frac{5}{y}$ is *not* a polynomial because the last term, $-\frac{5}{y}$, has a variable in the denominator.

Next we consider polynomial division in which the denominator has more than one term. The mechanics in the division process, sometimes called *long division*, closely parallels the procedure for dividing real numbers. We illustrate this parallel procedure with the quotients

$$\frac{1235}{23} \quad \text{and} \quad \frac{2x^2 + 5x + 5}{x + 1}.$$

We set up each problem with a similar arrangement.

$$23\,\overline{)\,1235} \qquad\qquad\qquad\qquad x + 1\,\overline{)\,2x^2 + 5x + 5}$$

Divide 23 into 123.   Divide x into $2x^2$.

$$
\begin{array}{r}
5 \\
23\,\overline{)\,1235} \\
\mathbf{115}\!\!\downarrow \\
\hline
\mathbf{85}
\end{array}
\qquad
\begin{array}{r}
2x \\
x + 1\,\overline{)\,2x^2 + 5x + 5} \\
\mathbf{2x^2 + 2x}\!\!\downarrow \\
\hline
\mathbf{3x + 5}
\end{array}
$$

5(23) ⟵ multiply ⟶ 2x(x + 1)

85 ⟵ subtract and bring down next term ⟶ 3x + 5

Divide 23 into 85.   Divide x into $3x$.

$$
\begin{array}{r}
53 \\
23\,\overline{)\,1235} \\
115 \\
\hline
85 \\
\mathbf{69} \\
\hline
\mathbf{16}
\end{array}
\qquad
\begin{array}{r}
2x + 3 \\
x + 1\,\overline{)\,2x^2 + 5x + 5} \\
2x^2 + 2x \\
\hline
3x + 5 \\
\mathbf{3x + 3} \\
\hline
\mathbf{2}
\end{array}
$$

3(23) ⟵ multiply ⟶ 3(x + 1)

16 ⟵ subtract ⟶ 2

Thus

$$\frac{1235}{23} = 53 + \frac{16}{23} = 53\frac{16}{23}.$$

Similarly, we write

$$\frac{2x^2 + 5x + 5}{x + 1} = 2x + 3 + \frac{2}{x + 1}.$$

In general, we write

$$\boxed{\frac{P(x)}{D(x)} = Q(x) + \frac{R(x)}{D(x)}} \qquad\qquad (1)$$

when the polynomial $P(x)$, called the **dividend**, is divided by the polynomial $D(x)$, called the **divisor**, yielding a polynomial $Q(x)$, called the **quotient**, and a polynomial $R(x)$, called the **remainder.** The division is not complete until $R(x) = 0$ or the degree of the remainder polynomial $R(x)$ is *less* than the degree of the dividing polynomial $D(x)$.

The checking procedure that we use on polynomials also parallels the checking procedure for real numbers. We check using:

$$\text{divisor} \times \text{quotient} + \text{remainder} = \text{dividend}.$$

Thus

$$23(53) + 16 = 1219 + 16 = 1235$$

and

$$(x + 1)(2x + 3) + 2 = 2x^2 + 5x + 3 + 2 = 2x^2 + 5x + 5.$$

In general, for polynomials we have

$$D(x)Q(x) + R(x) = P(x).$$

EXAMPLE 4 Divide and write the result in the form given in equation (1).

$$\frac{1 + x^3 + 4x^5 - 3x^2}{2x^2 + 2 - x}$$

SOLUTION We write each polynomial in decreasing powers of x and also notice that there are missing terms in the dividend. Each power of x *must* appear, so we supply coefficients of 0 for those missing powers of x.

Divide $2x^2$ into $4x^5$. $2x^2 - x + 2 \overline{)4x^5 + 0x^4 + x^3 - 3x^2 + 0x + 1}$
Multiply: $2x^3(2x^2 - x + 2)$. $\underline{4x^5 - 2x^4 + 4x^3}$
Subtract. Divide $2x^2$ into $2x^4$. $2x^4 - 3x^3 - 3x^2$
Multiply: $x^2(2x^2 - x + 2)$. $\underline{2x^4 - x^3 + 2x^2}$
Subtract. Divide $2x^2$ into $-2x^3$. $-2x^3 - 5x^2 + 0x$
Multiply: $-x(2x^2 - x + 2)$. $\underline{-2x^3 + x^2 - 2x}$
Subtract. Divide $2x^2$ into $-6x^2$. $-6x^2 + 2x + 1$
Multiply: $-3(2x^2 - x + 2)$. $\underline{-6x^2 + 3x - 6}$
Subtract. $-x + 7$

with quotient $2x^3 + x^2 - x - 3$ above.

Since the degree of $-x + 7$ is less than the degree of $2x^2 - x + 2$, the division is complete. We write our result as

$$\frac{4x^5 + x^3 - 3x^2 + 1}{2x^2 - x + 2} = 2x^3 + x^2 - x - 3 + \frac{-x + 7}{2x^2 - x + 2}.$$

PRACTICE PROBLEM 2 (Solution on page 169) Divide and write the result in the form given by equation (1).

$$\frac{x^3 - 8}{x - 2}$$

Restrict the value of the variable so that the quotient is defined. (See Example 1 and Practice Problem 1.)

1. $\dfrac{3x + 2}{4x}$

2. $\dfrac{2x^2 - x + 3}{-5x^2}$

3. $\dfrac{10x^3 - x + 3}{x - 1}$

4. $\dfrac{1 - x^2 + x^3}{2 - x}$

5. $\dfrac{3y^4 + 2y^2 + 5}{(y - 1)(y + 2)}$

6. $\dfrac{9y - 2y^4 + y^{10}}{(y - 3)(y + 1)}$

7. $\dfrac{5y^4 + 3y^3 - 7y^2}{(2y - 1)(3y + 9)}$

8. $\dfrac{10x^3}{(2x + 5)(4x - 1)}$

9. $\dfrac{a^3 - b^3}{a - b}$

10. $\dfrac{x^2 - 4xy + 4y^2}{x - 2y}$

Write each quotient as a sum and simplify. (See Examples 2 and 3.)

11. $\dfrac{8x^5 + 9x^4 + 2x^3}{x^3}$

12. $\dfrac{15x^7 - 20x^5 + 45x^4}{5x^3}$

13. $\dfrac{12x^5y^7 + 36x^6y^6 - 72x^7y^5}{12x^3y^3}$

14. $\dfrac{50a^{10}b^5 - 40a^8b^7}{10a^6b^5}$

15. $\dfrac{42x^3 + 21x^2 + 7x - 56}{7x^2}$

16. $\dfrac{x^3 + 7x^2 - x}{2x^3}$

17. $\dfrac{5a^5b + 10a^4b^2 - 20a^3b^3}{40a^5b^5}$

18. $\dfrac{4r^3s^3 + 17r^6s^6}{r^5s^5}$

19. $\dfrac{(3x)^5 - (3x)^4}{(3x)^2}$

20. $\dfrac{(5y)^7 + (5y)^6 + 2(5y)^5}{(5y)^5}$

21. $\dfrac{5(a - b)^3 + 2(a - b)^2}{(a - b)^2}$

22. $\dfrac{22(x - 2y)^5 - 77(x - 2y)^7}{11(x - 2y)^5}$

23. $\dfrac{(a + b)^7 + 8(a + b)^4}{(a + b)^5}$

24. $\dfrac{8(3x + 2y)^9 - 9(3x + 2y)^8}{6(3x + 2y)^{10}}$

Divide and write the result in the form of equation (1). (See Example 4 and Practice Problem 2.)

25. $\dfrac{x^2 - 5x + 6}{x - 3}$

26. $\dfrac{x^3 + 14x^2 + 49x}{x + 7}$

27. $\dfrac{x^2 - 5x - 10}{2 + x}$

28. $\dfrac{2x^2 - 5 + 5x}{3 + x}$

29. $\dfrac{6x^2 - 3 + 13x}{2x + 5}$

30. $\dfrac{8x^2 + 8 - 14x}{2x - 3}$

31. $\dfrac{2x^3 + 13x^2 + 9x - 6}{2x + 3}$

32. $\dfrac{6a^3 - 19a^2 + a + 6}{3a - 2}$

33. $\dfrac{4y^4 + 25y^3 - 33y^2 + 5y + 3}{4y - 3}$

34. $\dfrac{6b^4 + 17b^3 + b^2 - 7b - 1}{2b + 1}$

35. $\dfrac{x^4 - 3x^3 + 2x^2 - 5x + 2}{x - 3}$

36. $\dfrac{10x^3 + x^2 + 7x - 2}{5x + 3}$

37. $\dfrac{6x + 4x^4 - 2 - x^2}{2x + 1}$

38. $\dfrac{5x + 5 + 9x^3}{3x + 1}$

39. $\dfrac{2x^4 - 3x^3 - x^2 + 3x + 1}{x^2 - 1}$

40. $\dfrac{2x^4 - 4x^3 - 5x^2 - 2x - 3}{2x^2 + 1}$

41. $\dfrac{x^3 + x^2 - 5x - 1}{x^2 + 2x - 1}$

42. $\dfrac{2y^3 - y^2 - 2y + 2}{y^2 - y + 2}$

43. $\dfrac{x^4 + x^2 + 2x^5 + 2x^3 + 2 - 5x}{2x^2 + x}$

44. $\dfrac{5x + 3x^3 - 15x^2 - 10}{3x^2 + 2}$

45. $\dfrac{x^5 - 4x^4 - x^2 + 2}{x^3 - 2x^2}$

46. $\dfrac{x^6 + 7x^3 - 2}{x^3 + 2x}$

47. $\dfrac{4x^4 + 3x^2 + \frac{1}{2}}{2x + 5}$

48. $\dfrac{x^4 + 3x^2}{x + 3}$

49. $\dfrac{x^3 - 1}{x + 2}$

50. $\dfrac{x^4 + 2}{x + 1}$

51. $\dfrac{x^2 + 2x - 3}{2x - 3}$

52. $\dfrac{x^2 - 5x + 7}{3x - 2}$

53. $\dfrac{2x^3 + 4x - 3}{4x + 2}$

54. $\dfrac{2x^3 + 2x^2 + 5}{6x - 3}$

SOLUTIONS FOR PRACTICE PROBLEMS

1. (a) If $x = y$, the denominator is equal to zero. Thus the restriction is $x \neq y$.
   (b) The denominator becomes zero when $x = 1$, $x = 2$ or $x = 3$. Hence the restriction is $x \neq 1$, $x \neq 2$, $x \neq 3$.

2. In the dividend we leave space for those terms with zero coefficient.

$$
\begin{array}{r}
x^2 + 2x\ + 4 \\
x - 2 \overline{\smash{\big)}\ x^3 - 8} \\
\underline{x^3 - 2x^2 } \\
2x^2 \\
\underline{2x^2 - 4x } \\
4x - 8 \\
\underline{4x - 8} \\
0
\end{array}
$$

Thus

$$\frac{x^3 - 8}{x - 2} = x^2 + 2x + 4 + \frac{0}{x - 2} = x^2 + 2x + 4.$$

PRACTICE TEST for Chapter 6

Simplify each of the following by using the laws of exponents. Assume that all denominators are nonzero.

1. (a) $4x^2y \cdot 9xy^3$ (b) $(-5x^2y^3)^3$

2. (a) $\dfrac{3a^2b^4}{9ab^2}$ (b) $\dfrac{(2r^2s)^5(rs)^0}{(2rs)^3s}$

3. If $P(x) = 3x^2 - 4x + 5$, determine
   (a) $P(0)$ (b) $P(-1)$.

4. Perform the indicated operations and write the resulting polynomial in simplest form.
   (a) $3(2x^3 + 4x - 6) + 2(-x^2 - 7x + 3x + 8)$
   (b) $(4x^4 - 2x^2 + x - 4) - (5x^4 - x^3 + 4x^2 - 5x + 7)$

Perform the following multiplications using the special product formulas when applicable.

5. (a) $(2x - y)(3x + 4y)$ (b) $(x^2 - 2x - 5)(x + 3)$

6. (a) $(x - 6)(x + 6)$ (b) $(2x - 7)^2$

7. (a) $(x - 2)(x^2 + 2x + 4)$
   (b) $x - 2[x - 2(x - 2)] - (x - 2)^2$

Perform the following divisions.

8. $\dfrac{9x^3y^5 - 3x^4y^4}{-3x^3y^2}$

9. $\dfrac{2x^3 - x^2 - 25x - 20}{2x + 5}$

10. $\dfrac{2x^5 - 6x^4 + 3x^3 + 3x^2 - 4}{x^2 - 3x + 2}$

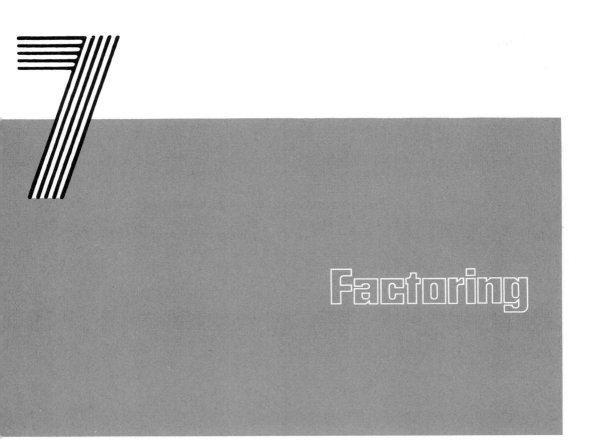

Factoring

7-1
The Distributive
Property

Factoring is the reverse process of multiplication. For example, we multiply 2 and 3 to obtain the product 6.

$$\text{MULTIPLY:} \quad 2 \cdot 3 = 6$$

Reversing the process, we factor 6 as the product of 2 and 3.

$$\text{FACTOR:} \quad 6 = 2 \cdot 3$$

A **prime number** is any positive integer (different from 1) whose only positive factors are itself and 1. The first few prime numbersare

$$2, 3, 5, 7, 11, 13, \ldots.$$

A positive integer is said to be **completely factored** if it is written as the product of its prime factors. A negative integer is completely factored if it is written as the product of -1 and its prime factors.

EXAMPLE 1   Factor completely:

(a) 39   (b) 12   (c) -108 (d) -32

SOLUTION   (a) $39 = 3 \cdot 13$
(b) $12 = 2 \cdot 2 \cdot 3 = 2^2 \cdot 3$
(c) $-108 = (-1)(108) = (-1) \cdot 9 \cdot 12 = (-1) \cdot 3^3 \cdot 2^2$
(d) $-32 = (-1) \cdot 4 \cdot 8 = (-1) \cdot 2^2 \cdot 2^3 = (-1) \cdot 2^5$

The greatest common factor of two integers a and b is the largest integer that is a factor of both a and b. For example, 7 is a common factor of 42 and 56 but 14 is the greatest common factor of 42 and 56.

The greatest common factor (abbreviated GCF) of two or more monomials can be determined by following the two steps outlined below.

To find the GCF, we

1. Factor each monomial completely, and

2. Form the product of all the common factors, with each common factor raised to the least power with which it appears in any factorization.

EXAMPLE 2   Determine the greatest common factor of $36x^3y$, $84x^2y^2$, and $-24x^2y^4$.

SOLUTION   The complete factorization of each expression is

$$36x^3y = 3^2 2^2 x^3 y$$

$$84x^2y^2 = 7 \cdot 3 \cdot 2^2 x^2 y^2$$

$$-24x^2y^4 = (-1)3 \cdot 2^3 x^2 y^4.$$

Since 3 occurs in each factorization at least once, 2 occurs in each factorization at least twice, x occurs in each factorization at least twice, and y occurs in each factorization at least once, the greatest common factor is

$$3 \cdot 2^2 \cdot x^2 y = 12x^2 y.$$

PRACTICE PROBLEM 1   (Solution on page 176) Determine the greatest common factor of $33(x - 2)^3$ and $99(x - 2)^5$.

In earlier chapters we used the distributive property to rewrite a product as a sum.

$$\text{MULTIPLY:} \quad \underbrace{a(b+c)}_{\text{product}} = \underbrace{ab+ac}_{\text{sum}}$$

Factoring is the reverse process of multiplication. Thus the distributive property is used to rewrite (hence factor) a sum as a product.

$$\text{FACTOR:} \quad \underbrace{ab+ac}_{\text{sum}} = \underbrace{a(b+c)}_{\text{product}}$$

In this chapter our goal is to factor polynomials. We consider only polynomials whose coefficients are integers, and we require that all factors be polynomials that have integers as coefficients. Even though we can multiply

$$\tfrac{1}{2}x(2x+4) = x^2 + 2x,$$

we do *not* allow the factorization

$$x^2 + 2x = \tfrac{1}{2}x(2x+4),$$

since the polynomial, $\tfrac{1}{2}x$, does not have integral coefficients.

A polynomial with integral coefficients is said to be **completely factored** if it is written as a product of polynomials with integral coefficients and none of the nonconstant polynomial factors themselves can be written as a product of two or more polynomials.

The first step in factoring polynomials is to use the distributive property to factor out the greatest common factor of all the terms of the polynomial.

EXAMPLE 3 Factor

$$9x^2 + 12x^3 - 6x^7.$$

SOLUTION The greatest common factor of the three terms $9x^2$, $12x^3$, and $-6x^7$ is $3x^2$, and hence can be factored out using the distributive property. Since

$$9x^2 = 3x^2 \cdot 3$$
$$12x^3 = 3x^2 \cdot 4x$$
$$-6x^7 = 3x^2 \cdot -2x^5,$$

we have

$$9x^2 + 12x^3 - 6x^7 = 3x^2(3 + 4x - 2x^5).$$

The greatest common factor of two or more polynomials is found by following the same procedure as was described for monomials. This is illustrated in the next example.

EXAMPLE 4   Factor
$$8(x - y)^3 - 6(x - y)^5.$$

SOLUTION   The greatest common factor of $8(x - y)^3$ and $-6(x - y)^5$ is
$$2(x - y)^3,$$
and since
$$8(x - y)^3 = 2(x - y)^3 \cdot 4$$
$$-6(x - y)^5 = 2(x - y)^3 \cdot (-3)(x - y)^2,$$
then
$$8(x - y)^3 - 6(x - y)^5 = 2(x - y)^3[4 - 3(x - y)^2].$$

PRACTICE PROBLEM 2   (Solution on page 176) Factor:

(a) $27a^3b^2 - 15a^3b^4$
(b) $15y^2(x - y)^2 + 10xy(x - y)^2$

The distributive property is also used to factor a negative number out of an expression. We have

$$a - b = -(-a + b) = -(b - a)$$
$$\underset{\text{Distributive Property}}{\nwarrow} \qquad \underset{\substack{\text{Commutative Property} \\ \text{of Addition}}}{\nwarrow}$$

and

$$-a - b = -(a + b).$$

These two uses of the distributive property are particularly helpful in "factoring by grouping" studied later in this chapter.

EXAMPLE 5   Factor completely using -1 (or some other negative number) as one of the factors.

(a) $5 - x$
(b) $-10x - 15y$

SOLUTION   (a) $5 - x = (-1)(-5 + x) = -(x - 5)$
(b) $-10x - 15y = -5(2x + 3y)$

PRACTICE PROBLEM 3 (Solution on page 176) Factor completely using a negative number as one of the factors. All variables represent positive numbers.

(a) $t^2 - st$ (b) $-8z^3 - 16z$

EXERCISES 7-1

Factor completely. (See Example 1.)

1. 8   2. 42
3. -18 4. -60
5. -23 6. -47
7. 120   8. 540

Determine the greatest common factor. (See Example 2 and Practice Problem 1.)

9. 70, 45   10. $8x^2y, 40xy^2$
11. $3z^5y, z^2y^2$ 12. $16a^2b^2c^8, 12a^3b^3c^3$
13. 14, 18, 27   14. $(x + y)^2, (x - y)^2$
15. $2(x - y)^2, 3(x - y), 5(x - y)^3$ 16. $4(a - b)^3, 16(a - b)^5, 64(a - b)^7$

Factor completely. (See Examples 3 and 4 and Practice Problem 2.)

17. $3a - ax$ 18. $cy - 5y$
19. $9xz^4 - 10x^2z^3$ 20. $4x^2y^3 - 3xy^5$
21. $a^2x + ax^2$ 22. $xy^2 - x^2y$
23. $10x^2 + 15xy$ 24. $-24xy + 42x^2$
25. $x^3 + x^2 + x$ 26. $a^4 - 2a^2 + 2a$
27. $8x^2y + 6xy^2 - 2x^2y^2$ 28. $6xz^2 + 3yz + 3z^3$
29. $4(a - 2b) - a(a - 2b)$ 30. $8x(x + y) + 3y(x + y)$
31. $2(y^3 - 4) - y(y^3 - 4)$ 32. $y^3(2 - y) - 4(2 - y)$
33. $15(a - b)^3 + 9(a - b)^2$ 34. $(x - 2)^5 + 5y(x - 2)^4$
35. $(x - 1)^3 + (x - 1)^2 + 3(x - 1)$
36. $y(z + x)^5 + 2y(z + x)^4 + 3y(z + x)^3$
37. $x(x^2 - 3x + 1) - 2(x^2 - 3x + 1)$
38. $y(y^2 + y + 1) + 3(y^2 + y + 1)$
39. $(x - 3)(x + 2) + (2x - 1)(x + 2)$
40. $(5 - y)(3y + 1) + (2 - y)(3y + 1)$
*41. $x^{70} - 8x^{68}$
*42. $y^{300} + 2y^{301} + 7y^{302}$

*43. $6a^{53}b^{37} - 10a^{35}b^{42} + 8a^{20}b^{30}$

*44. $12y^{15}z^{40} + 20y^{16}z^{40} - 12y^{16}z^{38}$

In problems 45–50, n is a positive integer.

*45. $x^n - x^{n+1}$ *46. $x^{3n} + x^n$

*47. $y^{2n+2} + 2y^{2n}$ *48. $3a^{n-1} + 4a^{n+1}$

*49. $x^{8n} + x^{6n} + x^{4n}$ *50. $y^{3n+5} - 2y^{3n+3} + 5y^{3n+1}$

Factor completely using a negative number as one of the factors. All variables represent positive numbers. (See Example 5 and Practice Problem 3.)

51. $x - y$ 52. $4 - x$

53. $-ab - a^2$ 54. $-x - x^2$

55. $-xy - z$ 56. $-3a^2x - 4$

57. $-20 - 4x$ 58. $-6 - 3y$

59. $2xy - 2x^2$ 60. $-5z^3 - 5z$

61. $ab^2 - a^2b$ 62. $3a^3 - 2a^4$

SOLUTIONS FOR PRACTICE PROBLEMS

1. $33(x - 2)^3 = 3 \cdot 11(x - 2)^3$
   $99(x - 2)^5 = 3^2 \cdot 11(x - 2)^5$
   greatest common factor $= 3 \cdot 11(x - 2)^3 = 33(x - 2)^3$
2. (a) $27a^3b^2 - 15a^3b^4 = 3a^3b^2(9 - 5b^2)$
   (b) $15y^2(x - y)^2 + 10xy(x - y)^2 = 5y(x - y)^2(3y + 2x)$
3. (a) $t^2 - st = -t(-t + s) = -t(s - t)$
   (b) $-8z^3 - 16z = -8z(z^2 + 2)$

7-2
Special Products

The special products studied in Section 6-3 are especially important in the study of factoring. Since factoring and multiplication are reverse processes, we rewrite the special product formulas here in the form to be used for factoring.

DIFFERENCE OF TWO SQUARES:	$x^2 - y^2 = (x + y)(x - y)$
SQUARE OF A BINOMIAL:	$\begin{cases} x^2 + 2xy + y^2 = (x + y)^2 \\ x^2 - 2xy + y^2 = (x - y)^2 \end{cases}$

To apply the "difference of two squares" formula, we must be able to recognize that the polynomial can be expressed as

(something squared) $-$ (something else squared).

EXAMPLE 1 Factor

$$4x^2 - 9.$$

SOLUTION Since

$$4x^2 - 9 = (2x)^2 - 3^2,$$

then we have the difference of two squares, and

$$4x^2 - 9 = (2x)^2 - 3^2 = (2x + 3)(2x - 3).$$

EXAMPLE 2 Factor

$$50x^3 - 98xy^2.$$

SOLUTION Recall that the first step in factoring is to look for factors common to all terms of the polynomial, and then factor out the greatest common factor. Thus, factoring out $2x$ yields

$$50x^3 - 98xy^2 = 2x(25x^2 - 49y^2),$$

and since

$$25x^2 - 49y^2 = (5x)^2 - (7y)^2 = (5x + 7y)(5x - 7y),$$

the complete factorization is

$$50x^3 - 98xy^2 = 2x(5x + 7y)(5x - 7y).$$

*EXAMPLE 3 Factor

$$(a - b)^2 - (a + b)^2.$$

SOLUTION Again we have the difference of two squares. Factoring and simplifying, we have

$$\begin{aligned}
(a - b)^2 - (a + b)^2 &= [(a - b) + (a + b)][(a - b) - (a + b)] \\
&= [a - b + a + b][a - b - a - b] \\
&= (2a)(-2b) \\
&= -4ab.
\end{aligned}$$

PRACTICE PROBLEM 1 (Solution on page 181) Factor completely:

(a) $36y^2 - 16x^2$

*(b) $9 - (a - b)^2$

To apply the "square of a binomial" formulas, we must be able to recognize that the polynomial to be factored is formed using the sum of the squares of two terms and twice the product of the two terms.

EXAMPLE 4   Factor

$$x^2 - 6xy + 9y^2.$$

SOLUTION   Since

$$x^2 - 6xy + 9y^2 = \underset{\substack{\text{first term} \\ \text{squared}}}{x^2} - \underset{\substack{\text{twice the} \\ \text{product}}}{2x(3y)} + \underset{\substack{\text{second term} \\ \text{squared}}}{(3y)^2},$$

this polynomial can be factored as the square of a binomial formed with the terms x and $3y$:

$$x^2 - 6xy + 9y^2 = (x - 3y)^2.$$

EXAMPLE 5   Factor

$$36a^2 + 60ab + 25b^2.$$

SOLUTION   Since $36a^2 = (6a)^2$, $25b^2 = (5b)^2$ and $60ab = 2(6a)(5b)$, then

$$36a^2 + 60ab + 25b^2 = (6a + 5b)^2.$$

PRACTICE PROBLEM 2   (Solution on page 181) Factor completely:

(a) $16a^2 - 24ab + 9b^2$
(b) $25x^3 + 20x^2y + 4xy^2$

There are two more special forms of polynomials that can be factored. They are the **sum of two cubes** and the **difference of two cubes**. The factorizations can be readily verified by direct multiplication.

SUM OF TWO CUBES:	$x^3 + y^3 = (x + y)(x^2 - xy + y^2)$
DIFFERENCE OF TWO CUBES:	$x^3 - y^3 = (x - y)(x^2 + xy + y^2)$

Just as in the factorization of the difference of two squares, to apply the formulas above we must recognize that the polynomial in question can be expressed as

(something cubed) + (something else cubed)

or

(something cubed) — (something else cubed).

EXAMPLE 6 Factor

$$x^3 - 27y^3.$$

SOLUTION Since

$$x^3 - 27y^3 = (x)^3 - (3y)^3,$$

we factor as the difference of two cubes. Hence

$$x^3 - 27y^3 = (x)^3 - (3y)^3$$
$$= (x - 3y)[x^2 + x(3y) + (3y)^2]$$
$$= (x - 3y)(x^2 + 3xy + 9y^2).$$

EXAMPLE 7 Factor

$$64a^3(a - b) + b^3(a - b).$$

SOLUTION First factor out the common factor $(a - b)$.

$$64a^3(a - b) + b^3(a - b) = (a - b)(64a^3 + b^3)$$

Then, since

$$64a^3 + b^3 = (4a)^3 + b^3$$
$$= (4a + b)[(4a)^2 - 4a(b) + b^2]$$
$$= (4a + b)(16a^2 - 4ab + b^2),$$

the complete factorization appears as

$$64a^3(a - b) + b^3(a - b) = (a - b)(4a + b)(16a^2 - 4ab + b^2).$$

PRACTICE PROBLEM 3 (Solution on page 181) Factor completely:

(a) $a^5 + 125a^2$

*(b) $(x - y)^3 - (x + y)^3$

It is worthwhile to note at this point that

$x^2 + y^2$ does **NOT** factor

as a product of polynomials with integral coefficients.

179

Factor completely. (Remember to first factor out the greatest common factor.)

DIFFERENCE OF TWO SQUARES

(See Examples 1–3 and Practice Problem 1.)

1. $a^2 - b^2$
2. $x^2 - 25$
3. $16b^2 - a^2$
4. $36a^2 - 1$
5. $49z^2 - 81w^2$
6. $100r^2 - 9s^2$
7. $144r^2s^2 - 1$
8. $x^2y^2z^2 - 4$
9. $242x^2 - 162y^2$
10. $x^3 - x$
11. $-3y^2 + 12$
12. $-98y^2 + 2x^2$

SQUARE OF A BINOMIAL

(See Examples 4 and 5 and Practice Problem 2.)

13. $x^2 + 4x + 4$
14. $x^2 + 8x + 16$
15. $y^2 - 6y + 9$
16. $a^2 - 10a + 25$
17. $64 - 16x + x^2$
18. $100 - 20a + a^2$
19. $-81x^2 - 18x - 1$
20. $-x^2 + 2x - 1$
21. $4x^2 + 12x + 9$
22. $9x^2 - 24xy + 16y^2$
23. $4a^2 + 20ab + 25b^2$
24. $49y^2 + 28yz + 4z^2$

SUM OR DIFFERENCE OF TWO CUBES

(See Examples 6 and 7 and Practice Problem 3.)

25. $x^3 - 1$
26. $y^3 - 27$
27. $x^3 + 8$
28. $x^3 + 27$
29. $64a^3 + 1$
30. $125x^3 + 1$
31. $8a^3 - b^3$
32. $27y^3 - z^3$
33. $8a^3 - 27$
34. $64a^3 - 125$
35. $125x^3 + 8y^3$
36. $27x^3 + 64y^3$

GENERAL

37. $100 - x^2$
38. $49x^2 - 1$
39. $4x^2 - 9y^2$
40. $16a^2 - 25b^2$
41. $x^2 + 10x + 25$
42. $y^2 + 18y + 81$
43. $4a^2 + 36ab + 81b^2$
44. $25x^2 + 30xy + 9y^2$
45. $125x^3 - 1$
46. $27x^3 - 1$
47. $-1 - 8y^3$
48. $-64 - a^3$
49. $x^2 + 1$
50. $a^2 + 100$
51. $-y^2 - z^2$
52. $-x - x^3$
53. $32x^2 - 50y^2$
54. $243r^2 - 27s^2$
55. $5s^3 + 10s^2 + 5s$
56. $3ab^2 - 24ab + 48a$
57. $xy^3 + 6xy^2 + 9xy$
58. $x^3z^3 + 16x^3z^2 + 64x^3z$
59. $x^3y - xy^3$
60. $3x^2 - 3$

61. $x^3y^3 + x^3$

62. $x^4y^4 + xy$

*63. $(a - b)^2 - 1$

*64. $(2x + 3y)^2 - 4$

*65. $(3r)^2 - (r - 2s)^2$

*66. $(2c - d)^2 - (2c + d)^2$

*67. $(x - y)^2 + 4(x - y) + 4$

*68. $(3x - 1)^2 - 6(3x - 1) + 9$

*69. $(abc)^2 - 2(abc) + 1$

*70. $(xz^2)^2 + 10(xz^2) + 25$

*71. $(x - y)^3 + (x + y)^3$

*72. $(x + 1)^3 + (x - 1)^3$

*73. $(a + 2)^3 - (a - 2)^3$

*74. $(c - 1)^3 - (c + 1)^3$

In problems 75–80, all variables in exponents represent positive integers.

*75. $9x^{2n} - 16$

*76. $4y^{2n} - 25$

*77. $9y^{4m} - 12y^{2m} + 4$

*78. $4x^{6r} - 20x^{3r} + 25$

*79. $z^{3r} - 8$

*80. $w^{3m} - 27$

SOLUTIONS FOR PRACTICE PROBLEMS

1. (a) $36y^2 - 16x^2 = 4(9y^2 - 4x^2)$
$$= 4[(3y)^2 - (2x)^2]$$
$$= 4(3y + 2x)(3y - 2x)$$
   *(b) $9 - (a - b)^2 = 3^2 - (a - b)^2$
$$= [3 + (a - b)][3 - (a - b)]$$
$$= (3 + a - b)(3 - a + b)$$

2. (a) $16a^2 - 24ab + 9b^2 = (4a)^2 - 2(4a)(3b) + (3b)^2 = (4a - 3b)^2$
   (b) $25x^3 + 20x^2y + 4xy^2 = x(25x^2 + 20xy + 4y^2)$
$$= x[(5x)^2 + 2(5x)(2y) + (2y)^2]$$
$$= x(5x + 2y)^2$$

3. (a) $a^5 + 125a^2 = a^2(a^3 + 125)$
$$= a^2(a^3 + 5^3)$$
$$= a^2(a + 5)(a^2 - 5a + 25)$$
   *(b) $(x - y)^3 - (x + y)^3$
$$= [(x - y) - (x + y)][(x - y)^2 + (x - y)(x + y) + (x + y)^2]$$
$$= (x - y - x - y)(x^2 - 2xy + y^2 + x^2 - y^2 + x^2 + 2xy + y^2)$$
$$= (-2y)(3x^2 + y^2)$$

7-3
Trinomials
and Quadratic
Equations

The product of the two binomials $x + a$ and $x + b$ yields a trinomial as given in the following multiplication.

MULTIPLY: $(x + a)(x + b) = x^2 + (a + b)x + ab$

In this section we reverse the multiplication process and factor the trinomial as a product of two binomials.

FACTOR: $x^2 + (a + b)x + ab = (x + a)(x + b)$

The "trick" in factoring trinomials is to determine the quantities a and b whose product is the constant term and whose sum is the coefficient of the linear term of the trinomial under consideration. We illustrate the procedure in the next examples.

EXAMPLE 1   Factor the trinomial
$$x^2 - 9x + 14.$$

SOLUTION   We need two integers a and b whose product is 14 and whose sum is -9. Both a and b must be negative since their product is positive and their sum is negative. The two possible pairs are listed below.

Possible Choices	Sum	
−14, −1	−15	
−7, −2	−9	CORRECT SUM

Thus -7 and -2 are the correct choices for a and b, and we factor
$$x^2 - 9x + 14 = (x - 7)(x - 2).$$

EXAMPLE 2   Factor
$$x^2 - 9xy - 10y^2.$$

SOLUTION   We search for two quantities whose product is $-10y^2$ and whose sum is $-9y$. Since the product is negative, the two quantities must be opposite in sign. Writing out each possibility and considering each sum, we can find the correct choice.

Possible Choices	Sum	
−5y, 2y	−3y	
5y, −2y	3y	
10y, −y	9y	
−10y, y	−9y	CORRECT SUM

Thus
$$x^2 - 9xy - 10y^2 = (x - 10y)(x + y).$$

PRACTICE PROBLEM 1 (Solution on page 188) Factor
$$x^2 - 11x + 30.$$

Factoring trinomials becomes more difficult when the trinomial is not monic. The multiplication problem,

MULTIPLY: $(ax + b)(cx + d) = acx^2 + (ad + bc)x + bd,$

will reverse to yield the factorization,

FACTOR: $acx^2 + (ad + bc)x + bd = (ax + b)(cx + d).$

Thus we must look for integers a, b, c, and d such that the product ac is the coefficient of x^2, the product bd is the constant term, and the coefficient of the linear term "works out correctly." We resort to a trial-and-error method which we illustrate in the next examples.

EXAMPLE 3 Factor
$$2x^2 + 11x + 12.$$

SOLUTION We consider possible binomial factors such that the product of the first terms of the binomials yield $2x^2$ and the product of the last terms of the binomials yield 12. The correct choice will be the binomials whose product contains middle term $11x$.

Possible Factors	Product	
$(2x + 1)(x + 12)$	$2x^2 + 25x + 12$	
$(2x + 12)(x + 1)$	$2x^2 + 14x + 12$	
$(2x + 2)(x + 6)$	$2x^2 + 14x + 12$	
$(2x + 6)(x + 2)$	$2x^2 + 10x + 12$	
$(2x + 3)(x + 4)$	$2x^2 + 11x + 12$	CORRECT
$(2x + 4)(x + 3)$	$2x^2 + 10x + 12$	

Thus

$$2x^2 + 11x + 12 = (2x + 3)(x + 4).$$

EXAMPLE 4 Factor

$$5x^2 - 9xy - 2y^2.$$

SOLUTION The possible binomial factors whose product has $5x^2$ as the first term and $-2y^2$ as the last term are listed and multiplied so that the correct choice can be made.

Possible Factors	Product
$(5x - 2y)(x + y)$	$5x^2 + 3xy - 2y^2$
$(5x + 2y)(x - y)$	$5x^2 - 3xy - 2y^2$
$(5x - y)(x + 2y)$	$5x^2 + 9xy - 2y^2$
$(5x + y)(x - 2y)$	$5x^2 - 9xy - 2y^2$ CORRECT

Thus

$$5x^2 - 9xy - 2y^2 = (5x + y)(x - 2y).$$

If all possible choices for the binomial factors fail to yield the correct trinomial product, then the trinomial is said to be a **prime polynomial**. This occurs in the next example.

EXAMPLE 5 Factor

$$3x^2 - 6x - 2.$$

SOLUTION We list all possible choices for the binomial factors and check their products.

Possible Factors	Product
$(3x - 2)(x + 1)$	$3x^2 + x - 2$
$(3x + 2)(x - 1)$	$3x^2 - x - 2$
$(3x - 1)(x + 2)$	$3x^2 + 5x - 2$
$(3x + 1)(x - 2)$	$3x^2 - 5x - 2$

Since none of the possibilities yields the correct product, $3x^2 - 6x - 2$ is a prime polynomial.

PRACTICE PROBLEM 2   (Solution on page 188) Factor
$$9x^2 + 12xy - 5y^2.$$

The method of factoring is often extremely useful in solving quadratic equations. First we define the standard form of a quadratic equation.

Definition 7-1 A **quadratic (second-degree) equation** in one variable is any equation that can be put in the form, called *standard form*,

$$ax^2 + bx + c = 0,$$

where a, b, and c are constants with $a \neq 0$.

For example, the quadratic equation

$$x^2 = 9x - 20$$

can be put into standard form

$$x^2 - 9x + 20 = 0.$$

The trinomial on the left can be factored and the quadratic equation can be written as

$$(x - 5)(x - 4) = 0.$$

Since the only way a product can be zero is for one or both of the factors to be zero, we set each linear factor equal to zero, and solve the resulting linear equations:

$$x - 5 = 0 \quad \text{or} \quad x - 4 = 0$$
$$x = 5 \qquad\qquad x = 4.$$

The values $x = 5$ and $x = 4$ check in the original equation:

$$5^2 = 9(5) - 20 \quad \text{and} \quad 4^2 = 9(4) - 20.$$

Thus the solution set is $\{5, 4\}$.

EXAMPLE 6   Solve by factoring:

$$5x^2 + 13x - 6 = 0.$$

SOLUTION   Factoring the trinomial on the left yields
$$(5x - 2)(x + 3) = 0.$$

Setting each linear factor equal to zero and solving the two resulting linear equations gives
$$5x - 2 = 0 \quad \text{or} \quad x + 3 = 0$$
$$x = \tfrac{2}{5} \qquad\qquad x = -3.$$

These values for x check in the original equation:
$$5(\tfrac{2}{5})^2 + 13(\tfrac{2}{5}) - 6 = \tfrac{4}{5} + \tfrac{26}{5} - 6 = 0,$$
$$5(-3)^2 + 13(-3) - 6 = 45 - 39 - 6 = 0,$$

and the solution set is $\{\tfrac{2}{5}, -3\}$.

Not all quadratic equations can be solved by factoring since not all trinomials will factor (see Example 5). Later, in Chapter 10, we will examine other methods of solving quadratic equations.

The method of factoring can be applied to any polynomial equation, that is, any equation of the form

$$P(x) = 0,$$

where $P(x)$ is a polynomial in x, if $P(x)$ can be factored. It is important to note that one side of the equation *must* be zero before we factor the polynomial on the other side. Consider the next example.

EXAMPLE 7   Solve by factoring:

$$x^3 = 16x.$$

SOLUTION Moving all the nonzero terms to one side of the equation and factoring, we have

$$x^3 - 16x = 0$$
$$x(x^2 - 16) = 0$$
$$x(x - 4)(x + 4) = 0.$$

In order for the product $x(x - 4)(x + 4)$ to be zero, one or more of the linear factors must equal zero. Hence we set each linear factor equal to zero and solve the resulting linear equations.

$$x = 0 \quad \text{or} \quad x - 4 = 0 \quad \text{or} \quad x + 4 = 0$$
$$x = 4 \qquad\qquad x = -4$$

The solutions are $x = 0, 4, -4$. ·

PRACTICE PROBLEM 3 (Solution on page 188) Solve by factoring:
(a) $2x^2 + 12 = 11x$
(b) $x^3 - 5x^2 = 0$

EXERCISES 7-3

Factor completely. (See Examples 1 and 2 and Practice Problem 1.)

1. $x^2 + 6x + 8$ 2. $x^2 + 4x + 3$
3. $x^2 - 4x + 3$ 4. $x^2 - 7x + 10$
5. $x^2 + 3x - 4$ 6. $x^2 - 2x - 15$
7. $x^2 - 5xy - 14y^2$ 8. $x^2 + 8xy - 20y^2$
9. $a^2 + 2ab - 3b^2$ 10. $a^2 - 8ab + 12b^2$
11. $r^2 + 2rs - 63s^2$ 12. $r^2 - rs - 110s^2$
13. $z^2 - 9zw - 190w^2$ 14. $w^2 - 13wz + 22z^2$
15. $x^2 + 17xy + 72y^2$ 16. $x^2 + 12xy + 27y^2$

Factor completely. (See Examples 3–5 and Practice Problem 2.)

17. $6x^2 - x - 1$ 18. $12x^2 + 7x + 1$
19. $4a^2 - a - 5$ 20. $6a^2 - 7a + 1$
21. $3x^2 - 19x - 14$ 22. $2x^2 - 13x + 15$
23. $2r^2 - 5r + 3$ 24. $2r^2 + 11r - 6$
25. $9x^2 + 9xy + 2y^2$ 26. $3x^2 + 11xy + 10y^2$
27. $44a^2 - 15ab + b^2$ 28. $50a^2 - 15ab + b^2$
29. $4y^2 - 18yz + 20z^2$ 30. $21y^2 - 8yz - 4z^2$
31. $10x^2 + 9xy - 22y^2$ 32. $8y^2 - 26yz + 21z^2$

Factor completely.

33. $a^3 - 11a^2 + 18a$

34. $2r + 16r^2 + 30r^3$

35. $x^5 - 4x^4 - 21x^3$

36. $y^6 - 13y^5 + 36y^4$

37. $x^2 + x + 1$

38. $x^2 + 2x + 2$

39. $3x^2 + 3x + 1$

40. $4x^2 + x + 1$

41. $y^2x^2 - 3y^2x + 4y^2$

42. $a^3b^2 + 7a^3b + 10a^3$

43. $-x^2 + 9x - 8$

44. $-a^2 - 11a - 10$

45. $-2r^2 - 2rs + 12s^2$

46. $-3x^2 - 3xy + 6y^2$

47. $33 - 14c + c^2$

48. $7 + 6z - z^2$

49. $6x^3 - 15x^2 + 6x$

50. $6a^3 + 4a^2 - 2a$

51. $-12x^3 - 8x^2y + 32xy^2$

52. $-45x^2y + 140xy^2 - 15y^3$

Solve by factoring. (See Examples 6 and 7 and Practice Problem 3.)

53. $x^2 + x - 2 = 0$

54. $x^2 - 7x + 10 = 0$

55. $x^2 + x = 12$

56. $x^2 + 8x = -7$

57. $x^2 - 9 = 0$

58. $x^2 - 16 = 0$

59. $4y^2 = 25$

60. $16y^2 = 9$

61. $x^2 + 4x + 4 = 0$

62. $x^2 - 6x + 9 = 0$

63. $25a^2 = 10a - 1$

64. $4x^2 = 12x - 9$

65. $x^2 - 3x = 0$

66. $x^2 + 7x = 0$

67. $3a^2 = 4a$

68. $2b^2 = 7b$

69. $2x^2 - 7x + 6 = 0$

70. $3x^2 + 5x - 12 = 0$

71. $3x^2 = 4x - 1$

72. $21x^2 = 8 - 22x$

73. $x^7 - x^5 = 0$

74. $x^3 - 4x^2 + 4x = 0$

75. $y^4 - 4y^2 = 0$

76. $a^5 - a^3 = 0$

77. $(a - 1)(a - 2)(a - 3)(a - 4) = 0$

78. $(z - 1)z(z + 1)(z + 2) = 0$

SOLUTIONS FOR PRACTICE PROBLEMS

1. $x^2 - 11x + 30 = (x - 5)(x - 6)$

2. $9x^2 + 12xy - 5y^2 = (3x + 5y)(3x - y)$

3. (a)
$$2x^2 + 12 = 11x$$
$$2x^2 - 11x + 12 = 0$$
$$(2x - 3)(x - 4) = 0$$
$$2x - 3 = 0 \quad \text{or} \quad x - 4 = 0$$
$$2x = 3 \qquad\qquad x = 4$$
$$x = \tfrac{3}{2}$$
Solution set: $\{\tfrac{3}{2}, 4\}$

(b)
$$x^3 - 5x^2 = 0$$
$$x^2(x - 5) = 0$$
$$x^2 = 0 \quad \text{or} \quad x - 5 = 0$$
$$x = 0 \qquad\qquad x = 5$$
Solution set: $\{0, 5\}$

7-4

More on Factoring

Often, a polynomial of degree larger than 3 will fit the form of one of the special products or of the quadratic trinomial as studied in the last two sections. If this is the case, the polynomial can be factored. Consider the next examples.

EXAMPLE 1 Factor completely:

$$x^4 - 16.$$

SOLUTION This fourth-degree polynomial can be expressed as the difference of two squares and then factored,

$$x^4 - 16 = (x^2)^2 - 4^2$$
$$= (x^2 - 4)(x^2 + 4).$$

Next we consider the two factors of $x^4 - 16$. Since

$$x^2 - 4 = (x - 2)(x + 2)$$

and

$$x^2 + 4 \text{ does not factor,}$$

the complete factorization is

$$x^4 - 16 = (x - 2)(x + 2)(x^2 + 4).$$

PRACTICE PROBLEM 1

(Solution on page 193) Factor completely:

$$x^6 - y^6.$$

EXAMPLE 2 Factor completely:

$$x^6 + 7x^3 - 8.$$

SOLUTION This sixth-degree polynomial can be expressed in the form of a quadratic trinomial

$$(x^3)^2 + 7x^3 - 8,$$

which factors as the product of two binomials

$$(x^3 - 1)(x^3 + 8).$$

Each of these binomial factors can be factored and we have

$$x^6 + 7x^3 - 8 = (x^3)^2 + 7x^3 - 8$$
$$= (x^3 - 1)(x^3 + 8)$$
$$= (x - 1)(x^2 + x + 1)(x + 2)(x^2 - 2x + 4).$$

PRACTICE PROBLEM 2 (Solution on page 193) Factor completely:

$$x^4 - 8x^2 + 16.$$

If a polynomial has more than three terms, it is often necessary to group some of the terms in order to factor. We illustrate this method of **factoring by grouping** in the next examples.

EXAMPLE 3 Factor

$$ac + ad + bc + bd.$$

SOLUTION Grouping the first two terms and the last two terms gives
$$ac + ad + bc + bd = (ac + ad) + (bc + bd).$$
Next, we use the distributive property to factor each group:
$$ac + ad = a(c + d)$$
$$bc + bd = b(c + d),$$
and we note that $(c + d)$ is a factor common to each group. Thus

$$
\begin{aligned}
ac + ad + bc + bd &= (ac + ad) + (bc + bd) & \text{(Grouping)}\\
&= a(c + d) + b(c + d) & \text{(Distributive Property)}\\
&= (a + b)(c + d) & \text{(Distributive Property)}
\end{aligned}
$$

The next example of factoring by grouping eventually leads to the difference of two squares.

EXAMPLE 4 Factor

$$x^2 - y^2 + 4x + 4.$$

SOLUTION Since addition is commutative and associative, we can rearrange the terms so as to group together a trinomial in x which factors:

$$
\begin{aligned}
x^2 - y^2 + 4x + 4 &= (x^2 + 4x + 4) - y^2 & \text{Grouping}\\
&= (x + 2)^2 - y^2 & \text{Factoring } x^2 + 4x + 4
\end{aligned}
$$

This results in a polynomial that fits the form of the difference of two squares which will factor:

$$
\begin{aligned}
(x + 2)^2 - y^2 &= [(x + 2) + y][(x + 2) - y]\\
&= (x + 2 + y)(x + 2 - y).
\end{aligned}
$$

Hence the complete factorization is

$$x^2 - y^2 + 4x + 4 = (x + 2 + y)(x + 2 - y).$$

We end this section (and chapter) with an outline of the general procedure for factoring.

Procedure for Factoring

1. Look for factors common to each term and factor out the greatest common factor.

2. If the polynomial is a binomial, determine if it will factor as the difference of two squares or the sum or difference of two cubes. If so, then factor using the special product formulas.

3. If the polynomial is a quadratic trinomial, determine if it can be written as a perfect square binomial. If not, use the trial-and-error method to factor as the product of two binomials.

4. If the polynomial is of degree larger than three, determine if it will fit one of the special forms for factoring. If so, factor using the special product formulas.

5. For a polynomial with more than three terms, use the method of factoring by grouping.

6. Finally, check each individual factor of the polynomial to determine if each factor is completely factored.

PRACTICE PROBLEM 3

(Solution on page 193) Factor completely:

$$3x^5 - 9x^3 - 30x.$$

$3x(x^4 - 3x^2 - 10)$
$3x(x^2 - 5)(x^2 - 2)$

EXERCISES 7-4

Factor completely. (See Examples 1 and 2 and Practice Problems 1 and 2).

1. $x^4 - 1$ 2. $x^4 - 81$

3. $(2a)^4 - 1$ 4. $(ab)^4 - c^4$

5. $x^6 + 9x^3 + 8$ 6. $x^6 - 9x^3 + 8$

7. $x^4 - 2x^2 + 1$ 8. $x^4 - 18x^2 + 81$

9. $x^2y^2 - 4xy + 3$ 10. $a^2b^2 + 5ab + 6$

11. $(a - 3)^2 + 2(a - 3) + 1$ 12. $(2a + 5)^2 + 2(2a + 5) - 3$

13. $x^8 - x^4y^4$ 14. $(2a - 3)^2 - (2a - 3)^3$

15. $-5x^3 + 10x^2 - 5x$ 16. $-2y^5 - 5y^4 - 3y^3$

Factor by grouping. (See Examples 3 and 4.)

17. $xy + xz + y^2 + yz$ 18. $ax + 4x + 2ay + 8y$

19. $xy + 3y + 3x + 9$ 20. $5a - a^2 + 5b - ab$

21. $r^2 + 2r + 1 - s^2$ 22. $p^2 + 4p + 4 - 4q^2$

23. $c^2 + 2c + 1 + cd + d$ 24. $a^2 + 4a + 4 - ab - 2b$

25. $x^2 - y^2 + 5x + 5y$ 26. $x^2 - y^2 - x + y$

27. $k^2 + 4k - h^2 - 4h$ 28. $r^2 - r - s^2 - s$

29. $x^3 + 3x^2 - x - 3$ 30. $y^3 + y^2 - y - 1$

31. $2x^3 + x^2 - 8x - 4$ 32. $4x^3 - 3x^2 - 4x + 3$

*33. $x^4 + x^2y^2 + y^4$ (*Hint:* $x^4 + x^2y^2 + y^4 = x^4 + 2x^2y^2 + y^4 - x^2y^2$.)

*34. $x^4 - 3x^2y^2 + y^4$ (*Hint:* Add and subtract x^2y^2.)

*35. $a^4 + 4$ (*Hint:* Add and subtract $4a^2$.)

*36. $a^4 + 64$ (*Hint:* Add and subtract $16a^2$.)

Factor completely using the methods of this chapter.

37. $100 - 36x^2$ 38. $49a^2 - 25b^2$

39. $x^3 - 1000$ 40. $27 + y^3$

41. $z^2 - 7z + 12$ 42. $w^2 + 2w - 3$

43. $6b^2 + 7b + 2$ 44. $8y^2 - 10y - 25$

45. $4r^2 - 12r + 9$ 46. $9s^2 + 6s + 1$

47. $2x^2 - 4xy + 2y^2$ 48. $3z^2 + 6zw + 3w^2$

49. $4x^2 + 4x + 4$ 50. $9x^2 + 9$

51. $(ab)^2 - (cd)^2$ 52. $(a + b)^2 - (c + d)^2$

53. $k^3 + k^2 - 2k$ 54. $4y^3 - 4y$

55. $2p - 16p^2$ 56. $9m^3 + 18m^2$

57. $40r^2 + rs - 6s^2$ 58. $34e^2 + 49ef - 3f^2$

59. $63t^2 + 41t + 6$ 60. $7x^2 - 86xy + 99y^2$

61. $2abx + a^2x + b^2x$ 62. $20x - 5x^2 - 20$

63. $x^2(x^2 + 2x + 1) - 25(x^2 + 2x + 1)$

64. $y^2(y^2 - 4y + 4) - 16(y^2 - 4y + 4)$

65. $x(x^2 - y^2) - y(x^2 - y^2)$ 66. $x(x - y)^2 - y(x - y)^2$

67. $x^4 + y^4$ 68. $x^8 + y^8$

69. $x^{20} + 1$ 70. $a^{100} + 1$

71. $a^2 + a^3 - 20a$ 72. $-7z^2 - 4z + 2z^3$

73. $2r^5 + 10r^3 + 12r$ 74. $9a^7 + 27a^4 - 90a$

75. $3x^{18} - x^{14} - 2x^{10}$ 76. $x^{50} + 10x^{30} + 25x^{10}$

193

Section 7-4
More on Factoring

*77. $4x^{2p} - 12x^p - 40$

*78. $5x^{2m} + 10x^m - 40$

*79. $6y^{2n} - 5y^n - 4$

*80. $6z^{2n} - 5z^n - 14$

*81. $15z^{4q} + 11z^{2q} - 14$

*82. $14y^{4p} + 13y^{2p} - 12$

*83. $16u^{4p} - v^{4q}$

*84. $w^{4m} - 81z^{4n}$

SOLUTIONS FOR PRACTICE PROBLEMS

1. $x^6 - y^6 = (x^3)^2 - (y^3)^2$
$$= (x^3 - y^3)(x^3 + y^3)$$
$$= (x - y)(x^2 + xy + y^2)(x + y)(x^2 - xy + y^2)$$

2. $x^4 - 8x^2 + 16 = (x^2)^2 - 8x^2 + 16$
$$= (x^2 - 4)^2$$
$$= [(x - 2)(x + 2)]^2$$
$$= (x - 2)^2(x + 2)^2$$

3. $3x^5 - 9x^3 - 30x = 3x(x^4 - 3x^2 - 10)$
$$= 3x[(x^2)^2 - 3x^2 - 10]$$
$$= 3x(x^2 - 5)(x^2 + 2)$$

PRACTICE TEST for Chapter 7

1. Determine the greatest common factor.
   (a) $20x^2y^2$, $45xy^3$ (b) $(a+b)^2$, $(a+b)^5$

In problems 2–9, factor each polynomial completely.

2. (a) $20a^2b - 5ab^2$ (b) $18(r+s)^3 - 4(r+s)^4$

3. (a) $x^2 - 9$ (b) $81a^2 - 64b^2$

4. (a) $a^2 - 2a + 1$ (b) $x^2 + 14xy + 49y^2$

5. (a) $x^3 - 64$ (b) $3a^3 - 3$

6. (a) $1 + x^3$ (b) $x^4 + xy^3$

7. (a) $x^2 + 2xy - 35y^2$ (b) $6z^2 - 11z + 4$

8. (a) $(r-s)^2 - 5(r-s) + 6$ (b) $x^4 + 2x^2 - 3$

9. $2x^3 - 2x^2 - 2x + 2$

10. Solve the quadratic equation by factoring.

$$2x^2 = 5x + 7$$

Rational Expressions

8-1
Reduction to
Lowest Terms

There is a close analogy between rational expressions and rational numbers, beginning with their definitions. We recall from Section 1-1 that

a **rational number** is a quotient $\dfrac{a}{b}$ of integers, with $b \neq 0$.

In close similarity,

a **rational expression** is a quotient $\dfrac{P}{Q}$ of polynomials, with $Q \neq 0$.

Thus rational numbers and rational expressions are both fractions. In fact, every rational number can be regarded as a rational expression, since a nonzero constant can be regarded as a polynomial of degree 0. Also, any polynomial can be regarded as a rational expression by considering it to be a quotient with denominator 1:

$$P = P/1.$$

EXAMPLE 1 Some specific examples of rational expressions are given by

$$\frac{x+y}{x-y}, \quad \frac{x+y}{x^2-y^2}, \quad -2, \quad x^3, \quad \text{and} \quad \frac{5}{x^2-4}.$$

The rational expressions that we work with in this section and most of this chapter are quotients of polynomials that have integral coefficients.* For this kind of rational expression, polynomials play the same role in rational expressions that integers play in rational numbers.

As in Chapters 6 and 7, it is understood that the variables in polynomials have their domains in the real numbers, and that polynomials assume real values. Just as in the study of division of polynomials (Section 6-4), we must restrict the variables from assuming values that cause the denominator to take on the value zero, since division by zero is undefined.

EXAMPLE 2 Restrict the values of the variables so that the rational expression is defined.

(a) $\dfrac{x+y}{x-y}$ (b) $\dfrac{x+y}{x^2-y^2}$ (c) $\dfrac{1}{x^2-4}$

SOLUTION

(a) The denominator $x - y$ is zero when $x = y$. Thus the restriction is: $x \neq y$.

(b) The denominator $x^2 - y^2$ is zero when $x^2 = y^2$, and this happens when either $x = y$ or $x = -y$. Thus the restriction is: $x \neq y$ and $x \neq -y$. (The fact that $x = -y$ also makes the numerator zero is of no significance, since $0/0$ is undefined.)

(c) The values of x that make the denominator zero are $x = 2$ and $x = -2$. Hence the restriction must be: $x \neq 2$ and $x \neq -2$.

PRACTICE PROBLEM 1 (Solution on page 202) Restrict the values of the variables so that the rational expression is defined.

(a) $\dfrac{x+3y}{2xy^2}$ (b) $\dfrac{y^2-1}{x(y-1)}$ (c) $\dfrac{x^2+2x}{x^2+1}$

Since rational expressions represent real numbers, all the properties of real numbers carry over to rational expressions. In particular, the Basic Formulas for Fractions listed in Section 1-5 hold for rational expressions. The first property in the list can be used to express equality of rational expressions in terms of polynomial equality.

*This type of rational expression is frequently called a *rational integral expression.*

> **Equality of Rational Expressions**
>
> $$\frac{P}{Q} = \frac{R}{S} \qquad \text{if and only if } PS = QR,$$
>
> where $Q \neq 0$ and $S \neq 0$.

EXAMPLE 3   The rational expressions $\dfrac{x+y}{x^2-y^2}$ and $\dfrac{1}{x-y}$ are equal:

$$\frac{x+y}{x^2-y^2} = \frac{1}{x-y},$$

since

$$(x+y)(x-y) = (x^2-y^2)(1).$$

It is understood that $x \neq y$ and $x \neq -y$ in the equation

$$\frac{x+y}{x^2-y^2} = \frac{1}{x-y}.$$

For the remainder of this chapter, *we assume that all necessary restrictions are made so that the denominators in rational expressions are nonzero.* This frees us from the nuisance of continually noting restrictions in our work with rational expressions.

The next property is so important that it is known as the

> **Fundamental Principle of Fractions**
>
> $$\frac{PR}{QR} = \frac{P}{Q}, \qquad \text{where } Q \neq 0 \text{ and } R \neq 0.$$

This principle can be regarded in two ways. It allows us to divide out, or to remove, any nonzero factor that the numerator and denominator have in common. On the other hand, it also allows us to multiply numerator and denominator by the same nonzero quantity, if we wish.

The Fundamental Principle of Fractions is used most commonly in reducing fractions. The equality

$$\frac{x+y}{x^2-y^2} = \frac{1}{x-y}$$

in Example 3 could be approached from this point of view:

$$\frac{x+y}{x^2-y^2} = \frac{(1)(x+y)}{(x-y)(x+y)}$$

$$= \frac{1}{x-y},$$

where the factor $x + y$ is divided out of the numerator and denominator by the Fundamental Principle. In making reductions such as this, we shall be concerned only with factoring polynomials which have coefficients that are integers, and we shall require that all factors be polynomials which have integers as coefficients. With these restrictions on the factors, it is meaningful to speak of reducing a rational expression to lowest terms.

> A rational expression is in **lowest terms** if the only common factors in the numerator and denominator are 1 or -1.

To reduce a rational expression to lowest terms, we follow this procedure:

> Factor numerator and denominator completely, then divide out all common factors.

EXAMPLE 4   Reduce each of the following to lowest terms.

(a) $\dfrac{21x^4y^2z^3}{14xy^6z^6}$

(b) $\dfrac{3x^4 - 4x^3 - 4x^2}{x^2 - x - 2}$

SOLUTION

(a) In factoring numerator and denominator, we keep an eye out for common factors.

$$\frac{21x^4y^2z^3}{14xy^6z^6} = \frac{3 \cdot \overset{1}{\cancel{7}} \cdot \cancel{x} \cdot x^3 \cdot \overset{1}{\cancel{y^2}} \cdot \overset{1}{\cancel{z^3}}}{2 \cdot \underset{1}{\cancel{7}} \cdot \underset{1}{\cancel{x}} \cdot \cancel{y^2} \cdot y^4 \cdot z^3 \cdot \underset{1}{\cancel{z^3}}}$$ (Displaying common factors)

$$= \frac{3x^3}{2y^4z^3}$$ (Dividing out the common factors)

The slashes are used to keep track of the factors that have been divided out.

(b) This time, factoring is a significant part of our work.

$$\frac{3x^4 - 4x^3 - 4x^2}{x^2 - x - 2} = \frac{x^2(3x^2 - 4x - 4)}{(x - 2)(x + 1)}$$

$$= \frac{x^2(3x + 2)(\cancel{x - 2})^{1}}{(\cancel{x - 2})_{1}(x + 1)}$$

$$= \frac{x^2(3x + 2)}{x + 1}$$

This result could just as well be written as

$$\frac{3x^3 + 2x^2}{x + 1},$$

but we normally leave the answer in factored form.

It is tempting to many people to make one or both of the following errors.

(a) It is wrong to remove x and reduce $\frac{3x + 2}{x + 2}$ to $\frac{5}{3}$;

$$\frac{3x + 2}{x + 2} \neq \frac{3 + 2}{1 + 2}.$$

(b) It is wrong to remove the 2 and reduce $\frac{3x + 2}{x + 2}$ to $\frac{3x}{x}$;

$$\frac{3x + 2}{x + 2} \neq \frac{3x}{x}.$$

These incorrect reductions are basically the same kind of error: each removes a quantity that is *not a factor. The quantity divided out must be a factor of the entire numerator and of the entire denominator.* Only common factors of numerator and denominator can be divided out.

PRACTICE PROBLEM 2 (Solution on page 203) Reduce each of the following to lowest terms.

(a) $\dfrac{x^2 - x - 6}{x^2 - 2x - 3}$ *(b) $\dfrac{2x^2 + ax - 4x - 2a}{2x^2 - ax - 4x + 2a}$

It is worth noting here that the factors $a - b$ and $b - a$ are negatives of each other:

$$a - b = -(b - a).$$

Regardless of the simplicity, these types of factors are frequently troublesome, and we devote the next example to them.

EXAMPLE 5 Reduce to lowest terms.

(a) $\dfrac{x^2 - y^2}{y - x}$ (b) $\dfrac{3x^2 - 8x + 4}{6 + x - 2x^2}$

SOLUTION   (a) $\dfrac{x^2 - y^2}{y - x} = \dfrac{\overset{1}{\cancel{(x - y)}}(x + y)}{\underset{-1}{-\cancel{(x - y)}}}$

$= \dfrac{x + y}{-1}$

$= -(x + y)$

$= -x - y$

(b) $\dfrac{3x^2 - 8x + 4}{6 + x - 2x^2} = \dfrac{(3x - 2)(x - 2)}{(3 + 2x)(2 - x)}$

$= \dfrac{(3x - 2)\cancel{(x - 2)}}{(-1)(3 + 2x)\cancel{(x - 2)}}$

$= -\dfrac{3x - 2}{3 + 2x}$

$= \dfrac{2 - 3x}{3 + 2x}$

The Fundamental Principle of Fractions is sometimes used to build fractions to higher terms instead of reducing them to lower terms. This procedure is frequently necessary in order to add rational numbers. Consider, for example,

$$\frac{2}{3} + \frac{1}{4} = \frac{2 \cdot 4}{3 \cdot 4} + \frac{1 \cdot 3}{4 \cdot 3}$$

$$= \frac{8}{12} + \frac{3}{12}$$

$$= \frac{11}{12}.$$

For similar reasons, rational expressions are sometimes raised to higher terms. This is illustrated in Example 6.

EXAMPLE 6   Supply the missing numerator so as to make a true equality of rational expressions.

$$\frac{2x - 1}{x + 3} = \frac{?}{x^2 + 4x + 3}$$

SOLUTION   To discover the appropriate multiplier, we first factor the denominator on the right:

$$\frac{2x - 1}{x + 3} = \frac{?}{(x + 3)(x + 1)}.$$

It is now clear that the required multiplier is $x + 1$, and

$$\frac{2x - 1}{x + 3} = \frac{(2x - 1)(x + 1)}{(x + 3)(x + 1)}$$

$$= \frac{2x^2 + x - 1}{x^2 + 4x + 3}.$$

200

Restrict the values of the variables so that the given rational expression is defined. (See Example 2 and Practice Problem 1.)

1. $\dfrac{3x}{3x-2}$ 2. $\dfrac{10x}{5x+3}$ 3. $\dfrac{9x^2-y^2}{3x-y}$

4. $\dfrac{x-4}{x^2-16}$ 5. $\dfrac{4x}{x^2+4}$ 6. $\dfrac{3x}{x^2+9}$

Determine whether or not the given pair of rational expressions are equal. (See Example 3.)

7. $\dfrac{6x-3}{4x^2-1}, \dfrac{3}{2x+1}$ 8. $\dfrac{x^2-3x}{2x^2-18}, \dfrac{x}{2x+6}$

9. $\dfrac{2x+5}{x+5}, \dfrac{7}{6}$ 10. $\dfrac{5x+3}{x+3}, \dfrac{5x}{x}$

Reduce each of the following to lowest terms. (See Examples 4 and 5 and Practice Problem 2.)

11. $\dfrac{108}{252}$ 12. $\dfrac{30}{276}$

13. $\dfrac{x-2}{2-x}$ 14. $\dfrac{6-2x}{x-3}$

15. $\dfrac{132x^3y^9}{55x^6y^3}$ 16. $\dfrac{54x^5y^4}{81x^2y^6}$

17. $\dfrac{42a^3b^4c^8}{39ab^2c^4}$ 18. $\dfrac{56a^6b^8c^4}{20a^2b^2c^2}$

19. $\dfrac{21u^2(v-4)^3}{3u^5(v-4)}$ 20. $\dfrac{16u^3(v+8)}{12u^2(v+4)}$

21. $\dfrac{18x^2(x+2)^6(2x-1)}{15x^3(2x-1)^3(x+2)^2}$ 22. $\dfrac{26x^3(x-3)^2(x+6)^3}{78x^4(x+6)^2(x-3)^6}$

23. $\dfrac{(3+x)(2-x)}{(x-2)(-3x+5)}$ 24. $\dfrac{(3-2x)(4-x)}{(x-4)(x+5)}$

25. $\dfrac{y^2-1}{1-y}$ 26. $\dfrac{w^2-4}{2-w}$

27. $\dfrac{x^2-9}{15-5x}$ 28. $\dfrac{x^2-4}{6-3x}$

29. $\dfrac{x^2-4x}{x^2-16}$ 30. $\dfrac{x^2-x}{x^2-1}$

31. $\dfrac{a^3b-ab^3}{a^2b-ab^2}$ 32. $\dfrac{a^2b+ab^2}{a+b}$

33. $\dfrac{x^2+x-12}{9-x^2}$ 34. $\dfrac{x^2+x-20}{25-x^2}$

35. $\dfrac{a^2-1}{a^2-2a+1}$ 36. $\dfrac{z^2-4}{z^2-4z+4}$

37. $\dfrac{y^2 - 9}{y^2 + 6y + 9}$

38. $\dfrac{w^2 - 4}{w^2 + 4w + 4}$

39. $\dfrac{x^2 - 3x - 4}{x^2 + 5x + 4}$

40. $\dfrac{u^2 - 4u - 5}{u^2 + 6u + 5}$

41. $\dfrac{3p - 5q}{9p^2 - 25q^2}$

42. $\dfrac{2b - 3c}{4b^2 - 9c^2}$

43. $\dfrac{4m^2 + 4mn - 3n^2}{4m^2 + 12mn + 9n^2}$

44. $\dfrac{4u^2 - 16uv + 7v^2}{4u^2 - 28uv + 49v^2}$

45. $\dfrac{2x^2 + 3x - 9}{2x^2 - 5x - 12}$

46. $\dfrac{2x^2 + 5x - 12}{2x^2 + 9x - 9}$

47. $\dfrac{3y^2 - 11y + 6}{3y^2 + y - 2}$

48. $\dfrac{4y^2 - y - 5}{4y^2 - 7y - 15}$

*49. $\dfrac{2x - 2}{x^3 - 1}$

*50. $\dfrac{3x - 6}{x^3 - 8}$

*51. $\dfrac{4x^2 - 9y^2}{8x^3 + 27y^3}$

*52. $\dfrac{3x^2 - 12}{3x^3 + 24}$

*53. $\dfrac{ab + ax - 2bx - 2x^2}{2x^2 - ax + 4bx - 2ab}$

*54. $\dfrac{ab - ax - bx + x^2}{x^2 - ax - 2bx + 2ab}$

In each of the following, supply the missing numerator so as to make a true equality of rational expressions. (See Example 6.)

55. $\dfrac{2x}{3y} = \dfrac{?}{18x^2y^2}$

56. $\dfrac{3x}{5y} = \dfrac{?}{30x^3y^3}$

57. $\dfrac{5a}{2} = \dfrac{?}{6a^2(a + 1)}$

58. $\dfrac{3b}{7} = \dfrac{?}{21b^3(b - 1)}$

59. $\dfrac{3z + 1}{z - 2} = \dfrac{?}{z^2 + z - 6}$

60. $\dfrac{2z - 3}{z + 2} = \dfrac{?}{2z^2 + z - 6}$

61. $\dfrac{w - 14}{w - 7} = \dfrac{?}{w^2 - 3w - 28}$

62. $\dfrac{w - 10}{w + 5} = \dfrac{?}{w^2 + 3w - 10}$

63. $\dfrac{3x + 2}{x - 5} = \dfrac{?}{2x^2 - 13x + 15}$

64. $\dfrac{2x + 3}{x - 6} = \dfrac{?}{2x^2 - 15x + 18}$

65. $\dfrac{m + n}{m - 2n} = \dfrac{?}{m^2 - 3mn + 2n^2}$

66. $\dfrac{m + n}{m + 3n} = \dfrac{?}{m^2 - 4mn - 21n^2}$

67. $\dfrac{2x - z}{3x + 2z} = \dfrac{?}{3x^2 - 7xz - 6z^2}$

68. $\dfrac{x - 4z}{2x - 3z} = \dfrac{?}{4x^2 - 4xz - 3z^2}$

SOLUTIONS FOR PRACTICE PROBLEMS

1. (a) $\dfrac{x + 3y}{2xy^2}$.   Restriction: $x \neq 0$ and $y \neq 0$.

   (b) $\dfrac{y^2 - 1}{x(y - 1)}$.   Restriction: $x \neq 0$ and $y \neq 1$.

   (c) $\dfrac{x^2 + 2x}{x^2 + 1}$.   Restriction: none, since $x^2 + 1$ is always positive.

2. (a) $\dfrac{x^2 - x - 6}{x^2 - 2x - 3} = \dfrac{\cancel{(x-3)}(x + 2)}{\cancel{(x-3)}(x + 1)} = \dfrac{x + 2}{x + 1}$

*(b) $\dfrac{2x^2 + ax - 4x - 2a}{2x^2 - ax - 4x + 2a} = \dfrac{x(2x + a) - 2(2x + a)}{x(2x - a) - 2(2x - a)}$

$\qquad\qquad\qquad = \dfrac{\cancel{(x-2)}(2x + a)}{\cancel{(x-2)}(2x - a)}$

$\qquad\qquad\qquad = \dfrac{2x + a}{2x - a}$

8-2
Multiplication
and Division

It was pointed out in Section 8-1 that, since rational expressions represent real numbers, the Basic Formulas for Fractions listed in Section 1-5 hold for rational expressions. In Section 8-1 we worked with two items from the list: Equality of Rational Expressions and the Fundamental Principle of Fractions. In this section we use two more of these basic formulas in connection with two of the fundamental operations on rational expressions.

With rational expressions, just as it is with rational numbers, multiplication and division are easier to work with than addition and subtraction. For this reason, we consider multiplication and division of rational expressions in this section, and defer addition and subtraction until Section 8-3.

The fifth item in the list of Basic Formulas for Fractions provides us with the following.

Product Rule for Rational Expressions

$$\frac{P}{Q} \cdot \frac{R}{S} = \frac{PR}{QS}, \qquad \text{where } Q \neq 0 \text{ and } S \neq 0.$$

In words, this rule says that the product of two rational expressions is the product of their numerators over the product of their denominators.

Just as with rational numbers, it is considered good procedure to reduce results of operations to lowest terms. For this reason, we do not multiply the numerators and denominators together as we did in Section 6-3 when working with polynomials. Rather, we write the products in factored form and divide out all common factors. This is demonstrated in Example 1.

EXAMPLE 1 Perform the following multiplications, and reduce each result to lowest terms.

(a) $\dfrac{3a}{4b^2c} \cdot \dfrac{10bc^2}{9a^3}$

(b) $\dfrac{6x^2y^5}{8xz^4} \cdot \dfrac{14xyz^2}{15x^2y^3}$

(a) If we follow the product rule exactly, we write the product of the numerators over the product of the denominators.

$$\frac{3a}{4b^2c} \cdot \frac{10bc^2}{9a^3} = \frac{(3a)(10bc^2)}{(4b^2c)(9a^3)}$$

This result can then be reduced to lowest terms:

$$\frac{3a}{4b^2c} \cdot \frac{10bc^2}{9a^3} = \frac{\overset{1}{\cancel{(3)}}\overset{1}{\cancel{(2)}}(5)\overset{1\cdot1\cdot c}{\cancel{abc^2}}}{\underset{2\cdot3\cdot a^2b\cdot1}{\cancel{2^2}\cdot\cancel{3^2}\cdot\cancel{a^3}b^2\cancel{c}}}$$

$$= \frac{5c}{6a^2b}.$$

(b) Once the idea is grasped, it is easy to see that the factoring can be done at the same time we are writing the product of the numerators over the product of the denominators. Common factors can then be divided out.

$$\frac{6x^2y^5}{8xz^4} \cdot \frac{14xyz^2}{15x^2y^3} = \frac{\overset{1}{\cancel{2^2}}\cdot\overset{1}{\cancel{3}}\cdot 7\overset{1}{\cancel{x^2}}\overset{y^3}{\cancel{y^5}}\overset{1}{\cancel{z^2}}}{\underset{2\cdot1\quad 1\cdot1\cdot z^2}{\cancel{2^3}\cdot\cancel{3}\cdot 5\cancel{x^3}\cancel{y^3}\cancel{z^4}}}$$

$$= \frac{7y^3}{10z^2}$$

The next example is more typical of the kind of problem that is usually encountered, because factoring is usually a major portion of the work required.

EXAMPLE 2   Write each of the following products as a rational expression in lowest terms.

(a) $\dfrac{m^2 + 2mn + n^2}{n^2 - m^2} \cdot \dfrac{2m^2 - 3mn + n^2}{2m^2 + 3mn + n^2}$

(b) $\dfrac{6x^2 - 5x - 6}{4x^2 - 8x + 3} \cdot \dfrac{4x^2 - 4x + 1}{6x^2 + 13x + 6}$

Whenever the factoring gets to be complicated, as it is in these problems, it is better to factor each of the numerators and denominators first, and then multiply. Common factors can be removed from the indicated product. This is illustrated in the solutions to both (a) and (b).

(a) $\dfrac{m^2 + 2mn + n^2}{n^2 - m^2} \cdot \dfrac{2m^2 - 3mn + n^2}{2m^2 + 3mn + n^2}$

$$= \frac{\overset{1}{\cancel{(m+n)^2}}}{\underset{1}{\cancel{(n+m)}}\underset{1}{\cancel{(n-m)}}} \cdot \frac{(2m - n)\overset{(-1)}{\cancel{(m-n)}}}{(2m + n)\underset{1}{\cancel{(m+n)}}}$$

$$= \frac{(2m - n)(-1)}{2m + n}$$

$$= \frac{n - 2m}{n + 2m}$$

(b) $\dfrac{6x^2 - 5x - 6}{4x^2 - 8x + 3} \cdot \dfrac{4x^2 - 4x + 1}{6x^2 + 13x + 6}$

$$= \dfrac{\overset{1}{\cancel{(2x-3)}}\overset{1}{\cancel{(3x+2)}}}{\underset{1}{\cancel{(2x-3)}}\underset{1}{\cancel{(2x-1)}}} \cdot \dfrac{\overset{1}{\cancel{(2x-1)^2}}}{\underset{1}{\cancel{(3x+2)}}(2x+3)}$$

$$= \dfrac{2x - 1}{2x + 3}.$$

PRACTICE
PROBLEM 1

(Solution on page 208) Write each of the following products as a rational expression in lowest terms.

(a) $\dfrac{4x^2 + 11xy - 3y^2}{2x^2 + xy - 28y^2} \cdot \dfrac{4x^2 + 15xy - 4y^2}{2x^2 - xy - 21y^2}$

*(b) $\dfrac{ay + 2a + xy + 2x}{by - 3b + xy - 3x} \cdot \dfrac{by + xy - 2b - 2x}{ay + xy - 3a - 3x}$

In considering division of rational expressions, we return once again to the list of Basic Formulas for Fractions in Section 1-5. The last item in the list provides us with the

Quotient Rule for Rational Expressions

$$\frac{P}{Q} \div \frac{R}{S} = \frac{P}{Q} \cdot \frac{S}{R} = \frac{PS}{QR},$$

where $Q \neq 0$, $S \neq 0$, and $R \neq 0$.

Some special cases of the Quotient Rule are important enough to merit special attention:

$$\frac{P}{Q} \div R = \frac{P}{Q} \cdot \frac{1}{R} = \frac{P}{QR}, \qquad \text{for } Q \neq 0 \text{ and } R \neq 0;$$

$$P \div \frac{R}{S} = P \cdot \frac{S}{R} = \frac{PS}{R}, \qquad \text{for } R \neq 0 \text{ and } S \neq 0;$$

$$1 \div \frac{R}{S} = 1 \cdot \frac{S}{R} = \frac{S}{R}, \qquad \text{for } R \neq 0 \text{ and } S \neq 0.$$

EXAMPLE 3 Perform the indicated operations and reduce the result to lowest terms.

(a) $\dfrac{9bc}{2a} \cdot \dfrac{4a^2c}{3a^2b^4} \div \dfrac{6ab^2}{5bc^6}$

(b) $\dfrac{4x^2 - 4x - 15}{1 - 16x^2} \div \dfrac{4x^2 + 12x + 9}{4x^2 - 13x + 3}$

SOLUTION (a) $\dfrac{9bc}{2a} \cdot \dfrac{4a^2c}{3a^2b^4} \div \dfrac{6ab^2}{5bc^6} = \dfrac{\overset{3}{\cancel{9}}bc}{\underset{1}{\cancel{2}}a} \cdot \dfrac{\overset{2\cdot1}{\cancel{4}a^2c}}{\underset{1\cdot1}{\cancel{3}a^2b^4}} \cdot \dfrac{\overset{1}{\cancel{5}}bc^6}{\underset{b}{6ab^2}}$

$= \dfrac{\overset{1}{\cancel{6}} \cdot 5 \cdot \overset{1}{\cancel{b}} \cdot c^8}{\underset{1}{\cancel{6}} \cdot a^2 \cdot \underset{b^4}{\cancel{b^5}}}$

$= \dfrac{5c^8}{a^2b^4}$

(b) $\dfrac{4x^2 - 4x - 15}{1 - 16x^2} \div \dfrac{4x^2 + 12x + 9}{4x^2 - 13x + 3}$

$= \dfrac{(2x - 5)(2x + 3)}{\underset{1}{(1 - 4x)}(1 + 4x)} \cdot \dfrac{\overset{(-1)}{(4x - 1)}(x - 3)}{(2x + 3)^{\cancel{2}\,1}}$

$= -\dfrac{(2x - 5)(x - 3)}{(4x + 1)(2x + 3)}$

PRACTICE PROBLEM 2 (Solution on page 209) Perform the indicated operations and reduce each result to lowest terms.

(a) $\dfrac{6x^2 + 17x + 12}{3x + 2} \div (2x + 3)$

*(b) $\left(\dfrac{u^2 - 4v^2}{u^2 - 3uv + 2v^2} \div \dfrac{u^2 - v^2}{u^2 - uv - 2v^2} \right) \cdot \dfrac{u^2 - 2uv + v^2}{u^2 - 4uv + 4v^2}$

EXERCISES 8-2

Perform the indicated operations and write the results in lowest terms.

MULTIPLICATION (See Example 1.)

1. $\dfrac{6}{25} \cdot \dfrac{10}{9}$ 2. $\dfrac{8}{9} \cdot \dfrac{15}{28}$

3. $\dfrac{3a}{2b} \cdot \dfrac{10b^2}{9a}$ 4. $\dfrac{6a^2}{5b} \cdot \dfrac{b}{4a}$

5. $\dfrac{5w^3}{9z^2} \cdot \dfrac{12z}{7w}$ 6. $\dfrac{9r}{10s^2} \cdot \dfrac{15s^3}{12r^2}$

7. $\dfrac{2xy}{6y^2} \cdot \dfrac{3xy}{4x^3y}$ 8. $\dfrac{6x^2y}{12y^3} \cdot \dfrac{3y}{8x^3y}$

DIVISION   (See Example 3.)

9. $\dfrac{3x}{10yz} \div \dfrac{6xy}{5z}$

10. $\dfrac{2xy}{21z} \div \dfrac{8y}{9xz}$

11. $\dfrac{8m^3}{6mn} \div \dfrac{2m}{12n^2}$

12. $\dfrac{3m^2n}{4m} \div \dfrac{9m^3}{6n^2}$

GENERAL   (See Example 3.)

13. $\left(\dfrac{3x^4}{y^2} \div \dfrac{6x}{y^3}\right) \cdot \dfrac{y}{4x^3}$

14. $\left(\dfrac{x^4}{2y^6} \div \dfrac{x^2}{6y^2}\right) \cdot \dfrac{y}{9x^3}$

15. $\dfrac{3x^4}{y^2} \div \left(\dfrac{6x}{y^3} \cdot \dfrac{y}{4x^3}\right)$

16. $\dfrac{x^4}{2y^6} \div \left(\dfrac{x^2}{6y^2} \cdot \dfrac{y}{9x^3}\right)$

17. $\dfrac{4a^2b}{3b^2c} \cdot \dfrac{6ac}{10b^2} \div \dfrac{ac^2}{5b}$

18. $\dfrac{6pq^2}{5qr} \cdot \dfrac{3p^2q^2}{4p^2r} \div \dfrac{9pq}{2r}$

19. $\dfrac{2xy^3}{3x^2z} \cdot \dfrac{9yz^2}{8x^2z^3} \div \dfrac{3x}{10y^3z^2}$

20. $\dfrac{4x^2z}{3xy^3} \cdot \dfrac{12yz^2}{5x} \div \dfrac{8x^3}{3y^2z}$

Perform the following multiplications or divisions, and write each result as a rational expression in lowest terms. (See Examples 2 and 3 and Practice Problems 1 and 2.)

21. $\dfrac{2ab^2}{a+b} \cdot \dfrac{a+b}{6ab}$

22. $\dfrac{3a^2b^2}{a-b} \cdot \dfrac{a-b}{12a^3b}$

23. $\dfrac{6m^2n^3}{2m+n} \cdot \dfrac{n+2m}{2mn}$

24. $\dfrac{10m^3n^3}{5m+2n} \cdot \dfrac{2n+5m}{15mn^2}$

25. $\dfrac{2x-1}{x} \div \dfrac{2x+1}{x}$

26. $\dfrac{3y-2}{y} \div \dfrac{3y-4}{2y}$

27. $\dfrac{z-2}{z} \div \dfrac{z^2-4}{3z}$

28. $\dfrac{x+3}{x^2} \div \dfrac{x^2-9}{3x}$

29. $\dfrac{x^2-9}{3x-6} \div (2x+6)$

30. $\dfrac{x^2-16}{2x-8} \div (3x+12)$

31. $(x^2-4) \div \dfrac{x^2+2x}{x-2}$

32. $(x^2-25) \div \dfrac{x^2+5x}{x-5}$

33. $\dfrac{x+2}{x^3+2x^2} \cdot \dfrac{x^2}{x-4}$

34. $\dfrac{w-4}{w^3-4w^2} \cdot \dfrac{w}{w+2}$

35. $\dfrac{p+2}{p^2-4} \div \dfrac{2p-4}{p^2-4p+4}$

36. $\dfrac{y+3}{y^2-9} \div \dfrac{2y-6}{y^2-6y+9}$

37. $\dfrac{4x^2-1}{x^2-9} \cdot \dfrac{x^2+3x}{2x+1}$

38. $\dfrac{a^2+3a-4}{a+3} \cdot \dfrac{a^2+3a}{a^2+4a}$

39. $\dfrac{x^2-4}{x^2+x-6} \div \dfrac{x^2+x-2}{x^2+4x+3}$

40. $\dfrac{x^2-6x+9}{x^2-2x-3} \cdot \dfrac{x^2-x-6}{x^2-1}$

41. $\dfrac{z^2-z-12}{z^2-2z-15} \div \dfrac{z^2-3z-10}{8+2z-z^2}$

42. $\dfrac{z^2+5z-14}{z^2+6z-7} \cdot \dfrac{z^2+5z-6}{8-2z-z^2}$

43. $\dfrac{y^2+4y-4}{y+2} \div \dfrac{y^2+2y-1}{y+2}$

44. $\dfrac{w^2+6w-9}{w+3} \div \dfrac{w^2-2w-1}{w+3}$

207

45. $\dfrac{x^3y - xy^3}{x^2y + xy^2} \cdot \dfrac{x^2 + xy}{x^2 - y^2}$ 46. $\dfrac{x^3y^2 - x^2y^3}{x^2 - xy} \cdot \dfrac{x^2y^2 + x^2}{xy^4 + xy^2}$

47. $\dfrac{2x^2 + x - 3}{3x - 6x^2} \cdot \dfrac{2x^2 + x - 1}{x^2 - 1}$ 48. $\dfrac{8x^2 - 21x - 9}{2x - 8x^2} \cdot \dfrac{4x^2 + 11x - 3}{x^2 - 9}$

*49. $\dfrac{x^3 - 8}{x^2} \div \dfrac{x - 2}{x}$ *50. $\dfrac{x^3 - 8y^3}{x^2 + 2xy + 4y^2} \div \dfrac{x - 2y}{x + y}$

*51. $\dfrac{3x^2 - 3}{2x - 1} \div \dfrac{x + 1}{1 - 8x^3}$ *52. $\dfrac{w^2 - 3w - 4}{w - 3} \div \dfrac{w^2 - 1}{27 - w^3}$

*53. $\dfrac{aw^2 + a - 3w^2 - 3}{aw - a + 2w - 2} \cdot \dfrac{a + 2}{aw + a - 3w - 3}$

*54. $\dfrac{3ax - 6x - 4ay + 8y}{2ax - 4x + ay - 2y} \cdot \dfrac{ax + ay + 2x + 2y}{6x^2 - 5xy - 4y^2}$

*55. $\dfrac{ab + aq + pb + pq}{ab + aq - pb - pq} \cdot \dfrac{ab - aq + pb - pq}{pb + pq - ab - aq}$

*56. $\dfrac{ab + 2a - 2bp - 4p}{ab - 2a + 2bp - 4p} \cdot \dfrac{ab + 2a + 2bp + 4p}{ab - 2a - 2bp + 4p}$

Perform the indicated operations, and leave the results in lowest terms. (See Example 3 and Practice Problem 2.)

*57. $\dfrac{x^2y + xy^2}{xy - x^2} \div \left(\dfrac{x^2 + 2xy + y^2}{x^2 - y^2} \div \dfrac{xy + y^2}{x^2 - 2xy + y^2} \right)$

*58. $\dfrac{x^3 + y^3}{x^2 - 2xy + y^2} \div \left(\dfrac{x^2 - xy + y^2}{x^2 - y^2} \div \dfrac{x^2y - xy^2}{x^2 + 2xy + y^2} \right)$

*59. $\left(\dfrac{x^2y + xy^2}{xy - x^2} \div \dfrac{x^2 + 2xy + y^2}{x^2 - y^2} \right) \div \dfrac{xy + y^2}{x^2 - 2xy + y^2}$

*60. $\left(\dfrac{x^3 + y^3}{x^2 - 2xy + y^2} \div \dfrac{x^2 - xy + y^2}{x^2 - y^2} \right) \div \dfrac{x^2y - xy^2}{x^2 + 2xy + y^2}$

SOLUTIONS FOR PRACTICE PROBLEMS

1. (a) $\dfrac{4x^2 + 11xy - 3y^2}{2x^2 + xy - 28y^2} \cdot \dfrac{4x^2 + 15xy - 4y^2}{2x^2 - xy - 21y^2}$

$$= \dfrac{(4x - y)\cancel{(x + 3y)}^{1}}{(2x - 7y)\cancel{(x + 4y)}} \cdot \dfrac{(4x - y)\cancel{(x + 4y)}^{1}}{(2x - 7y)\cancel{(x + 3y)}}$$

$$= \dfrac{(4x - y)^2}{(2x - 7y)^2}$$

*(b) $\dfrac{ay + 2a + xy + 2x}{by - 3b + xy - 3x} \cdot \dfrac{by + xy - 2b - 2x}{ay + xy - 3a - 3x}$

$$= \dfrac{a(y + 2) + x(y + 2)}{b(y - 3) + x(y - 3)} \cdot \dfrac{y(b + x) - 2(b + x)}{y(a + x) - 3(a + x)}$$

$$= \dfrac{\cancel{(a + x)}^{1}(y + 2)}{\cancel{(b + x)}(y - 3)} \cdot \dfrac{(y - 2)\cancel{(b + x)}^{1}}{(y - 3)\cancel{(a + x)}}$$

$$= \dfrac{(y + 2)(y - 2)}{(y - 3)^2}$$

2. (a) $\dfrac{6x^2 + 17x + 12}{3x + 2} \div (2x + 3) = \dfrac{(3x + 4)\cancel{(2x + 3)}^{1}}{3x + 2} \cdot \dfrac{1}{\cancel{2x + 3}_{1}}$

$$= \frac{3x + 4}{3x + 2}$$

*(b) $\left(\dfrac{u^2 - 4v^2}{u^2 - 3uv + 2v^2} \div \dfrac{u^2 - v^2}{u^2 - uv - 2v^2}\right) \cdot \dfrac{u^2 - 2uv + v^2}{u^2 - 4uv + 4v^2}$

$$= \frac{\cancel{(u - 2v)}^{1}(u + 2v)}{\cancel{(u - 2v)}_{1}\cancel{(u - v)}_{1}} \cdot \frac{\cancel{(u - 2v)}^{1}\cancel{(u + v)}^{1}}{\cancel{(u - v)}_{1}\cancel{(u + v)}_{1}} \cdot \frac{\cancel{(u - v)}^{2}}{(u - 2v)^{2}}$$

$$= \frac{u + 2v}{u - 2v}$$

8-3
Addition and
Subtraction

Sections 8-1 and 8-2 have shown something about how polynomials play the same kind of role in rational expressions that integers play in rational numbers. With addition and subtraction of rational expressions, the analogy is even clearer.

Addition of rational numbers is easy enough when the two fractions have the same denominator:

$$\frac{a}{b} + \frac{c}{b} = \frac{a + c}{b}, \qquad \text{where } b \neq 0.$$

A minor complication which sometimes occurs is that a sum may need to be reduced. For instance,

$$\frac{5}{24} + \frac{11}{24} = \frac{5 + 11}{24}$$

$$= \frac{16}{24}$$

$$= \frac{2}{3}.$$

Since rational expressions represent real numbers, they follow the same basic formula.

Addition Rule for Rational Expressions

$$\frac{P}{Q} + \frac{R}{Q} = \frac{P + R}{Q}, \qquad \text{where } Q \neq 0.$$

Subtraction of $\dfrac{R}{Q}$ from $\dfrac{P}{Q}$ is, by definition, the same as adding the opposite of $\dfrac{R}{Q}$ to $\dfrac{P}{Q}$. Thus

$$\frac{P}{Q} - \frac{R}{Q} = \frac{P}{Q} + \left(\frac{-R}{Q}\right)$$

$$= \frac{P + (-R)}{Q}$$

$$= \frac{P - R}{Q}$$

and the same sort of rule holds for subtraction as for addition:

$$\frac{P}{Q} - \frac{R}{Q} = \frac{P - R}{Q}, \qquad \text{where } Q \neq 0.$$

These same rules extend to sums or differences with more than three terms. For example,

$$\frac{P}{Q} - \frac{R}{Q} + \frac{S}{Q} = \frac{P - R + S}{Q}.$$

EXAMPLE 1 Perform the indicated operations, and write each result as a rational expression in lowest terms.

(a) $\dfrac{6x}{2x + 1} + \dfrac{3}{2x + 1}$

(b) $\dfrac{x}{x^2 - 4} + \dfrac{2}{x^2 - 4}$

(c) $\dfrac{2x^2}{x - 3} - \dfrac{x^2 + 14}{x - 3} + \dfrac{5}{x - 3}$

SOLUTION

(a) $\dfrac{6x}{2x + 1} + \dfrac{3}{2x + 1} = \dfrac{6x + 3}{2x + 1}$

$$= \frac{3\overset{1}{\cancel{(2x + 1)}}}{\underset{1}{\cancel{2x + 1}}}$$

$$= 3$$

(b) $\dfrac{x}{x^2 - 4} + \dfrac{2}{x^2 - 4} = \dfrac{x + 2}{x^2 - 4}$

$$= \frac{\overset{1}{\cancel{x + 2}}}{(x - 2)\underset{1}{\cancel{(x + 2)}}}$$

$$= \frac{1}{x - 2}$$

(c) $\dfrac{2x^2}{x-3} - \dfrac{x^2+14}{x-3} + \dfrac{5}{x-3} = \dfrac{2x^2 - (x^2+14) + 5}{x-3}$

$= \dfrac{2x^2 - x^2 - 14 + 5}{x-3}$

$= \dfrac{x^2 - 9}{x-3}$

$= \dfrac{\overset{1}{\cancel{(x-3)}}(x+3)}{\underset{1}{\cancel{x-3}}}$

$= x + 3$

**PRACTICE
PROBLEM 1**   (Solution on page 217) Combine into a rational expression in lowest terms.

(a) $\dfrac{y}{x^2 - y^2} - \dfrac{x}{x^2 - y^2}$

(b) $\dfrac{4x}{x^2 - 1} - \dfrac{2x+1}{x^2 - 1} + \dfrac{3}{x^2 - 1}$

Addition of rational numbers is much more complicated when the fractions involved do not have the same denominator. Before the addition can be performed, the Fundamental Principle of Fractions must be used to convert the fractions to fractions with the same denominator. As an example,

$$\frac{1}{25} + \frac{7}{10} = \frac{(1)(2)}{(25)(2)} + \frac{(7)(5)}{(10)(5)}$$

$$= \frac{2}{50} + \frac{35}{50}$$

$$= \frac{37}{50}.$$

This example can be used to illustrate another important point. In the list of Basic Formulas for Fractions in Section 1-5, the fourth item states that

$$\frac{a}{b} + \frac{c}{d} = \frac{ad+bc}{bd}, \qquad \text{where } b \neq 0 \text{ and } d \neq 0.$$

It is worth noting that we *did not* use the formula to add $\frac{1}{25}$ and $\frac{7}{10}$, and the reason is simple: It would have resulted in a larger denominator (250 instead of 50). It is much more efficient to use the smallest denominator possible.

The point to the discussion in the preceding paragraph applies to rational expressions as well as rational numbers. The formula

$$\frac{P}{Q} + \frac{R}{S} = \frac{PS + QR}{QS}, \qquad \text{where } Q \neq 0 \text{ and } S \neq 0,$$

is valid, but it has limited usefulness. To work efficiently, we should find the least common multiple of the denominators, and change the fractions involved to fractions with this denominator.

The least common multiple (abbreviated LCM) of a set of polynomials† is the polynomial of smallest degree which has each polynomial as a factor, and has the coefficient of the highest-degree term as the smallest possible positive integer.

To Find the LCM

1. **Factor each polynomial completely, using integer coefficients, and**
2. **Form the product of all the different factors, with each factor raised to the highest power with which it appears in any of the polynomials.**

This is essentially the same procedure as is used to find the LCM of integers. It is illustrated in Example 2.

EXAMPLE 2   Find the LCM of each of the following sets of polynomials.

  (a) 90, 40, 75
  (b) $6x^2y$, $9xy^3$, $24y^2$
  (c) $x^2 - 4x + 4$, $3x^2 - 12$

SOLUTION   (a) Factoring completely, we have

$$90 = 9 \cdot 10 = 2 \cdot 3^2 \cdot 5$$
$$40 = 8 \cdot 5 = 2^3 \cdot 5$$
$$75 = 3 \cdot 25 = 3 \cdot 5^2.$$

The different factors that occur in these factorizations are 2, 3, and 5:

  2 occurs to the powers 1 and 3, with 3 the highest of these;

  3 occurs to the powers 2 and 1, with 2 the highest of these;

  5 occurs to the powers 1, 1, and 2, with 2 the highest of these.

The LCM is the product with each factor raised to the highest power with which it appears in any of the factorizations:

---

†The restriction made at the first of this chapter is in effect here: We are working with polynomials that have integral coefficients.

$$\text{LCM} = 2^3 \cdot 3^2 \cdot 5^2$$
$$= 1800.$$

(b) We first factor each polynomial completely:

$$6x^2y = 2 \cdot 3 \cdot x^2 \cdot y,$$
$$9xy^3 = 3^2 \cdot x \cdot y^3,$$
$$24y^2 = 2^3 \cdot 3 \cdot y^2.$$

We then form the product with each factor raised to the highest power to which it has occurred:

$$\text{LCM} = 2^3 \cdot 3^2 \cdot x^2 \cdot y^3$$
$$= 72x^2y^3.$$

(c) Factoring completely, we obtain

$$x^2 - 4x + 4 = (x - 2)^2,$$
$$3x^2 - 12 = 3(x^2 - 4)$$
$$= 3(x - 2)(x + 2),$$

and the LCM is given by

$$\text{LCM} = 3(x - 2)^2(x + 2).$$

As mentioned before, the most efficient denominator to use in adding rational expressions is the least common multiple of the denominators, which is called the **least common denominator** (abbreviated LCD). To add or subtract rational expressions that are in lowest terms, we follow these steps:

1. **Find the LCD. (This is the least common multiple of the denominators.)**
2. **Convert each rational expression to a fraction having the LCD as its denominator.**
3. **Combine the new numerators, and place the result over the LCD.**
4. **Reduce to lowest terms.**

EXAMPLE 3 Combine each of the following into a single fraction in lowest terms.

(a) $\dfrac{3}{2x - 6} - \dfrac{5}{4x}$

(b) $\dfrac{3}{t - 2} - \dfrac{12}{t^2 - 4}$

SOLUTION We follow the steps listed in the box preceding this example.

(a) $\dfrac{3}{2x - 6} - \dfrac{5}{4x} = \dfrac{3}{2(x - 3)} - \dfrac{5}{2^2x}$ $\left(\begin{array}{l}\text{Factoring to} \\ \text{find the LCD}\end{array}\right)$

$\qquad = \dfrac{3(2x)}{[2(x - 3)](2x)} - \dfrac{5(x - 3)}{2^2x(x - 3)}$ $\left(\begin{array}{l}\text{Converting to} \\ \text{fractions with} \\ \text{LCD as denom-} \\ \text{inator}\end{array}\right)$

$\qquad = \dfrac{6x}{4x(x - 3)} - \dfrac{5x - 15}{4x(x - 3)}$

$\qquad = \dfrac{6x - (5x - 15)}{4x(x - 3)}$ $\left(\begin{array}{l}\text{Combining} \\ \text{numerators}\end{array}\right)$

$\qquad = \dfrac{x + 15}{4x(x - 3)}$

(b) $\dfrac{3}{t - 2} - \dfrac{12}{t^2 - 4} = \dfrac{3}{t - 2} - \dfrac{12}{(t - 2)(t + 2)}$ $\left(\begin{array}{l}\text{Factoring to} \\ \text{find LCD}\end{array}\right)$

$\qquad = \dfrac{3(t + 2)}{(t - 2)(t + 2)} - \dfrac{12}{(t - 2)(t + 2)}$ $\left(\begin{array}{l}\text{Converting} \\ \text{to LCD as} \\ \text{denominator}\end{array}\right)$

$\qquad = \dfrac{3t + 6 - 12}{(t - 2)(t + 2)}$ $\left(\begin{array}{l}\text{Combining} \\ \text{numerators}\end{array}\right)$

$\qquad = \dfrac{3t - 6}{(t - 2)(t + 2)}$

$\qquad = \dfrac{3\overset{1}{\cancel{(t - 2)}}}{\underset{1}{\cancel{(t - 2)}}(t + 2)}$ $\left(\begin{array}{l}\text{Reducing to} \\ \text{lowest terms}\end{array}\right)$

$\qquad = \dfrac{3}{t + 2}$

If there are more than two terms involved in a sum, the procedure is essentially the same. This is illustrated in the next example.

EXAMPLE 4 Perform the indicated operations, and write each result as a rational expression in lowest terms.

(a) $\dfrac{3}{x - 3} + 2 - \dfrac{2x^2}{x^2 - 9}$

(b) $\dfrac{2}{y(y + 2)} + \dfrac{2}{(y + 2)^2} + \dfrac{4}{y(y + 2)^2}$

SOLUTION (a) $\dfrac{3}{x - 3} + 2 - \dfrac{2x^2}{x^2 - 9} = \dfrac{3}{x - 3} + \dfrac{2}{1} - \dfrac{2x^2}{(x - 3)(x + 3)}$

$\qquad = \dfrac{3(x + 3) + 2(x - 3)(x + 3) - 2x^2}{(x - 3)(x + 3)}$

$\qquad = \dfrac{3x + 9 + 2x^2 - 18 - 2x^2}{(x - 3)(x + 3)}$

$$= \frac{3x - 9}{(x - 3)(x + 3)}$$

$$= \frac{\overset{1}{3(\cancel{x - 3})}}{\underset{1}{(\cancel{x - 3})(x + 3)}}$$

$$= \frac{3}{x + 3}$$

(b) $\dfrac{2}{y(y + 2)} + \dfrac{2}{(y + 2)^2} + \dfrac{4}{y(y + 2)^2} = \dfrac{2(y + 2) + 2(y) + 4}{y(y + 2)^2}$

$$= \frac{2y + 4 + 2y + 4}{y(y + 2)^2}$$

$$= \frac{4y + 8}{y(y + 2)^2}$$

$$= \frac{\overset{1}{4(\cancel{y + 2})}}{y(y + 2)\cancel{^2}}$$

$$= \frac{4}{y(y + 2)}$$

PRACTICE PROBLEM 2 (Solution on page 217) Combine each of the following into a single fraction in lowest terms.

(a) $\dfrac{7}{3z^2 + 5z - 2} - \dfrac{11}{6z^2 + 7z - 3}$

(b) $1 + \dfrac{x}{x - 2} - \dfrac{2x^2}{x^2 - 4}$

EXERCISES 8-3

Find the LCM. (See Example 2.)

1. $6, 9, 10$ 2. $4, 12, 15$
3. $6, 8, 9$ 4. $21, 28, 42$
5. $6, 2x$ 6. $4, 6y$
7. $9xy, 6x^2$ 8. $9x^2y, 12xy^2$
9. $2p, 10q, 5r$ 10. $3a, 6b, 4c$
11. $6r^2s, 9s^2t, 15rt^3$ 12. $12u^3v^3, 20uv^2w, 45vw^2$
13. $25(x - 1)^2, 15x(x - 1)$ 14. $16x^2(x + 2), 24x(x + 2)^3$
15. $y^2 - 4, 3(y - 2)$ 16. $y^2 - 9, 2(y + 3)$
17. $a^2 - 1, a^2 - 2a + 1$ 18. $a^2 - 4, a^2 + 4a + 4$
19. $w^2 - 2w, 3w - 6$ 20. $z^2 + 3z, 2z^3 + 6z^2$
21. $3x^2 - 6x + 9, x^2 - 4x + 4$ 22. $2x^2 - 8x + 6, x^2 - 6x + 9$
23. $6x^2 - 3x, 4x^2 - 1, 2x^3 - x^2$ 24. $4y^2 + 8y, 6y^3 + 12y^2, y^2 - 4$

Perform the following additions or subtractions, and write each result as a rational expression in lowest terms. (See Example 1 and Practice Problem 1.)

25. $\dfrac{2x}{7} + \dfrac{5}{7}$

26. $\dfrac{2a}{5} + \dfrac{3b}{5}$

27. $\dfrac{5}{x} - \dfrac{7}{x}$

28. $\dfrac{3}{y} - \dfrac{8}{y}$

29. $\dfrac{x}{x+2} + \dfrac{2}{x+2}$

30. $\dfrac{y}{y+7} + \dfrac{7}{y+7}$

31. $\dfrac{3}{w-3} - \dfrac{w}{w-3}$

32. $\dfrac{5}{2z-5} - \dfrac{2z}{2z-5}$

33. $\dfrac{x}{x^2-9} + \dfrac{3}{x^2-9}$

34. $\dfrac{a}{a^2-b^2} + \dfrac{b}{a^2-b^2}$

Combine each of the following into a single fraction in lowest terms. (See Examples 3 and 4 and Practice Problem 2.)

35. $\dfrac{5}{a-1} + \dfrac{3}{1-a}$

36. $\dfrac{4}{t-2} + \dfrac{1}{2-t}$

37. $\dfrac{4a}{a-b} - \dfrac{2b}{b-a}$

38. $\dfrac{3x}{x-y} - \dfrac{2y}{y-x}$

39. $\dfrac{5}{x+3} - \dfrac{3}{2x+6}$

40. $\dfrac{5}{x-2} - \dfrac{4}{3x-6}$

41. $\dfrac{x-2y}{2y} + \dfrac{x-y}{x}$

42. $\dfrac{x-2}{x} + \dfrac{2x}{3y}$

43. $\dfrac{2}{t-2} + \dfrac{3}{t}$

44. $\dfrac{3}{r-3} + \dfrac{2}{r}$

45. $\dfrac{5}{3a} - \dfrac{1}{2a^2}$

46. $\dfrac{4}{5y} - \dfrac{3}{2y^2}$

47. $\dfrac{2+x}{2-x} + 1$

48. $\dfrac{3+y}{3-y} + 1$

49. $\dfrac{1}{x-1} - \dfrac{1}{x+2}$

50. $\dfrac{1}{y+1} - \dfrac{1}{y+2}$

51. $\dfrac{3}{2z} + \dfrac{1}{z-2}$

52. $\dfrac{1}{3z} + \dfrac{2}{z-3}$

53. $\dfrac{3}{x-1} + \dfrac{6}{1-x^2}$

54. $\dfrac{3}{r-2} + \dfrac{12}{4-r^2}$

55. $\dfrac{3}{a+2} + \dfrac{a-2}{(a+2)^2}$

56. $\dfrac{w+3}{w-3} + \dfrac{9}{(w-3)^2}$

57. $\dfrac{5}{p+2} + \dfrac{10}{(p-1)(p+2)}$

58. $\dfrac{4}{q-2} - \dfrac{20}{(q+3)(q-2)}$

59. $\dfrac{4}{t^2+2t-3} - \dfrac{2}{t^2-1}$

60. $\dfrac{12}{t^2-9} - \dfrac{10}{t^2+t-6}$

61. $\dfrac{x+1}{x^2-4} - \dfrac{x}{x^2+x-6}$

62. $\dfrac{x}{x^2-16} - \dfrac{x+1}{x^2-3x-4}$

63. $\dfrac{1}{w^2 - 3w + 2} - \dfrac{5}{w^2 + w - 6}$

64. $\dfrac{6}{w^2 + w - 2} - \dfrac{2}{w^2 + 3w + 2}$

65. $m - \dfrac{3}{2 - m} - \dfrac{m^3}{m^2 - 4}$

66. $m - \dfrac{1}{1 - m} - \dfrac{m^3}{m^2 - 1}$

67. $\dfrac{2}{z - 3} + \dfrac{3}{z + 3} + \dfrac{18}{z^2 - 9}$

68. $\dfrac{3}{z - 2} + \dfrac{3}{z + 2} + \dfrac{12}{z^2 - 4}$

*69. $\dfrac{x + y}{x^2 - 3xy + 2y^2} + \dfrac{x + y}{2x^2 - 3xy + y^2}$

*70. $\dfrac{x - y}{4x^2 + 7xy - 2y^2} + \dfrac{x - y}{x^2 - 2xy - 8y^2}$

*71. $\dfrac{p - q}{p^2 - pq - 2q^2} + \dfrac{p + q}{p^2 - 3pq + 2q^2}$

*72. $\dfrac{p - q}{3p^2 + pq - 2q^2} + \dfrac{3p + 2q}{p^2 + 2pq + q^2}$

*73. $\dfrac{2r - s}{6r^2 - rs - s^2} + \dfrac{2r + 2s}{3r^2 - 2rs - s^2}$

*74. $\dfrac{r + 2s}{3r^2 + 4rs - 4s^2} + \dfrac{2r - s}{3r^2 - 5rs + 2s^2}$

SOLUTIONS FOR PRACTICE PROBLEMS

1. (a) $\dfrac{y}{x^2 - y^2} - \dfrac{x}{x^2 - y^2} = \dfrac{y - x}{x^2 - y^2}$

$$= \dfrac{y - x}{(x - y)(x + y)} = \dfrac{(-1)\overset{1}{\cancel{(x - y)}}}{\underset{1}{\cancel{(x - y)}}(x + y)} = -\dfrac{1}{x + y}$$

(b) $\dfrac{4x}{x^2 - 1} - \dfrac{2x + 1}{x^2 - 1} + \dfrac{3}{x^2 - 1} = \dfrac{4x - 2x - 1 + 3}{x^2 - 1}$

$$= \dfrac{2x + 2}{x^2 - 1}$$

$$= \dfrac{2\overset{1}{\cancel{(x + 1)}}}{(x - 1)\underset{1}{\cancel{(x + 1)}}}$$

$$= \dfrac{2}{x - 1}$$

2. (a) $\dfrac{7}{3z^2 + 5z - 2} - \dfrac{11}{6z^2 + 7z - 3} = \dfrac{7}{(3z - 1)(z + 2)} - \dfrac{11}{(3z - 1)(2z + 3)}$

$$= \dfrac{7(2z + 3) - 11(z + 2)}{(3z - 1)(z + 2)(2z + 3)}$$

$$= \dfrac{14z + 21 - 11z - 22}{(3z - 1)(z + 2)(2z + 3)}$$

$$= \dfrac{\overset{1}{\cancel{3z - 1}}}{\underset{1}{\cancel{(3z - 1)}}(z + 2)(2z + 3)}$$

$$= \dfrac{1}{(z + 2)(2z + 3)}$$

(b) $1 + \dfrac{x}{x-2} - \dfrac{2x^2}{x^2-4} = \dfrac{(1)(x-2)(x+2) + x(x+2) - 2x^2(1)}{(x-2)(x+2)}$

$$= \dfrac{x^2 - 4 + x^2 + 2x - 2x^2}{(x-2)(x+2)}$$

$$= \dfrac{2x - 4}{(x-2)(x+2)}$$

$$= \dfrac{\overset{1}{2(\cancel{x-2})}}{\underset{1}{(\cancel{x-2})(x+2)}}$$

$$= \dfrac{2}{x+2}$$

8-4
Solving Fractional
Equations

In this section we solve equations that involve rational expressions. In very simple equations of this type, all of the denominators are constants, as they are in

$$\frac{5}{8}x - \frac{1}{6} = \frac{1}{4}x + \frac{1}{2}.$$

Theorem 2-4(b) of Chapter 2 allows us to obtain an equivalent equation by multiplying both sides of an equation by the same nonzero quantity. If this quantity is chosen properly, the resulting equation will be free of fractions. The most efficient choice of multiplier for this purpose is the LCD of all the fractions in the equation. In the equation

$$\frac{5}{8}x - \frac{1}{6} = \frac{1}{4}x + \frac{1}{2},$$

the LCD is 24. Multiplying both sides by 24, we have

$$(\mathbf{24})\left(\frac{5}{8}x - \frac{1}{6}\right) = (\mathbf{24})\left(\frac{1}{4}x + \frac{1}{2}\right)$$

$$\overset{3}{(\cancel{24})}\left(\frac{5}{8}x\right) - \overset{4}{(\cancel{24})}\left(\frac{1}{6}\right) = \overset{6}{(\cancel{24})}\left(\frac{1}{4}x\right) + \overset{12}{(\cancel{24})}\left(\frac{1}{2}\right)$$

$$15x - 4 = 6x + 12.$$

Once the equation is free of fractions, it is easy to solve:

$$15x - 6x = 12 + 4$$

$$9x = 16$$

$$x = \frac{16}{9}.$$

As a check on our work, we can test the value $x = \frac{16}{9}$ in each side of the original equation to see if it gives a true equality. We shall use LHS and RHS to indicate the left-hand side and right-hand side, respectively, of the original equation.

$$Check: \quad x = \frac{16}{9}$$

$$LHS = \frac{5}{8}\left(\frac{16}{9}\right) - \frac{1}{6} = \frac{10}{9} - \frac{1}{6} = \frac{20}{18} - \frac{3}{18} = \frac{17}{18}$$

$$RHS = \frac{1}{4}\left(\frac{16}{9}\right) + \frac{1}{2} = \frac{4}{9} + \frac{1}{2} = \frac{8}{18} + \frac{9}{18} = \frac{17}{18}$$

Since LHS = RHS when $x = \frac{16}{9}$, the solution set of the equation is $\{\frac{16}{9}\}$.

A more complicated equation is solved in the next example.

EXAMPLE 1 Solve:

$$\frac{2y + 1}{2y - 5} = \frac{y}{y - 4}.$$

SOLUTION We multiply both sides by the LCD, which is $(2y - 5)(y - 4)$.

$$(2y - 5)(y - 4)\frac{2y + 1}{2y - 5} = (2y - 5)(y - 4)\frac{y}{y - 4}$$

$$(y - 4)(2y + 1) = (2y - 5)(y)$$

$$2y^2 + y - 8y - 4 = 2y^2 - 5y$$

$$2y^2 - 2y^2 - 7y + 5y = 4$$

$$-2y = 4$$

$$y = -2$$

$$Check: \quad y = -2$$

$$LHS = \frac{2(-2) + 1}{2(-2) - 5} = \frac{-4 + 1}{-4 - 5} = \frac{-3}{-9} = \frac{1}{3}$$

$$RHS = \frac{-2}{-2 - 4} = \frac{-2}{-6} = \frac{1}{3}$$

Since LHS = RHS, -2 is the solution to the equation.

The testing of a solution in the original equation always provides a check against errors in our work. But when both sides of an equation have been multiplied by an expression that contains a variable, there is a more serious reason for checking: The proposed solution may make the multiplier zero, and multiplication of both sides by zero *does not* yield an equivalent equation. For this reason, it is *absolutely necessary* to verify that the proposed solution does not make the multiplier zero, and it is really best to check the solution in the original equation.

EXAMPLE 2   Solve:

$$\frac{3}{x-2} + \frac{5}{x+2} = \frac{12}{x^2-4}.$$

SOLUTION   Since $x^2 - 4 = (x-2)(x+2)$, the LCD is $x^2 - 4$. Multiplying both sides by this expression, we have

$$(x-2)(x+2)\left(\frac{3}{x-2} + \frac{5}{x+2}\right) = (x-2)(x+2)\frac{12}{x^2-4}$$

$$(\overset{1}{\cancel{x-2}})(x+2)\frac{3}{\underset{1}{\cancel{x-2}}} + (x-2)(\overset{1}{\cancel{x+2}})\frac{5}{\underset{1}{\cancel{x+2}}} = (\overset{1}{\cancel{x^2-4}})\frac{12}{\underset{1}{\cancel{x^2-4}}}$$

$$(x+2)(3) + (x-2)(5) = 12$$
$$3x + 6 + 5x - 10 = 12$$
$$8x - 4 = 12$$
$$8x = 16$$
$$x = 2.$$

We need to check this proposed solution in the original equation.

Check: $x = 2$

$$\text{LHS} = \frac{3}{2-2} + \frac{5}{2+2} = \frac{3}{0} + \frac{5}{4}$$

$$\text{RHS} = \frac{12}{4-4} = \frac{12}{0}$$

Since division by 0 is undefined, $x = 2$ is not a solution. This means that there is no real number which is a solution to the equation

$$\frac{3}{x-2} + \frac{5}{x+2} = \frac{12}{x^2-4}.$$

In other words, the solution set in $\varnothing$.

Example 2 shows that a proposed solution (one obtained after clearing of fractions) is not always a solution to the original equation. Such solutions are called **extraneous solutions**. We would say that $x = 2$ is an extraneous solution in Example 2.

EXAMPLE 3 Solve:

$$\frac{2}{x-1} + \frac{1}{x+1} = \frac{3x+5}{x^2+x}.$$

SOLUTION Since $x^2 + x = x(x+1)$, the LCD is $x(x-1)(x+1)$. We multiply both sides by this expression:

$$x(x-1)(x+1)\left(\frac{2}{x-1} + \frac{1}{x+1}\right) = x(x-1)(x+1)\frac{3x+5}{x(x+1)}$$

$$x\overset{1}{\cancel{(x-1)}}(x+1)\frac{2}{\cancel{x-1}}\underset{1}{} + x(x-1)\overset{1}{\cancel{(x+1)}}\frac{1}{\cancel{x+1}}\underset{1}{}$$

$$= \overset{1}{\cancel{x}}\overset{1}{\cancel{(x-1)}}(x+1)\frac{3x+5}{\underset{1}{\cancel{x}}(\underset{1}{\cancel{x+1}})}$$

$$2x(x+1) + x(x-1) = (x-1)(3x+5)$$
$$2x^2 + 2x + x^2 - x = 3x^2 + 5x - 3x - 5$$
$$3x^2 + x = 3x^2 + 2x - 5$$
$$3x^2 - 3x^2 + x - 2x = -5$$
$$-x = -5$$
$$x = 5$$

Check: $x = 5$

$$\text{LHS} = \frac{2}{5-1} + \frac{1}{5+1} = \frac{2}{4} + \frac{1}{6} = \frac{6}{12} + \frac{2}{12} = \frac{8}{12} = \frac{2}{3}$$

$$\text{RHS} = \frac{3(5)+5}{5^2+5} = \frac{15+5}{25+5} = \frac{20}{30} = \frac{2}{3}$$

Thus LHS = RHS, and the solution set is $\{5\}$.

PRACTICE PROBLEM 1 (Solution on page 224) Find the solution set for the equation

$$\frac{y^2 - y - 6}{y^2 - 4} = 0.$$

EXERCISES 8-4

Find the solution set for each of the following equations.

1. $\frac{x}{3} - 4 = x$

2. $x + 8 = \frac{x}{5}$

3. $\frac{1}{2}y - \frac{1}{6} = \frac{1}{3}y + 2$

4. $\frac{1}{2}y + \frac{3}{10} = \frac{1}{5}y + \frac{1}{5}$

5. $\frac{1}{6}z + \frac{3}{10} = \frac{1}{15}z + \frac{1}{2}$

6. $\frac{1}{3}z - \frac{1}{5} = \frac{2}{15}z + \frac{1}{15}$

7. $\frac{2}{x} - \frac{3}{5} = 1$

8. $\frac{3}{x} + \frac{5}{2x} = \frac{5}{2}$

9. $\frac{2}{y} + \frac{3}{4} = \frac{4+y}{2y}$

10. $\frac{5}{y} - \frac{7}{2} = \frac{y-5}{4y}$

11. $\frac{x-2}{x-3} = 0$

12. $\frac{2x-7}{x+3} = 0$

13. $\frac{3x+4}{(2x-3)^2} = 0$

14. $\frac{5x-12}{(5x+2)^2} = 0$

15. $\frac{x}{x-2} + 3 = \frac{2}{x-2}$

16. $\frac{x}{x+3} = 5 - \frac{3}{x+3}$

17. $\frac{3}{y-2} = \frac{2}{y-3}$

18. $\frac{2}{y+1} = \frac{5}{y+2}$

19. $\frac{z}{2z-3} = \frac{z}{2z+1}$

20. $\frac{2r}{2r+1} = \frac{r}{r+3}$

21. $\frac{2}{p-1} + \frac{1}{2} = \frac{p+3}{p-1}$

22. $\frac{3}{t+1} - \frac{1}{3} = \frac{2t+7}{t+1}$

23. $\frac{2}{x-2} + \frac{5}{2x-4} = \frac{3}{4}$

24. $\frac{1}{m+3} + \frac{7}{3m+9} = \frac{5}{6}$

25. $\frac{w+1}{2w+3} - \frac{1}{2} = \frac{3w+4}{2w+3}$

26. $\frac{2w-1}{3w+4} = \frac{5w+3}{3w+4} - \frac{5}{2}$

27. $\frac{x^2-4}{(4x-1)(x-3)} = 0$

28. $\frac{x^2-25}{(x+3)(2x-5)} = 0$

29. $\frac{16x^2-81}{(x-1)(x+5)(x-2)} = 0$

30. $\frac{9x^2-25}{(x-7)(x+2)(3x-1)} = 0$

31. $\frac{z}{z^2+3z} = 0$

32. $\frac{2t}{t^7+4t^6-t^5} = 0$

33. $\frac{y+2}{y^2-4} = 0$

34. $\frac{y-8}{y^2-64} = 0$

35. $\frac{5}{m-2} + \frac{3}{m+2} = \frac{12}{m^2-4}$

36. $\frac{3}{t+4} + \frac{2}{t-4} = \frac{11}{t^2-16}$

37. $\frac{x^2+3}{x^2} = \frac{x-2}{x}$

38. $\frac{2x^2+1}{2x^2} = \frac{x-1}{x}$

39. $\frac{6}{x} - \frac{7}{x-1} = \frac{3}{x^2-x}$

40. $\frac{5}{y} - \frac{3}{y+1} = \frac{21}{y^2+y}$

41. $\frac{y^2+4y-21}{y^2-49} = 0$

42. $\frac{z^2-z-6}{z^2-4} = 0$

43. $\frac{6r^2+5r-25}{4r^2-25} = 0$

44. $\frac{4s^2+8s+3}{4s^2-9} = 0$

45. $\frac{4}{t+2} + \frac{3}{t+3} = \frac{4}{t^2+5t+6}$

46. $\frac{3}{v-1} + \frac{2}{v+3} = \frac{2}{v^2+2v-3}$

47. $\frac{5}{y-3} - \frac{3}{y+2} = \frac{25}{y^2-y-6}$

48. $\frac{3}{z+2} + \frac{4}{z-1} = \frac{12}{z^2+z-2}$

49. $\dfrac{3}{2x - 4} - \dfrac{2}{3x - 6} + \dfrac{1}{4x - 8} = \dfrac{13}{3}$

50. $\dfrac{1}{2x + 6} - \dfrac{3}{x + 3} + \dfrac{5}{3x + 9} = \dfrac{5}{6}$

51. $\dfrac{z + 2}{z - 1} - \dfrac{z - 2}{z + 1} = \dfrac{z - 10}{z^2 - 1}$

52. $\dfrac{z + 1}{z - 2} - \dfrac{z + 3}{z + 2} = \dfrac{2z - 6}{z^2 - 4}$

53. $\dfrac{6}{y} - \dfrac{7}{y + 1} = \dfrac{5 - y}{y^2 - 1}$

54. $\dfrac{4}{y} - \dfrac{3}{y - 2} = \dfrac{y - 4}{y^2 - 4}$

*55. $\dfrac{1}{t^2 + 2t - 3} - \dfrac{2}{t^2 + 5t + 6} = \dfrac{3}{t^2 + t - 2}$

*56. $\dfrac{2}{t^2 - t - 2} - \dfrac{4}{t^2 + t - 6} = \dfrac{5}{t^2 + 4t + 3}$

*57. $\dfrac{1}{x^2 - x} + \dfrac{1}{x^2 - 2x + 1} - \dfrac{2}{x^2 + x} = 0$

*58. $\dfrac{1}{x^2 + 2x} + \dfrac{2}{x^2 + 4x + 4} - \dfrac{3}{x^2 - 2x} = 0$

*59. $\dfrac{(x + 3)^2 - (x - 2)2(x + 3)}{(x + 3)^4} = 0$

*60. $\dfrac{(r - 1)^2 - (r + 1)2(r - 1)}{(r - 1)^4} = 0$

*61. $\dfrac{(z + 1)^2 2z - z^2(2)(z + 1)}{(z + 1)^4} = 0$

*62. $\dfrac{(2y - 3)^2 2y - y^2(2)(2y - 3)2}{(2y - 3)^4} = 0$

63. Suppose that Cal's total flight time from Mt. Morris to Hazelwood and back is 3 hours and 7.5 minutes. The one-way distance between the two cities is 450 miles. Cal's jet flies 300 miles per hour in still air, but there is a steady wind blowing in the direction from Hazelwood to Mt. Morris during both trips. Find the speed of the wind.

64. It takes the tugboat *Ole River* 1 hour 4 minutes to travel 10 miles upriver and 10 miles back. If *Ole River*'s speed in still water is 20 miles per hour, what is the speed of the current of the river?

65. Grandma was gone from her home in Quitman for 2 hours on a grocery shopping trip to Ruston, 15 miles away. She bought ice cream and was afraid it would melt before she returned, so she drove 5 miles per hour faster returning to Quitman than she did going to Ruston. If she spent 1 hour 22 minutes shopping, how fast did she drive on her way to Ruston?

66. An empty pulpwood truck can drive 10 miles per hour less than twice as fast as it can when it is loaded with hardwood pulpwood. If it takes 26 minutes to unload the pulpwood truck at the paper mill, which is 20 miles away from the woods, and the round trip to the mill and back takes $1\frac{1}{2}$ hours, how fast can the pulpwood truck travel when it is empty and when it is loaded?

1. Multiplying both sides of

$$\frac{y^2 - y - 6}{y^2 - 4} = 0$$

by $y^2 - 4$ yields

$$(y^2 - 4)\left(\frac{y^2 - y - 6}{y^2 - 4}\right) = (y^2 - 4) \cdot 0$$

$$y^2 - y - 6 = 0$$

$$(y - 3)(y + 2) = 0$$

$$y = 3 \quad \text{or} \quad y = -2.$$

Check: $y = 3$

$$\text{LHS} = \frac{3^2 - 3 - 6}{3^2 - 4} = \frac{9 - 3 - 6}{9 - 4} = \frac{0}{5} = 0 = \text{RHS}$$

Thus $y = 3$ is a solution since LHS = RHS, when $y = 3$.

Check: $y = -2$

$$\text{LHS} = \frac{(-2)^2 + 2 - 6}{(-2)^2 - 4} = \frac{4 + 2 - 6}{4 - 4} = \frac{0}{0}$$

Since the LHS is undefined when $y = -2$, then $y = -2$ is not a solution. The solution set is $\{3\}$.

8-5
Complex Fractions

A **complex fraction** is a fraction that has fractions in its numerator or its denominator (that is, a fraction that has fractions in it). A quotient of mixed numbers such as

$$\frac{1\frac{5}{6}}{7\frac{1}{3}}$$

is a relatively simple type of complex fraction. Some more complicated examples of complex fractions are

$$\frac{x + \dfrac{1}{x}}{x + \dfrac{2}{3}}, \qquad \frac{1 - \dfrac{2}{x + 3}}{x - 2 + \dfrac{4}{x + 2}}, \qquad \frac{x}{1 + \dfrac{2}{3 + \dfrac{4}{x}}}.$$

In contrast to a complex fraction, a fraction that is a quotient of polynomials with integral coefficients is called a **simple fraction.**‡ In other words, a simple fraction is the same thing as a rational expression.

‡Sometimes called a *single fraction.*

Any complex fraction can be expressed as a simple fraction by using either of two methods. In the first method, the indicated operations internal to the numerator and denominator are performed first, and followed by the division. As an illustration,

$$\frac{1\frac{5}{6}}{7\frac{1}{3}} = \frac{1 + \frac{5}{6}}{7 + \frac{1}{3}} = \frac{\frac{(1)(6) + 5}{6}}{\frac{(7)(3) + 1}{3}}$$

$$= \frac{\frac{11}{6}}{\frac{22}{3}} = \frac{\overset{1}{\cancel{11}}}{\underset{2}{\cancel{6}}} \cdot \frac{\overset{1}{\cancel{3}}}{\underset{2}{\cancel{22}}} = \frac{1}{4}.$$

In the second method, the Fundamental Principle of Fractions is used to multiply the numerator and denominator of the complex fraction by the LCD of all the fractions that appear internally in the complex fraction. Using this method, we would write

$$\frac{1\frac{5}{6}}{7\frac{1}{3}} = \frac{6\left(1 + \frac{5}{6}\right)}{6\left(7 + \frac{1}{3}\right)} = \frac{6(1) + 6\left(\frac{5}{6}\right)}{6(7) + 6\left(\frac{1}{3}\right)}$$

$$= \frac{6 + 5}{42 + 2} = \frac{11}{44} = \frac{1}{4}.$$

Other illustrations of both methods are given in the following examples. In a particular problem, one method may be easier to use than the other, but neither of them is always best. Both are always effective.

EXAMPLE 1 Express as a simple fraction in lowest terms:

$$\frac{x - \frac{9}{4x}}{x + \frac{3}{2}}.$$

SOLUTION   *Method 1* We first perform the internal operations, then invert the denominator of the complex fraction and multiply. As the last step, the result is reduced to lowest terms.

$$\frac{x - \dfrac{9}{4x}}{x + \dfrac{3}{2}} = \frac{\dfrac{x(4x) - 9}{4x}}{\dfrac{x(2) + 3}{2}}$$

$$= \frac{\dfrac{4x^2 - 9}{4x}}{\dfrac{2x + 3}{2}}$$

$$= \frac{4x^2 - 9}{4x} \cdot \frac{2}{2x + 3}$$

$$= \frac{(2x - 3)(2x + 3)}{4x} \cdot \frac{2}{2x + 3}$$

$$= \frac{2x - 3}{2x}$$

Method 2   With this method, we multiply numerator and denominator by the LCD of all the internal fractions, and then reduce to lowest terms. The LCD of $4x$ and 2 is $4x$.

$$\frac{x - \dfrac{9}{4x}}{x + \dfrac{3}{2}} = \frac{4x\left(x - \dfrac{9}{4x}\right)}{4x\left(x + \dfrac{3}{2}\right)}$$

$$= \frac{4x(x) - 4x\left(\dfrac{9}{4x}\right)}{4x(x) + 4x\left(\dfrac{3}{2}\right)}$$

$$= \frac{4x^2 - 9}{4x^2 + 6x}$$

$$= \frac{(2x - 3)(2x + 3)}{2x(2x + 3)}$$

$$= \frac{2x - 3}{2x}$$

This agrees with the result obtained by method 1.

EXAMPLE 2   Express as a simple fraction in lowest terms:

$$\frac{\dfrac{x}{y} + 2 + \dfrac{y}{x}}{\dfrac{x}{y} - \dfrac{y}{x}}.$$

Method 1

$$\frac{\dfrac{x}{y} + 2 + \dfrac{y}{x}}{\dfrac{x}{y} - \dfrac{y}{x}} = \frac{\dfrac{x^2 + 2xy + y^2}{xy}}{\dfrac{x^2 - y^2}{xy}}$$

$$= \frac{x^2 + 2xy + y^2}{xy} \cdot \frac{xy}{x^2 - y^2}$$

$$= \frac{(x + y)^2}{xy} \cdot \frac{xy}{(x - y)(x + y)}$$

$$= \frac{x + y}{x - y}.$$

Method 2   The denominators of the internal fractions are x and y, and the LCD is xy.

$$\frac{\dfrac{x}{y} + 2 + \dfrac{y}{x}}{\dfrac{x}{y} - \dfrac{y}{x}} = \frac{xy\left(\dfrac{x}{y} + 2 + \dfrac{y}{x}\right)}{xy\left(\dfrac{x}{y} - \dfrac{y}{x}\right)}$$

$$= \frac{x^2 + 2xy + y^2}{x^2 - y^2}$$

$$= \frac{(x + y)^2}{(x - y)(x + y)}$$

$$= \frac{x + y}{x - y}.$$

In working with complex fractions, it is common to use the instruction "simplify" as meaning "express as a simple fraction in lowest terms."

EXAMPLE 3   Simplify:

$$\frac{a + 2 - \dfrac{1}{a + 2}}{a + \dfrac{1}{a + 2}}.$$

SOLUTION   The method of multiplying numerator and denominator by the LCD is more efficient here. The LCD is $a + 2$, and

$$\frac{(a+2) - \dfrac{1}{a+2}}{a + \dfrac{1}{a+2}} = \frac{(a+2)\left(a+2 - \dfrac{1}{a+2}\right)}{(a+2)\left(a + \dfrac{1}{a+2}\right)}$$

$$= \frac{(a+2)(a+2) - (a+2)\dfrac{1}{a+2}}{(a+2)(a) + (a+2)\dfrac{1}{a+2}}$$

$$= \frac{a^2 + 4a + 4 - 1}{a^2 + 2a + 1}$$

$$= \frac{a^2 + 4a + 3}{a^2 + 2a + 1}$$

$$= \frac{(a+3)(a+1)}{(a+1)^2}$$

$$= \frac{a+3}{a+1}.$$

PRACTICE PROBLEM 1   (Solution on page 230) Simplify:

$$\frac{x}{x + \dfrac{x}{1 + \dfrac{1}{x-1}}}$$

EXERCISES 8-5

Express each of the following as a simple fraction in lowest terms.

1. $\dfrac{\dfrac{1}{2}}{\dfrac{3}{4}}$

2. $\dfrac{\dfrac{5}{6}}{\dfrac{7}{8}}$

3. $\dfrac{\dfrac{1}{2} - \dfrac{1}{3}}{\dfrac{1}{4} - \dfrac{1}{6}}$

4. $\dfrac{\dfrac{1}{3} - \dfrac{1}{5}}{\dfrac{1}{5} - \dfrac{1}{9}}$

5. $\dfrac{2 - \dfrac{2}{5}}{1 + \dfrac{13}{15}}$

6. $\dfrac{3 - \dfrac{5}{6}}{2 + \dfrac{3}{5}}$

7. $\dfrac{2\dfrac{3}{8}}{3\dfrac{1}{6}}$

8. $\dfrac{2\dfrac{5}{8}}{2\dfrac{4}{5}}$

9. $\dfrac{\dfrac{5}{x}}{\dfrac{8}{3x}}$

10. $\dfrac{\dfrac{3}{2x}}{\dfrac{7}{6x}}$

11. $\dfrac{\dfrac{3}{x^2}}{\dfrac{6y}{x}}$

12. $\dfrac{\dfrac{2x}{3y}}{\dfrac{4}{5xy}}$

13. $\dfrac{2 - \dfrac{1}{x}}{2 + \dfrac{1}{x}}$

14. $\dfrac{1}{2 - \dfrac{1}{x}}$

15. $\dfrac{\dfrac{1+a}{a}}{\dfrac{1-a}{a}}$

16. $\dfrac{1 + \dfrac{1}{x}}{1 - \dfrac{1}{x}}$

17. $\dfrac{\dfrac{1}{x} + \dfrac{1}{y}}{\dfrac{1}{x} - \dfrac{1}{y}}$

18. $\dfrac{\dfrac{1}{x^2} - \dfrac{1}{y^2}}{\dfrac{1}{x} - \dfrac{1}{y}}$

19. $\dfrac{\dfrac{1}{a} - \dfrac{1}{b}}{a - b}$

20. $\dfrac{\left(\dfrac{x}{y} + \dfrac{y}{x}\right) - 1}{\left(\dfrac{x}{y} + \dfrac{y}{x}\right) + 1}$

21. $\dfrac{\dfrac{x - y}{3x}}{\dfrac{x^2 - y^2}{6x}}$

22. $\dfrac{\dfrac{w - 2}{6w}}{\dfrac{w^2 + w - 6}{8w^2}}$

23. $\dfrac{\dfrac{z}{2} - \dfrac{2}{z}}{\dfrac{z - 2}{z}}$

24. $\dfrac{\dfrac{t}{3} - \dfrac{3}{t}}{2 + \dfrac{t + 9}{t}}$

25. $\dfrac{1 - \dfrac{2}{x}}{x - \dfrac{4}{x}}$

26. $\dfrac{\dfrac{x^2}{x - 1} - x}{\dfrac{1}{x - 1} + 1}$

27. $\dfrac{\dfrac{1}{x} + \dfrac{1}{x + 2}}{\dfrac{1}{x} - \dfrac{1}{x + 2}}$

28. $\dfrac{z - \dfrac{4}{z + 3}}{z + \dfrac{z}{z + 3}}$

29. $\dfrac{x + 1 - \dfrac{6}{x + 2}}{x + 3 - \dfrac{2}{x + 2}}$

30. $\dfrac{\dfrac{y + 2}{y - 2} + \dfrac{y - 2}{y + 2}}{\dfrac{y + 2}{y - 2} - \dfrac{y - 2}{y + 2}}$

31. $z - \dfrac{z}{3 + \dfrac{1}{z}}$

32. $3 + \dfrac{2}{1 + \dfrac{4z}{z - 1}}$

33. $1 - \dfrac{1}{1 - \dfrac{1}{1 + x}}$

34. $1 - \dfrac{1}{1 - \dfrac{1}{x}}$

*35. $\dfrac{y + \dfrac{1}{y - \dfrac{x}{y}}}{y - \dfrac{1}{y - \dfrac{x}{y}}}$

*36. $1 + \dfrac{1}{1 + \dfrac{1}{1 + \dfrac{1}{x - 1}}}$

SOLUTION FOR PRACTICE PROBLEM

*1. It is easier to use the method of performing the internal operations, proceeding one step at a time from the last division bar. (This corresponds to removing the innermost symbol of grouping first.)

$$\cfrac{x}{x + \cfrac{x}{1 + \cfrac{1}{x-1}}} = \cfrac{x}{x + \cfrac{x}{\cfrac{1(x-1)+1}{x-1}}}$$

$$= \cfrac{x}{x + \cfrac{x}{\cfrac{x}{x-1}}}$$

$$= \cfrac{x}{x + \cfrac{x}{1} \cdot \cfrac{x-1}{x}}$$

$$= \frac{x}{x + x - 1}$$

$$= \frac{x}{2x - 1}$$

PRACTICE TEST for Chapter 8

1. Reduce each of the following to lowest terms.

   (a) $\dfrac{x^2 - 3x - 10}{x^2 - 25}$

   (b) $\dfrac{2x^2 + 7x + 3}{14x^2 + x - 3}$

2. Supply the missing numerator so as to make a true equality of rational expressions.

   (a) $\dfrac{3y}{2z} = \dfrac{?}{12y^2z^2}$

   (b) $\dfrac{t + 2}{t - 5} = \dfrac{?}{t^2 - 3t - 10}$

Perform the indicated operations, and leave the result in lowest terms.

3. (a) $\dfrac{2x^6y}{21y^2z} \div \dfrac{4x^3}{7y^3}$

   (b) $\dfrac{3ab^2}{8c^3} \cdot \dfrac{12bc^2}{5c} \div \dfrac{3a^2b^3}{4c^2}$

4. (a) $\dfrac{9m^2 - 1}{m^2 - 4} \cdot \dfrac{m^2 + 2m}{3m + 1}$

   (b) $\dfrac{6t^2 - 5t - 4}{2t^2 + 5t + 2} \div \dfrac{9t^2 - 16}{6t + 8}$

5. Find the LCM.

   (a) $p^2 - 9,\ 2p + 6$

   (b) $q^2 - 6q + 9,\ 3q^2 - 12q + 9$

6. Perform the indicated operations, and write the result as a rational expression in lowest terms.

   (a) $\dfrac{1}{4z^2 - 1} - \dfrac{2z}{4z^2 - 1}$

   (b) $\dfrac{2}{r^2 - 1} - \dfrac{7}{r^2 - 5r - 6}$

Find the solution set for each of the following equations.

7. $\dfrac{2}{x - 1} = 3 + \dfrac{x}{x - 1}$

8. $\dfrac{3}{x - 2} - \dfrac{2}{x + 1} = \dfrac{6}{x^2 - x - 2}$

Express each of the following as a simple fraction in lowest terms.

9. $\dfrac{1 + \dfrac{2}{t}}{1 - \dfrac{4}{t^2}}$

10. $\dfrac{p + \dfrac{12}{p - 7}}{p + \dfrac{3p}{p - 7}}$

Exponents, Radicals, and Complex Numbers

9-1
Integral Exponents

In Theorem 6-3 of Section 6-1, the Laws of Exponents were presented in this form: If m, n are nonnegative integers (whole numbers), and x, y are real numbers such that x^m, x^n and y^n are defined, then

(a) $x^m \cdot x^n = x^{m+n}$

(b) $(x^m)^n = x^{mn}$

(c) $\dfrac{x^m}{x^n} = \begin{cases} x^{m-n} & \text{if } x \neq 0 \text{ and } m \geq n \\ \dfrac{1}{x^{n-m}} & \text{if } x \neq 0 \text{ and } n > m \end{cases}$

(d) $(xy)^n = x^n y^n$

(e) $\left(\dfrac{x}{y}\right)^n = \dfrac{x^n}{y^n}$ if $y \neq 0$

In order that these laws hold for the exponent 0 as well as for positive integral exponents, the zero power was defined in Definition 6-2 by

$$x^0 = 1 \quad \text{if } x \neq 0;$$
$$0^0 \text{ is undefined.}$$

Our first goal in this section is to define exponentials with negative integral exponents, and to do this in a way so that all of the laws listed above hold for all integral exponents (positive, zero, or negative), whenever the quantities involved are defined.

To begin our development of negative exponents, let us consider a particular example, say 3^{-1}. If the law

$$3^m \cdot 3^n = 3^{m+n}$$

is to hold, then it must be true that

$$3^1 \cdot 3^{-1} = 3^{1+(-1)} = 3^0.$$

But $3^0 = 1$, so we must have

$$3 \cdot 3^{-1} = 1,$$

and therefore

$$3^{-1} = \frac{1}{3}.$$

Pursuing this same sort of reasoning, the requirement $3^m \cdot 3^n = 3^{m+n}$ leads to

$$3^{-2} = 3^{(-1)+(-1)}$$
$$= 3^{-1} \cdot 3^{-1}$$
$$= \frac{1}{3} \cdot \frac{1}{3}$$
$$= \frac{1}{3^2},$$

and similarly to

$$3^{-3} = \frac{1}{3^3}, \quad 3^{-4} = \frac{1}{3^4}, \quad 3^{-5} = \frac{1}{3^5}, \quad \text{and so on.}$$

This leads us to make the following definition.

Definition 9-1 If n is an integer, then

$$x^{-n} = \frac{1}{x^n} \quad \text{for } x \neq 0.$$

This defines x^{-n} as the reciprocal of x^n:

$$x^{-n} = \frac{1}{x^n} = (x^n)^{-1}.$$

It follows from this definition that

$$\frac{1}{3^{-4}} = \frac{1}{\frac{1}{3^4}} = 3^4,$$

and generally that for any integer n,

$$\frac{1}{x^{-n}} = x^n \qquad \text{for } x \neq 0.$$

It amounts to this: Each of x^{-n} and x^n is the reciprocal of the other.

EXAMPLE 1   Find the value of each of the following.

  (a) 2^{-4} (b) -2^{-4}

  (c) $(-2)^{-4}$ (d) $\left(-\dfrac{5}{2}\right)^{-3}$

SOLUTION

  (a) $2^{-4} = \dfrac{1}{2^4} = \dfrac{1}{16}$

  (b) $-2^{-4} = -\dfrac{1}{2^4} = -\dfrac{1}{16}$

  (c) $(-2)^{-4} = \dfrac{1}{(-2)^4} = \dfrac{1}{16}$

  (d) $\left(-\dfrac{5}{2}\right)^{-3} = \dfrac{1}{\left(-\dfrac{5}{2}\right)^3} = \dfrac{1}{-\dfrac{125}{8}} = -\dfrac{8}{125}$

Although all our emphasis has been placed on part (a) of Theorem 6-3, the other parts are also valid for all integers m and n. This is stated in the next theorem.

Theorem 9-2 (**Laws of Exponents**) If m, n are integers and x, y are real numbers such that x^m, x^n and y^n are defined, then

(a) $x^m \cdot x^n = x^{m+n}$ **(product rule)**

(b) $(x^m)^n = x^{mn}$ **(power rule)**

(c) $\dfrac{x^m}{x^n} = = x^{m-n}$ for $x \neq 0$ **(quotient rule)**

(d) $(xy)^n = x^n y^n$

(e) $\left(\dfrac{x}{y}\right)^n = \dfrac{x^n}{y^n}$ for $y \neq 0$

With negative integral exponents defined, there is no need for different cases in the quotient rule.

For the remainder of this section, we work extensively with rational expressions. To avoid continually placing restrictions on the variables, *we shall assume that all denominators are nonzero.*

Various uses of the Laws of Exponents are made in the following examples.

EXAMPLE 2   Use the product rule [Theorem 9-2(a)] to compute the value if possible; otherwise, express as a rational expression in lowest terms.

(a) $3^{-6} \cdot 3^2$ (b) $(-4)^{-1}(-4)^{-2}$

(c) $(-r)^3(-r)^{-5}$ (d) $(x - y)^{-4}(x - y)^6$

SOLUTION   (a) $3^{-6} \cdot 3^2 = 3^{-6+2} = 3^{-4} = \dfrac{1}{3^4} = \dfrac{1}{81}$

(b) $(-4)^{-1}(-4)^{-2} = (-4)^{-3} = \dfrac{1}{(-4)^3} = -\dfrac{1}{64}$

(c) $(-r)^3(-r)^{-5} = (-r)^{-2} = \dfrac{1}{(-r)^2} = \dfrac{1}{r^2}$

(d) $(x - y)^{-4}(x - y)^6 = (x - y)^2$

EXAMPLE 3   Evaluate if possible; otherwise, express as a rational expression in lowest terms. [See the power rule in Theorem 9-2(b).]

(a) $(5^{-2})^{-1}$ (b) $(3^{-2})^0$

(c) $-(2^{-3})^2$ (d) $(x^{-2})^{-3}$

SOLUTION   (a) $(5^{-2})^{-1} = 5^{(-2)(-1)} = 5^2 = 25$

(b) $(3^{-2})^0 = 3^{(-2)(0)} = 3^0 = 1$

(c) $-(2^{-3})^2 = -2^{-6} = -\dfrac{1}{2^6} = -\dfrac{1}{64}$

(d) $(x^{-2})^{-3} = x^6$

EXAMPLE 4 Use the quotient rule [Theorem 9-2(c)] to evaluate or express as a rational expression in lowest terms.

(a) $\dfrac{4^{-5}}{4^{-2}}$

(b) $\dfrac{x^{-3}}{x^{-6}}$

(c) $\dfrac{y^{-9}}{y^{-3}}$

(d) $\dfrac{(5-t)^{-6}}{(5-t)^2}$

SOLUTION

(a) $\dfrac{4^{-5}}{4^{-2}} = 4^{-5-(-2)} = 4^{-5+2} = 4^{-3} = \dfrac{1}{4^3} = \dfrac{1}{64}$

(b) $\dfrac{x^{-3}}{x^{-6}} = x^{-3+6} = x^3$

(c) $\dfrac{y^{-9}}{y^{-3}} = y^{-9+3} = y^{-6} = \dfrac{1}{y^6}$

(d) $\dfrac{(5-t)^{-6}}{(5-t)^2} = (5-t)^{-6-2} = (5-t)^{-8} = \dfrac{1}{(5-t)^8}$

PRACTICE PROBLEM 1 (Solution on page 239) Compute the value if possible; otherwise, use the Laws of Exponents to simplify the given expression to a rational expression in lowest terms.

(a) -3^{-4}

(b) $(-2)^{-3}(-2)^{-2}$

(c) $-(2^3)^{-2}$

(d) $\dfrac{(x-1)^{-4}}{(x-1)^{-2}}$

EXAMPLE 5 Use the Laws of Exponents to express each of the following as a rational expression in lowest terms.

(a) $(-3u)^{-4}$

(b) $-(2uv^{-2})^{-4}$

(c) $\left(\dfrac{r^2}{s}\right)^{-3}$

(d) $\left(\dfrac{2x^{-1}}{3y^2}\right)^{-2}$

SOLUTION

(a) $(-3u)^{-4} = \dfrac{1}{(-3u)^4} = \dfrac{1}{(-3)^4 u^4} = \dfrac{1}{81u^4}$

(b) $-(2uv^{-2})^{-4} = -2^{-4}u^{-4}(v^{-2})^{-4} = -\dfrac{1}{2^4} \cdot \dfrac{1}{u^4} \cdot v^8 = -\dfrac{v^8}{16u^4}$

(c) $\left(\dfrac{r^2}{s}\right)^{-3} = \dfrac{(r^2)^{-3}}{s^{-3}} = \dfrac{r^{-6}}{s^{-3}} = \dfrac{s^3}{r^6}$

(d) $\left(\dfrac{2x^{-1}}{3y^2}\right)^{-2} = \dfrac{2^{-2}x^2}{3^{-2}y^{-4}} = \dfrac{3^2 x^2 y^4}{2^2} = \dfrac{9x^2y^4}{4}$

EXAMPLE 6 Express each of the following as a rational expression in lowest terms.

(a) $\dfrac{5a^{-2}b^3c^{-1}}{4a^3b^{-4}c^{-3}}$

(b) $\left(\dfrac{p^{-2}q^{-3}}{p^3q^{-2}}\right)^{-1} \cdot \left(\dfrac{p^4q^0}{p^{-1}q^{-4}}\right)^{-2}$

SOLUTION (a) $\dfrac{5a^{-2}b^3c^{-1}}{4a^3b^{-4}c^{-3}} = \dfrac{5}{4} \cdot \dfrac{a^{-2}}{a^3} \cdot \dfrac{b^3}{b^{-4}} \cdot \dfrac{c^{-1}}{c^{-3}}$

$$= \dfrac{5}{4} \cdot \dfrac{1}{a^5} \cdot \dfrac{b^7}{1} \cdot \dfrac{c^2}{1}$$

$$= \dfrac{5b^7c^2}{4a^5}$$

(b) $\left(\dfrac{p^{-2}q^{-3}}{p^3q^{-2}}\right)^{-1} \cdot \left(\dfrac{p^4q^0}{p^{-1}q^{-4}}\right)^{-2} = \dfrac{p^2q^3}{p^{-3}q^2} \cdot \dfrac{p^{-8}(1)}{p^2q^8}$

$$= \dfrac{p^{-6}q^3}{p^{-1}q^{10}}$$

$$= \dfrac{1}{p^5q^7}$$

There is usually no one correct way to work a problem involving exponents. Most can be worked by more than one sequence of steps, depending on the order in which the Laws of Exponents are used.

PRACTICE PROBLEM 2 (Solution on page 239) Express each of the following as a rational expression in lowest terms.

(a) $[(r^{-2}s^2)^{-3}]^{-2}$

(b) $\dfrac{x^{-2} - y^{-2}}{x^{-1} + y^{-1}}$

EXERCISES 9-1

Find the value of each of the following.

(See Examples 1 and 2.)

1. -3^{-2}

2. -2^{-4}

3. $(-3)^{-2}$

4. $(-5)^{-2}$

5. $\left(\dfrac{2}{5}\right)^{-3}$

6. $\left(\dfrac{3}{2}\right)^{-4}$

7. $\dfrac{1}{4^{-3}}$

8. $\dfrac{1}{5^{-2}}$

9. $4^{-5} \cdot 4^3$

10. $2^{-6} \cdot 2^3$

11. $10^8 \cdot 10^{-8}$

12. $9^{-7} \cdot 9^7$

(See Examples 3 and 4.)

13. $(2^{-3})^2$

14. $(2^3)^{-2}$

15. $(2^{-3})^{-2}$

16. $(10^{-3})^{-2}$ 17. $(2^{-3})^0$ 18. $(5^0)^{-3}$

19. $\dfrac{2^3}{2^{-2}}$ 20. $\dfrac{3^2}{3^{-1}}$ 21. $\dfrac{5^{-3}}{5^{-3}}$

22. $\dfrac{7^{-9}}{7^{-9}}$ 23. $\dfrac{4^{-3}}{4^0}$ 24. $\dfrac{5^0}{5^{-3}}$

Use the Laws of Exponents to simplify the given expression to a rational expression in lowest terms. Assume that all variables are nonzero.

(See Examples 2–4 and Practice Problem 1.)

25. $x^{-6} \cdot x^2$ 26. $y^{-2} \cdot y$ 27. $x^{-2} \cdot x^{-3}$

28. $y^{-1} \cdot y^{-1}$ 29. $(t^{-2})^2$ 30. $(z^3)^{-2}$

31. $-(x^{-2})^{-4}$ 32. $(x^2)^{-3}$ 33. $(x^{-3})^0$

34. $(x^0)^0$ 35. $\dfrac{x^{-2}}{x^{-4}}$ 36. $\dfrac{y^{-3}}{y^{-6}}$

37. $(2a)^{-5}$ 38. $(4t)^{-3}$ 39. $(-5t)^{-2}$

40. $(-3z)^{-4}$ 41. $-5t^{-2}$ 42. $-3z^{-4}$

43. $(2x)^{-3}(2x)^{-2}$ 44. $(3t)^{-2}(3t)^{-1}$ 45. $(-2a)^5(-2a)^{-3}$

46. $(-3a)^2(-3a)^{-4}$ 47. $\left(\dfrac{r}{s}\right)^{-3}$ 48. $\left(\dfrac{2r}{3s}\right)^{-2}$

(See Examples 5 and 6 and Practice Problem 2.)

49. x^2y^{-5} 50. $x^{-3}y^4$

51. $2^{-3}z^{-1}t^3$ 52. $3^{-2}z^2t^{-3}$

53. $\dfrac{(2x^{-2})(6x^4)}{4x^{-8}}$ 54. $\dfrac{(4m^{-3})(9m^2)}{6m^{-7}}$

55. $\dfrac{(ab^{-3})(ab)^{-3}}{a^{-3}b^{-3}}$ 56. $\dfrac{(yz^{-2})(yz^{-2})^3}{y^{-2}z^{-3}}$

57. $\dfrac{-3x^{-2}}{(-3y)^{-2}}$ 58. $\dfrac{-2z^{-4}}{(-2w)^{-4}}$

59. $\dfrac{4^{-2}r^{-3}}{5^{-2}r^{-6}}$ 60. $\dfrac{3^{-2}u^{-4}}{4^{-3}u^{-8}}$

61. $\dfrac{2^{-3}x^{-2}w^{-2}}{3^{-2}x^{-2}w^{-3}}$ 62. $\dfrac{5^{-2}x^{-6}n^{-3}}{4^{-3}x^{-2}n^{-3}}$

63. $[(x^{-1}y^{-2})^3]^{-2}$ 64. $[(x^2y^{-3})^{-2}]^{-1}$

65. $\left(\dfrac{5r^{-3}s^{-2}}{6r^{-4}s^{-5}}\right)^0$ 66. $\left(\dfrac{3a^{-5}b^{-6}}{4a^{-2}b^{-3}}\right)^0$

67. $(3mn^{-2})^{-2}(3m^{-2}n^{-3})^2$ 68. $(2m^{-3}n^{-1})^{-2}(4m^2n^{-2})^{-1}$

69. $\dfrac{4^{-1}x^{-2}y^3}{(2xy)^{-3}}$ 70. $\dfrac{-3^{-2}x^{-1}y^{-2}}{(2x^{-2}y^{-1})^{-3}}$

71. $\dfrac{4^{-2}p^{-3}q^0}{(2pq)^{-5}}$ 72. $\dfrac{9^{-1}u^{-4}v^{-8}}{(3u^2v^{-1})^{-3}}$

73. $\left(\frac{3p^2q^{-1}}{(2pq)^{-3}}\right)^{-1}$

74. $\left(\frac{-2p^{-3}q^0}{(-2pq)^{-2}}\right)^{-1}$

75. $\left(\frac{3x^{-2}y^2}{2x^{-6}y^{-4}}\right)^{-2}$

76. $\left(\frac{4xy^{-3}}{8^{-2}x^{-3}y^{-1}}\right)^{-2}$

77. $\left(\frac{x^{-2}y^3}{z^{-3}}\right)^{-1} \cdot \left(\frac{x^0}{y^{-1}z^{-2}}\right)^{-3}$

78. $\left(\frac{x^{-3}y^0}{z^2}\right)^{-2} \cdot \left(\frac{x^{-4}}{y^3z^{-1}}\right)^{-3}$

79. $\left(\frac{x^0y^2}{z^2}\right)^{-1} \cdot \left(\frac{x^2z^3}{y^{-1}}\right)^{-2}$

80. $\left(\frac{x^{-2}z}{w^3y}\right)^{-2} \cdot \left(\frac{xw^{-1}}{yz^{-2}}\right)^{-3}$

81. $\left(\frac{-x^{-1}}{2y^{-2}}\right)^{-2}(x^{-1}y^{-2})^{-3}$

82. $\left(\frac{-x^{-1}}{z^{-1}}\right)^{-2}(2xy^{-1}z^{-1})^{-3}$

83. $2^{-3} + 2^{-1}$

84. $3^{-2} + 3^{-1}$

85. $m^0 + m^{-1}$

86. $m^{-1} + m^{-2}$

87. $x^{-1} + y^{-1}$

88. $(x + y)^{-1}$

89. $xy^{-1} + \left(\frac{x^{-1}}{y^{-1}}\right)^{-1}$

90. $(xy)^{-1} + x^{-1}y^{-1}$

91. $\frac{x^{-1} + y^{-1}}{(xy)^{-1}}$

92. $\frac{x^{-1} + y^{-1}}{(x + y)^{-1}}$

93. $\left(\frac{(x-y)^{-1}}{x^{-2} - y^{-2}}\right)^{-1}$

94. $\left(\frac{x^{-1} - y^{-1}}{x^{-2} - y^{-2}}\right)^{-1}$

In problems 95–98, n denotes a positive integer.

*95. $x^{2n} \cdot x^{-3n}$

*96. $x^n \cdot x^{1-n}$

*97. $\left(\frac{x^{2n}}{x^{n-1}}\right)^{-1}$

*98. $\left(\frac{(xy)^n}{y^{2n}}\right)^{-2}$

Evaluate each of the following.

C99. $(-3.21)^{-2}$

C100. $(-0.571)^{-9}$

C101. $\frac{(-4.11)^{-5}}{(-24.9)^{-4}}$

C102. $\frac{(27.4)^0}{(3.45)^{-3}(1.21)^{-5}}$

C103. $[(1.13)^{-3}(2.67)^{-2}]^{-2}$

C104. $[(3.79)^{-5}(0.307)^{-3}]^{-2}$

SOLUTIONS FOR PRACTICE PROBLEMS

1. (a) $-3^{-4} = -\frac{1}{3^4} = -\frac{1}{81}$

   (b) $(-2)^{-3}(-2)^{-2} = (-2)^{-5} = \frac{1}{(-2)^5} = -\frac{1}{32}$

   (c) $-(2^3)^{-2} = -(-8)^{-2} = -\frac{1}{(-8)^2} = -\frac{1}{64}$

   (d) $\frac{(x-1)^{-4}}{(x-1)^{-2}} = = (x-1)^{-4+2} = (x-1)^{-2} = \frac{1}{(x-1)^2}$

2. (a) $[(r^{-2}s^2)^{-3}]^{-2} = (r^{-2}s^2)^6 = r^{-12}s^{12} = \frac{s^{12}}{r^{12}}$

(b) $\dfrac{x^{-2} - y^{-2}}{x^{-1} + y^{-1}} = \dfrac{\left(\dfrac{1}{x^2} - \dfrac{1}{y^2}\right)(x^2 y^2)}{\left(\dfrac{1}{x} + \dfrac{1}{y}\right)(x^2 y^2)} = \dfrac{y^2 - x^2}{xy^2 + x^2 y} = \dfrac{(y - x)(y + x)}{xy(y + x)}$

$$= \dfrac{y - x}{xy}$$

9-2
Scientific
Notation

In measurement of physical quantities, and in scientific work in general, it is not unusual to work with very large numbers or extremely small numbers. A blue whale (the largest animal) may weigh as much as 120,000,000 grams, while a fairy fly (the smallest insect) may weigh as little as 0.00000501 gram. Measurements of distances in astronomy yield enormous numbers, and measurements of ion concentrations in chemistry yield minute numbers. When working with numbers of this sort, it is convenient to write the numbers in a form called *scientific notation*.

In scientific notation, the weights above would be written as

$$120{,}000{,}000 = 1.2 \times 10^8$$

and

$$0.00000501 = 5.01 \times 10^{-6},$$

where each is expressed as the product of a power of 10 and a number between 1 and 10.

Any positive number N can be written in the form

$$N = a \times 10^m,$$

with $1 \leq a < 10$ and m an integer. The expression $a \times 10^m$ is called the **scientific notation** for N.

One nice feature of integral powers of 10 is that the exponent indicates the placing of the decimal, starting from 1.0.

$$10^1 = 10 \qquad 10^{-1} = 0.1$$
$$10^2 = 100 \qquad 10^{-2} = 0.01$$
$$10^3 = 1000 \qquad 10^{-3} = 0.001$$

Multiplication by an integral power of 10 can be accomplished by simply moving the decimal an appropriate number of places. In multiplying 3.142 by 10^5,

$$3.142 \times 10^5 = (3.142)(100{,}000)$$
$$= 314{,}200,$$

the decimal is moved five places to the right:

$$3.142 \times 10^5 = 314200.$$

5 places

Similarly, multiplication by 10^{-5} moves the decimal five places to the left:

$$3.142 \times 10^{-5} = (3.142)(0.00001)$$
$$= 0.00003142.$$

5 places

These observations illustrate the following rule.

**Changes from Scientific Notation
to Decimal Notation**

1. To change $a \times 10^m$, where $m > 0$, move the decimal m places to the right in a.

2. To change $a \times 10^{-m}$, where $-m < 0$, move the decimal m places to the left in a.

EXAMPLE 1 Change the following numbers from scientific notation to decimal notation.

(a) 7.315×10^6 (b) 1.627×10^2

(c) 4.1×10^{-4} (d) 6.0135×10^{-1}

SOLUTION

(a) $7.315 \times 10^6 = 7.315000 \times 10^6 = 7,315,000$

6 places

(b) $1.627 \times 10^2 = 1.627 \times 10^2 = 162.7$

2 places

(c) $4.1 \times 10^{-4} = 0004.1 \times 10^{-4} = 0.00041$

4 places

(d) $6.0135 \times 10^{-1} = 6.0135 \times 10^{-1} = 0.60135$

1 place

To change from decimal notation to scientific notation, we perform the following procedure.

> **Changes from Decimal Notation
> to Scientific Notation**
>
> 1. Move the decimal so that the resulting number has one nonzero digit to the left of the decimal.
>
> 2. The original number equals the product of this number times 10^m, where $|m|$ is the number of places the decimal was moved.
>
> 3. The exponent m is positive if the original number is greater than 10, and m is negative if the original number is less than 1.

EXAMPLE 2   Write the following numbers in scientific notation.

    (a) 3,180,000   (b) 428.53

    (c) 0.0003   (d) 0.617

SOLUTION   (a) $3,180,000 = 3.\underbrace{180000}_{6 \text{ places}} \times 10^6 = 3.18 \times 10^6$

    (b) $428.53 = 4.\underbrace{2853}_{2 \text{ places}} \times 10^2 = 4.2853 \times 10^2$

    (c) $0.0003 = \underbrace{00003}_{4 \text{ places}}. \times 10^{-4} = 3 \times 10^{-4}$

    (d) $0.617 = 0\underbrace{6}_{1 \text{ place}}.17 \times 10^{-1} = 6.17 \times 10^{-1}$

Scientific notation is frequently helpful in numerical calculations. This is illustrated in the next example.

EXAMPLE 3   Evaluate the following expressions and write the result both in scientific notation and in decimal form.

    (a) $\dfrac{3}{4 \times 10^5}$ (b) $\dfrac{0.00783 \times 175,000}{26,100,000 \times 0.000875}$

SOLUTION   (a) $\dfrac{3}{4 \times 10^5} = \dfrac{3}{4} \times \dfrac{1}{10^5} = 0.75 \times 10^{-5}$

                            $= 7.5 \times 10^{-1} \times 10^{-5}$

                            $= 7.5 \times 10^{-6}$ in scientific notation,

                            $= 0.0000075$ in decimal notation.

(b) $\dfrac{0.00783 \times 175,000}{26,100,000 \times 0.000875} = \dfrac{7.83 \times 10^{-3} \times 1.75 \times 10^5}{2.61 \times 10^7 \times 8.75 \times 10^{-4}}$

$$= \dfrac{\overset{3}{\cancel{7.83}} \times \overset{1}{\cancel{1.75}} \times 10^2}{\underset{1}{\cancel{2.61}} \times \underset{5}{\cancel{8.75}} \times 10^3}$$

$$= \dfrac{3}{5} \times 10^{-1}$$

$$= 0.6 \times 10^{-1}$$

$$= 6 \times 10^{-1} \times 10^{-1}$$

$$= 6 \times 10^{-2} \text{ in scientific notation,}$$

$$= 0.06 \text{ in decimal form.}$$

PRACTICE
PROBLEM 1
(Solution on page 244) Evaluate the following expression, and write the result both in scientific notation and in decimal form.

$$\frac{15,000 \times 0.16}{0.00064 \times 7500}$$

EXERCISES 9-2

Change the following numbers to decimal notation. (See Example 1.)

1. 4.3×10^2	2. 1.25×10^3	3. 6.81×10^4
4. 6.79×10^4	5. 7.92×10^6	6. 2.78×10^5
7. 8.58×10^{-1}	8. 9.17×10^{-1}	9. 5.33×10^{-3}
10. 2.54×10^{-2}	11. 6.14×10^{-4}	12. 5.74×10^{-5}

Express each of the following in scientific notation. (See Example 2.)

13. 538	14. 62	15. 5781
16. 64,430	17. 317,500,000	18. 13,455
19. 0.0042	20. 0.00061	21. 0.308
22. 0.0112	23. 0.00008	24. 0.000007

Use scientific notation to help evaluate the following numbers, and express each result both in scientific notation and in decimal form. (See Example 3 and Practice Problem 1.)

25. $\dfrac{1}{4 \times 10^2}$	26. $\dfrac{1}{5 \times 10^3}$
27. $\dfrac{3}{5 \times 10^3}$	28. $\dfrac{4}{5 \times 10^2}$
29. $\dfrac{3 \times 10^2}{4 \times 10^4}$	30. $\dfrac{9 \times 10^3}{2 \times 10^5}$

31. $\dfrac{3 \times 10^2}{6 \times 10^{-3}}$

32. $\dfrac{2.4 \times 10^3}{8 \times 10^{-2}}$

33. $\dfrac{(4.2 \times 10^{-3})(3 \times 10^2)}{2.1 \times 10^{-5}}$

34. $\dfrac{(9.3 \times 10^{-2})(4 \times 10^{-3})}{3.1 \times 10^{-6}}$

35. $\dfrac{(6 \times 10^{-2})^2(4 \times 10^3)}{(2 \times 10^{-1})^3}$

36. $\dfrac{(4 \times 10^{-2})^2(3 \times 10^{-1})^4}{(6 \times 10^{-2})^2}$

37. $\dfrac{0.00085}{170}$

38. $\dfrac{77,000}{0.022}$

39. $\dfrac{0.0008}{20,000}$

40. $\dfrac{0.000012}{3000}$

41. $\dfrac{0.00018 \times 500,000}{90,000}$

42. $\dfrac{0.0008 \times 6,000}{0.0016}$

43. $\dfrac{0.00002 \times 1500}{300,000 \times 0.004}$

44. $\dfrac{0.00042 \times 480,000}{70,000 \times 0.0000018}$

45. $\dfrac{0.00016 \times 10,500,000}{0.000014 \times 60,000}$

46. $\dfrac{0.009 \times 121,000}{0.011 \times 1,800,000}$

47. $\dfrac{0.000012 \times 0.00084}{0.00028 \times 0.0000045}$

48. $\dfrac{0.000015 \times 0.0064}{0.0008 \times 0.016}$

In problems 49–52, express the value of each expression in scientific notation, rounded to four digits.

C49. $\dfrac{439,200 \times 0.000363}{53,780 \times 0.00295}$

C50. $\dfrac{81,340 \times 0.00684}{429,500 \times 0.0000741}$

C51. $\dfrac{62,480 \times 0.00916 \times 0.0557}{341,400 \times 0.00822}$

C52. $\dfrac{731,800 \times 61,400 \times 0.00428}{3,481,000 \times 0.000667}$

SOLUTION FOR PRACTICE PROBLEM

1. $\dfrac{15,000 \times 0.16}{0.00064 \times 7500} = \dfrac{1.5 \times 10^4 \times 1.6 \times 10^{-1}}{6.4 \times 10^{-4} \times 7.5 \times 10^3}$

$$= \dfrac{\overset{1}{\cancel{1.5}} \times \overset{1}{\cancel{1.6}} \times 10^3}{\underset{4}{\cancel{6.4}} \times \underset{5}{\cancel{7.5}} \times 10^{-1}}$$

$$= \dfrac{1}{20} \times 10^4$$

$$= 0.05 \times 10^4$$

$$= 5 \times 10^{-2} \times 10^4$$

$$= 5 \times 10^2 \text{ in scientific notation,}$$

$$= 500 \text{ in decimal form.}$$

9-3
Principal nth
Roots

Roots of real numbers are studied in this section. In the section following this one, the development of rational exponents is based on this material.

A square root of a real number a is a number b whose square is a: $b^2 = a$. For example, a square root of 4 is a number b such that $b^2 = 4$. Now

$$(2)^2 = 4 \quad \text{and} \quad (-2)^2 = 4,$$

so there are two numbers, 2 and -2, whose square is 4. Each of 2 and -2 is called a **square root** of 4, but 2 is called the **principal square root of 4**, and the symbol $\sqrt{4}$ is used to denote the principal square root. We write

$$\sqrt{4} = 2.$$

A discussion similar to the preceding can be made for any real number a that is positive:* There are two square roots of a, and one is designated as the principal square root of a, as follows.

Definition 9-3 If a is a *nonnegative number*, the **principal square root** of a is the *nonnegative number* $\sqrt{a}$ such that

$$(\sqrt{a})^2 = a.$$

The symbol $\sqrt{}$ is called the **radical sign**.

It is correct use of the notation to write

$$\sqrt{4} = 2, \quad -\sqrt{4} = -2, \quad \sqrt{9} = 3, \quad -\sqrt{9} = -3.$$

EXAMPLE 1 Find the principal square root of each of the following numbers.

(a) 49

(b) $\dfrac{4}{25}$

(c) 0.04

(d) 0

SOLUTION

(a) $\sqrt{49} = 7$ since 7 is nonnegative and $7^2 = 49$.

(b) $\sqrt{\dfrac{4}{25}} = \dfrac{2}{5}$ since $\dfrac{2}{5}$ is nonnegative and $\left(\dfrac{2}{5}\right)^2 = \dfrac{4}{25}$.

(c) $\sqrt{0.04} = 0.2$ since 0.2 is nonnegative and $(0.2)^2 = 0.04$.

(d) $\sqrt{0} = 0$ since 0 is nonnegative and $0^2 = 0$.

Roots other than square roots are defined in a similar way:

A **cube root** of a is a number b such that $b^3 = a$;

a **fourth root** of a is a number b such that $b^4 = a$;

*If a is negative, it is not the square of any real number. If $a = 0$, its only square root is 0.

and, for any positive integer n,

an **nth root** of a is a number b such that $b^n = a$.

As examples,

-2 is a cube root of -8 since $(-2)^3 = -8$;

3 is a fourth root of 81 since $3^4 = 81$;

-3 is a fourth root of 81 since $(-3)^4 = 81$.

We shall soon define principal roots for orders† higher than 2, but some more preliminary observations need to be made first.

Since the square b^2 of a real number b is never negative, *a negative real number does not have a square root in the set of real numbers.* For example, -4 does not have a real square root since the equation

$$b^2 = -4$$

does *not* have a solution in the real numbers.

On the other hand, every positive number a has two square roots, and we have designated them by $\sqrt{a}$ and $-\sqrt{a}$. These square roots are not always rational numbers. The number $\sqrt{3}$ is such a number. Using the symbol "$\approx$" to mean "approximately equals," we can write

$\sqrt{3} \approx 1.7$, to one decimal place;

$\sqrt{3} \approx 1.73$, to two decimal places;

$\sqrt{3} \approx 1.732$, to three decimal places;

and these approximations can be made to any desired degree of accuracy. However, these decimal representations do not terminate, and they do not form a repeating decimal. This is a reflection of the fact that $\sqrt{3}$ is an irrational number.

The situation with cube roots is simpler than it is with square roots, because every real number a has exactly one real cube root. This cube root of a is designated as the principal cube root of a, and is denoted by $\sqrt[3]{a}$. Some examples are:

$\sqrt[3]{8} = 2$ since $2^3 = 8$;

$\sqrt[3]{-64} = -4$ since $(-4)^3 = -64$;

$\sqrt[3]{125} = 5$ since $5^3 = 125$.

Cube roots are not always rational. For instance, $\sqrt[3]{6}$ is an irrational

†An nth root of a is also called a root of *order n*.

number approximated to three decimal places by

$$\sqrt[3]{6} \approx 1.817.$$

EXAMPLE 2 Find the principal cube root of each of the following numbers.

(a) -1 (b) $\dfrac{8}{27}$

(c) -216 (d) 0

SOLUTION

(a) $\sqrt[3]{-1} = -1$ since $(-1)^3 = -1.$

(b) $\sqrt[3]{\dfrac{8}{27}} = \dfrac{2}{3}$ since $\left(\dfrac{2}{3}\right)^3 = \dfrac{8}{27}.$

(c) $\sqrt[3]{-216} = -6$ since $(-6)^3 = -216.$

(d) $\sqrt[3]{0} = 0$ since $0^3 = 0.$

The discussion for square roots can be extended to 4th roots, 6th roots, 8th roots, and all other even-numbered roots. For example, 16 has two real fourth roots, 2 and -2. On the other hand, -16 has no real fourth roots. For roots of even order, a positive number has two real roots of that order, and a negative number has none.

For roots of odd-numbered order, every real number has exactly one real root of that order.

With these facts in mind, we make the following definition.

Definition 9-4 Let n be a positive integer. The **principal nth root** of a real number a is the real number $\sqrt[n]{a}$ defined by the following statements:

1. If n is even and $a \geq 0$, then $\sqrt[n]{a}$ is the *nonnegative number* such that

$$(\sqrt[n]{a})^n = a.$$

2. If n is odd, then $\sqrt[n]{a}$ is the real number such that

$$(\sqrt[n]{a})^n = a.$$

The symbol $\sqrt[n]{a}$ is called a **radical**, a is called the **radicand**, and n is called the **index** or **order** of the radical.

When it applies, this definition defines *one and only one real number* $\sqrt[n]{a}$ such that $(\sqrt[n]{a})^n = a$. If n is even, the principal nth root of a negative number is undefined at this point in our work. After complex numbers are introduced in Section 9-7, $\sqrt[n]{a}$ can be defined for all real numbers a and all positive integers n.

EXAMPLE 3 Find the value of each of the following.

(a) $\sqrt[4]{81}$
(b) $\sqrt[5]{-32}$

(c) $\sqrt[4]{\dfrac{16}{81}}$
(d) $\sqrt[5]{-x^5}$

SOLUTION

(a) $\sqrt[4]{81} = 3$ since 3 is nonnegative and $3^4 = 81$.

(b) $\sqrt[5]{-32} = -2$ since $(-2)^5 = -32$.

(c) $\sqrt[4]{\dfrac{16}{81}} = \dfrac{2}{3}$ since $\dfrac{2}{3}$ is nonnegative and $\left(\dfrac{2}{3}\right)^4 = \dfrac{16}{81}$.

(d) $\sqrt[5]{-x^5} = -x$ since $(-x)^5 = -x^5$.

We have noted earlier that $\sqrt{4} = 2$ and $\sqrt{4} \neq -2$, because of the condition that $\sqrt[n]{a}$ be nonnegative when n is even. The same condition requires that $\sqrt{x^2}$ be the nonnegative number that gives x^2 when it is squared, and this means that $\sqrt{x^2}$ and x are opposites of each other when x is negative. For example, $\sqrt{(-2)^2} = \sqrt{4} \neq -2$. However, we can *always* write

$$\boxed{\sqrt{x^2} = |x| \qquad \text{for all } x,}$$

and similarly that

$$\boxed{\sqrt[n]{x^n} = |x| \qquad \text{for } n \text{ even and any } x.}$$

When n is odd, a real number has only one real nth root, and

$$\boxed{\sqrt[n]{x^n} = x \qquad \text{for } n \text{ odd and any } x.}$$

This discussion is summarized in part (b) of the next theorem. Part (a) of the theorem follows directly from the definition of $\sqrt[n]{x}$, and the other parts are consequences of the Laws of Exponents [Theorem 9-2(d) and (e)].

Theorem 9-5 (Basic Properties of Radicals) Let n be a positive integer, and let x and y be real numbers. Then

(a) $(\sqrt[n]{x})^n = x$ if $\sqrt[n]{x}$ is defined;

(b) $\sqrt[n]{x^n} = \begin{cases} x & \text{if } n \text{ is odd,} \\ |x| & \text{if } n \text{ is even;} \end{cases}$

(c) $\sqrt[n]{x} \cdot \sqrt[n]{y} = \sqrt[n]{xy}$ if $\sqrt[n]{x}$ and $\sqrt[n]{y}$ are defined;

(d) $\dfrac{\sqrt[n]{x}}{\sqrt[n]{y}} = \sqrt[n]{\dfrac{x}{y}}$ if $\sqrt[n]{x}$ and $\sqrt[n]{y}$ are defined.

In the following Example 4 and Practice Problem 1, we make the assumption that all letters represent positive numbers (this makes certain that all indicated roots are defined), that all denominators are not zero, and that part (b) of Theorem 9-5 occurs only in the form $\sqrt[n]{x^n} = x$.

EXAMPLE 4   Use the Basic Properties of Radicals (Theorem 9-5) to find the value of the given expression. (All letters represent positive numbers.)

(a) $\sqrt{(-5)^2}$

(b) $\sqrt{x^6}$

(c) $\sqrt[3]{-8p^6q^{12}}$

(d) $-\sqrt[4]{\dfrac{243z^2w^{-1}}{3z^6w^{11}}}$

SOLUTION

(a) $\sqrt{(-5)^2} = \sqrt{25} = 5$

(b) $\sqrt{x^6} = \sqrt{(x^3)^2} = x^3$ since x is positive

(c) $\sqrt[3]{-8p^6q^{12}} = \sqrt[3]{-8} \cdot \sqrt[3]{p^6} \cdot \sqrt[3]{q^{12}}$
$= \sqrt[3]{(-2)^3} \cdot \sqrt[3]{(p^2)^3} \cdot \sqrt[3]{(q^4)^3}$
$= -2p^2q^4$

(d) $-\sqrt[4]{\dfrac{243z^2w^{-1}}{3z^6w^{11}}} = -\sqrt[4]{\dfrac{81}{z^4w^{12}}}$

$= -\dfrac{\sqrt[4]{81}}{\sqrt[4]{z^4}\sqrt[4]{w^{12}}}$

$= -\dfrac{3}{zw^3}$ since z and w are positive

PRACTICE PROBLEM 1   (Solution on page 252) Find the value of each of the following. (All letters represent positive numbers.)

(a) $(\sqrt[4]{16})^4$

(b) $-\sqrt[4]{(-3)^4}$

(c) $\sqrt[3]{xy^4}\,\sqrt[3]{x^2y^2}$

(d) $\sqrt[5]{\dfrac{-2x^8y^2}{64x^{-2}y^{12}}}$

If we remove the assumption that all letters represent positive numbers, much more care must be used in evaluating radicals.

EXAMPLE 5 In the following expressions, letters represent arbitrary real numbers, not necessarily positive. Use absolute values as needed to evaluate these expressions.

(a) $\sqrt{9x^2}$

(b) $\sqrt{x^4}$

(c) $\sqrt[4]{(x+1)^4}$

(d) $\sqrt{x^2 + 2xy + y^2}$

SOLUTION

(a) $\sqrt{9x^2} = \sqrt{9} \cdot \sqrt{x^2} = 3|x|$

(b) $\sqrt{x^4} = \sqrt{(x^2)^2} = |x^2| = x^2$ since x^2 is nonnegative

(c) $\sqrt[4]{(x+1)^4} = |x+1|$

(d) $\sqrt{x^2 + 2xy + y^2} = \sqrt{(x+y)^2} = |x+y|$

EXERCISES 9-3

Find the principal square root of each of the following numbers. (See Example 1.)

1. 16

2. 25

3. $\frac{1}{9}$

4. $\frac{1}{4}$

5. $\frac{4}{9}$

6. $\frac{36}{49}$

7. $\frac{169}{144}$

8. $\frac{81}{16}$

9. $\frac{64}{49}$

10. $\frac{121}{100}$

11. 0.09

12. 0.01

13. 0.16

14. 0.25

15. 1.44

16. 1.21

17. 0.0025

18. 0.0036

Find the principal cube root of each of the following numbers. (See Example 2.)

19. 27

20. 64

21. $-\frac{1}{125}$

22. $-\frac{1}{27}$

23. $-\frac{8}{216}$

24. $-\frac{8}{125}$

25. $\frac{1000}{27}$

26. $\frac{343}{64}$

27. 0.027

28. 0.125

29. -0.343

30. -0.216

Find the value of each of the following. (See Example 3.)

31. $-\sqrt{49}$

32. $-\sqrt{36}$

33. $\sqrt[4]{81}$

34. $\sqrt[6]{64}$

35. $\sqrt[5]{-1}$

36. $\sqrt[3]{-8}$

37. $\sqrt[5]{32}$

38. $\sqrt[5]{-243}$

39. $\sqrt[3]{0.001}$

40. $\sqrt[3]{1000}$ 41. $-\sqrt[4]{\dfrac{81}{16}}$ 42. $-\sqrt[4]{\dfrac{256}{10,000}}$

Use the Basic Properties of Radicals (Theorem 9-5) to find the value of the given expression. Assume that all letters represent positive numbers. (See Example 4 and Practice Problem 1.)

43. $\sqrt[4]{1}$ 44. $\sqrt[6]{1}$ 45. $\sqrt[5]{-1}$

46. $\sqrt[7]{-1}$ 47. $\sqrt{(-3)^2}$ 48. $\sqrt{(-4)^2}$

49. $\sqrt{x^2}$ 50. $\sqrt{y^4}$ 51. $\sqrt[3]{a^3}$

52. $\sqrt[3]{b^6}$ 53. $\sqrt{9z^2}$ 54. $\sqrt{4w^2}$

55. $-\sqrt{9p^6}$ 56. $-\sqrt{16w^8}$ 57. $\sqrt{16x^8}$

58. $\sqrt{81y^{12}}$ 59. $(\sqrt{ab^3})^2$ 60. $(\sqrt[4]{r^2s^3})^4$

61. $(\sqrt{a^2b^4})^3$ 62. $(\sqrt[3]{a^3b^6})^2$ 63. $\sqrt[3]{-27t^3}$

64. $\sqrt[3]{-8z^3}$ 65. $\sqrt[3]{a^3b^3}$ 66. $\sqrt[3]{-a^3b^3}$

67. $\sqrt[3]{-8x^3y^6}$ 68. $\sqrt[3]{-27u^6v^9}$ 69. $\sqrt[4]{16m^4n^{12}}$

70. $\sqrt[5]{32s^{10}t^{20}}$ 71. $\sqrt[5]{-\dfrac{1}{x^5}}$ 72. $\sqrt[7]{-\dfrac{1}{x^7}}$

73. $\left(\sqrt[3]{\dfrac{x^2}{y^4}}\right)^3$ 74. $\left(\sqrt[4]{\dfrac{x^3}{y^5}}\right)^4$ 75. $-\sqrt[3]{\dfrac{-8}{27}}$

76. $-\sqrt[3]{-\dfrac{27}{125}}$ 77. $\sqrt[3]{\dfrac{8}{b^6}}$ 78. $\sqrt[3]{\dfrac{27}{b^9}}$

79. $\sqrt{ab}\,\sqrt{ab^5}$ 80. $\sqrt[3]{ab}\,\sqrt[3]{a^2b^5}$ 81. $\sqrt[3]{x^2}\,\sqrt[3]{x^4}$

82. $\sqrt[5]{y^2}\,\sqrt[5]{y^3}$ 83. $\sqrt[3]{xy^2}\,\sqrt[3]{x^2y}$ 84. $\sqrt[4]{a^2b}\,\sqrt[4]{a^2b^3}$

85. $-\sqrt{\dfrac{m^2}{n^4}}$ 86. $-\sqrt{\dfrac{m^4}{n^6}}$ 87. $\sqrt[3]{-\dfrac{x^6}{8y^{12}}}$

88. $\sqrt[3]{-\dfrac{x^9}{27y^6}}$ 89. $\sqrt[4]{x^4y^{-8}}$ 90. $\sqrt[4]{p^4q^{-12}}$

91. $\sqrt[4]{\dfrac{x^5y^2}{xy^{10}}}$ 92. $\sqrt[4]{\dfrac{p^9q^2}{pq^6}}$ 93. $\dfrac{\sqrt[3]{u^4v^{11}}}{\sqrt[3]{uv^2}}$

94. $\dfrac{\sqrt{u^3v^5}}{\sqrt{uv}}$ 95. $\sqrt{(x+y)^{-2}}$ 96. $\sqrt[3]{(x+y)^{-3}}$

In problems 97–102, letters represent arbitrary real numbers and all denominators are assumed to be nonzero. Use absolute values as needed to evaluate the given expression. (See Example 5.)

*97. $-\sqrt{16m^2}$ *98. $\sqrt[4]{x^8}$

*99. $(\sqrt[4]{x^2})^4$ *100. $\sqrt{(x^2+4)^2}$

*101. $\sqrt{\dfrac{4}{x^2+2x+1}}$ *102. $\sqrt{\dfrac{x^4+2x^2+1}{x^2-4xy+4y^2}}$

Evaluate each of the following. Round each answer to the nearest thousandth.

C103. $\sqrt{3.214}$ C104. $\sqrt{7.879}$

C105. $\dfrac{\sqrt[3]{-12.16}}{\sqrt[4]{8.962}}$

C106. $\dfrac{\sqrt[3]{-552.2}}{\sqrt{9.358}\,\sqrt[4]{16.97}}$

C107. $\sqrt{\sqrt[3]{13.47}\,\sqrt{2.681}}$

C108. $\sqrt[3]{\sqrt{43.78}\,\sqrt[4]{8.563}}$

SOLUTION FOR PRACTICE PROBLEM

1. (a) $(\sqrt[4]{16})^4 = 16$

   (b) $-\sqrt[4]{(-3)^4} = -\sqrt[4]{81} = -3$

   (c) $\sqrt[3]{xy^4}\,\sqrt[3]{x^2y^2} = \sqrt[3]{x^3y^6} = \sqrt[3]{x^3} \cdot \sqrt[3]{y^6} = xy^2$

   (d) $\sqrt[5]{\dfrac{-2x^8y^2}{64x^{-2}y^{12}}} = \sqrt[5]{\dfrac{-x^{10}}{32y^{10}}} = \dfrac{\sqrt[5]{-x^{10}}}{\sqrt[5]{32}\,\sqrt[5]{y^{10}}} = -\dfrac{x^2}{2y^2}$

9-4
Radicals and
Rational
Exponents

In defining exponentials with zero exponent or negative integral exponents, we made our definitions under the condition that the Laws of Exponents (Theorem 9-2) should hold for all exponents. Our goal now is to define exponentials with rational numbers as exponents so that the same condition is still satisfied: The Laws of Exponents are to hold for all exponents.

We consider first an exponential of the form $x^{1/n}$, say $5^{1/2}$. If the law of exponents

$$(5^m)^n = 5^{mn}$$

is to hold, we must have

$$(5^{1/2})^2 = 5^{(1/2)(2)} = 5^1 = 5.$$

That is, $5^{1/2}$ must be a square root of 5. The natural choice is to make the definition

$$5^{1/2} = \sqrt{5}.$$

For any positive integer n, this example generalizes to $x^{1/n}$. If the Law of Exponents

$$(x^m)^n = x^{mn}$$

is to hold, then we must have

$$(x^{1/n})^n = x^{n/n} = x^1 = x.$$

This leads us to make the following definition.

Definition 9-6 For any positive integer n and any real number x, we define

$$x^{1/n} = \sqrt[n]{x},$$

under the condition that $x \geq 0$ if n is even.

It should be noted that

$x^{1/n}$ is not defined when n is even and x is negative,

just as $\sqrt[n]{x}$ is not defined when n is even and x is negative.

EXAMPLE 1   Evaluate each of the following.

(a) $64^{1/3}$ (b) $(-64)^{1/3}$

(c) $-64^{1/6}$ (d) $\left(\dfrac{27}{64}\right)^{1/3}$

SOLUTION

(a) $64^{1/3} = \sqrt[3]{64} = \sqrt[3]{(4)^3} = 4$

(b) $(-64)^{1/3} = \sqrt[3]{-64} = \sqrt[3]{(-4)^3} = -4$

(c) $-64^{1/6} = -(64)^{1/6} = -\sqrt[6]{64} = -\sqrt[6]{2^6} = -2$

(d) $\left(\dfrac{27}{64}\right)^{1/3} = \sqrt[3]{\dfrac{27}{64}} = \sqrt[3]{\left(\dfrac{3}{4}\right)^3} = \dfrac{3}{4}$

As an example to guide us with more complicated rational exponents, let us consider $5^{3/2}$. If $(5^m)^n = 5^{mn}$ is to hold for all m and n, we must have

$$5^{3/2} = 5^{(1/2)(3)} = (5^{1/2})^3 = (\sqrt{5})^3,$$

and we must also have

$$5^{3/2} = 5^{(3)(1/2)} = (5^3)^{1/2} = \sqrt{5^3}.$$

The values $(\sqrt{5})^3$ and $\sqrt{5^3}$ have different appearances, but they are actually equal:

$$(\sqrt{5})^3 = \sqrt{5}\,\sqrt{5}\,\sqrt{5}$$
$$= \sqrt{5^2}\,\sqrt{5} \qquad \text{by Theorem 9-5(c)}$$
$$= \sqrt{5^3} \qquad \text{by Theorem 9-5(c).}$$

The example

$$5^{3/2} = (\sqrt{5})^3 = \sqrt{5^3}$$

generalizes to any $x^{m/n}$, where m and n are positive integers and $\sqrt[n]{x}$ is defined:

$$x^{m/n} = (\sqrt[n]{x})^m = \sqrt[n]{x^m}.$$

In the case of a negative rational exponent, we write the exponent as

$$\frac{-m}{n}, \quad \text{where } m \text{ and } n \text{ are positive.}$$

We then define

$$x^{-m/n} = \sqrt[n]{x^{-m}} = (\sqrt[n]{x})^{-m} = \frac{1}{x^{m/n}}.$$

This is stated more compactly in the next definition, where m is allowed to be any integer (positive, zero or negative).

Definition 9-7 If m is an integer and n is a positive integer then we define $x^{m/n}$ by

$$x^{m/n} = \sqrt[n]{x^m} = (\sqrt[n]{x})^m,$$

under the condition that **$x > 0$ if n is even.**
    Note that

$x^{m/n}$ is not defined when n is even and $x < 0$,

just as it was with $\sqrt[n]{x}$. Although we do not demonstrate it here, it is a consequence of this definition that

$$x^{-m/n} = \frac{1}{x^{m/n}},$$

where m is an integer, n is a positive integer, and $x > 0$ if n is even.
    Definition 9-7 allows us to change back and forth from a form involving a rational exponent to either one of two forms involving a radical. The form $x^{m/n}$ is called an **exponential form**, and either of $\sqrt[n]{x^m}$ or $(\sqrt[n]{x})^m$ is called a **radical form**. Such changes of form are shown in Example 2.

EXAMPLE 2 Change each of the following from exponential form to radical form, or from radical form to exponential form, whichever is appropriate. All variables represent positive numbers.

(a) $16x^{5/4}$

(b) $-9y^{3/2}$

(c) $\sqrt[6]{z^7}$

(d) $\sqrt[5]{(4a^2)^3}$

(a) $16x^{5/4} = 16\sqrt[4]{x^5}$ or $16(\sqrt[4]{x})^5$

(b) $-9y^{3/2} = -9\sqrt{y^3}$ or $-9(\sqrt{y})^3$

(c) $\sqrt[6]{z^7} = z^{7/6}$

(d) $\sqrt[5]{(4a^2)^3} = (4a^2)^{3/5}$

EXAMPLE 3 Evaluate each of the following by changing to radical form.

(a) $(-64)^{-1/3}$ 　　　　　　　　　　　(b) $\left(\dfrac{16}{81}\right)^{3/4}$

(c) $(-125)^{2/3}$

SOLUTION   (a) $(-64)^{-1/3} = \dfrac{1}{(-64)^{1/3}} = \dfrac{1}{\sqrt[3]{-64}} = \dfrac{1}{\sqrt[3]{(-4)^3}} = -\dfrac{1}{4}$

(b) $\left(\dfrac{16}{81}\right)^{3/4} = \left(\sqrt[4]{\dfrac{16}{81}}\right)^3 = \left(\sqrt[4]{\dfrac{2^4}{3^4}}\right)^3 = \left(\dfrac{2}{3}\right)^3 = \dfrac{8}{27}$

(c) $(-125)^{2/3} = (\sqrt[3]{-125})^2 = (-5)^2 = 25$

We have been guided in our definition of powers with rational exponents by the requirement that the Laws of Exponents hold for rational exponents. Although we make no attempt to verify it here, the definitions that we have made do indeed make these laws valid whenever the quantities involved are defined.

For simplicity, **we assume that all variables are positive real numbers for the remainder of this section.**

EXAMPLE 4 Use the Laws of Exponents to simplify the given expression to one in which all exponents are positive and no variable occurs more than once.

(a) $r^{3/4}r^{5/4}$ 　　　　　　　　　　　(b) $y^{3/5}y^{-3/5}$

(c) $(w^{-2/3})^6$ 　　　　　　　　　　　(d) $\dfrac{z^{3/7}}{z^{-2/7}}$

SOLUTION   (a) $r^{3/4}r^{5/4} = r^{3/4+5/4} = r^{8/4} = r^2$

(b) $y^{3/5}y^{-3/5} = y^{3/5-3/5} = y^0 = 1$

(c) $(w^{-2/3})^6 = w^{(-2/3)(6)} = w^{-4} = \dfrac{1}{w^4}$

(d) $\dfrac{z^{3/7}}{z^{-2/7}} = z^{3/7-(-2/7)} = z^{5/7}$

EXAMPLE 5 Simplify the given expression to one in which all exponents are positive and no variable occurs more than once.

(a) $(p^6q^{-9})^{-1/3}$

(b) $\dfrac{8x^{1/3}y^{-3/5}z^0}{9x^{-2/3}y^{2/5}z^{-1/2}}$

(c) $\left(\dfrac{4x^2y^{-1/3}z^{-1}}{x^{1/2}y^{2/3}z^{-1/3}}\right)^{-3/2}$

SOLUTION

(a) $(p^6q^{-9})^{-1/3} = (p^6)^{-1/3}(q^{-9})^{-1/3} = p^{-2}q^3 = \dfrac{q^3}{p^2}$

(b) $\dfrac{8x^{1/3}y^{-3/5}z^0}{9x^{-2/3}y^{2/5}z^{-1/2}} = \dfrac{8}{9} \cdot \dfrac{x^{1/3}}{x^{-2/3}} \cdot \dfrac{y^{-3/5}}{y^{2/5}} \cdot \dfrac{1}{z^{-1/2}}$

$= \dfrac{8}{9} \cdot \dfrac{x^1}{1} \cdot \dfrac{1}{y^1} \cdot \dfrac{z^{1/2}}{1}$

$= \dfrac{8xz^{1/2}}{9y}$

(c) $\left(\dfrac{4x^2y^{-1/3}z^{-1}}{x^{1/2}y^{2/3}z^{-1/3}}\right)^{-3/2} = \left(\dfrac{4x^{3/2}}{yz^{2/3}}\right)^{-3/2}$

$= \left(\dfrac{yz^{2/3}}{4x^{3/2}}\right)^{3/2}$

$= \dfrac{y^{3/2}z}{4^{3/2}x^{9/4}}$

$= \dfrac{y^{3/2}z}{8x^{9/4}}$

PRACTICE PROBLEM 1 (Solution on page 258) Perform the following multiplications, and write the results so that all exponents are positive and no variable occurs more than once in a term.

(a) $[9x^{-2/3}y^{1/2}]^{1/2}[4x^{-2/3}y^{3/4}]^{-1}$

(b) $\left(\dfrac{p^{3/2}q^{-1/4}r^{-1}}{p^{1/4}q^{1/2}r^0}\right)^{-2/3}\left(\dfrac{p^{-2/3}q^2r^{-1/2}}{p^{1/6}q^{1/2}}\right)^2$

(c) $(a^{-1/2} - b^{-1/2})(a^{-1/2} + b^{-1/2})$

EXERCISES 9-4

All variables in these exercises represent positive real numbers.
Evaluate each of the following expressions. (See Examples 1 and 3.)

1. $(144)^{1/2}$

2. $(121)^{1/2}$

3. $(-27)^{1/3}$

4. $(-125)^{1/3}$

5. $-25^{1/2}$

6. $-36^{1/2}$

7. $25^{-1/2}$

8. $36^{-1/2}$

9. $\left(\dfrac{9}{16}\right)^{1/2}$

10. $\left(\dfrac{4}{25}\right)^{1/2}$

11. $\left(\dfrac{16}{81}\right)^{-1/4}$

12. $\left(\dfrac{256}{625}\right)^{-1/4}$

Change each of the following from exponential form to radical form, or from radical form to exponential form, whichever is appropriate. (See Example 2.)

13. $x^{1/5}$

14. $x^{1/7}$

15. $y^{3/5}$

16. $y^{2/7}$

17. $\sqrt[4]{z}$

18. $\sqrt[6]{w}$

19. $\sqrt[3]{a^5}$

20. $\sqrt[4]{t^7}$

21. $\sqrt[4]{r^{12}}$

22. $\sqrt[3]{s^{12}}$

23. $\sqrt[5]{(x-y)^3}$

24. $\sqrt[4]{(x+2y)^3}$

25. $4x^{3/2}$

26. $9y^{5/2}$

27. $(xy^2)^{2/3}$

28. $(x^3y^2)^{1/6}$

29. $(3m^2n)^{2/5}$

30. $(2mn^2q)^{3/4}$

Evaluate if possible; otherwise, use the Laws of Exponents to simplify the given expression to a rational expression in lowest terms. (See Examples 3 and 4.)

31. $27^{2/3}$

32. $125^{2/3}$

33. $-27^{2/3}$

34. $-125^{2/3}$

35. $(-27)^{2/3}$

36. $(-125)^{2/3}$

37. $27^{-2/3}$

38. $125^{-2/3}$

39. $(-27)^{-2/3}$

40. $(-125)^{-2/3}$

41. $x^{1/5}x^{4/5}$

42. $x^{3/7}x^{4/7}$

43. $y^{4/3}y^{2/3}$

44. $y^{3/5}y^{7/5}$

45. $r^{-2/3}r^{5/3}$

46. $t^{-2/5}t^{7/5}$

47. $(x^6)^{3/2}$

48. $(y^6)^{2/3}$

49. $(x^{3/4})^8$

50. $(y^{4/3})^6$

51. $\dfrac{z^{3/5}}{z^{-2/5}}$

52. $\dfrac{w^{-2/3}}{w^{1/3}}$

53. $\dfrac{p^{-3/5}}{p^{7/5}}$

54. $\dfrac{w^{-2/3}}{w^{4/3}}$

Simplify each of the following expressions to one in which all exponents are positive and no variable occurs more than once. (See Example 5.)

55. $\dfrac{(x^{3/4})^2}{(x^4)^{1/2}}$

56. $\dfrac{(z^{3/5})^3}{(z^2)^{2/5}}$

57. $\left(\dfrac{x^{2/3}}{y^{3/2}}\right)^6$

58. $\left(\dfrac{p^{1/2}}{q^{3/4}}\right)^8$

59. $\dfrac{(8m^{4/3})(64m^{1/3})}{36m^{1/2}}$

60. $\dfrac{(4s^{3/2})(9s^{1/2})}{36s^{-5/2}}$

61. $(x^8y^4)^{1/4}$

62. $(x^6y^3)^{1/3}$

63. $(p^9q^{-6})^{-1/3}$

64. $(p^{-3}q^6)^{1/3}$

65. $(m^{-8}n^4)^{-1/2}$

66. $(m^8n^{-4})^{-1/4}$

67. $\dfrac{x^3y^0z^{2/5}}{x^{2/3}y^{1/4}z^{2/5}}$

68. $\dfrac{x^{2/3}y^{-1/3}z^{3/4}}{x^{-1/3}y^0z^{1/4}}$

69. $\dfrac{-8r^{1/3}t^{8/5}}{27r^{4/3}t^{-2/5}}$

70. $\dfrac{4x^{1/2}y^{3/4}}{9x^{-3/2}y^{-5/4}}$

71. $\dfrac{(4p)^{1/2}(27q)^{2/3}}{(8pq)^{1/3}}$

72. $\dfrac{(9u)^{1/2}(8v)^{1/3}}{(16uv)^{1/4}}$

73. $[(x^{1/2}y^{-2/3})^6]^{-1}$

74. $[(x^{-2/3}y^{5/2})^{-1/2}]^3$

75. $\left(\dfrac{a^{4/3}b^{-1}c^{-2/3}}{8a^{-3}b^{5/7}c^{1/6}}\right)^{0}$

76. $\left(\dfrac{3a^{3/5}b^{-2/5}c^{3}}{2a^{1/5}b^{-2}c^{3/5}}\right)^{0}$

77. $(4x^{1/3}y^{-2/5})^{2}(3x^{-2/3}y^{1/5})^{-1}$

78. $(3x^{-1/2}y^{3/4})^{2}(2x^{-1}y^{0})^{3}$

79. $\dfrac{(p^{3/4}q^{2/5}r^{-1})^{2}}{(p^{-1/4}q^{3/5}r)^{3}}$

80. $\dfrac{(p^{2/3}q^{-1/2}r^{0})^{3}}{(p^{1/5}q^{-3/4}r^{-2})^{-1}}$

81. $\dfrac{4^{-2}z^{-1/3}w^{4/3}}{(9z^{2/3}w^{-4/3})^{1/2}}$

82. $\dfrac{9^{-2}z^{-2/5}w^{3/5}}{(4z^{-4/5}w^{-1})^{-1/2}}$

83. $\left(\dfrac{x^{3/4}y^{0}}{x^{-1/2}z^{2/3}}\right)^{-1/2}$

84. $\left(\dfrac{4m^{3/4}n^{-3/5}}{m^{0}n^{3/5}}\right)^{-1/3}$

85. $\left(\dfrac{x^{2}y^{-4}}{z^{4}}\right)^{1/2}\left(\dfrac{x^{-2}y^{0}}{z^{-4}}\right)^{-1/2}$

86. $\left(\dfrac{xy^{1/2}}{z^{1/2}w^{3/2}}\right)^{-4}\left(\dfrac{y^{2}w^{2}}{x^{2}z^{4}}\right)^{-3/2}$

87. $\left(\dfrac{x^{0}y^{1/2}}{z^{4}}\right)^{1/2}\left(\dfrac{x^{3/5}y^{-3/4}}{z^{-3}}\right)^{-1/3}$

88. $\left(\dfrac{x^{-2}y^{0}}{y^{3}z^{-1}}\right)^{1/3}\left(\dfrac{x^{-4/3}y^{2/5}}{xy^{-2}}\right)^{-1/2}$

Perform the indicated operations, and write the results so that all exponents are positive and no variable occurs more than once in a term. (See Practice Problem 1.)

89. $x^{1/3}(x^{2/3} + x^{2})$

90. $x^{-4/5}(x^{9/5} - x^{4/5})$

91. $2p^{-2/5}(p^{7/5} - 3p^{2/5})$

92. $3q^{2/3}(q^{-1/3} + 4q^{4/3})$

93. $(x^{3/2} - y^{3/2})(x^{3/2} + y^{3/2})$

94. $(x^{1/2} - y^{1/2})(x^{1/2} + y^{1/2})$

95. $(u^{1/2} + v^{1/2})^{2}$

96. $(u^{1/2} - v^{1/2})^{2}$

In problems 97–104, assume that n is a positive integer.

*97. $(x^{3})^{2n}$

*98. $(x^{n+1})^{2}$

*99. $x^{2n} \cdot x^{1-n}$

*100. $x^{3n-1} \cdot x^{2-n}$

*101. $\left(\dfrac{x^{4n-1}}{x^{n+2}}\right)^{1/3}$

*102. $\left(\dfrac{x^{3n-1}}{x^{n+1}}\right)^{1/2}$

*103. $\left(\dfrac{x^{4n}}{y^{3}}\right)^{1/4}\left(\dfrac{x^{4}}{y^{-1/2}}\right)^{3/2}$

*104. $\left(\dfrac{x^{3n}}{y^{4}}\right)^{1/2}\left(\dfrac{x^{1/2}}{y^{3}}\right)^{n}$

Use the power rule [Theorem 9-2(b)] to express each of the following as a single radical.

*105. $\sqrt[3]{\sqrt{x}}$

*106. $\sqrt{\sqrt[3]{x}}$

*107. $\sqrt{\sqrt[4]{x}}$

*108. $\sqrt[5]{\sqrt{x}}$

*109. $\sqrt{\sqrt[5]{x}}$

*110. $\sqrt[4]{\sqrt[3]{x}}$

SOLUTION FOR PRACTICE PROBLEM

1. (a) $[9x^{-2/3}y^{1/2}]^{1/2}[4x^{-2/3}y^{3/4}]^{-1} = (9^{1/2}x^{-1/3}y^{1/4})(4^{-1}x^{2/3}y^{-3/4})$

$$= 3 \cdot 4^{-1}x^{1/3}y^{-1/2}$$

$$= \dfrac{3x^{1/3}}{4y^{1/2}}$$

(b) $\left(\dfrac{p^{3/2}q^{-1/4}r^{-1}}{p^{1/4}q^{1/2}r^0}\right)^{-2/3}\left(\dfrac{p^{-2/3}q^2r^{-1/2}}{p^{1/6}q^{1/2}}\right)^2 = \dfrac{p^{-1}q^{1/6}r^{2/3}}{p^{-1/6}q^{-1/3}(1)} \cdot \dfrac{p^{-4/3}q^4r^{-1}}{p^{1/3}q}$

$$= \dfrac{q^{1/2}r^{2/3}}{p^{5/6}} \cdot \dfrac{q^3}{p^{5/3}r}$$

$$= \dfrac{q^{7/2}}{p^{5/2}r^{1/3}}$$

(c) $(a^{-1/2} - b^{-1/2})(a^{-1/2} + b^{-1/2}) = a^{-1} + a^{-1/2}b^{-1/2} - a^{-1/2}b^{-1/2}$
$$- b^{-1}$$
$$= a^{-1} - b^{-1}$$
$$= \dfrac{1}{a} - \dfrac{1}{b}$$

9-5
Simplifying
Radicals

An expression containing one or more radicals is called a **radical expression**. The Basic Properties of Radicals (Theorem 9-5) can frequently be used to change the form of a radical expression. By convention, certain types of radical expressions are accepted as being simpler than others. Some of these conventions are illustrated in the following examples. **In these examples and for the remainder of this section, all variables are assumed to represent positive real numbers.**

EXAMPLE 1 **If a perfect *n*th power is factored out of the radicand, the result is simpler than the original.** As illustrations,

$$\sqrt{45} = \sqrt{3^2 \cdot 5} = \sqrt{3^2}\sqrt{5} = 3\sqrt{5}$$

and

$$\sqrt[3]{56} = \sqrt[3]{2^3 \cdot 7} = \sqrt[3]{2^3}\sqrt[3]{7} = 2\sqrt[3]{7}.$$

The form without a perfect *n*th power under the radical of order *n* is considered to be simpler: $3\sqrt{5}$ is simpler than $\sqrt{45}$, and $2\sqrt[3]{7}$ is simpler than $\sqrt[3]{56}$.

EXAMPLE 2 **If a fraction is rewritten without a radical in the denominator, the result is simpler than the original.** As an example,

$$\dfrac{\sqrt[3]{35}}{\sqrt[3]{5}} = \sqrt[3]{\dfrac{35}{5}} = \sqrt[3]{7}$$

and $\sqrt[3]{7}$ is simpler than $\dfrac{\sqrt[3]{35}}{\sqrt[3]{5}}$.

EXAMPLE 3   **If an expression is rewritten so that no negative or zero exponents occur, the result is simpler than the original.** As an illustration,

$$\sqrt[3]{\frac{7xy^0}{x^{-1}}} = \sqrt[3]{7x^2(1)} = \sqrt[3]{7x^2},$$

and $\sqrt[3]{7x^2}$ is simpler than $\sqrt[3]{\frac{7xy^0}{x^{-1}}}$.

EXAMPLE 4   **If the index of a radical is reduced to a smaller number, the result is simpler than the original.** For instance,

$$\sqrt[6]{8} = \sqrt[6]{2^3} = 2^{3/6} = 2^{1/2} = \sqrt{2},$$

and $\sqrt{2}$ is simpler than $\sqrt[6]{8}$.

The last example shows how the index of a radical can be reduced when the index and the exponent in the radicand have a positive integer greater than 1 as a common factor. To see how this works in general, suppose that $x^{m/n}$ is defined, and let p be a positive integer greater than 1. Then

$$\sqrt[pn]{x^{pm}} = x^{pm/pn} = x^{m/n} = \sqrt[n]{x^m}.$$

That is,

$$\sqrt[pn]{x^{pm}} = \sqrt[n]{x^m},$$

where p is a positive integer and $x^{m/n}$ is defined.

The four preceding examples illustrate four ways in which a radical can be changed to a simpler form. Of these four ways, the one illustrated in Example 2 is probably the most troublesome. For example, how can

$$\frac{5}{\sqrt{2}}$$

be rewritten without the radical in the denominator? The process of rewriting a quotient so that the denominator contains no radicals is called **rationalizing the denominator**. We rationalize the denominator in $5/\sqrt{2}$ by choosing a multiplier that would produce a perfect square under the radical. As a general procedure, we choose the multiplier so as to make a power under the radical in the denominator which is the same as the index of the radical. This is illustrated in the next example.

EXAMPLE 5   Rationalize the denominators of the following fractions.

(a) $\dfrac{5}{\sqrt{2}}$

(b) $\sqrt[3]{\dfrac{5}{4}}$

(c) $\dfrac{\sqrt[4]{2x^2}}{\sqrt[4]{9y^3z}}$

SOLUTION

(a) $\dfrac{5}{\sqrt{2}} = \dfrac{5\sqrt{2}}{\sqrt{2}\sqrt{2}} = \dfrac{5\sqrt{2}}{2}$

(b) $\sqrt[3]{\dfrac{5}{4}} = \dfrac{\sqrt[3]{5}}{\sqrt[3]{2^2}} = \dfrac{\sqrt[3]{5}\sqrt[3]{2}}{\sqrt[3]{2^2}\sqrt[3]{2}} = \dfrac{\sqrt[3]{10}}{\sqrt[3]{2^3}} = \dfrac{\sqrt[3]{10}}{2}$

(c) $\dfrac{\sqrt[4]{2x^2}}{\sqrt[4]{9y^3z}} = \dfrac{\sqrt[4]{2x^2}\sqrt[4]{3^2yz^3}}{\sqrt[4]{3^2y^3z}\sqrt[4]{3^2yz^3}}$

$= \dfrac{\sqrt[4]{18x^2yz^3}}{\sqrt[4]{3^4y^4z^4}}$

$= \dfrac{\sqrt[4]{18x^2yz^3}}{3yz}$

PRACTICE PROBLEM 1   (Solution on page 264) Rationalize the denominators.

(a) $\sqrt{\dfrac{2}{7}}$

(b) $\dfrac{4r}{\sqrt{2s}}$

(c) $\sqrt[3]{\dfrac{5x}{4yz^2}}$

In the next section we consider some more complicated cases for rationalizing the denominator.

The foregoing examples illustrate the conditions used in the definition of simplest radical form.

Definition 9-8   A radical expression is in **simplest radical form** if all of the following conditions are satisfied.

Conditions for Simplest Radical Form

(a) The expression contains no negative or zero exponents.

(b) No radicand contains a polynomial factor to a power equal to or greater than the index of the radical.

(c) No denominator contains a radical, and no fraction is under a radical sign.

(d) The index of the radical is as small as possible.

261

EXAMPLE 6 Change each of the following to simplest radical form.

$$\text{(a)} \quad \frac{\sqrt[3]{72}}{\sqrt[3]{5}}$$

$$\text{(b)} \quad \sqrt[3]{\frac{3p^4}{25qr^2}}$$

$$\text{(c)} \quad \sqrt[9]{8u^3v^6}$$

SOLUTION

$$\text{(a)} \quad \frac{\sqrt[3]{72}}{\sqrt[3]{5}} = \frac{\sqrt[3]{2^3 \cdot 3^2}\,\sqrt[3]{5^2}}{\sqrt[3]{5}\,\sqrt[3]{5^2}}$$

$$= \frac{2\sqrt[3]{9}\,\sqrt[3]{25}}{\sqrt[3]{5^3}}$$

$$= \frac{2\sqrt[3]{225}}{5}$$

$$\text{(b)} \quad \sqrt[3]{\frac{3p^4}{25qr^2}} = \frac{\sqrt[3]{3p^3p}\,\sqrt[3]{5q^2r}}{\sqrt[3]{5^2qr^2}\,\sqrt[3]{5q^2r}}$$

$$= \frac{p\sqrt[3]{3p}\,\sqrt[3]{5q^2r}}{\sqrt[3]{5^3q^3r^3}}$$

$$= \frac{p\sqrt[3]{15pq^2r}}{5qr}$$

$$\text{(c)} \quad \sqrt[9]{8u^3v^6} = \sqrt[9]{2^3u^3(v^2)^3}$$

$$= \sqrt[9]{(2uv^2)^3}$$

$$= (2uv^2)^{3/9}$$

$$= (2uv^2)^{1/3}$$

$$= \sqrt[3]{2uv^2}$$

PRACTICE PROBLEM 2 (Solution on page 265) Change to simplest radical form.

$$\text{(a)} \quad \sqrt{\frac{4}{3x^7}}$$

$$\text{(b)} \quad \sqrt[3]{(x + 1)^5}$$

$$\text{(c)} \quad \sqrt{\frac{18x^3y^3}{x^{-1}}}$$

EXERCISES 9-5

All variables in these exercises represent positive real numbers.
Simplify by removing all possible factors from the radicand. (See Example 1.)

1. $\sqrt{8}$
2. $\sqrt{18}$
3. $-\sqrt{300}$
4. $-\sqrt{125}$
5. $\sqrt[3]{-81}$
6. $\sqrt[3]{-250}$
7. $\sqrt[4]{32}$
8. $\sqrt[4]{243}$
9. $\sqrt{50x^3}$
10. $\sqrt{75y^5}$

11. $\sqrt[3]{40}$

12. $\sqrt[3]{54}$

13. $\sqrt[3]{27p^8}$

14. $\sqrt[3]{16q^7}$

15. $\sqrt[3]{-108x^4y^2}$

16. $\sqrt[3]{-250x^2y^5}$

17. $\sqrt[3]{-128(p+q)^5}$

18. $\sqrt[3]{-135(r+s)^7}$

19. $\sqrt[4]{80m^6n^7}$

20. $\sqrt[4]{162r^5s^6}$

21. $\sqrt[5]{-x^{12}y^7}$

22. $\sqrt[5]{-x^8y^{13}}$

23. $\sqrt[5]{-32u^8v^7}$

24. $\sqrt[5]{-243z^6w^9}$

Perform the indicated multiplications or divisions, and remove all factors possible from the radicand. (See Example 2.)

25. $\sqrt{6}\,\sqrt{15}$

26. $\sqrt{10}\,\sqrt{15}$

27. $\sqrt[3]{-3}\,\sqrt[3]{18}$

28. $\sqrt[3]{-5}\,\sqrt[3]{50}$

29. $\sqrt{y+z}\,\sqrt{(y+z)^3}$

30. $\sqrt{x^3(y-z)}\,\sqrt{x(y-z)}$

31. $\dfrac{\sqrt{6x}}{\sqrt{3x}}$

32. $\dfrac{\sqrt{10x}}{\sqrt{2x}}$

33. $\dfrac{\sqrt{12y^3}}{\sqrt{3y}}$

34. $\dfrac{\sqrt{18y^5}}{\sqrt{3y^3}}$

35. $\dfrac{\sqrt[3]{96a^4b^5c^5}}{\sqrt[3]{2a^2b^2c}}$

36. $\dfrac{\sqrt[3]{144a^5b^4c^3}}{\sqrt[3]{2abc}}$

Reduce the index as much as possible on the following radicals. (See Example 4.)

37. $\sqrt[4]{\dfrac{4}{25}}$

38. $\sqrt[4]{\dfrac{9}{16}}$

39. $\sqrt[6]{y^8}$

40. $\sqrt[9]{y^6}$

41. $\sqrt[12]{m^8}$

42. $\sqrt[12]{n^9}$

43. $\sqrt[6]{0.027x^3}$

44. $\sqrt[6]{0.008s^3}$

45. $\sqrt[6]{16x^4y^8}$

46. $\sqrt[6]{81x^8y^{12}}$

47. $\sqrt[12]{16p^8q^4}$

48. $\sqrt[12]{27p^9q^3}$

Rationalize the denominators. (See Example 5 and Practice Problem 1.)

49. $\dfrac{1}{\sqrt{3}}$

50. $\dfrac{1}{\sqrt{5}}$

51. $\sqrt{\dfrac{2}{3}}$

52. $\sqrt{\dfrac{5}{7}}$

53. $-\dfrac{2}{\sqrt{3}}$

54. $-\dfrac{5}{\sqrt{7}}$

55. $\sqrt{\dfrac{x}{2}}$

56. $\sqrt{\dfrac{y}{3}}$

57. $\sqrt{\dfrac{4}{x}}$

58. $\sqrt{\dfrac{9}{y}}$

59. $-\dfrac{1}{\sqrt{2x}}$

60. $-\dfrac{1}{\sqrt{3y}}$

61. $\dfrac{2r}{\sqrt{3rs}}$

62. $\dfrac{3s}{\sqrt{5rs}}$

63. $\sqrt{\dfrac{3x}{2y}}$

64. $\sqrt{\dfrac{5x}{3y}}$

65. $\dfrac{9p^2q}{\sqrt{3pq}}$

66. $\dfrac{4p^2}{\sqrt{2pq}}$

67. $\sqrt{\dfrac{3r^2}{4rs}}$

68. $\sqrt{\dfrac{5r}{9r^3s}}$

69. $\sqrt[3]{\dfrac{1}{4}}$

70. $\sqrt[3]{\dfrac{1}{9}}$

71. $\dfrac{1}{\sqrt[4]{8}}$

72. $\dfrac{1}{\sqrt[4]{27}}$

73. $\sqrt[3]{\dfrac{5}{9}}$

74. $\sqrt[3]{\dfrac{5}{32}}$

75. $\sqrt[3]{\dfrac{5a}{2b^2c}}$

76. $\sqrt[3]{\dfrac{7a^2}{9bc^2}}$

77. $\sqrt{\dfrac{x}{7^3z}}$

78. $\sqrt{\dfrac{3x}{yz^5}}$

79. $\dfrac{\sqrt{p^3q^4}}{\sqrt{pq}}$

80. $\dfrac{\sqrt{p^5q^3}}{\sqrt{pq}}$

81. $\sqrt[3]{\dfrac{7r^2s}{9rs^2}}$

82. $\sqrt[3]{\dfrac{5rs^3}{4r^3s}}$

83. $\sqrt[4]{\dfrac{2xy^2}{6x^3y}}$

84. $\sqrt[4]{\dfrac{3x^2y}{12x^2y^3}}$

Change to simplest radical form. (See Example 6 and Practice Problem 2.)

85. $\dfrac{2}{\sqrt{2}}$

86. $\dfrac{3}{\sqrt{3}}$

87. $2\cdot\sqrt{\dfrac{1}{3}}$

88. $3\cdot\sqrt{\dfrac{1}{2}}$

89. $\sqrt{\dfrac{25}{12}}$

90. $\sqrt{\dfrac{9}{20}}$

91. $\dfrac{x}{\sqrt{x}}$

92. $\dfrac{2x}{\sqrt{2x}}$

93. $\sqrt{\dfrac{8}{3x^3}}$

94. $\sqrt{\dfrac{9}{2x^5}}$

95. $\sqrt[3]{\dfrac{u^9}{v^5}}$

96. $\sqrt[3]{\dfrac{u^{12}}{v^8}}$

97. $\sqrt[4]{\dfrac{p^8}{q^7}}$

98. $\sqrt[4]{\dfrac{p^{12}}{q^9}}$

99. $\sqrt[3]{(a+b)^4}$

100. $\sqrt{(a-b)^3}$

101. $\dfrac{\sqrt{40u^2v^3}}{\sqrt{3w}}$

102. $\dfrac{\sqrt{150u^2v^5}}{\sqrt{7w}}$

103. $\sqrt[4]{\dfrac{81}{8}}$

104. $\sqrt[4]{\dfrac{16}{27}}$

105. $\sqrt[3]{\dfrac{2x^5}{49yz^3}}$

106. $\sqrt[3]{\dfrac{3x^4}{2y^3z^2}}$

107. $\sqrt[3]{\dfrac{125xy^4}{36z^5}}$

108. $\sqrt[3]{\dfrac{8x^7}{5y^4z^2}}$

109. $\sqrt[4]{\dfrac{7u^4}{8v^2w}}$

110. $\sqrt[4]{\dfrac{5u^8}{27vw^3}}$

111. $\sqrt[4]{\dfrac{4m^2}{9n^3p^2}}$

112. $\sqrt[4]{\dfrac{25m^2}{4np^3}}$

113. $\sqrt[4]{36}$

114. $\sqrt[4]{100}$

115. $\sqrt[6]{4x^4}$

116. $\sqrt[6]{9x^4}$

117. $\sqrt{r^7s^{-2}t^0}$

118. $\sqrt{r^5s^0t^{-3}}$

119. $\dfrac{a}{\sqrt{4b^{-2}}}$

120. $\sqrt[3]{\dfrac{x^{-1}}{xy^{-6}}}$

SOLUTIONS FOR PRACTICE PROBLEMS

1. (a) $\sqrt{\dfrac{2}{7}} = \dfrac{\sqrt{2}\sqrt{7}}{\sqrt{7}\sqrt{7}} = \dfrac{\sqrt{14}}{7}$

(b) $\dfrac{4r}{\sqrt{2s}} = \dfrac{4r\sqrt{2s}}{\sqrt{2s}\sqrt{2s}} = \dfrac{4r\sqrt{2s}}{2s} = \dfrac{2r\sqrt{2s}}{s}$

(c) $\sqrt[3]{\dfrac{5x}{4yz^2}} = \dfrac{\sqrt[3]{5x}\,\sqrt[3]{2y^2z}}{\sqrt[3]{2^2yz^2}\,\sqrt[3]{2y^2z}} = \dfrac{\sqrt[3]{10xy^2z}}{\sqrt[3]{2^3y^3z^3}} = \dfrac{\sqrt[3]{10xy^2z}}{2yz}$

2. (a) $\sqrt{\dfrac{4}{3x^7}} = \dfrac{\sqrt{2^2}}{\sqrt{3(x^3)^2x}} = \dfrac{2\sqrt{3x}}{x^3\sqrt{3x}\sqrt{3x}} = \dfrac{2\sqrt{3x}}{x^3(3x)} = \dfrac{2\sqrt{3x}}{3x^4}$

(b) $\sqrt[3]{(x+1)^5} = \sqrt[3]{(x+1)^3(x+1)^2} = (x+1)\sqrt[3]{(x+1)^2}$

(c) $\sqrt{\dfrac{18x^3y^3}{x^{-1}}} = \sqrt{18x^4y^3} = \sqrt{2\cdot 3^2(x^2)^2y^2y} = 3x^2y\sqrt{2y}$

9-6
Operations
on Radical
Expressions

The next step in our study of radical expressions is to consider the combination of radical expressions by use of the fundamental operations of addition, subtraction, multiplication, or division. We continue the restriction made earlier, and **assume that all variables represent positive real numbers throughout this section. We also assume that all denominators are nonzero.**

If a sum or difference involves radicals that have the same index and the same radicand, the terms can be combined by using the distributive property in the following fashion:

$$7\sqrt{2} - 3\sqrt{2} = (7-3)\sqrt{2} = 4\sqrt{2}.$$

It may happen that the terms do not have the same index and the same radicand at the beginning, but they do after each term is written in simplest radical form. An example of this type is provided by

$$\begin{aligned}
5\sqrt{48} - 6\sqrt{75} + 7\sqrt{27} &= 5\sqrt{4^2\cdot 3} - 6\sqrt{5^2\cdot 3} + 7\sqrt{3^2\cdot 3} \\
&= 5(4)\sqrt{3} - 6(5)\sqrt{3} + 7(3)\sqrt{3} \\
&= 20\sqrt{3} - 30\sqrt{3} + 21\sqrt{3} \\
&= (20 - 30 + 21)\sqrt{3} \\
&= 11\sqrt{3}.
\end{aligned}$$

Simplifications such as this cannot be performed if the terms do not have the same index and radicand when written in simplest radical form. Expressions such as $\sqrt{2} + \sqrt{3}$, $\sqrt[3]{5} + \sqrt[4]{5}$, and $2\sqrt{5} + 5\sqrt{2}$ cannot be simplified.

Summarizing this discussion, we handle sums and differences of radical expressions by the following procedure.

Addition or Subtraction of Radical Expressions

1. First, each term is written in simplest radical form.

2. Terms with the same index and the same radicand are then combined by using the distributive property.

EXAMPLE 1   Whenever possible, combine terms by use of the distributive property.

(a) $\sqrt{80} - \sqrt{45} + \sqrt{20}$
(b) $\sqrt{18} - \sqrt{12}$
(c) $7\sqrt[3]{24x^4y^7} - 5y\sqrt[3]{3x^4y^4}$

SOLUTION

(a) $\sqrt{80} - \sqrt{45} + \sqrt{20} = \sqrt{4^2 \cdot 5} - \sqrt{3^2 \cdot 5} + \sqrt{2^2 \cdot 5}$
$$= 4\sqrt{5} - 3\sqrt{5} + 2\sqrt{5}$$
$$= (4 - 3 + 2)\sqrt{5}$$
$$= 3\sqrt{5}$$

(b) $\sqrt{18} - \sqrt{12} = \sqrt{3^2 \cdot 2} - \sqrt{2^2 \cdot 3}$
$$= 3\sqrt{2} - 2\sqrt{3} \qquad \text{cannot be combined}$$

(c) $7\sqrt[3]{24x^4y^7} - 5y\sqrt[3]{3x^4y^4} = 7\sqrt[3]{2^3 \cdot 3x^3x(y^2)^3y} - 5y\sqrt[3]{3x^3xy^3y}$
$$= 7(2xy^2)\sqrt[3]{3xy} - 5y(xy)\sqrt[3]{3xy}$$
$$= 14xy^2\sqrt[3]{3xy} - 5xy^2\sqrt[3]{3xy}$$
$$= (14xy^2 - 5xy^2)\sqrt[3]{3xy}$$
$$= 9xy^2\sqrt[3]{3xy}$$

PRACTICE PROBLEM 1   (Solution on page 271) Whenever possible, combine terms by use of the distributive property.

(a) $4\sqrt{24x} + \sqrt{150x} - 2\sqrt{54x}$
(b) $\sqrt[3]{81x^4y} + 5\sqrt{12x^3y} - 2x\sqrt[3]{3xy} - 4x\sqrt{3xy}$

Since radical expressions represent real numbers, the distributive property holds when radical expressions are involved as factors or terms.

EXAMPLE 2   Use the distributive property to perform the following multiplications, and write the results in simplest radical form.

(a) $\sqrt{2}(\sqrt{3} + 5\sqrt{2})$ \qquad\qquad (b) $(\sqrt{5} + \sqrt{2})(\sqrt{5} - \sqrt{2})$

SOLUTION

(a) $\sqrt{2}(\sqrt{3} + 5\sqrt{2}) = \sqrt{2}(\sqrt{3}) + \sqrt{2}(5\sqrt{2})$
$$= \sqrt{6} + 5(\sqrt{2})^2$$
$$= \sqrt{6} + 5(2)$$
$$= \sqrt{6} + 10$$

(b) $(\sqrt{5} + \sqrt{2})(\sqrt{5} - \sqrt{2})$

$$= \sqrt{5}(\sqrt{5} - \sqrt{2}) + \sqrt{2}(\sqrt{5} - \sqrt{2})$$
$$= (\sqrt{5})^2 - \sqrt{5}\sqrt{2} + \sqrt{2}\sqrt{5} - (\sqrt{2})^2$$
$$= 5 - \sqrt{10} + \sqrt{10} - 2$$
$$= 3$$

The FOIL method and the special product rules in Chapter 6 also hold for radical expressions. Two illustrations are presented in the following example.

EXAMPLE 3   Perform the following multiplications, and write the results in simplest radical form.

(a) $(3 - 2\sqrt{5})^2$

(b) $(5\sqrt{6} + 2)(\sqrt{2} - 4\sqrt{3})$

SOLUTION   (a) The formula for the square of a binomial gives

$$(3 - 2\sqrt{5})^2 = 3^2 - 2(3)(2\sqrt{5}) + (2\sqrt{5})^2$$
$$= 9 - 12\sqrt{5} + 20$$
$$= 29 - 12\sqrt{5}.$$

(b) The FOIL method gives

$(5\sqrt{6} + 2)(\sqrt{2} - 4\sqrt{3})$

$$\overset{\mathbf{F}}{= (5\sqrt{6})(\sqrt{2})} + \overset{\mathbf{O}}{(5\sqrt{6})(-4\sqrt{3})} + \overset{\mathbf{I}}{2\sqrt{2}} + \overset{\mathbf{L}}{2(-4\sqrt{3})}$$
$$= 5\sqrt{12} - 20\sqrt{18} + 2\sqrt{2} - 8\sqrt{3}$$
$$= 5(2\sqrt{3}) - 20(3\sqrt{2}) + 2\sqrt{2} - 8\sqrt{3}$$
$$= 10\sqrt{3} - 60\sqrt{2} + 2\sqrt{2} - 8\sqrt{3}$$
$$= 2\sqrt{3} - 58\sqrt{2}.$$

The special product rule

$$(x + y)(x - y) = x^2 - y^2$$

is very useful in rationalizing denominators which are binomials formed using square roots. For example,

$$\frac{5}{\sqrt{7}+2} = \frac{5(\sqrt{7}-2)}{(\sqrt{7}+2)(\sqrt{7}-2)}$$
$$= \frac{5(\sqrt{7}-2)}{(\sqrt{7})^2 - (2)^2}$$
$$= \frac{5\sqrt{7}-10}{7-4}$$
$$= \frac{5\sqrt{7}-10}{3}.$$

The multiplier $\sqrt{7}-2$ was chosen so as to form a difference of two squares in the denominator. The numbers $\sqrt{7}+2$ and $\sqrt{7}-2$ are called **conjugates** of each other.

Generally, the expression obtained from a binomial by changing the sign of the second term is called the **conjugate** of the binomial. If the denominator of a fraction is a binomial containing one or more square roots, the denominator can be rationalized by multiplying numerator and denominator of the fraction by the conjugate of the denominator.

EXAMPLE 4 Rationalize the denominator and reduce the result to lowest terms.

$$\frac{\sqrt{3}}{\sqrt{6}-3}$$

SOLUTION

$$\frac{\sqrt{3}}{\sqrt{6}-3} = \frac{\sqrt{3}(\sqrt{6}+3)}{(\sqrt{6}-3)(\sqrt{6}+3)}$$
$$= \frac{\sqrt{3}\sqrt{6}+3\sqrt{3}}{(\sqrt{6})^2 - 3^2}$$
$$= \frac{\sqrt{18}+3\sqrt{3}}{6-9}$$
$$= \frac{3\sqrt{2}+3\sqrt{3}}{-3}$$
$$= -\frac{3(\sqrt{2}+\sqrt{3})}{3}$$
$$= -\sqrt{2}-\sqrt{3}$$

PRACTICE PROBLEM 2 (Solution on page 272) Rationalize the denominator and reduce to lowest terms.

$$\frac{6\sqrt{y}}{3\sqrt{x}-2\sqrt{y}}$$

As a final example, we consider some more complicated combinations of radical expressions.

EXAMPLE 5   Combine into a single fraction with a rationalized denominator.

(a) $\dfrac{3}{\sqrt{2}} - \dfrac{1}{\sqrt{3}}$ (b) $\sqrt{x-2} + \dfrac{2}{\sqrt{x-2}}$

SOLUTION   (a) $\dfrac{3}{\sqrt{2}} - \dfrac{1}{\sqrt{3}} = \dfrac{3\sqrt{2}}{2} - \dfrac{\sqrt{3}}{3}$

$$= \frac{3(3\sqrt{2}) - 2(\sqrt{3})}{6}$$

$$= \frac{9\sqrt{2} - 2\sqrt{3}}{6}$$

(b) $\sqrt{x-2} + \dfrac{2}{\sqrt{x-2}} = \dfrac{(\sqrt{x-2})^2 + 2}{\sqrt{x-2}}$

$$= \frac{x-2+2}{\sqrt{x-2}}$$

$$= \frac{x(\sqrt{x-2})}{\sqrt{x-2}\sqrt{x-2})}$$

$$= \frac{x\sqrt{x-2}}{x-2}$$

PRACTICE   (Solution on page 272) Combine into a single fraction with a rationalized
PROBLEM 3   denominator.

$$\sqrt{x^2+1} - \frac{x^2-1}{\sqrt{x^2+1}}$$

EXERCISES 9-6

All variables in these exercises represent positive numbers.
Whenever possible, combine terms by use of the distributive property. (See
Example 1 and Practice Problem 1.)

1. $2\sqrt{3} + 5\sqrt{3}$ 2. $7\sqrt{2} - 3\sqrt{2}$

3. $7\sqrt{2} - 4\sqrt{2} + 5\sqrt{2}$ 4. $8\sqrt{3} - 6\sqrt{3} + 4\sqrt{3}$

5. $6\sqrt{2} - \sqrt{8}$ 6. $5\sqrt{27} + 4\sqrt{3}$

7. $\sqrt{12} + \sqrt{75}$ 8. $\sqrt{18} + \sqrt{50}$

9. $3\sqrt{20} - 2\sqrt{45}$ 10. $6\sqrt{28} - 2\sqrt{63}$

11. $3\sqrt{98} - 2\sqrt{72} + 4\sqrt{8}$ 12. $5\sqrt{75} + 3\sqrt{12} - 6\sqrt{48}$

13. $5\sqrt[3]{x} - 2\sqrt[3]{x} + 4\sqrt[3]{x}$ 14. $7\sqrt[3]{xy} + 4\sqrt[3]{xy} - 6\sqrt[3]{xy}$

15. $\sqrt{x} + 2\sqrt{y} + \sqrt{y}$

16. $\sqrt{2x} - \sqrt{8x} + 2\sqrt{y}$

17. $\sqrt{80x} + \sqrt{45x}$

18. $\sqrt{405x} - \sqrt{45x}$

19. $\sqrt{8xy^2} - \sqrt{32xy^2} + y\sqrt{x}$

20. $5\sqrt{27x^2y} - 6\sqrt{24x^2y} + 3x\sqrt{y}$

21. $6\sqrt[3]{54z} - 8\sqrt[3]{250z}$

22. $7\sqrt[3]{24b} + 4\sqrt[3]{192b}$

23. $9\sqrt{200x^3} + 2x\sqrt{72x}$

24. $4\sqrt{108x} - 5\sqrt{75x^3}$

25. $5\sqrt[3]{16r^4s} + 6r\sqrt[3]{128rs}$

26. $9q\sqrt[3]{40pq} - 5\sqrt[3]{135pq^4}$

27. $4y\sqrt[3]{81x^4y^2} - 3x\sqrt[3]{375xy^5}$

28. $3k\sqrt[3]{24k^2m^5} - 2m\sqrt[3]{81k^5m^2}$

29. $3y\sqrt{12x^2y} - 5x\sqrt{75y^3} + \sqrt{18x^2y} - x\sqrt{50y}$

30. $6x\sqrt{54x^2y} + y\sqrt{12x} + 2\sqrt{24x^4y} - \sqrt{48xy^2}$

Perform the following multiplications and write the results in simplest radical form. (See Examples 2 and 3.)

31. $\sqrt{3}(\sqrt{3} - 1)$

32. $\sqrt{2}(\sqrt{2} - 1)$

33. $\sqrt{5}(\sqrt{5} + \sqrt{2})$

34. $\sqrt{3}(\sqrt{3} - \sqrt{2})$

35. $\sqrt{x}(3 - 2\sqrt{x})$

36. $\sqrt{y}(5 - 2\sqrt{y})$

37. $(\sqrt{5} + \sqrt{7})(\sqrt{5} - \sqrt{7})$

38. $(\sqrt{3} + \sqrt{5})(\sqrt{3} - \sqrt{5})$

39. $(\sqrt{x} + 2)(\sqrt{x} - 2)$

40. $(\sqrt{x} + \sqrt{y})(\sqrt{x} - \sqrt{y})$

41. $(\sqrt{x} + 5)(\sqrt{x} - 3)$

42. $(\sqrt{x} + 3)(\sqrt{x} - 1)$

43. $(2 + 5\sqrt{3})^2$

44. $(7 + 3\sqrt{2})^2$

45. $(7 + 3\sqrt{6})(4 - 5\sqrt{6})$

46. $(2 - 3\sqrt{7})(4 + \sqrt{7})$

47. $(\sqrt{3} + 5\sqrt{2})(4\sqrt{3} - \sqrt{2})$

48. $(2\sqrt{5} - \sqrt{3})(3\sqrt{5} - 4\sqrt{3})$

49. $(7\sqrt{6} - 1)(\sqrt{2} + 5\sqrt{3})$

50. $(9\sqrt{2} + 5)(\sqrt{6} - \sqrt{3})$

51. $(\sqrt{5} + 2)(\sqrt{2} - 3)$

52. $(\sqrt{7} - 1)(\sqrt{3} + 2)$

53. $(\sqrt[3]{x} - \sqrt[3]{y})(\sqrt[3]{x} + \sqrt[3]{y})$

54. $(\sqrt[3]{x} - \sqrt[3]{y})(\sqrt[3]{x^2} + \sqrt[3]{y^2})$

55. $(\sqrt[3]{x} - \sqrt[3]{y})(\sqrt[3]{x^2} + \sqrt[3]{x}\sqrt[3]{y} + \sqrt[3]{y^2})$

56. $(\sqrt[3]{x} + \sqrt[3]{y})(\sqrt[3]{x^2} - \sqrt[3]{x}\sqrt[3]{y} + \sqrt[3]{y^2})$

Rationalize the denominators and reduce the results to lowest terms. (See Example 4 and Practice Problem 2.)

57. $\dfrac{4}{\sqrt{3} + 1}$

58. $\dfrac{6}{\sqrt{5} - 1}$

59. $\dfrac{10}{\sqrt{5} - \sqrt{3}}$

60. $\dfrac{6}{\sqrt{7} - \sqrt{3}}$

61. $\dfrac{10}{5 - 2\sqrt{3}}$

62. $\dfrac{2}{4\sqrt{2} - \sqrt{3}}$

63. $\dfrac{\sqrt{5}}{\sqrt{10} - 5}$

64. $\dfrac{\sqrt{5}}{\sqrt{10} - \sqrt{5}}$

65. $\dfrac{\sqrt{5} - 2}{\sqrt{5} + \sqrt{3}}$

66. $\dfrac{\sqrt{5} + 3}{\sqrt{5} - \sqrt{2}}$

67. $\dfrac{2}{1+\sqrt{x}}$

68. $\dfrac{3}{1-\sqrt{2x}}$

69. $\dfrac{2\sqrt{x}}{3\sqrt{x}+1}$

70. $\dfrac{5\sqrt{x}}{2\sqrt{x}-3}$

71. $\dfrac{\sqrt{x}}{\sqrt{x}+\sqrt{y}}$

72. $\dfrac{\sqrt{x}-\sqrt{y}}{\sqrt{x}+\sqrt{y}}$

73. $\dfrac{2\sqrt{x}+\sqrt{y}}{3\sqrt{x}-2\sqrt{y}}$

74. $\dfrac{\sqrt{x}-4\sqrt{y}}{2\sqrt{x}+3\sqrt{y}}$

Combine into a single fraction with a rationalized denominator and in lowest terms. (See Example 5 and Practice Problem 3.)

75. $\dfrac{2}{\sqrt{3}}+\dfrac{1}{\sqrt{2}}$

76. $\sqrt{5}-\dfrac{4}{\sqrt{5}}$

77. $\sqrt{\dfrac{3}{2}}+\sqrt{\dfrac{2}{3}}$

78. $\sqrt{\dfrac{3}{2}}-\sqrt{\dfrac{2}{3}}$

79. $\sqrt[3]{54}-\dfrac{1}{\sqrt[3]{16}}$

80. $\sqrt[4]{48}-\dfrac{1}{\sqrt[4]{27}}$

81. $\sqrt{x+2}-\dfrac{x+1}{\sqrt{x+2}}$

82. $\sqrt{x}+\dfrac{1-x}{\sqrt{x}}$

83. $\dfrac{\sqrt{x^2-1}}{x-1}-\dfrac{x}{\sqrt{x^2-1}}$

84. $\dfrac{\sqrt{x^2-1}}{x}-\dfrac{x-1}{\sqrt{x^2-1}}$

Rationalize the numerators, and express the results in lowest terms.

*85. $\dfrac{2+3\sqrt{3}}{6}$

*86. $\dfrac{1+2\sqrt{2}}{6}$

*87. $\dfrac{\sqrt{12}+6}{10}$

*88. $\dfrac{\sqrt{45}+12}{15}$

*89. $\dfrac{6\sqrt{2}-\sqrt{8}}{14}$

*90. $\dfrac{7\sqrt{3}-\sqrt{2}}{10}$

SOLUTIONS FOR PRACTICE PROBLEMS

1. (a) $4\sqrt{24x}+\sqrt{150x}-2\sqrt{54x}=4\sqrt{2^2\cdot 6x}+\sqrt{5^2\cdot 6x}-2\sqrt{3^2\cdot 6x}$
   $$=4(2)\sqrt{6x}+5\sqrt{6x}-2(3)\sqrt{6x}$$
   $$=(8+5-6)\sqrt{6x}$$
   $$=7\sqrt{6x}$$

   (b) $\sqrt[3]{81x^4y}+5\sqrt{12x^3y}-2x\sqrt[3]{3xy}-4x\sqrt{3xy}$
   $$=\sqrt[3]{3^3\cdot 3x^3xy}+5\sqrt{2^2\cdot 3x^2xy}-2x\sqrt[3]{3xy}-4x\sqrt{3xy}$$
   $$=3x\sqrt[3]{3xy}+5(2x)\sqrt{3xy}-2x\sqrt[3]{3xy}-4x\sqrt{3xy}$$
   $$=x\sqrt[3]{3xy}+6x\sqrt{3xy}$$

2. $\dfrac{6\sqrt{y}}{3\sqrt{x}-2\sqrt{y}} = \dfrac{6\sqrt{y}(3\sqrt{x}+2\sqrt{y})}{(3\sqrt{x}-2\sqrt{y})(3\sqrt{x}+2\sqrt{y})}$

$\qquad\qquad = \dfrac{18\sqrt{xy}+12(\sqrt{y})^2}{(3\sqrt{x})^2-(2\sqrt{y})^2}$

$\qquad\qquad = \dfrac{18\sqrt{xy}+12y}{9x-4y}$

3. $\sqrt{x^2+1}-\dfrac{x^2-1}{\sqrt{x^2+1}} = \dfrac{(\sqrt{x^2+1})^2-(x^2-1)}{\sqrt{x^2+1}}$

$\qquad\qquad = \dfrac{x^2+1-x^2+1}{\sqrt{x^2+1}}$

$\qquad\qquad = \dfrac{2(\sqrt{x^2+1})}{\sqrt{x^2+1}(\sqrt{x^2+1})}$

$\qquad\qquad = \dfrac{2\sqrt{x^2+1}}{x^2+1}$

9-7
Complex Numbers

In Section 9-3 we observed that every positive real number a has two square roots, designated by $\sqrt{a}$ and $-\sqrt{a}$. We also noted a fundamental deficiency of the set of real numbers: *A negative real number does not have a square root in the set of real numbers*, because the square of a real number is never negative. This is a very unsatisfactory state of affairs mathematically, since simple equations such as

$$x^2 = -1$$

or

$$x^2 = -4$$

do not have solutions in the real numbers. This deficiency of the real numbers is the main reason for the construction of the set of complex numbers.

Our goal here is to extend the set of real numbers to a larger set, the complex numbers, in which negative numbers have square roots. Moreover, this extension is to be made in such a way that the Basic Properties listed in Section 1-3 (the field properties) hold for complex numbers as well as for real numbers, and also so that computations are consistent with those of the real numbers.

Definition 9-9 The number $i = \sqrt{-1}$ is by definition a number such that

$$\boxed{i^2 = -1.}$$

A **complex number** is an expression of the form

$$\boxed{a + bi,}$$

where a and b are real numbers. The number a is called the **real part** of $a + bi$, and b is called the **imaginary part**.

Examples of complex numbers are

$$1 + 2i, \quad 2 + (-3)i, \quad -5 + \tfrac{7}{2}i, \quad 6 + \sqrt{2}\,i, \quad 8 + 0i, \quad 0 + 7i.$$

If b is a negative number, as in $2 + (-3)i$, we drop the "+" sign and write $2 - 3i$ instead of $2 + (-3)i$.

A complex number of the form $a + 0i$ is regarded as being the same as the **real number** a. Any complex number $a + bi$ with $b \neq 0$ is called an **imaginary number**, and a number of the form $0 + bi$, with $b \neq 0$, is called a **pure imaginary number**.

In this section we define equality, addition, subtraction, multiplication, and division for complex numbers in ways so that the goal set forth just before Definition 9-9 is realized. We begin with the definition of equality.

Definition 9-10 Let $a + bi$ and $c + di$ be two complex numbers, where a, b, c, and d are real numbers. Then

$$a + bi = c + di$$

if and only if

$$a = c \quad \text{and} \quad b = d.$$

That is, two complex numbers are **equal** if and only if their real parts are equal and their imaginary parts are equal. As special cases, we take $a = a + 0i$ and $bi = 0 + bi$.

EXAMPLE 1 Solve for x and y in the following equations, where x and y are real numbers.

(a) $x + 6i = 4 + 3yi$
(b) $(3x + 2y) + (x - 5)i = (x + 5) + (2y - 1)i$

SOLUTION

(a) By Definition 9-10,

$$x + 6i = 4 + 3yi \quad \text{if and only if} \quad x = 4 \text{ and } 6 = 3y,$$

so we have the solution $x = 4$, $y = 2$.

(b) By the definition of equality,

$$(3x + 2y) + (x - 5)i = (x + 5) + (2y - 1)i$$

if and only if the following system is satisfied:

$$3x + 2y = x + 5$$
$$x - 5 = 2y - 1.$$

This system is equivalent to

$$2x + 2y = 5$$
$$x - 2y = 4.$$

Adding these equations, we get $3x = 9$ and $x = 3$. Substituting $x = 3$, we have

$$2(3) + 2y = 5$$
$$2y = -1$$
$$y = -\tfrac{1}{2}.$$

The solution is $x = 3$, $y = -\tfrac{1}{2}$.

Definition 9-11 **Addition** of complex numbers is defined by

$$(a + bi) + (c + di) = (a + c) + (b + d)i.$$

This means that the sum of two complex numbers is found by adding them in the same way that polynomials are added:

$$(a + bx) + (c + dx) = (a + c) + (b + d)x.$$

Definition 9-11 is consistent with addition of real numbers: If $a = a + 0i$ and $b = b + 0i$ are real numbers, their sum as complex numbers is

$$(a + 0i) + (b + 0i) = (a + b) + 0i,$$

which corresponds to $a + b$.

The complex number $0 = 0 + 0i$ is the **additive identity**, and the **additive inverse** of $a + bi$ is

$$-(a + bi) = -a + (-b)i$$

since

$$(a + bi) + (-a + (-b)i) = (a - a) + (b - b)i$$
$$= 0 + 0i$$
$$= 0.$$

Subtraction is performed in the same way as for binomials. To subtract $c + di$ from $a + bi$, we add the additive inverse of $c + di$ to $a + bi$:

$$(a + bi) - (c + di) = [a + bi] + [-(c + di)],$$

so

$$(a + bi) - (c + di) = (a - c) + (b - d)i.$$

EXAMPLE 2 Perform the following operations and write the results in the form $a + bi$.

(a) $(-5 + 7i) + (2 - 3i)$ (b) $(3 - 5i) - (4 - 7i)$

SOLUTION

(a) $(-5 + 7i) + (2 - 3i) = (-5 + 2) + (7 - 3)i$
$$= -3 + 4i$$
(b) $(3 - 5i) - (4 - 7i) = (3 - 4) + (-5 + 7)i$
$$= -1 + 2i$$

To form the product of two complex numbers, we multiply the same way as with binomials, and simplify the result by using $i^2 = -1$.

EXAMPLE 3 Perform the following multiplications, and write the results in the form $a + bi$.

(a) $(2 + 3i)(4 - 5i)$ (b) $(-i)(7 - 8i)$

SOLUTION

(a) Using the FOIL method for multiplying binomials, we have
$$(2 + 3i)(4 - 5i) = (2)(4) + (2)(-5i) + (3i)(4) + (3i)(-5i)$$
$$= 8 - 10i + 12i - 15i^2$$
$$= 8 + 2i - 15(-1)$$
$$= 23 + 2i.$$
(b) $(-i)(7 - 8i) = (-i)(7) + (-i)(-8i)$
$$= -7i + 8i^2$$
$$= -8 - 7i$$

If the same procedure is followed with arbitrary complex numbers $a + bi$ and $c + di$, the result gives the formula in Definition 9-12.

Definition 9-12 **Multiplication** of complex numbers is defined by

$$(a + bi)(c + di) = (ac - bd) + (ad + bc)i.$$

This formula can be used to evaluate a product, but the chance of error is much less if the multiplication is performed as it was done in Example 3.

The work done in the solutions to Examples 2 and 3 shows that a complex number can be written in many different forms (as a product, or as a sum, etc.). The form where the complex number is written as $a + bi$, with a and b real numbers, is called the **standard form** of the complex number.

PRACTICE PROBLEM 1 (Solution on page 281) Perform the multiplications, and write the results in standard form.

(a) $(6 - i)(-2 + 4i)$
(b) $(4 + 7i)(7 + 4i)$

In the set of complex numbers, negative real numbers have square roots.‡ For example, consider

$$(2i)^2 = 4i^2 = -4$$

and

$$(-2i)^2 = 4i^2 = -4.$$

Thus -4 has two square roots in the complex numbers, given by $2i$ and $-2i$. In analogy with the notation for square roots of positive real numbers, the square root that has the positive imaginary part is designated as the principal square root and is denoted by $\sqrt{-4}$. Thus

$$\sqrt{-4} = 2i \qquad \text{and} \qquad -\sqrt{-4} = -2i.$$

We use the same notation for arbitrary negative real numbers. For any positive real number a, the negative real number $-a$ has two square roots, $i\sqrt{a}$ and $-i\sqrt{a}$. The **principal square root** of $-a$ is

$$\boxed{\sqrt{-a} = i\sqrt{a}, \qquad \text{where } a > 0.}$$

EXAMPLE 4 Write the following expressions in terms of i, with radicals simplified as much as possible.

(a) $\sqrt{-9}$ (b) $-\sqrt{-16}$ (c) $\sqrt{-63}$

SOLUTION

(a) $\sqrt{-9} = i\sqrt{9} = 3i$
(b) $-\sqrt{-16} = -i\sqrt{16} = -4i$
(c) $\sqrt{-63} = i\sqrt{63} = i\sqrt{3^2 \cdot 7} = i(3\sqrt{7}) = 3i\sqrt{7}$

‡In trigonometry, it is shown that every complex number has a square root in the set of complex numbers.

It is common to leave the i to the left of the radical in a number such as $3i\sqrt{7}$, and not write $3\sqrt{7}i$. This is for clarity, to emphasize that i does not belong under the radical with the 7.

Some complications result from the extension of the principal square root notation to square roots of negative numbers. For example, the property, $\sqrt{a}\sqrt{b} = \sqrt{ab}$, where $a > 0$ and $b > 0$, for products of principal square roots of positive numbers *does not carry over to principal square roots of negative numbers*:

$$\sqrt{-4}\sqrt{-9} = (2i)(3i) = 6i^2 = -6$$

and

$$\sqrt{(-4)(-9)} = \sqrt{36} = 6 \neq \sqrt{-4}\sqrt{-9}.$$

Difficulties of this sort are best handled by converting all numbers involved to standard form $a + bi$, and then performing the operations as we have done in the preceding examples.

EXAMPLE 5 Perform the indicated operations.

(a) $\sqrt{-25}\sqrt{-4}$

(b) $\sqrt{-6}(\sqrt{-3} + \sqrt{2})$

(c) $(2 + \sqrt{-9})(2 - \sqrt{-9})$

SOLUTION

(a) $\sqrt{-25}\sqrt{-4} = (5i)(2i) = 10i^2 = -10$

(b) $\sqrt{-6}(\sqrt{-3} + \sqrt{2}) = i\sqrt{6}(i\sqrt{3} + \sqrt{2})$
$$= i^2\sqrt{6}\sqrt{3} + i\sqrt{6}\sqrt{2}$$
$$= (-1)\sqrt{18} + i\sqrt{12}$$
$$= -3\sqrt{2} + 2i\sqrt{3}$$

(c) $(2 + \sqrt{-9})(2 - \sqrt{-9}) = (2 + 3i)(2 - 3i)$
$$= 4 - 6i + 6i - 9i^2$$
$$= 4 - 9(-1)$$
$$= 13$$

In the solution to part (c) of Example 5, we have a product of the form $(a + bi)(a - bi)$. The value of such a product is always a nonnegative real number:

$$(a + bi)(a - bi) = a^2 - abi + abi - b^2i^2$$
$$= a^2 - b^2(-1)$$
$$= a^2 + b^2,$$

and $a^2 + b^2$ is a nonnegative real number. Extending the terminology we used in Section 9-6, $a + bi$ and $a - bi$ are called **conjugates** of each other.

In close similarity to our earlier work in rationalizing denominators, division of complex numbers is accomplished by multiplying numerator and denominator of a quotient by the conjugate of the denominator.

EXAMPLE 6 Perform the indicated division, and express the result in standard form.

$$\frac{3 + i}{4 - 7i}$$

SOLUTION

$$\frac{3 + i}{4 - 7i} = \frac{(3 + i)(4 + 7i)}{(4 - 7i)(4 + 7i)}$$

$$= \frac{12 + 25i + 7i^2}{16 - 49i^2}$$

$$= \frac{12 + 25i - 7}{16 + 49}$$

$$= \frac{5 + 25i}{65}$$

$$= \frac{5(1 + 5i)}{5(13)}$$

$$= \frac{1}{13} + \frac{5}{13}i$$

PRACTICE PROBLEM 2 (Solution on page 281) Perform the following division, and express the result in standard form.

$$\frac{17}{5 + 3i}$$

At this point, we have defined equality and the four fundamental operations for complex numbers. Although we do not verify it here, the Basic Properties listed in Section 1-3 are valid for complex numbers, and our objectives for this section are accomplished.

As a final item of interest, we consider the positive integral powers of the number i. We have

$$i^0 = 1$$

$$i^1 = i$$

$$i^2 = -1$$

$$i^3 = i^2 \cdot i = (-1)i = -i$$

$$i^4 = i^3 \cdot i = (-i)(i) = -i^2 = 1.$$

278

The fact that $i^4 = 1$ can be used to reduce any positive integral power i^n to one of the numbers 1, i, -1, and $-i$. This is accomplished by dividing n by 4 and using the Laws of Exponents as demonstrated in the next example.

EXAMPLE 7   Evaluate i^{55}.

SOLUTION   We first divide 55 by 4 which yields $55 = 4(13) + 3$. Then

$$i^{55} = i^{(4)(13)+3}$$
$$= i^{(4)(13)} \cdot i^3$$
$$= (i^4)^{13} \cdot i^3$$
$$= (1)^{13} \cdot i^3$$
$$= -i.$$

EXERCISES 9-7

Use the definition of equality of complex numbers to solve for x and y, where x and y are real numbers. (See Example 1.)

1. $3x - 6i = 12 + 2yi$
2. $15 - 4yi = 3x + 20i$
3. $(3x - 1) + (y + 2)i = (2x + 1) + (2y - 3)i$
4. $(2x + 5) + (y - 3)i = (5x + 8) + (9 - 2y)i$
5. $(2x - 1) + (12 - 2y)i = (2 - 9y) + (1 - 3x)i$
6. $(2y - 2) + (3x + 6)i = (2 - x) + (2y - 6)i$
7. $(7x - y) + (3x + 10)i = 9 + (3 - 5y)i$
8. $(4x + 3y) + (2x + 7)i = 1 + (5y - 12)i$

Perform the following additions or subtractions, and write the results in standard form. (See Example 2.)

9. $(7 + 2i) + (3 - 5i)$
10. $(6 + 9i) + (-2 + 8i)$
11. $(4 - 3i) - (-2 + i)$
12. $(-3 + 5i) - (-4 + 3i)$
13. $-11 - (-6 + 8i)$
14. $-4 - (-1 + 9i)$
15. $(-18 + 4i) + (14 - 10i)$
16. $(-34 + 9i) + (18 - 16i)$
17. $-(7 - 9i) - (-5 - 3i)$
18. $-(10 - 8i) - (-4 - 7i)$
19. $(16 + 17i) - 11$
20. $(13 - 6i) - 9$
21. $(-31 + 14i) + 8i$
22. $(28 - 15i) + 4i$
23. $(6 - 3i) + (4 + 6i) - (9 - 7i)$
24. $(5 + 7i) + (3 - 9i) - (4 - 6i)$

25. $(-3 + 5i) + (1 - 2i) - (-4 + 6i)$

26. $(-4 + 7i) + (3 - 3i) - (-2 + 4i)$

27. $(2 - 5i) - (3 + 4i) - (-2 + i)$

28. $(4 - i) - (2 + 3i) + (-4 + 5i)$

Perform the indicated multiplications, and leave the results in standard form. (See Example 3 and Practice Problem 1.)

29. $(3i)(4i)$

31. $(-5i)(2i)$

33. $2i(3 + 5i)$

35. $4i(5 - 3i)$

37. $(4 + 3i)(2 - i)$

39. $(1 + 3i)(2 - 5i)$

41. $(7 - 2i)(3 - i)$

43. $(4 + 5i)(4 - 5i)$

45. $(4 + 5i)(5 + 4i)$

47. $(2 + 3i)(2 - 3i)$

49. $(4 - 3i)(3 - 4i)$

51. $(4 + i)^2$

53. $i(3 - i)^2$

30. $(2i)(7i)$

32. $(6i)(-4i)$

34. $3i(2 + 7i)$

36. $5i(4 - 9i)$

38. $(3 - 5i)(4 - 2i)$

40. $(4 - 3i)(5 + 2i)$

42. $(2 + 3i)(-1 + 4i)$

44. $(6 + 8i)(6 - 8i)$

46. $(6 + 3i)(3 + 6i)$

48. $(2 + 5i)(2 - 5i)$

50. $(3 - 5i)(5 - 3i)$

52. $(2 - i)^2$

54. $i(3 + 2i)^2$

Write the following in terms of i, with radicals simplified as much as possible. (See Example 4.)

55. $\sqrt{-16}$

58. $\sqrt{-75}$

56. $\sqrt{-25}$

59. $-\sqrt{-45}$

57. $\sqrt{-50}$

60. $-\sqrt{-300}$

Solve the following equations.

*61. $x^2 = -64$

*64. $x^2 = -28$

*62. $x^2 = -36$

*65. $x^2 = -48$

*63. $x^2 = -20$

*66. $x^2 = -80$

Perform the indicated operations. Write the results in terms of i, with radicals simplified as much as possible. (See Example 5.)

67. $\sqrt{-16}\sqrt{-9}$

69. $\dfrac{\sqrt{-48}}{\sqrt{-3}}$

71. $\sqrt{-15}(\sqrt{-5} - \sqrt{3})$

68. $\sqrt{-25}\sqrt{-49}$

70. $\dfrac{\sqrt{-80}}{\sqrt{-5}}$

72. $\sqrt{-14}(\sqrt{-7} - \sqrt{2})$

Perform the following divisions, and express the results in standard form. (See Example 6 and Practice Problem 2.)

73. $\dfrac{6 + 8i}{2}$

74. $\dfrac{6 - 9i}{3}$

75. $\dfrac{3 + 4i}{i}$

76. $\dfrac{2 + i}{i}$

77. $\dfrac{1}{2 + i}$

78. $\dfrac{1}{3 - i}$

79. $\dfrac{5i}{3 + i}$

80. $\dfrac{10i}{2 - i}$

81. $\dfrac{2 + 3i}{3 + 2i}$

82. $\dfrac{3 + i}{1 + 2i}$

83. $\dfrac{3 - 2i}{4 - 3i}$

84. $\dfrac{3 + 2i}{5 + 3i}$

85. $\dfrac{1 + 3i}{-5 + 2i}$

86. $\dfrac{2 + i}{-8 + 6i}$

87. $\dfrac{1 + i}{1 - 3i}$

88. $\dfrac{1 + i}{3 - 2i}$

89. $\dfrac{5 - 2i}{5 + 2i}$

90. $\dfrac{3 + 4i}{3 - 4i}$

Write each of the following as 1, i, -1, or $-i$. (See Example 7.)

91. i^9

92. i^7

93. i^{23}

94. i^{25}

95. i^{68}

96. i^{58}

97. i^{74}

98. i^{77}

99. i^{115}

100. i^{175}

*101. i^{-23}

*102. i^{-19}

SOLUTIONS FOR PRACTICE PROBLEMS

1. (a) $(6 - i)(-2 + 4i) = -12 + 24i + 2i - 4i^2$
$$= -12 + 26i + 4$$
$$= -8 + 26i$$

(b) $(4 + 7i)(7 + 4i) = 28 + 16i + 49i + 28i^2$
$$= 28 + 65i - 28$$
$$= 65i$$

2. $\dfrac{17}{5 + 3i} = \dfrac{17(5 - 3i)}{(5 + 3i)(5 - 3i)} = \dfrac{17(5 - 3i)}{25 - 9i^2} = \dfrac{17(5 - 3i)}{34} = \dfrac{5}{2} - \dfrac{3}{2}i$

PRACTICE TEST for Chapter 9

Assume that all variables represent positive numbers.

1. Simplify each expression to a rational expression in lowest terms.

   (a) $\dfrac{x^{-2}w^{-1}y^0}{x^{-3}w^3y^{-4}}$

   (b) $\left(\dfrac{x^{-1}y^2}{z^{-2}}\right)^{-2}\left(\dfrac{xy^0}{z^2}\right)^{-1}$

2. Use scientific notation to help evaluate the following numbers, and express each result both in scientific notation and in decimal form.

   (a) $\dfrac{0.00065}{260}$

   (b) $\dfrac{0.000042 \times 16,000}{280,000 \times 0.003}$

3. Find the value of the given expression.

   (a) $-\sqrt{25p^2q^6}$

   (b) $\sqrt[3]{\dfrac{x^8y^7z^{-1}}{x^{-1}yz^2}}$

4. Evaluate.

   (a) $-64^{2/3}$

   (b) $(-8)^{-2/3}$

5. Perform the indicated operations, and write the results so that all exponents are positive and no variable occurs more than once in a term.

   (a) $\dfrac{(9p^2)^{1/2}(8q)^{2/3}}{(27p^2q)^{1/3}}$

   (b) $(x^{-3/2} + y^{-3/2})(x^{-3/2} - y^{-3/2})$

6. Perform the indicated multiplication or division, and remove all factors possible from the radicand.

   (a) $\sqrt{10x}\sqrt{6x^3}$

   (b) $\dfrac{\sqrt{96a^3b^5}}{\sqrt{2ab}}$

7. Whenever possible, combine terms by use of the distributive property.

   (a) $5\sqrt{3} + 4\sqrt{3}$

   (b) $3x\sqrt{8xy} + 5\sqrt{2x^3y} - 4x\sqrt{2xy}$

8. Rationalize the denominators and reduce the results to lowest terms.

   (a) $\dfrac{2x}{\sqrt{3xy}}$

   (b) $\sqrt[3]{\dfrac{6a^2}{9xy^3}}$

   (c) $\dfrac{10}{\sqrt{5}+1}$

   (d) $\dfrac{\sqrt{5}}{\sqrt{7}+\sqrt{5}}$

In problems 9 and 10, perform the indicated operations and write the results in standard form.

9. (a) $(3 - 2i) + (-7 + 6i)$

   (b) $(4 - 3i) - (6 - 8i)$

10. (a) $(4 + 3i)(4 - 3i)$

    (b) $\dfrac{2 + 5i}{2 - 5i}$

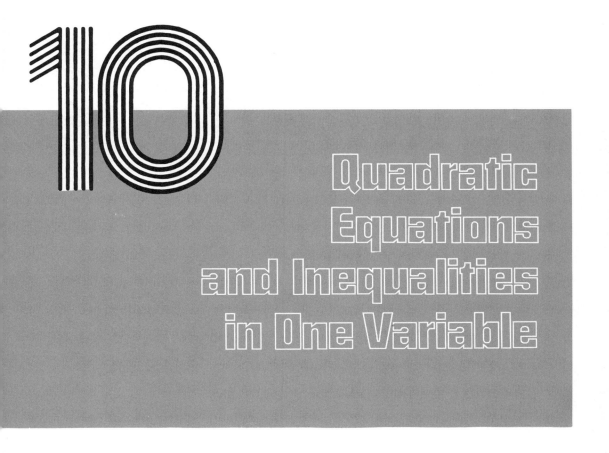

10

10-1
Solution
by Completing
the Square

In Section 7-3 we described a quadratic equation in one variable as any equation that can be put in the following form.

> **Standard Form of a Quadratic Equation**
> $$ax^2 + bx + c = 0, \qquad a \neq 0$$

If it is possible to factor the quadratic expression

$$ax^2 + bx + c$$

as a product of linear factors, then the solutions to the linear equations formed by setting each linear factor equal to zero will be the solutions to the quadratic equation.

The following is an outline of the procedure for solving quadratic equations by factoring.

> **Solution by Factoring**
>
> 1. Rewrite, if necessary, the quadratic equation in standard form.
> 2. Factor the quadratic expression as a product of linear factors.
> 3. Set each linear factor equal to zero.
> 4. Solve the resulting linear equations.

EXAMPLE 1   Solve each quadratic equation by factoring.

(a) $7x^2 + 19x = 6$ (b) $x^2 - 9 = 0$

SOLUTION

(a) $7x^2 + 19x = 6$
$7x^2 + 19x - 6 = 0$
$(7x - 2)(x + 3) = 0$
$7x - 2 = 0 \qquad x + 3 = 0$
$7x = 2 \qquad\qquad x = -3$
$x = \frac{2}{7}$
Solution set $= \{\frac{2}{7}, -3\}$

(b) $x^2 - 9 = 0$
$(x - 3)(x + 3) = 0$
$x - 3 = 0 \qquad x + 3 = 0$
$x = 3 \qquad\qquad x = -3$
Solution set $= \{3, -3\}$

PRACTICE
PROBLEM 1

(Solution on page 290) Solve by factoring.

(a) $x = \dfrac{9}{15 - 4x}$ (b) $9(y - 2)^2 = 4$

Let us return to part (b) of Example 1. The solutions $x = 3$ and $x = -3$ are those numbers whose square is 9. These solutions could have been found by considering the equation in the form

$$x^2 = 9.$$

Since

$$3^2 = 9 \quad \text{or} \quad (-3)^2 = 9,$$

we have

$$x = 3 \quad \text{or} \quad x = -3,$$

which we write compactly as

$$x = \pm 3.$$

The symbol "$\pm$" is read "plus or minus."

In general, the quadratic equation written in the form

$$(x + h)^2 = k^2,$$

with constants h and k, can be solved by taking the square root of both sides:

$$x + h = \pm k.$$

Solving for x yields

$$x = -h \pm k.$$

We illustrate this method of *taking the square root* of both sides in the next example.

EXAMPLE 2 Solve each quadratic equation by taking the square root of both sides.

(a) $4x^2 - 25 = 0$

(b) $4z^2 + 1 = 0$

(c) $\left(y - \dfrac{2}{3}\right)^2 - 1 = 0$

SOLUTION

(a) $4x^2 - 25 = 0$

$\qquad 4x^2 = 25$ (Adding 25 to both sides)

$\qquad (2x)^2 = 5^2$ (Writing each side as a perfect square)

$\qquad 2x = \pm 5$ (Taking the square root of both sides)

$\qquad x = \pm \dfrac{5}{2}$ (Dividing both sides by 2)

(b) $4z^2 + 1 = 0$

$\qquad 4z^2 = -1$ (Adding -1 to both sides)

$\qquad (2z)^2 = i^2$ (Writing each side as a perfect square)

$\qquad 2z = \pm i$ (Taking the square root of both sides)

$\qquad z = \pm \dfrac{i}{2}$ (Dividing both sides by 2)

(c) $\left(y - \dfrac{2}{3}\right)^2 - 1 = 0$

$\qquad \left(y - \dfrac{2}{3}\right)^2 = 1$ (Adding 1 to both sides)

$\qquad \left(y - \dfrac{2}{3}\right)^2 = 1^2$ (Writing each side as a perfect square)

$\qquad y - \dfrac{2}{3} = \pm 1$ (Taking the square root of both sides)

$\qquad y = \dfrac{2}{3} \pm 1$ $\left(\text{Adding } \dfrac{2}{3} \text{ to both sides}\right)$

$\qquad y = \begin{cases} \dfrac{2}{3} + 1 = \dfrac{5}{3} & \text{(Using the "}+\text{" sign)} \\[2ex] \dfrac{2}{3} - 1 = -\dfrac{1}{3} & \text{(Using the "}-\text{" sign)} \end{cases}$

The solution set is $\left\{\dfrac{5}{3}, -\dfrac{1}{3}\right\}$.

Any quadratic equation can be put in the form

$$(x + h)^2 = k^2$$

or

$$x^2 + 2hx + h^2 = k^2.$$

The procedure of changing the quadratic equation

$$ax^2 + bx + c = 0$$

to

$$(x + h)^2 = k^2$$

involves *completing the square*, and we illustrate this procedure in the next example.

EXAMPLE 3   Solve the quadratic equation

$$x^2 = 6x - 8$$

by completing the square.

SOLUTION   Our goal is to find constants h and k so that the equation

$$x^2 = 6x - 8$$

is equivalent to one in the form

$$x^2 + 2hx + h^2 = k^2.$$

We concentrate on the constant h. First we write the equation so that only the variable terms appear on the left side.

$$x^2 - 6x = -8$$

Since

$$x^2 - 6x = x^2 + 2(-3)x,$$

we see that $h = -3$. Notice that -3 is one-half the coefficient of the linear term. Thus $h^2 = (-3)^2 = 9$ and we add 9 to both sides of the equation.

$$x^2 - 6x + 9 = -8 + 9$$
$$x^2 - 6x + 9 = 1. \qquad (x^2 + 2hx + h^2 = k^2)$$

The left side now factors as a perfect square binomial and we write each side as a perfect square.

$$(x - 3)^2 = 1^2 \qquad [(x + h)^2 = k^2]$$

Taking the square root of both sides gives

$$x - 3 = \pm 1, \qquad (x + h = \pm k)$$

and solving for x yields
$$x = 3 \pm 1. \qquad (x = -h \pm k)$$

Thus
$$x = \begin{cases} 3 + 1 = 4 & \text{(using the "+" sign)} \\ 3 - 1 = 2 & \text{(using the "−" sign)} \end{cases}$$

and the solutions are $x = 4, 2$.

EXAMPLE 4   Solve the quadratic equation
$$3x^2 - 12x + 15 = 0$$
by completing the square.

SOLUTION   Again we must write the equation in the form
$$x^2 + 2hx + h^2 = k^2.$$
Thus after moving the constant to the right-hand side,
$$3x^2 - 12x = -15,$$
we divide both sides by 3, the coefficient of the x^2 term.
$$x^2 - 4x = -5$$
Next we add
$$(\tfrac{1}{2} \cdot \text{coefficient of } x)^2 = [\tfrac{1}{2}(-4)]^2 = 4$$
to both sides, yielding
$$x^2 - 4x + 4 = -5 + 4$$
or
$$x^2 - 4x + 4 = -1. \qquad (x^2 + 2hx + h^2 = k^2)$$
The left side factors as a perfect square binomial and we write each side as a perfect square.
$$(x - 2)^2 = i^2 \qquad [(x + h)^2 = k^2]$$
Taking the square root of both sides gives
$$x - 2 = \pm i, \qquad (x + h = \pm k)$$
and finally we solve for x:
$$x = 2 \pm i.$$
The two solutions are $2 + i$ and $2 - i$.

The steps for solving a quadratic equation by completing the square are summarized below.

> **Completing the Square to Solve**
> $$ax^2 + bx + c = 0, \qquad a \neq 0.$$
> 1. Isolate the constant term on one side of the equation.
> 2. Divide both sides of the equation by the coefficient of the x^2 term.
> 3. Compute $\frac{1}{2}$ times the coefficient of x, square the result, and add this to both sides of the equation.
> 4. Factor the quadratic as a perfect square binomial.
> 5. Take the square root of both sides.
> 6. Solve the resulting linear equations.

EXAMPLE 5 Solve by completing the square.

$$2x^2 + x - 2 = 0$$

SOLUTION We follow the steps outlined above.

Steps	*Equation*
1. Isolate the constant term on one side of the equation.	$2x^2 + x = 2$
2. Divide both sides of the equation by the coefficient of the x^2 term.	$x^2 + \dfrac{1}{2}x = 1$
3. Compute $\frac{1}{2}$ times the coefficient of x.	$\dfrac{1}{2}\left(\dfrac{1}{2}\right) = \dfrac{1}{4}$
Square the result.	$\left(\dfrac{1}{4}\right)^2 = \dfrac{1}{16}$
Add this to both sides of the equation.	$x^2 + \dfrac{1}{2}x + \dfrac{1}{16} = 1 + \dfrac{1}{16}$
	$x^2 + \dfrac{1}{2}x + \dfrac{1}{16} = \dfrac{17}{16}$
4. Factor the quadratic as a perfect square binomial.	$\left(x + \dfrac{1}{4}\right)^2 = \dfrac{17}{16}$
5. Take the square root of both sides.	$x + \dfrac{1}{4} = \pm\dfrac{\sqrt{17}}{4}$
6. Solve the resulting linear equations.	$x = -\dfrac{1}{4} \pm \dfrac{\sqrt{17}}{4} = \dfrac{-1 \pm \sqrt{17}}{4}$

The solutions are $\dfrac{-1 + \sqrt{17}}{4}$ and $\dfrac{-1 - \sqrt{17}}{4}$.

PRACTICE PROBLEM 2   (Solution on page 291) Solve by completing the square.

$$4x^2 - 8x + 20 = 0$$

EXERCISES 10-1

Solve by factoring. (See Example 1 and Practice Problem 1.)

1. $x^2 - 5x + 6 = 0$

2. $x^2 - 8x + 12 = 0$

3. $b^2 + 4b - 5 = 0$

4. $c^2 + 3c + 2 = 0$

5. $2x^2 + x = 1$

6. $3x^2 + 7x = -2$

7. $10m^2 = 1 - 3m$

8. $11h = 3 - 4h^2$

9. $a^2 - 1 = 0$

10. $x^2 - 16 = 0$

11. $9x^2 - 100 = 0$

12. $25x^2 - 36 = 0$

13. $r^2 - 4r = 0$

14. $s^2 + 9s = 0$

15. $3x^2 - x = 0$

16. $5x^2 + 4x = 0$

17. $\dfrac{x^2}{x + 4} = 2$

18. $x = \dfrac{7}{2x + 13}$

19. $2x = \dfrac{15 - 7x}{x}$

20. $\dfrac{4}{x} = 13 - 3x$

21. $x^3 = 2x^2$

22. $x^2 = x$

23. $z^3 = 9z$

24. $w^3 = w$

Solve by the method of taking the square root of both sides. (See Example 2.)

25. $y^2 = 9$

26. $z^2 = 16$

27. $4a^2 = 1$

28. $100b^2 = 36$

29. $(x - 1)^2 = 100$

30. $(y + 2)^2 = 9$

31. $(z + 11)^2 = 81$

32. $(x - 4)^2 = 4$

33. $\left(x - \dfrac{1}{2}\right)^2 = \dfrac{9}{4}$

34. $\left(x - \dfrac{2}{5}\right)^2 = \dfrac{1}{25}$

35. $\left(y + \dfrac{1}{3}\right)^2 = \dfrac{16}{9}$

36. $\left(z - \dfrac{1}{4}\right)^2 = \dfrac{9}{64}$

37. $x^2 + 4x + 4 = 9$

38. $x^2 - 18x + 81 = 100$

39. $9x^2 - 6x + 1 = 1$

40. $16x^2 + 8x + 1 = 64$

41. $y^2 = 2$

42. $a^2 = 7$

43. $(x - 1)^2 = 3$

44. $(x + 3)^2 = 5$

45. $(x - 2)^2 = -16$

46. $(t + 2)^2 = -100$

47. $(w + 11)^2 = -3$

48. $(d + 5)^2 = -5$

49. $\left(t - \dfrac{1}{2}\right)^2 = -\dfrac{1}{4}$

50. $\left(c - \dfrac{1}{3}\right)^2 = -\dfrac{16}{9}$

C51. $(x - 1.53)^2 = 8.41$

C52. $(y + 3.21)^2 = 9.61$

289

Solve by completing the square. (See Examples 3–5 and Practice Problem 2.)

53. $x^2 - 4x - 21 = 0$ 54. $x^2 + 6x - 16 = 0$

55. $x^2 = 10x - 16$ 56. $x^2 = -4x - 3$

57. $2x^2 - 4x = 6$ 58. $3x^2 = 18x + 120$

59. $5x^2 + 5x = 10$ 60. $4x^2 + 24 = 20x$

61. $2x^2 + 2x - 1 = 0$ 62. $3x^2 + x - 3 = 0$

63. $5x^2 + 10x - 4 = 0$ 64. $2x^2 - 3x = 6$

65. $-x^2 + x + 1 = 0$ 66. $-x^2 + 2x + 2 = 0$

67. $-2x^2 + 6x + 4 = 0$ 68. $-5x^2 + 20x + 10 = 0$

69. $x^2 - 2x + 5 = 0$ 70. $x^2 + 2x + 2 = 0$

71. $x^2 + 4x + 13 = 0$ 72. $x^2 - 8x + 17 = 0$

73. $2x^2 - 2x + 1 = 0$ 74. $9x^2 - 6x + 17 = 0$

75. $4x^2 + 16x + 17 = 0$ 76. $2x^2 + 2x + 13 = 0$

*77. $x^2 - 2ax = 0$

*78. $x^2 + ax + b = 0$, if $a^2 - 4b \geq 0$

SOLUTIONS FOR PRACTICE PROBLEMS

1. (a)
$$x = \frac{9}{15 - 4x}$$
$$(15 - 4x)x = 9$$
$$15x - 4x^2 = 9$$
$$0 = 4x^2 - 15x + 9$$
$$0 = (4x - 3)(x - 3)$$
$$4x - 3 = 0 \quad \text{or} \quad x - 3 = 0$$
$$4x = 3 \qquad\qquad x = 3$$
$$x = \tfrac{3}{4}$$

The solution set is $\{\tfrac{3}{4}, 3\}$.

(b)
$$9(y - 2)^2 = 4$$
$$9(y - 2)^2 - 4 = 0$$
$$[3(y - 2)]^2 - 2^2 = 0$$
$$[3(y - 2) + 2][3(y - 2) - 2] = 0$$
$$(3y - 6 + 2)(3y - 6 - 2) = 0$$
$$(3y - 4)(3y - 8) = 0$$
$$3y - 4 = 0 \quad \text{or} \quad 3y - 8 = 0$$
$$3y = 4 \qquad\qquad 3y = 8$$
$$y = \tfrac{4}{3} \qquad\qquad y = \tfrac{8}{3}$$

The solution set is $\{\tfrac{4}{3}, \tfrac{8}{3}\}$.

2. $\qquad 4x^2 - 8x + 20 = 0$

Step 1. $\qquad 4x^2 - 8x = -20$

Step 2. $\qquad x^2 - 2x = -5$

Step 3. $\qquad [\frac{1}{2}(-2)]^2 = (-1)^2 = 1$

$$x^2 - 2x + 1 = -5 + 1$$

$$x^2 - 2x + 1 = -4$$

Step 4. $\qquad (x - 1)^2 = -4$

Step 5. $\qquad x - 1 = \pm 2i$

Step 6. $\qquad x = 1 \pm 2i$

10-2
*The Quadratic
Formula*

Since any quadratic equation can be solved by completing the square, then certainly the general quadratic equation

$$ax^2 + bx + c = 0, \qquad a \neq 0$$

can be solved by this method. We follow the steps outlined in the last section.

Steps	*Equation*
1. Isolate the constant term on one side of the equation.	$ax^2 + bx = -c$
2. Divide both sides of the equation by the coefficient of the x^2 term.	$x^2 + \dfrac{b}{a}x = -\dfrac{c}{a}$
3. Compute $\frac{1}{2}$ times the coefficient of x.	$\dfrac{1}{2}\left(\dfrac{b}{a}\right) = \dfrac{b}{2a}$
Square the result.	$\left(\dfrac{b}{2a}\right)^2 = \dfrac{b^2}{4a^2}$
Add this to both sides of the equation.	$x^2 + \dfrac{b}{a}x + \dfrac{b^2}{4a^2} = \dfrac{b^2}{4a^2} - \dfrac{c}{a}$
	$x^2 + \dfrac{b}{a}x + \dfrac{b^2}{4a^2} = \dfrac{b^2 - 4ac}{4a^2}$
4. Factor the quadratic as a perfect square binomial.	$\left(x + \dfrac{b}{2a}\right)^2 = \dfrac{b^2 - 4ac}{4a^2}$
5. Take the square root of both sides.	$x + \dfrac{b}{2a} = \pm\dfrac{\sqrt{b^2 - 4ac}}{2a}$
6. Solve the resulting linear equations.	$x = -\dfrac{b}{2a} \pm \dfrac{\sqrt{b^2 - 4ac}}{2a}$
	$x = \dfrac{-b \pm \sqrt{b^2 - 4ac}}{2a}$

This result is known as the **Quadratic Formula** and gives the solutions to any quadratic equation.

> **Quadratic Formula**
>
> The solutions to the quadratic equation
>
> $$ax^2 + bx + c = 0, \qquad a \neq 0$$
>
> are given by the quadratic formula
>
> $$x = \frac{-b \pm \sqrt{b^2 - 4ac}}{2a}.$$

The steps for solving a quadratic equation by the quadratic formula are listed next.

> **Using the Quadratic Formula to Solve**
> $$ax^2 + bx + c = 0, \qquad a \neq 0.$$
> 1. Rewrite, if necessary, the equation into standard form.
> 2. Identity the coefficients:
>   > a is the coefficient of x^2,
>   >
>   > b is the coefficient of x,
>   >
>   > c is the constant term.
> 3. Determine the solutions by substituting the values of a, b, and c into the quadratic formula.

The quadratic formula is valid whenever the coefficients a, b, and c are complex numbers, but we restrict our attention to the case where a, b, and c are real numbers.

EXAMPLE 1 Use the quadratic formula to solve

$$3x^2 + 4x = 4.$$

SOLUTION We follow the steps outlined above.

Steps	*Equation*
1. Rewrite the equation in standard form.	$3x^2 + 4x - 4 = 0$
2. Identify the coefficients.	$a = 3,\ b = 4,\ c = -4$
3. Replace a, b, and c by these values in the quadratic formula.	$x = \dfrac{-4 \pm \sqrt{4^2 - 4(3)(-4)}}{2(3)}$

$$= \frac{-4 \pm \sqrt{16 + 48}}{6}$$

$$= \frac{-4 \pm \sqrt{64}}{6}$$

$$= \frac{-4 \pm 8}{6}$$

Thus

$$x = \begin{cases} \dfrac{-4 + 8}{6} = \dfrac{4}{6} = \dfrac{2}{3} & \text{(Using the "+" sign)} \\[2ex] \dfrac{-4 - 8}{6} = \dfrac{-12}{6} = -2 & \text{(Using the "−" sign).} \end{cases}$$

The solution set is $\{\frac{2}{3}, -2\}$.

EXAMPLE 2 Solve, using the quadratic formula.

(a) $4x^2 = 20x - 25$ (b) $x^2 - 4x + 13 = 0$

SOLUTION Again we follow the steps outlined above.

(a) $4x^2 - 20x + 25 = 0$

$a = 4, \quad b = -20, \quad c = 25$

$$x = \frac{-(-20) \pm \sqrt{(-20)^2 - 4(4)(25)}}{2(4)}$$

$$= \frac{20 \pm \sqrt{400 - 400}}{8}$$

$$= \frac{20 \pm \sqrt{0}}{8}$$

$$= \frac{20}{8}$$

$$= \frac{5}{2}$$

Solution: $\frac{5}{2}$

(b) $x^2 - 4x + 13 = 0$

$a = 1, \quad b = -4, \quad c = 13$

$$x = \frac{-(-4) \pm \sqrt{(-4)^2 - 4(1)(13)}}{2(1)}$$

$$= \frac{4 \pm \sqrt{16 - 52}}{2}$$

$$= \frac{4 \pm \sqrt{-36}}{2}$$

$$= \frac{4 \pm 6i}{2}$$

$$= \frac{2(2 \pm 3i)}{2}$$

$$= 2 \pm 3i$$

Solutions: $2 + 3i, 2 - 3i$

(Solution on page 297) **PRACTICE PROBLEM 1** Solve, using the quadratic formula.

(a) $x^2 = 6x + 16$ (b) $8x^2 + 4x + \frac{1}{2} = 0$

Equations of degree greater than two can sometimes be solved by using the method of factoring in combination with the quadratic formula. This is illustrated in the next example.

EXAMPLE 3 Solve the equation

$$z^3 + 8 = 0.$$

SOLUTION We begin by factoring the left member as the sum of two cubes.

$$z^3 + 2^3 = 0$$

$$(z + 2)(z^2 - 2z + 4) = 0$$

Next, we solve the equations formed by setting each factor equal to zero.

$$z + 2 = 0 \qquad\qquad z^2 - 2z + 4 = 0$$

$$z = -2 \qquad\qquad z = \frac{2 \pm \sqrt{4 - 4(1)(4)}}{2(1)}$$

$$= \frac{2 \pm \sqrt{-12}}{2}$$

$$= \frac{2 \pm 2i\sqrt{3}}{2}$$

$$= \frac{2(1 \pm i\sqrt{3})}{2}$$

$$= 1 \pm i\sqrt{3}$$

The solution set is $\{-2, 1 + i\sqrt{3}, 1 - i\sqrt{3}\}$.

We now direct our attention to a part of the quadratic formula, called the discriminant. The **discriminant** is

$$b^2 - 4ac.$$

The sign of the discriminant determines the type of solutions of the quadratic equation.

Discriminant	Types of Solutions	Example
$b^2 - 4ac > 0$	two unequal real solutions	Example 1 $3x^2 + 4x = 4$ $b^2 - 4ac = 64 > 0$ Solutions: $\frac{2}{3}$, -2
$b^2 - 4ac = 0$	one real solution	Example 2(a) $4x^2 = 20x - 25$ $b^2 - 4ac = 0$ Solution: $\frac{5}{2}$
$b^2 - 4ac < 0$	two imaginary solutions (complex conjugates)	Example 2(b) $x^2 - 4x + 13 = 0$ $b^2 - 4ac = -36$ Solutions: $2 \pm 3i$

EXERCISES 10-2

Use the quadratic formula to solve each quadratic equation. (See Examples 1 and 2 and Practice Problem 1.)

1. $x^2 - 7x + 6 = 0$
2. $y^2 + 7y + 12 = 0$
3. $-x^2 + x + 6 = 0$
4. $-y^2 - 2y + 15 = 0$
5. $-3a^2 + 5a - 2 = 0$
6. $-6b^2 - 11b + 2 = 0$
7. $5y^2 - y = 0$
8. $20z^2 + 8z = 0$
9. $x^2 - 2x + 1 = 0$
10. $x^2 - 20x + 100 = 0$
11. $2x^2 - 8x + 8 = 0$
12. $2x^2 - 12x + 18 = 0$
13. $-9y^2 - 6y - 1 = 0$
14. $-64r^2 - 16r - 1 = 0$
15. $4a^2 - 12a + 9 = 0$
16. $25c^2 + 20c + 4 = 0$
17. $x^2 - 2x - 4 = 0$
18. $2x^2 - 4x - 1 = 0$
19. $a^2 + a - 5 = 0$
20. $c^2 + 4c - 6 = 0$
21. $-r^2 + r + 1 = 0$
22. $-2t^2 + 3t + 1 = 0$
23. $x^2 - 2 = 0$
24. $9x^2 - 8 = 0$
25. $x^2 + x + 1 = 0$
26. $t^2 + 2t + 2 = 0$
27. $-z^2 + 2z - 7 = 0$
28. $-2w^2 + w + 7 = 0$
29. $a^2 + 1 = 0$
30. $r^2 + 9 = 0$
31. $4x^2 + 4x + 5 = 0$
32. $9x^2 - 12x + 5 = 0$

In problems 33–64, rewrite each quadratic equation in standard form and then solve by using the quadratic formula.

33. $3x^2 = 4x + 7$

34. $a = \dfrac{9}{a - 8}$

35. $x + 3 - \dfrac{5}{x} = \dfrac{x + 3}{x}$

36. $x + 1 = 4 + \dfrac{5}{x + 1}$

37. $6(x + 1)^2 + 7x = -9$

38. $6(x^2 + 1) = 13x$

39. $(x - 1)(x + 1) = 5(x + 1)$

40. $(2x - 3)(x + 2) = x + 2$

41. $x^2 + 25 = 10x$

42. $2x - x^2 = 1$

43. $y = \dfrac{9}{6 - y}$

44. $x + 3 = -\dfrac{9}{4x}$

45. $3r(r - 5) + 16 = -r$

46. $100 = a(20 - a)$

47. $x^2 + 4(x + 1) = 0$

48. $y^2 = 9(2y - 9)$

49. $x^2 - 3 = x$

50. $y^2 - 1 = 5 - 2y$

51. $x + 3 = \dfrac{3}{x}$

52. $r = \dfrac{5}{r + 2}$

53. $3a(a + 2) + 1 = 0$

54. $-4c^2 = 9c + 2$

55. $m^2 + 1 = \dfrac{1 - 5m}{2}$

56. $2k = \dfrac{2}{k + 1}$

57. $x = \dfrac{-4}{x}$

58. $y + \dfrac{9}{y} = 0$

59. $(x + 9)(x - 3) = -37$

60. $(x + 3)(x + 1) = -5$

61. $2 - x = \dfrac{5}{x}$

62. $4 - x = \dfrac{29}{x}$

In problems 63 and 64, round the answers to the nearest hundredth.

C63. $4.21x(x + 2.01) = 13.1$

C64. $\dfrac{2.63(x^2 - 4)}{x} = -6.91$

Solve the following equations. (See Example 3.)

65. $y^3 - 1 = 0$

66. $y^3 + 1 = 0$

67. $x^3 + 27 = 0$

68. $x^3 - 27 = 0$

69. $w^3 = -64$

70. $w^3 = 64$

71. $t^3 = 8$

72. $t^3 = 125$

Describe the type of solutions of each quadratic equation by evaluating the discriminant. Do not solve the quadratic equation.

73. $3x^2 + 3 = 10x$

74. $2(w^2 + 1) = 5w$

75. $9r^2 = 4r$

76. $9y^2 = 4$

77. $36y^2 = 12y - 1$

78. $4x(x + 7) + 49 = 0$

79. $\dfrac{x}{3} = \dfrac{2x-3}{x}$

80. $\dfrac{x^2}{2x+1} = -1$

81. $4x^2 + 7 = 0$

82. $2t^2 + 3t + 4 = 0$

83. $\dfrac{x}{17} = \dfrac{1}{8-x}$

84. $\dfrac{2x}{-5} = \dfrac{1}{x+3}$

SOLUTION FOR PRACTICE PROBLEM

1. (a) $x^2 = 6x + 16$

$x^2 - 6x - 16 = 0$

$a = 1, b = -6, c = -16$

$x = \dfrac{-(-6) \pm \sqrt{(-6)^2 - 4(1)(-16)}}{2(1)}$

$= \dfrac{6 \pm \sqrt{36 + 64}}{2}$

$= \dfrac{6 \pm \sqrt{100}}{2}$

$= \dfrac{6 \pm 10}{2}$

$= \begin{cases} \dfrac{6+10}{2} = 8 \\ \dfrac{6-10}{2} = -2 \end{cases}$

Solutions: $8, -2$

(b) $8x^2 + 4x + \frac{1}{2} = 0$

$a = 8, b = 4, c = \frac{1}{2}$

$x = \dfrac{-4 \pm \sqrt{4^2 - 4(8)(\frac{1}{2})}}{2(8)}$

$= \dfrac{-4 \pm \sqrt{16 - 16}}{16}$

$= \dfrac{-4 \pm \sqrt{0}}{16}$

$= \dfrac{-4}{16}$

$= -\dfrac{1}{4}$

Solution: $-\frac{1}{4}$

10-3
Applications
Many physical problems can be expressed mathematically in the form of a linear equation and hence solved (see Chapter 3). Similarly, we might be faced with the problem of determining and solving a quadratic equation.

EXAMPLE 1
A gardener wants the width of his rectangular-shaped garden to be 10 feet less than half its length and to be large enough to contain 4000 square feet. Find the dimensions of his garden.

SOLUTION Let l represent the length of the garden in feet. Then the width is given by $\frac{1}{2}l - 10$.

$$\boxed{4000 = \text{area}} \qquad \tfrac{1}{2}l - 10 = \text{width}$$

$$l = \text{length}$$

Since the area of a rectangle is the product of its length and width, we have the quadratic equation

$$l(\tfrac{1}{2}l - 10) = 4000.$$

length · width = area

We rewrite this equation in standard form and solve by using the quadratic formula.

$$\tfrac{1}{2}l^2 - 10l - 4000 = 0$$

$$a = \tfrac{1}{2}, \quad b = -10, \quad c = -4000$$

$$l = \frac{-(-10) \pm \sqrt{(-10)^2 - 4(\tfrac{1}{2})(-4000)}}{2(\tfrac{1}{2})}$$

$$= \frac{10 \pm \sqrt{100 + 8000}}{1}$$

$$= 10 \pm \sqrt{8100}$$

$$= 10 \pm 90$$

$$= \begin{cases} 10 + 90 = 100 \\ 10 - 90 = -80 \end{cases}$$

Since $l = -80$ is meaningless as a possible length of the garden, we exclude it as a possible solution. With $l = 100$, we find the width to be

$$\tfrac{1}{2}l - 10 = \tfrac{1}{2}(100) - 10 = 40,$$

and the garden is 100 feet long and 40 feet wide.

PRACTICE PROBLEM 1 (Solution on page 300) Suppose that the profit P of selling x bicycles is given by

$$P = 24x - x^2.$$

How many bicycles must be sold to earn a profit of $80?

EXERCISES 10-3

Solve the following word problems. (See Example 1 and Practice Problem 1.)

1. What are the dimensions of a wall that is 2 feet longer than it is high and can be covered by 80 square feet of wallpaper?

2. What are the dimensions of a surface that can be covered by 55 square feet of wallpaper if the height is $\frac{1}{2}$ foot more than half the length?

3. What are the dimensions of a room if the width is $\frac{3}{4}$ of the length and the ceiling can be covered by 300 square feet of acoustic tile?

4. What are the dimensions of a room if the width is 1 foot less than half the length and the floor can be covered by 112 square feet of carpet?

5. How much fencing is needed to enclose a square pasture containing 4 square miles of area?

6. How much fencing is needed to enclose a rectangular-shaped pasture containing 5000 square meters if the pasture is twice as long as it is wide?

7. How much fencing is needed to enclose a dog pen covering 120 square feet where 3 times the width is 6 more than twice the length?

8. Find the length of a strand of Christmas lights needed to trim a window containing 24 square feet of glass where the height is 2 feet less than twice the width.

9. If we disregard air resistance, the number of feet s that a body falls from rest during t seconds is given by

$$s = 16t^2.$$

How long will it take for a suitcase to reach the ground if it falls from an airplane flying at an altitude of 14,400 feet?

10. How long will it take a free-falling elevator to reach the bottom floor of a building if the cables broke when the elevator was at a height of 256 feet? Use the formula given in problem 9.

11. Disregarding air resistance, a ball thrown vertically upward with initial velocity of 48 feet per second reaches a height h, in feet, after t seconds given by

$$h = 48t - 16t^2.$$

How long will it take the ball to reach a height of 32 feet on its way up? On its way down?

12. A bullet shot vertically upward with initial velocity of 2000 feet per second reaches a height of h feet in t seconds given by the equation

$$h = 2000t - 16t^2,$$

disregarding air resistance. How long will it take the bullet to reach a height of 9600 feet on its way up? On its way down?

13. Suppose that the cost, C, of producing x canoes is given, in dollars, by

$$C = 1500 - 60x + 3x^2.$$

How many canoes can be produced at a cost of $1200?

14. Suppose that the profit, P, of selling x cars in 1 year is given, in dollars, by

$$P = -96,000 + 1800x - 6x^2.$$

How many cars must be sold to earn a profit of $39,000?

15. Suppose that the revenue, R, for selling x handmade lamps at the arts and crafts show is given, in dollars, by

$$R = 40x - x^2 - 150.$$

How many lamps must be sold so that the revenue is $250?

16. Suppose that the cost, C, of producing x wind chimes is given, in dollars, by

    $$C = 20 - 12x + 2x^2.$$

    How many wind chimes can be produced at a cost of $2?

17. The Acme Boat Company has discovered that the minimum price p, in dollars, that it can afford to sell its boats for, is given by $p = 15,000 - 150b$, where b is the number of boats sold. The revenue R, in dollars, produced from the sale of b boats is the product of p and b. Find a formula for R, and find the number of boats that will produce $240,000 in revenue.

18. Acme Manufacturing can produce small boat anchors and make a total profit P, in dollars, given by $P = 80a - 0.02a^2$, where a is the number of anchors produced. How many anchors should be produced to make a total profit of $1592 on small anchors?

19. Ace Gravel Company can produce t tons of gravel at a profit of $P = 4t - 150 - 0.02t^2$, where P is in hundreds of dollars. How many tons of gravel must be produced for a profit of $5000 ($P = 50$)?

20. Roy Ballantine has found that the sale of y loads of firewood from his wood lot results in a profit P, in dollars, which is given by $P = 54y - y^2 - 9$. How many loads of wood must be sold to bring Roy a profit of $720?

21. The demand D for Pedalex cars, in thousands of cars, is given by $D = 5 + 10p - p^2$, where p is the price in thousands of dollars. What price on the car will produce a demand for 29,000 cars ($D = 29$)?

22. The demand D for the new book *Algebra for Everybody* is given by $D = 10 + 4p - 0.5p^2$, where D is the demand in thousands of books and p is the price of the book in dollars. What price of the book will result in a demand for 16,000 books ($D = 16$)?

23. (See problem 21.) The supply S of Pedalex cars, in thousands of cars, is given by $S = p^2 + 4p - 31$, where p is the price in thousands of dollars. Find the price for which $S = D$. (This is the *equilibrium price*.)

24. (See problem 22.) The supply S of copies of *Algebra for Everybody* is given by $S = p^2 - 2p - 8$, where S is the supply in thousands of books, and p is the price of the book in dollars. Find the price for which $S = D$ (the *equilibrium price*).

SOLUTION FOR PRACTICE PROBLEM

1. Replacing P by 80 and solving the quadratic equation yields

$$80 = 24x - x^2$$
$$x^2 - 24x + 80 = 0$$
$$(x - 20)(x - 4) = 0$$
$$x - 20 = 0 \quad \text{or} \quad x - 4 = 0$$
$$x = 20 \qquad\qquad x = 4.$$

Thus selling either 4 or 20 bicycles will yeild a profit of $80.

Any equation that can be put in the standard quadratic form

$$ax^2 + bx + c = 0, \qquad a \neq 0,$$

where x might represent an expression in some other variable, is said to be *quadratic in form*. Some examples of equations quadratic in form are listed next.

$$y^4 - y^2 - 20 = 0 \qquad \text{is quadratic in } y^2.$$
$$(t - 1)^2 - 5(t - 1) + 6 = 0 \qquad \text{is quadratic in } t - 1.$$
$$\frac{1}{z^2} - \frac{1}{z} - 2 = 0 \qquad \text{is quadratic in } \frac{1}{z}.$$
$$\left(x - \frac{8}{x}\right)^2 + 4\left(x - \frac{8}{x}\right) + 4 = 0 \qquad \text{is quadratic in } x - \frac{8}{x}.$$

Each of these can be solved by first making a substitution.

EXAMPLE 1   Solve

$$y^4 - y^2 - 20 = 0.$$

SOLUTION   Since this equation is quadratic in y^2, we make the substitution $x = y^2$. Thus $x^2 = (y^2)^2 = y^4$ and we solve a quadratic equation for x.

$$y^4 - y^2 - 20 = 0$$

SUBSTITUTION: $x = y^2$
$$x^2 - x - 20 = 0$$
$$(x - 5)(x + 4) = 0$$
$$x - 5 = 0 \quad \text{or} \quad x + 4 = 0$$
$$x = 5 \qquad\qquad x = -4$$

But we must find solutions for y. Thus we use the substitution again.

$$x = 5 \qquad\qquad x = -4$$

SUBSTITUTION: $x = y^2$
$$y^2 = 5 \qquad\qquad y^2 = -4$$
$$y = \pm\sqrt{5} \qquad\quad y = \pm 2i$$

Thus the solution set is $\{\sqrt{5}, -\sqrt{5}, 2i, -2i\}$.

**PRACTICE
PROBLEM 1**   (Solution on page 303) Solve

$$z^4 - 7z^2 - 8 = 0.$$

EXAMPLE 2   Solve

$$\frac{1}{z^2} - \frac{1}{z} - 2 = 0.$$

This equation is quadratic in $\frac{1}{z}$. We make the substitution $x = \frac{1}{z}$ and first solve for x.

$$\frac{1}{z^2} - \frac{1}{z} - 2 = 0$$

SUBSTITUTION: $\quad x = \frac{1}{z} \qquad\qquad x^2 - x - 2 = 0$

$$(x - 2)(x + 1) = 0$$

$$x - 2 = 0 \quad \text{or} \quad x + 1 = 0$$

$$x = 2 \qquad\qquad\qquad x = -1$$

We make our substitution again to solve for z.

$$x = 2 \qquad\qquad x = -1$$

SUBSTITUTION: $\quad x = \frac{1}{z} \qquad \frac{1}{z} = 2 \qquad\qquad \frac{1}{z} = -1$

$$1 = 2z \qquad\qquad 1 = -z$$

$$\frac{1}{2} = z \qquad\qquad -1 = z$$

The solution set is $\{\frac{1}{2}, -1\}$.

PRACTICE PROBLEM 2

(Solution on page 303) Solve

$$2(t + 3)^2 + 5(t + 3) - 12 = 0.$$

EXERCISES 10-4

Solve. (See Example 1 and Practice Problem 1.)

1. $y^4 - 5y^2 + 4 = 0$

2. $z^4 - 10z^2 + 9 = 0$

3. $64y^4 - 20y^2 + 1 = 0$

4. $9r^4 - 13r^2 + 4 = 0$

5. $a^4 - 8a^2 + 15 = 0$

6. $t^4 - 9t^2 + 14 = 0$

7. $2b^4 - 7b^2 + 5 = 0$

8. $9b^4 - 27b^2 + 20 = 0$

9. $x^4 + x^2 - 2 = 0$

10. $x^4 + 2x^2 - 35 = 0$

11. $4y^4 + 13y^2 + 9 = 0$

12. $4z^4 + 99z^2 - 25 = 0$

Solve. (See Practice Problem 2.)

13. $(t - 1)^2 - 2(t - 1) - 15 = 0$

14. $(r + 2)^2 + 10(r + 2) + 24 = 0$

15. $(2y + 3)^2 - (2y + 3) - 42 = 0$

16. $(3x - 1)^2 - 7(3x - 1) - 18 = 0$

17. $2(y + 2)^2 + 5(y + 2) - 12 = 0$

18. $10(y - 1)^2 + 17(y - 1) + 3 = 0$

19. $6(3x - 1)^2 - 13(3x - 1) + 6 = 0$

20. $8(4x + 5)^2 - 14(4x + 5) + 3 = 0$

21. $(y + 2)^2 - 2(y + 2) + 1 = 0$

22. $(r + 4)^2 + 4(r + 4) + 4 = 0$

23. $(2z - 3)^2 + 6(2z - 3) + 9 = 0$

24. $(3z - 5)^2 - 10(3z - 5) + 25 = 0$

Solve. (See Example 2.)

25. $\dfrac{1}{k^2} + \dfrac{1}{k} - 20 = 0$

26. $\dfrac{1}{z^2} + \dfrac{8}{z} - 20 = 0$

27. $\dfrac{1}{y^2} - \dfrac{2}{y} - 35 = 0$

28. $\dfrac{1}{t^2} - \dfrac{3}{t} - 28 = 0$

29. $\dfrac{6}{(t + 1)^2} + \dfrac{1}{t + 1} - 1 = 0$

30. $\dfrac{12}{(y + 2)^2} + \dfrac{1}{y + 2} - 1 = 0$

31. $\dfrac{4}{(z - 3)^2} + \dfrac{7}{z - 3} + 3 = 0$

32. $\dfrac{9}{(y - 4)^2} - \dfrac{11}{y - 4} + 2 = 0$

33. $\dfrac{2}{(2r + 3)^2} + \dfrac{9}{2r + 3} - 5 = 0$

34. $\dfrac{10}{(5y - 1)^2} + \dfrac{7}{5y - 1} - 3 = 0$

35. $\dfrac{7}{(7x + 1)^2} + \dfrac{50}{7x + 1} + 7 = 0$

36. $\dfrac{2}{(2y - 3)^2} + \dfrac{25}{2y - 3} + 72 = 0$

*37. $x^6 - 1 = 0$

*38. $x^6 - 64 = 0$

*39. $z^6 - 7z^3 - 8 = 0$

*40. $z^6 - 65z^3 + 64 = 0$

*41. $8y^6 - 9y^3 + 1 = 0$

*42. $27y^6 + 28y^3 + 1 = 0$

*43. $27z^6 + 217z^3 + 8 = 0$

*44. $64y^6 + 511y^3 - 8 = 0$

SOLUTIONS FOR PRACTICE PROBLEMS

1. $z^4 - 7z^2 - 8 = 0$

SUBSTITUTION: $x = z^2$
$x^2 - 7x - 8 = 0$
$(x - 8)(x + 1) = 0$
$x - 8 = 0$ or $x + 1 = 0$
$\quad\quad x = 8 \quad\quad\quad\quad x = -1$

SUBSTITUTION: $x = z^2$
$z^2 = 8 \quad\quad\quad\quad z^2 = -1$
$z = \pm 2\sqrt{2} \quad\quad z = \pm i$
Solution set $= \{\pm 2\sqrt{2}, \pm i\}$.

2. $2(t + 3)^2 + 5(t + 3) - 12 = 0$

SUBSTITUTION: $x = t + 3$
$2x^2 + 5x - 12 = 0$
$(2x - 3)(x + 4) = 0$
$2x - 3 = 0$ or $x + 4 = 0$
$\quad 2x = 3 \quad\quad\quad\quad x = -4$
$\quad\quad x = \dfrac{3}{2}$

SUBSTITUTION: $x = t + 3$
$t + 3 = \dfrac{3}{2} \quad\quad\quad t + 3 = -4$
$t = \dfrac{3}{2} - 3 \quad\quad\quad t = -7$
$t = -\dfrac{3}{2}$

Solution set $= \left\{ -\dfrac{3}{2}, -7 \right\}$.

In this section we consider equations in one variable that contain a radical in one or more terms. Several examples are

$$\sqrt{2x - 3} = 15,$$
$$\sqrt{2y + 1} = y - 3,$$
$$\sqrt[3]{y - 5} = 1,$$
$$\sqrt{x + 4} - \sqrt{13 - x} = 3.$$

The method we use to solve an equation involving a square root is to isolate the radical on one side of the equation, square both sides to eliminate that radical, and then solve the resulting equation. It is important to note that "squaring both sides" of an equation does not necessarily yield an equivalent equation (an equation with the same solutions). Consider, for example, the equation

$$x = -1,$$

whose solution is -1. Squaring both sides yields the equation

$$x^2 = 1,$$

whose solutions are 1 and -1. The "extra" solution "1" is called an **extraneous solution** since it does not satisfy the original equation

$$x = -1.$$

It is true that the solutions to a certain equation will also be solutions to the equation formed by squaring both sides, but the reverse is not always true. Hence one of the most *critical* steps in solving equations involving radicals is to check the solutions in the original equation, and *discard* those extraneous solutions.

EXAMPLE 1 Solve

$$\sqrt{2x - 3} = 15.$$

SOLUTION Squaring both sides yields the linear equation

$$2x - 3 = 225,$$

which we solve:

$$2x = 228$$
$$x = 114.$$

Next we check to see if $x = 114$ satisfies the original equation. As in Chapter 8, we use LHS and RHS to indicate the left-hand side and the right-hand side, respectively, of the original equation. When $x = 114$,

$$\text{LHS} = \sqrt{2(114) - 3} = \sqrt{228 - 3} = \sqrt{225} = 15 = \text{RHS}.$$

Thus $x = 114$ is the solution to the original equation, and the solution set is $\{114\}$.

PRACTICE PROBLEM 1   (Solution on page 309) Solve
$$\sqrt{x - 1} = \sqrt{5 - 2x}.$$

EXAMPLE 2   Solve
$$\sqrt[3]{y - 5} = 1.$$

SOLUTION   We eliminate the radical by raising both sides of the equation to the third power, and solve the resulting linear equation.

$$(\sqrt[3]{y - 5})^3 = 1^3$$
$$y - 5 = 1$$
$$y = 6$$

Check: $y = 6$
$$\text{LHS} = \sqrt[3]{6 - 5} = \sqrt[3]{1} = 1 = \text{RHS}$$

Since LHS = RHS when $y = 6$, then $y = 6$ is a solution.

Thus the solution set is $\{6\}$.

EXAMPLE 3   Solve
$$\sqrt{2y} + 1 = y - 3.$$

SOLUTION   Before squaring both sides, we isolate the radical on the left by adding -1 to both sides of the equation.

$$\sqrt{2y} = y - 4$$

We next eliminate the radical by squaring both sides of the equation, and solve the resulting quadratic equation.

$$(\sqrt{2y})^2 = (y - 4)^2$$
$$2y = y^2 - 8y + 16$$
$$0 = y^2 - 10y + 16$$
$$0 = (y - 8)(y - 2)$$
$$y - 8 = 0 \quad \text{or} \quad y - 2 = 0$$
$$y = 8 \qquad\qquad y = 2$$

The possible solutions are 8 and 2. But we *must* check to see if either or both of these are extraneous.

Check: $y = 8$

$$\text{LHS} = \sqrt{2(8)} + 1 = \sqrt{16} + 1 = 4 + 1 = 5$$
$$\text{RHS} = 8 - 3 = 5$$

Thus LHS = RHS when $y = 8$ and $y = 8$ is a solution.

Check: $y = 2$

$$\text{LHS} = \sqrt{2(2)} + 1 = \sqrt{4} + 1 = 2 + 1 = 3$$
$$\text{RHS} = 2 - 3 = -1$$

Since LHS $\neq$ RHS when $y = 2$ then $y = 2$ is an extraneous solution.

Hence the solution set is $\{8\}$.

Often it is necessary to square both sides of an equation involving radicals twice to eliminate all the radicals. This is illustrated in the next example.

EXAMPLE 4 Solve

$$\sqrt{x + 4} - \sqrt{13 - x} = 3.$$

SOLUTION To eliminate the radical $\sqrt{x + 4}$, we first isolate it on the left-hand side of the equation by adding $\sqrt{13 - x}$ to both sides.

$$\sqrt{x + 4} = 3 + \sqrt{13 - x}$$

Squaring both sides gives

$$(\sqrt{x + 4})^2 = (3 + \sqrt{13 - x})^2.$$

Squaring on the left-hand side eliminates that radical while *squaring the binomial* on the right *yields a trinomial*.

$$x + 4 = 3^2 + 2 \cdot 3\sqrt{13 - x} + (\sqrt{13 - x})^2$$
$$x + 4 = 9 + 6\sqrt{13 - x} + 13 - x$$

To eliminate the radical $\sqrt{13 - x}$, we first isolate it on the right-hand side by adding $x - 22$ to both sides.

$$2x - 18 = 6\sqrt{13 - x}$$

Dividing both sides by 2 further simplifies the equation.

$$x - 9 = 3\sqrt{13 - x}$$

We now eliminate the radical by squaring both sides again and then solve the resulting quadratic equation.

$$(x - 9)^2 = (3\sqrt{13 - x})^2$$
$$x^2 - 18x + 81 = 9(13 - x)$$
$$x^2 - 18x + 81 = 117 - 9x$$
$$x^2 - 9x - 36 = 0$$
$$(x - 12)(x + 3) = 0$$
$$x - 12 = 0 \quad \text{or} \quad x + 3 = 0$$
$$x = 12 \qquad x = -3$$

The possible solutions are 12 and -3. Each one must be checked in the *original* equation.

Check: $x = 12$

$$\text{LHS} = \sqrt{12 + 4} - \sqrt{13 - 12} = \sqrt{16} - \sqrt{1} = 4 - 1 = 3 = \text{RHS}$$

Since LHS = RHS when $x = 12$, then $x = 12$ is a solution.

Check: $x = -3$

$$\text{LHS} = \sqrt{-3 + 4} - \sqrt{13 - (-3)} = \sqrt{1} - \sqrt{16}$$
$$= 1 - 4 = -3 \neq \text{RHS}$$

Since LHS $\neq$ RHS when $x = -3$, then $x = -3$ is an extraneous solution.

Thus the solution set is $\{12\}$.

PRACTICE PROBLEM 2 (Solution on page 309) Solve
$$\sqrt{4 + 3x} - \sqrt{2x + 2} = 1.$$

We summarize the procedure for solving equations involving radicals with the following steps.

Solving Equations Involving Radicals

1. Isolate the radical on one side of the equation.

2. Raise both sides of the equation to the smallest power that will eliminate the radical.

3. If the resulting equation contains another radical, repeat steps 1 and 2; otherwise, solve the resulting equation.

4. CHECK the solutions in the ORIGINAL equation and discard any extraneous solutions.

308

EXERCISES 10-5

Chapter 10
Quadratic Equations
and Inequalities in One
Variable

Determine the solution set for each of the following. Be sure to check each possible solution and discard any extraneous solutions.

(See Example 1 and Practice Problem 1.)

1. $\sqrt{x} = 4$ 2. $\sqrt{x} = 2$

3. $\sqrt{x-1} = 1$ 4. $\sqrt{x+2} = 5$

5. $\sqrt{4x+1} = \sqrt{11-x}$ 6. $\sqrt{1-5x} = \sqrt{x+19}$

7. $\sqrt{2x+1} = -\sqrt{x+13}$ 8. $\sqrt{x+3} = -\sqrt{4x+9}$

9. $\sqrt{7x+1} - \sqrt{8x-4} = 0$ 10. $\sqrt{4x+9} - \sqrt{9-3x} = 0$

11. $\sqrt{x+10} - \sqrt{2-7x} = 0$ 12. $\sqrt{x+6} - \sqrt{2x+11} = 0$

13. $\sqrt{5x} + \sqrt{6x-20} = 0$ 14. $\sqrt{1-8x} + \sqrt{-10x-19} = 0$

15. $\sqrt{3x+4} + \sqrt{4x-3} = 0$ 16. $\sqrt{x-4} + \sqrt{3x-14} = 0$

(See Example 2.)

17. $\sqrt[3]{2x-3} = 1$ 18. $\sqrt[3]{5x-7} = 2$

In problems 19 and 20, round the answers to the nearest tenth.

C19. $\sqrt[3]{1-2x} = -5.21$ C20. $\sqrt[3]{4x-12} = -4.33$

(See Example 3.)

21. $\sqrt{y} = 2 - y$ 22. $\sqrt{x} = 6 - x$

23. $\sqrt{r} = 6r - 1$ 24. $\sqrt{z} = 20 - z$

25. $x + 2 = 2\sqrt{2x+1}$ 26. $\sqrt{x+3} = x + 1$

27. $\sqrt{2x+3} = x - 6$ 28. $\sqrt{x-1} = 7 - x$

29. $\sqrt{x-4} + 6 = x$ 30. $\sqrt{t+1} + t = 5$

31. $\sqrt{1-x} - x = 11$ 32. $\sqrt{5-x} - x = 1$

33. $\sqrt{a^2 - 3a} = 2$ 34. $\sqrt{2x^2 + 3x} = 3$

35. $\sqrt{a^2 - 4a} + \sqrt{5} = 0$ 36. $\sqrt{15x^2 + 7x + 2} = 0$

(See Example 4 and Practice Problem 2.)

37. $\sqrt{2u+7} = \sqrt{u} - 2$ 38. $\sqrt{3a-11} = \sqrt{a} + 1$

39. $\sqrt{x+4} = 3 - \sqrt{x}$ 40. $\sqrt{x+5} = \sqrt{x} - 3$

41. $\sqrt{r} - \sqrt{2r-2} = 1$ 42. $2 = \sqrt{x} - \sqrt{2x+7}$

43. $\sqrt{z-3} - \sqrt{z} = 1$ 44. $\sqrt{x-8} + \sqrt{x} = 4$

45. $\sqrt{2x+1} = \sqrt{x+9} - 2$ 46. $\sqrt{3x-5} = \sqrt{x-1} - 2$

47. $\sqrt{2t-1} = 1 + \sqrt{t-1}$ 48. $\sqrt{x+1} = \sqrt{2x+3} - 1$

49. $\sqrt{3x-5} - \sqrt{x+2} = 1$ 50. $\sqrt{7x+4} - \sqrt{5x+1} = 1$

51. $\sqrt{x+12} - \sqrt{1-5x} = 1$ 52. $\sqrt{2x+15} - \sqrt{1-8x} = 2$

1. Original equation.
   Squaring both sides.

   $$\sqrt{x-1} = \sqrt{5-2x}$$
   $$(\sqrt{x-1})^2 = (\sqrt{5-2x})^2$$
   $$x - 1 = 5 - 2x$$

   Solving the linear equation. $3x = 6$
   Possible solution. $x = 2$

   Check: $x = 2$

   $$\text{LHS} = \sqrt{2-1} = \sqrt{1} = 1$$
   $$\text{RHS} = \sqrt{5 - 2(2)} = \sqrt{1} = 1$$

   Since LHS = RHS when $x = 2$, then $x = 2$ is a solution.

   Solution set = $\{2\}$.

2. Original equation.
   Isolating $\sqrt{4 + 3x}$.
   Squaring both sides.

   $$\sqrt{4 + 3x} - \sqrt{2x + 2} = 1$$
   $$\sqrt{4 + 3x} = 1 + \sqrt{2x + 2}$$
   $$(\sqrt{4 + 3x})^2 = (1 + \sqrt{2x + 2})^2$$
   $$4 + 3x = 1 + 2\sqrt{2x + 2} + 2x + 2$$

   Isolating $\sqrt{2x + 2}$. $x + 1 = 2\sqrt{2x + 2}$
   Squaring both sides. $(x + 1)^2 = (2\sqrt{2x + 2})^2$

   $$x^2 + 2x + 1 = 4(2x + 2)$$

   Solving the quadratic
   equation.

   $$x^2 + 2x + 1 = 8x + 8$$
   $$x^2 - 6x - 7 = 0$$
   $$(x - 7)(x + 1) = 0$$
   $$x - 7 = 0 \quad \text{or} \quad x + 1 = 0$$

   Possible solutions. $x = 7 \qquad\qquad x = -1$

   Check: $x = 7$

   $$\text{LHS} = \sqrt{4 + 3(7)} - \sqrt{2(7) + 2} = \sqrt{25} - \sqrt{16} = 5 - 4 = 1 = \text{RHS}$$

   Since LHS = RHS when $x = 7$, then $x = 7$ is a solution.

   Check: $x = -1$

   $$\text{LHS} = \sqrt{4 + 3(-1)} - \sqrt{2(-1) + 2} = \sqrt{1} - \sqrt{0} = 1 = \text{RHS}$$

   Since LHS = RHS when $x = -1$, then $x = -1$ is a solution.

   Solution set = $\{7, -1\}$.

10-6
*Quadratic
Inequalities in
One Variable*

Inequalities involving products or quotients of two linear expressions are called **quadratic inequalities** in one variable. Some examples are

$$(x - 5)(x + 3) \geq 0;$$
$$x^2 - 4x + 3 < 0;$$
$$\frac{2x - 1}{x + 3} \leq 0;$$
$$\frac{1}{x - 2} > \frac{1}{x}.$$

One method of solution is called the **sign graph method**, which we describe in the next examples.

EXAMPLE 1   Solve

$$(x - 5)(x + 3) \geq 0.$$

SOLUTION   The quadratic equation

$$(x - 5)(x + 3) = 0$$

has solutions $x = 5$ and $x = -3$. The sign of each factor $x - 5$ and $x + 3$, and hence the product $(x - 5)(x + 3)$, depends on the value of x. We first consider the sign of each factor. The factor $x - 5$ satisfies the following conditions:

$$x - 5 > 0 \quad \text{when} \quad x > 5$$
$$x - 5 = 0 \quad \text{when} \quad x = 5$$
$$x - 5 < 0 \quad \text{when} \quad x < 5.$$

This is illustrated on the number line in Figure 10.1.

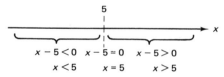

FIGURE 10.1

Similarly, the factor $x + 3$ satisfies the conditions:

$$x + 3 > 0 \quad \text{when} \quad x > -3$$
$$x + 3 = 0 \quad \text{when} \quad x = -3$$
$$x + 3 < 0 \quad \text{when} \quad x < -3.$$

which we illustrate on the number line in Figure 10.2.

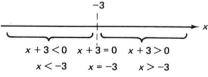

FIGURE 10.2

To solve the quadratic inequality, $(x - 5)(x + 3) \geq 0$, we must examine the sign of the product $(x - 5)(x + 3)$. This is most easily done on the sign graph. The sign graph is drawn by first locating the solutions to the quadratic equation on a number line. To indicate the sign of each factor we place "+" signs in the interval where each factor is positive, and "−" signs where each is negative, and "0" where each assumes the value zero. Finally, we consider the product of the two factors. Since quantities with "like" signs multiply to yield a positive product and quantities with "opposite" signs multiply to yield a negative product, we can determine the sign of the product. Thus the solution to the quadratic inequality

$$(x - 5)(x + 3) \geq 0$$

is the set of real numbers in the intervals where the product is positive or zero (see Figure 10.3). Hence the solution set is

$$\{x \mid x \leq -3 \quad \text{or} \quad x \geq 5\}.$$

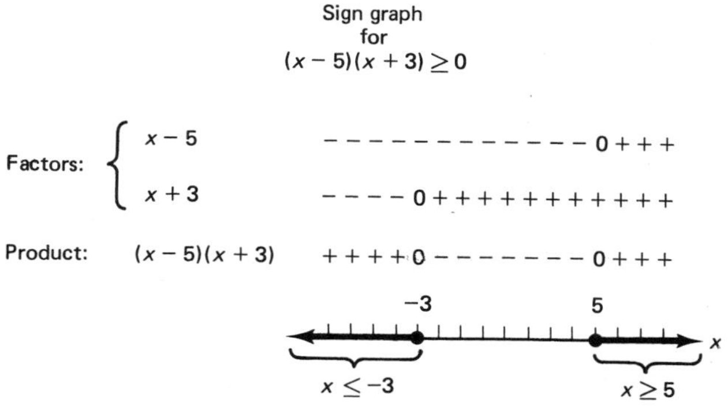

Sign graph
for
$(x - 5)(x + 3) \geq 0$

FIGURE 10.3

EXAMPLE 2 Use a sign graph to solve the quadratic inequality

$$x^2 - 4x + 3 < 0.$$

SOLUTION Factoring the quadratic, we have

$$(x - 3)(x - 1) < 0.$$

We determine the signs of each factor,

x − 3

Sign	Interval
+	$x > 3$
0	$x = 3$
−	$x < 3$

x − 1

Sign	Interval
+	$x > 1$
0	$x = 1$
−	$x < 1$

and use this information to draw the sign graph in Figure 10.4.

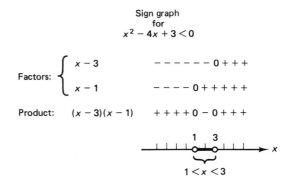

FIGURE 10.4

The solution set for the quadratic inequality

$$x^2 - 4x + 3 < 0$$

is the set of real numbers in the interval where the product is negative. Hence the solution set is

$$\{x \mid 1 < x < 3\}.$$

PRACTICE PROBLEM 1   (Solution on page 316) Use a sign graph to solve the inequality

$$x^2 - x - 12 \le 0.$$

This sign graph method also applies to inequalities involving quotients.

EXAMPLE 3   Use a sign graph to solve

$$\frac{2x - 1}{x + 3} \le 0.$$

SOLUTION   Again we consider the sign of each factor in the quotient,

2x − 1	
Sign	**Interval**
+	$x > \frac{1}{2}$
0	$x = \frac{1}{2}$
−	$x < \frac{1}{2}$

x + 3	
Sign	**Interval**
+	$x > -3$
0	$x = -3$
−	$x < -3$

and use this information to draw the sign graph in Figure 10.5. Here we shall use "U" to indicate that the quotient is undefined.

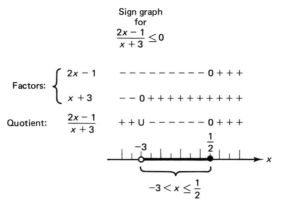

FIGURE 10.5

Hence the solution set for the inequality

$$\frac{2x - 1}{x + 3} \le 0$$

is

$$\{x \mid -3 < x \le \tfrac{1}{2}\}.$$

To use the sign graph method, one side of the inequality *must be zero* and the other side must be written as a product or a quotient of linear factors. Consider the next example.

EXAMPLE 4   Use a sign graph to solve

$$\frac{1}{x - 2} > \frac{1}{x}.$$

SOLUTION   Writing this inequality in the form described in the preceding paragraph, we have

$$\frac{1}{x - 2} - \frac{1}{x} > 0$$

$$\frac{x - (x - 2)}{(x - 2)x} > 0$$

$$\frac{2}{(x - 2)x} > 0.$$

This inequality has its sign graph as in Figure 10.6.

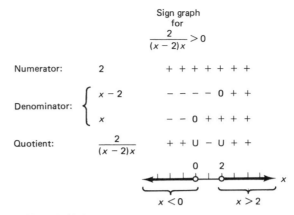

FIGURE 10.6

The solution set for the inequality

$$\frac{1}{x-2} > \frac{1}{x}$$

is

$$\{x \mid x < 0 \quad \text{or} \quad x > 2\}.$$

EXERCISES 10-6

Solve the following quadratic inequalities and draw a graph of each solution set.

(See Example 1.)

1. $x(x + 3) < 0$
2. $r(r - 1) < 0$
3. $(t + 1)(t - 5) < 0$
4. $(t - 2)(t - 7) < 0$
5. $(x + 4)(x + 3) \leq 0$
6. $(x - 2)(x + 3) \leq 0$
7. $(4 - z)(2 - z) \leq 0$
8. $(1 - w)(3 + w) \leq 0$
9. $(x - 2)(x + 4) > 0$
10. $(x + 3)(x + 2) > 0$
11. $(y - 1)(y + 3) > 0$
12. $(a - 7)(a + 2) > 0$
13. $(x + 1)(x + 5) \geq 0$
14. $(x - 1)(x - 3) \geq 0$
15. $(1 - x)(2 + x) \geq 0$
16. $(4 - x)(1 + x) \geq 0$

(See Example 2 and Practice Problem 1.)

17. $x^2 - 7x + 10 < 0$
18. $x^2 - x - 6 < 0$
19. $x^2 + 6x + 5 > 0$
20. $x^2 + x - 12 > 0$
21. $a^2 - 4 \leq 0$
22. $b^2 - 9 \leq 0$

23. $x^2 - 1 \geq 0$

24. $x^2 - 25 \geq 0$

25. $r^2 - 4r \leq 0$

26. $r^2 + 2r \leq 0$

27. $2x^2 + x > 0$

28. $3x^2 + 5x > 0$

Solve the following quadratic inequalities involving quotients. Draw a graph of each solution set. (See Example 3.)

29. $\dfrac{x}{x + 2} < 0$

30. $\dfrac{y}{y - 3} < 0$

31. $\dfrac{z + 1}{z - 3} \leq 0$

32. $\dfrac{x + 4}{x - 7} \leq 0$

33. $\dfrac{t - 1}{t + 1} > 0$

34. $\dfrac{y - 4}{y - 2} > 0$

35. $\dfrac{y + 3}{y - 1} \geq 0$

36. $\dfrac{y - 2}{y + 2} \geq 0$

37. $\dfrac{1}{x(x + 3)} \leq 0$

38. $\dfrac{2}{x(x - 5)} \leq 0$

39. $\dfrac{-4}{(x - 1)(x + 1)} \geq 0$

40. $\dfrac{-7}{(x + 2)(x - 3)} \geq 0$

41. $\dfrac{5}{(x - 3)(2 - x)} > 0$

42. $\dfrac{-1}{(1 + t)(2 - t)} < 0$

Solve each of the following inequalities involving a product of three linear factors. Draw a graph of each solution set.

43. $x(x - 1)(x + 2) \leq 0$

44. $y(y + 3)(y - 2) \leq 0$

45. $(2x - 1)(3x - 2)(x) > 0$

46. $(5x - 3)(x + 2)(x - 3) > 0$

47. $(x^2 - 1)(x + 3) \geq 0$

48. $(y^2 - 4)(y + 1) \geq 0$

49. $(x^2 + 4x + 4)(x + 1) < 0$

50. $(y^2 + 2y + 1)(y - 1) < 0$

Solve by first combining the terms into a single fraction. Draw a graph of each solution set. (See Example 4.)

51. $\dfrac{2}{r} - \dfrac{3}{r - 1} > 0$

52. $\dfrac{1}{x + 2} - \dfrac{2}{x - 1} \geq 0$

53. $\dfrac{5}{y - 3} - \dfrac{3}{y + 1} \leq 0$

54. $\dfrac{1}{a + 3} - \dfrac{1}{2a - 3} < 0$

55. $\dfrac{1}{x + 3} \geq \dfrac{1}{x - 1}$

56. $\dfrac{2}{x + 1} \leq \dfrac{1}{x + 2}$

57. $\dfrac{1}{2 - p} > \dfrac{-1}{p + 1}$

58. $\dfrac{4}{r + 3} \geq \dfrac{1}{1 - r}$

59. $\dfrac{x}{x - 5} \leq 1$

60. $\dfrac{y + 1}{y - 3} < 2$

61. $\dfrac{t}{2 - t} \geq 1$

62. $\dfrac{2x - 7}{3 - x} \leq -1$

63. $\dfrac{y+4}{y+3} \geq -2$

64. $\dfrac{x}{x+2} > -7$

*65. $\dfrac{x}{x-2} \leq x$

*66. $\dfrac{4x}{x+1} \leq x$

*67. $\dfrac{-2}{x+3} > x$

*68. $\dfrac{-2}{1-y} < y$

SOLUTION FOR PRACTICE PROBLEM

1.
$$x^2 - x - 12 \leq 0$$
$$(x-4)(x+3) \leq 0 \qquad \text{(see Figure 10.7)}$$

x − 4

Sign	Interval
+	$x > 4$
0	$x = 4$
−	$x < 4$

x + 3

Sign	Interval
+	$x > -3$
0	$x = -3$
−	$x < -3$

Sign graph
for
$(x-4)(x+3) \leq 0$

Factors:
$\begin{cases} x-4 \qquad -------- 0++ \\ x+3 \qquad ---0++++++++++ \end{cases}$

Product: $(x-4)(x+3) \qquad +++0------0++$

$-3 \leq x \leq 4$

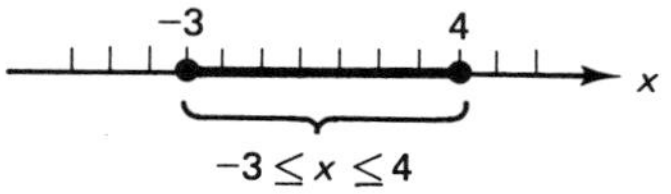

FIGURE 10.7

Solution set $= \{x \mid -3 \leq x \leq 4\}$.

PRACTICE TEST for Chapter 10

1. (a) Solve by factoring.
$$2x^2 + 10 = 9x$$
   (b) Solve by the method of taking the square root of both sides.
$$(x + 5)^2 = 49$$

2. Solve by completing the square.
   (a) $x^2 = 16 - 6x$ (b) $-x^2 - 4x + 20 = 0$

3. Solve by using the quadratic formula.
   (a) $4x^2 = 9x$ (b) $x(3x - 2) = 5$

4. Describe the type of solutions of each quadratic equation by evaluating the discriminant. Do not solve the equation.
   (a) $x^2 + 7x = 5$ (b) $3x(3x + 4) + 4 = 0$
   (c) $x = 9x^2 + 4$ (d) $\dfrac{6x^2 - 5}{x} = 13$

5. A ball dropped from a height of 196 feet is h feet above the ground after t seconds, where
$$h = 196 - 16t^2.$$
   How long does it take the ball to reach the ground?

6. Solve the following equations, which are quadratic in form.
   (a) $(2x - 1)^2 - (2x - 1) - 12 = 0$
   (b) $x^4 - 13x^2 + 36 = 0$

In problems 7 and 8, find the solution set for each equation involving radicals.

7. $x + 1 = \sqrt{5x + 11}$
8. $\sqrt{4 + x} - \sqrt{15 + 2x} = 2$

In problems 9 and 10, solve each inequality and graph the solution set.

9. $x^2 - 2x - 3 > 0$

10. $\dfrac{x}{x + 1} \leq 2$

Quadratic Equations and Inequalities in Two Variables

11-1
Parabolas

In Chapter 4 we saw that the graphs of equations which are linear in two real variables

$$ax + by = c, \qquad \text{not both } a \text{ and } b \text{ zero,}$$

are straight lines. In this section we consider equations that are quadratic in one real variable and linear in the other,

$$y = ax^2 + bx + c, \qquad a \neq 0$$

with a, b, and c real. The graphs of equations of this type are "bullet-shaped" curves called **parabolas**. The shape and position of the parabola depends on the constants a, b and c (see Figure 11.1).

The parabola

$$y = ax^2 + bx + c$$

opens upward when $a > 0$ and downward when $a < 0$ (see Figure 11.1).

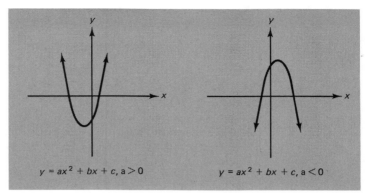

FIGURE 11.1

There is then either a lowest point or a highest point on the parabola. This point, which we label (x_0, y_0), is called the **vertex** of the parabola (see Figure 11.2). The parabola is symmetric about the straight line that goes

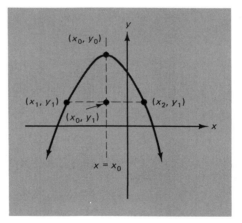

FIGURE 11.2

through the vertex parallel to the y-axis. This straight line is called the **axis of symmetry** and has the equation

$$x = x_0.$$

Exactly one-half of the parabola lies on either side of the axis of symmetry. Given any two points on the parabola with the same y-coordinate, say (x_1, y_1) and (x_2, y_1), the line joining these two points will intersect with the axis of symmetry at a point whose x-coordinate is x_0, the x-coordinate of the vertex. The fact that the parabola is symmetric means that x_0 is half-way between x_1 and x_2, or

$$x_0 = \frac{x_1 + x_2}{2}.$$

We will use this idea to graph parabolas.

To graph any equation we look for the ordered pairs (x, y) that satisfy the equation. Because of the special shape of the parabolas we can choose as few as three ordered pairs to plot in order to sketch any parabola. But those three ordered pairs must be *wisely* chosen to get a good idea of the shape and position of the parabola. The three ordered pairs to choose are **two symmetric points and the vertex.**

EXAMPLE 1   Graph the parabola

$$y = x^2 + 4x + 1.$$

SOLUTION   To find two symmetric points, set $y = 1$, the constant on the right, and solve for x:

$$1 = x^2 + 4x + 1$$
$$0 = x^2 + 4x$$
$$0 = x(x + 4)$$
$$x_1 = 0, \qquad x_2 = -4.$$

The two symmetric points are $(0, 1)$, $(-4, 1)$.

To find the vertex, we first locate the x-coordinate, x_0, halfway between the x-coordinates of the two symmetric points.

$$x_0 = \frac{0 + (-4)}{2} = -2$$

This also gives the equation of the axis of symmetry: $x = -2$.

To locate the y-coordinate, y_0, of the vertex, we substitute x_0 into the equation of the parabola and solve for y_0.

$$y_0 = (-2)^2 + 4(-2) + 1 = -3.$$

Thus the vertex is $(-2, -3)$. The parabola opens upward since $a = 1 > 0$.

We now have enough information to sketch the parabola, in Figure 11.3.

This method also works for parabolas written in the form

$$y = a(x - h)^2 + k,$$

as illustrated in the next example.

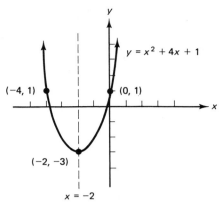

FIGURE 11.3

EXAMPLE 2   Graph the parabola

$$2y = -(x - 3)^2 + 1.$$

SOLUTION   We divide both sides of the equation by 2 so that the equation is expressed in the desired form.

$$y = -\tfrac{1}{2}(x - 3)^2 + \tfrac{1}{2}$$

Since $a = -\tfrac{1}{2} < 0$, the parabola opens downward. We locate three points. First, set $y = \tfrac{1}{2}$, and solve for x.

$$\tfrac{1}{2} = -\tfrac{1}{2}(x - 3)^2 + \tfrac{1}{2}$$
$$0 = -\tfrac{1}{2}(x - 3)^2$$
$$0 = (x - 3)^2$$
$$0 = x - 3$$
$$x = 3$$

Since we find only *one* value of x, then we have the coordinates of the vertex.

Vertex: $(3, \tfrac{1}{2})$

Next we set $x = 3 \pm 1$.

If $x = 3 + 1 = 4$, $y = -\tfrac{1}{2}(4 - 3)^2 + \tfrac{1}{2} = -\tfrac{1}{2} + \tfrac{1}{2} = 0.$
If $x = 3 - 1 = 2$, $y = -\tfrac{1}{2}(2 - 3)^2 + \tfrac{1}{2} = -\tfrac{1}{2} + \tfrac{1}{2} = 0.$

The two symmetric points are

$$(4, 0) \text{ and } (2, 0),$$

and the graph is as seen in Figure 11.4.

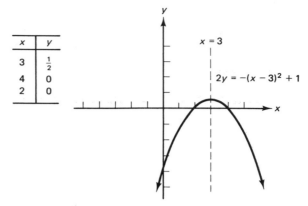

x	y
3	$\frac{1}{2}$
4	0
2	0

FIGURE 11.4

We summarize these results for graphing parabolas in the following.

Graphing the Parabola

$$y = ax^2 + bx + c, \qquad a \neq 0$$

1. If $a > 0$, the parabola opens upward and the vertex is the lowest point. If $a < 0$, the parabola opens downward and the vertex is the highest point.

2. Three points can be located in the following manner.

   Set $y = c$, and solve for x.

   (a) If there are two solutions x_1 and x_2 with $x_1 \neq x_2$, then (x_1, c) and (x_2, c) are **two symmetric points** on the parabola.

   (b) To locate the **vertex** (x_0, y_0): set

   $$x_0 = \frac{x_1 + x_2}{2};$$

   substitute $x = x_0$ into the equation and solve for $y = y_0$.

   (a) If there is one solution x_0, then this is the x-coordinate of the **vertex**,

   $$(x_0, y_0) = (x_0, c).$$

   (b) To find **two symmetric points** substitute $x = x_0 \pm k$, k any convenient nonzero value, into the equation and solve for y.

3. The equation of the **axis of symmetry** is

   $$x = x_0.$$

4. Draw a smooth curve, symmetric with respect to the axis of symmetry, through the three points.

PRACTICE
PROBLEM 1
(Solution on page 326) Graph

$$y = -2x^2 + 3x + 1.$$

The graphs of equations that are quadratic in y and linear in x,

$$x = ay^2 + by + c, \qquad a \neq 0$$

are parabolas, which open to the right when $a > 0$, and to the left when $a < 0$ (see Figure 11.5). The point that lies either farthest to the left or farthest to the right is the **vertex**, (x_0, y_0). The **axis of symmetry** is a straight line parallel to the x-axis passing through the vertex. It has equation $y = y_0$.

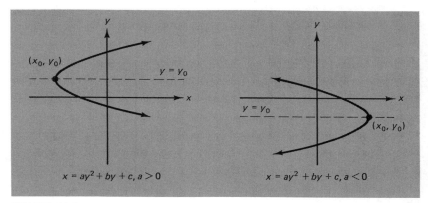

FIGURE 11.5

The procedure for graphing parabolas of this type is exactly the same as for parabolas opening upward or downward except that the roles of x and y are interchanged.

EXAMPLE 3   Graph the parabola

$$x + 2y^2 + 4y = 3.$$

SOLUTION   Isolating x on the left yields

$$x = -2y^2 - 4y + 3.$$

This is a parabola opening to the left since $a = -2 < 0$. Setting $x = 3$, the constant on the right, then solving for y,

$$3 = -2y^2 - 4y + 3$$
$$0 = -2y^2 - 4y$$
$$0 = -2y(y + 2)$$
$$-2y = 0 \qquad y + 2 = 0$$
$$y = 0 \qquad\qquad y = -2.$$

Two symmetric points are $(3, 0)$ and $(3, -2)$.

To locate the vertex we set

$$y_0 = \frac{0 + (-2)}{2} = -1$$

and substitute this into the equation of the parabola to find x_0. The vertex is $(5, -1)$, and the equation of the axis of symmetry is $y = -1$. The graph can be seen in Figure 11.6.

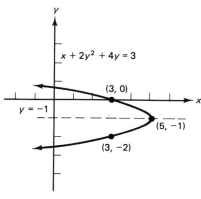

FIGURE 11.6

PRACTICE PROBLEM 2 (Solution on page 326) Graph the parabola

$$x = (y + 1)^2 + 2.$$

EXERCISES 11-1

Graph the parabolas.

(See Example 1 and Practice Problem 1.)

1. $y = x^2 + 2x + 4$ 2. $y = x^2 + 2x - 3$

3. $y = x^2 - 5x + 3$ 4. $y = x^2 - 4x + 3$

5. $y = 2x^2 + 4x - 3$

6. $y = 2x^2 + 4x + 3$

7. $y = 3x^2 + 3x + 4$

8. $y = 3x^2 + 6x - 2$

9. $y = -x^2 + 2x - 3$

10. $y = -x^2 + 4x + 5$

11. $y = -x^2 - 4x + 2$

12. $y = -x^2 + 2x - 4$

13. $y = -2x^2 - 2x + 3$

14. $y = -4x^2 - 8x + 9$

15. $y = -3x^2 + 4x - 3$

16. $y = -2x^2 - 4x + 2$

17. $y = x^2 - 2x$

18. $y = x^2 + 4x$

19. $y = -2x^2 + x$

20. $y = -2x^2 + 6x$

21. $y - x^2 + 4x = 0$

22. $y - x^2 - x = 0$

23. $4y + x^2 - 2x = 0$

24. $3y + 3x^2 + x = 0$

In problems 25–28, round the coordinates to the nearest hundredth.

C25. $y = x^2 + 1.02x - 3.71$

C26. $y = -x^2 + 4.75x + 3.59$

C27. $y = -1.02(x - 1.18)^2 + 2.93$

C28. $y = 1.71(x + 1.32)^2 - 1.22$

(See Example 2.)

29. $y = x^2$

30. $y = -x^2$

31. $y = x^2 - 4$

32. $y = 2x^2 + 5$

33. $y = -3x^2 + 7$

34. $y = -x^2 - 2$

35. $2y = -x^2 + 8$

36. $3y = x^2 + 6$

37. $y = -(x + 3)^2$

38. $y = 2(x - 1)^2$

39. $y = (x - 5)^2 + 2$

40. $y = (x - 2)^2 + 1$

41. $y = \frac{1}{2}(x + 1)^2 - 1$

42. $y = \frac{1}{3}(x + 3)^2 - 2$

43. $y = -2(x + 3)^2 - 3$

44. $y = -3(x + 1)^2 + 1$

(See Example 3 and Practice Problem 2.)

45. $x = y^2$

46. $x = -y^2$

47. $x = -(y - 1)^2$

48. $x = (y - 1)^2$

49. $x = y^2 + 2y + 1$

50. $x = y^2 + 3y - 1$

51. $x = 2y^2 - 4y + 5$

52. $x = 3y^2 + 4y - 2$

53. $x = -y^2 - y - 3$

54. $x = -y^2 + 2y - 1$

55. $2x + y^2 = 4$

56. $4x - 3y^2 = 5$

57. $x = (y - 1)^2 + 5$

58. $x = (y - 2)^2 + 1$

59. $2x = -(y + 1)^2$

60. $4x = -2(y + 3)^2 - 3$

1. The parabola $y = -2x^2 + 3x + 1$ opens downward since $a = -2 < 0$. Set $y = 1$, and solve for x.

$$1 = -2x^2 + 3x + 1$$
$$0 = -2x^2 + 3x$$
$$0 = x(-2x + 3)$$
$$x = 0, \qquad x = \tfrac{3}{2}$$

Two symmetric points: $(0, 1)$, $(\tfrac{3}{2}, 1)$
Locate vertex: (x_0, y_0)

$$x_0 = \frac{\tfrac{3}{2} + 0}{2} = \frac{3}{4}$$

$$y_0 = -2\left(\frac{3}{4}\right)^2 + 3\left(\frac{3}{4}\right) + 1 = \frac{17}{8}$$

A graph of this parabola is shown in Figure 11.7.

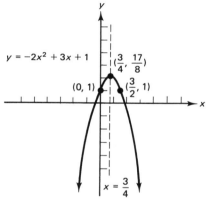

FIGURE 11.7

2. The parabola $x = (y + 1)^2 + 2$ opens to the right since $a = 1 > 0$. Set $x = 2$ and solve for y.

$$2 = (y + 1)^2 + 2$$
$$0 = (y + 1)^2$$
$$y = -1$$

Vertex: $(2, -1)$.
Set $y = -1 \pm 1$ and solve for x.

$$y = -1 + 1 = 0, \qquad x = (0 + 1)^2 + 2 = 1^2 + 2 = 3$$
$$y = -1 - 1 = -2, \qquad x = (-2 + 1)^2 + 2 = (-1)^2 + 2 = 3$$

Two symmetric points: $(3, 0)$, $(3, -2)$
A graph of this parabola is shown in Figure 11.8.

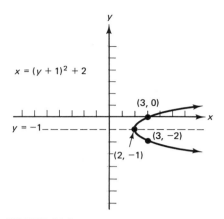

$x = (y + 1)^2 + 2$

FIGURE 11.8

11-2 Distances are useful in describing circles, ellipses, and hyperbolas. The
The Distance distance formula is derived from the Pythagorean Theorem, which estab-
Formula and lishes a relationship between the lengths of the sides of a right triangle.
Circles If c is the length of the hypothenuse and a and b are the lengths of the
sides forming the right angle [see Figure 11.9(a)], then the Pythagorean
Theorem states

$$c^2 = a^2 + b^2$$

or

$$c = \sqrt{a^2 + b^2}.$$

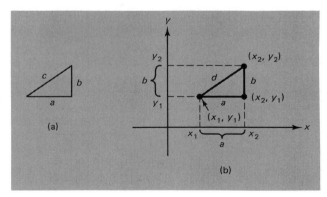

FIGURE 11.9

Given any two points (x_1, y_1) and (x_2, y_2), the distance, d, between
those points is the length of the hypothenuse of a right triangle with vertices as shown in Figure 11.9(b). With

$d =$ distance between (x_1, y_1) and (x_2, y_2),

$b = |y_2 - y_1|$ and $b^2 = (y_2 - y_1)^2$,

$a = |x_2 - x_1|$ and $a^2 = (x_2 - x_1)^2$,

we have

$$d = \sqrt{a^2 + b^2}$$
$$= \sqrt{(x_2 - x_1)^2 + (y_2 - y_1)^2}.$$

This result is known as the distance formula.

Distance Formula

The distance, d, between two points (x_1, y_1) and (x_2, y_2) is

$$d = \sqrt{(x_2 - x_1)^2 + (y_2 - y_1)^2}.$$

EXAMPLE 1   Find the distance between $(3, 6)$ and $(0, 10)$.

SOLUTION   It makes no difference which point we choose to label (x_1, y_1) or (x_2, y_2) since

$$(x_2 - x_1)^2 = (x_1 - x_2)^2 \quad \text{and} \quad (y_2 - y_1)^2 = (y_1 - y_2)^2.$$

Let $(x_1, y_1) = (3, 6)$ and $(x_2, y_2) = (0, 10)$. Then

$$d = \sqrt{(0 - 3)^2 + (10 - 6)^2} = \sqrt{9 + 16} = \sqrt{25} = 5$$

is the distance between $(3, 6)$ and $(0, 10)$.

EXAMPLE 2   Show that $(-1, 1)$, $(5, 3)$ and $(0, -2)$ are vertices of a right triangle.

SOLUTION   Our "game plan" is to compute the distances d_1, d_2, and d_3 between each pair of points and then check to see if these distances satisfy the Pythagorean Theorem (see Figure 11.10).

The distance, d_1, between $(0, -2)$ and $(5, 3)$ is

$$d_1 = \sqrt{(5 - 0)^2 + (3 - (-2))^2} = \sqrt{25 + 25} = \sqrt{50}.$$

The distance, d_2, between $(-1, 1)$ and $(5, 3)$ is

$$d_2 = \sqrt{(5 - (-1))^2 + (3 - 1)^2} = \sqrt{36 + 4} = \sqrt{40}.$$

The distance, d_3, between $(-1, 1)$ and $(0, -2)$ is

$$d_3 = \sqrt{(0 - (-1))^2 + (-2 - 1)^2} = \sqrt{1 + 9} = \sqrt{10}.$$

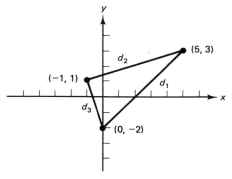

FIGURE 11.10

Since

$$(d_3)^2 + (d_2)^2 = 10 + 40 = 50 = (d_1)^2,$$

the Pythagorean Theorem is satisfied, and $(-1, 1)$, $(5, 3)$, and $(0, -2)$ are vertices of a right triangle.

As indicated earlier, distances are used to describe circles, and to write their equations.

Definition 11-1 A **circle** is the set of all points equally distant from a given point called the **center** of the circle. The distance between any point on the circle and its center is called the **radius** of the circle.

EXAMPLE 3 Use the distance formula to find the equation of a circle with center (h, k) and radius r.

SOLUTION Let (x, y) represent a point on the circle. Then the distance between (x, y) and (h, k) is r (see Figure 11.11). Using the distance formula, we have

$$r = \sqrt{(x - h)^2 + (y - k)^2}$$

or, equivalently,

$$r^2 = (x - h)^2 + (y - k)^2.$$

As a special case, the equation of a circle with center at the origin $(0, 0)$ and radius r is

$$x^2 + y^2 = r^2.$$

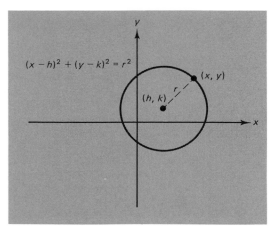

FIGURE 11.11

These results are summarized as follows.

Standard Equations of a Circle		
Equation	**Center**	**Radius**
$x^2 + y^2 = r^2$	$(0, 0)$	r
$(x - h)^2 + (y - k)^2 = r^2$	(h, k)	r

EXAMPLE 4   Write the equation of a circle with center at $(2, -1)$ and radius 3. Sketch the circle.

SOLUTION   Let (x, y) represent a point on the circle with center $(h, k) = (2, -1)$ and radius $r = 3$. Then the equation is

$$(x - h)^2 + (y - k)^2 = r^2$$
$$(x - 2)^2 + (y - (-1))^2 = 3^2$$
$$(x - 2)^2 + (y + 1)^2 = 9.$$

To sketch the circle we first locate the center and four points 3 units from the center. Then we draw a smooth curve connecting those four points (see Figure 11.12).

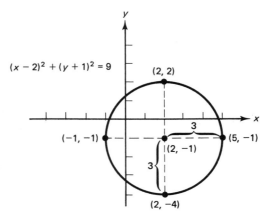

$(x - 2)^2 + (y + 1)^2 = 9$

FIGURE 11.12

EXAMPLE 5   Find the center and radius of the following circles.

(a) $x^2 + y^2 = 4$
(b) $(x - 1)^2 + y^2 = 5$
(c) $x^2 - 2x + y^2 + 6y = -6$

SOLUTION   Whenever the equation fits one of the standard forms for a circle, we can easily find the center and radius.

(a) We rewrite this equation as

$$x^2 + y^2 = 2^2.$$

Thus the center is $(0, 0)$ and radius, $r = 2$.

(b) We rewrite this equation as

$$(x - 1)^2 + (y - 0)^2 = (\sqrt{5})^2.$$

Thus the center is $(1, 0)$ and radius is $r = \sqrt{5}$.

(c) To rewrite

$$x^2 - 2x + y^2 + 6y = -6$$

so as to fit the second standard form, we add 1 to both sides to complete the square on x:

$$x^2 - 2x + \mathbf{1} + y^2 + 6y = -6 + \mathbf{1};$$

we add 9 to both sides to complete the square on y.

$$x^2 - 2x + 1 + y^2 + 6y + \mathbf{9} = -6 + 1 + \mathbf{9}$$

Factoring each quadratic yields

$$(x - 1)^2 + (y + 3)^2 = 4$$

or

$$(x - 1)^2 + (y - (-3))^2 = 2^2.$$

Thus the center is $(1, -3)$ and the radius is $r = 2$.

PRACTICE (Solution on page 333) Find the center and radius of the circle with
PROBLEM 1 equation

$$x^2 + y^2 + 3x + 2y = 1.$$

EXERCISES 11-2

Find the distance between each of the following pairs of points. (See Example 1.)

1. $(1, 2)$, $(4, -2)$ 2. $(6, 3)$, $(-6, -2)$

3. $(1, 4)$, $(1, -2)$ 4. $(-3, -1)$, $(4, -1)$

5. $(0, -2)$, $(4, -5)$ 6. $(5, 2)$, $(0, -10)$

7. $(-2, 3)$, $(-1, -4)$ 8. $(5, -8)$, $(-2, 1)$

9. $(6, -2)$,$(-4, 8)$ 10. $(-5, -1)$, $(-2, 1)$

In problems 11 and 12, round the answers to the nearest tenth.

C11. $(-1.1, 2.7)$, $(-3.2, -4.3)$ C12. $(0.27, -0.12)$, $(-0.58, 0.68)$

(See Example 2.)

13. Show that $(1, 3)$, $(-4, 0)$, and $(4, -2)$ are vertices of a right triangle.

14. Show that $(1, -1)$, $(4, 3)$, and $(-4, 9)$ are vertices of a right triangle.

15. Find the perimeter of the triangle with vertices at $(-5, -3)$, $(1, -1)$, and $(0, 2)$.

16. Find the perimeter of the diamond with vertices at $(0, 4)$, $(0, -4)$, $(2, 0)$, and $(-2, 0)$.

17. Find the perimeter of the parallelogram with vertices at $(-3, 8)$, $(7, 8)$, $(-8, -4)$, and $(2, -4)$.

18. Find the perimeter of the parallelogram with vertices at $(-6, -4)$, $(0, -4)$, $(0, 4)$, and $(6, 4)$.

Write an equation of the circle with center and radius given. (See Example 4.)

	Center	Radius		Center	Radius
19.	$(0, 0)$	3	20.	$(0, 0)$	1
21.	$(0, 0)$	$\frac{4}{3}$	22.	$(0, 0)$	$\frac{1}{5}$

23. $(2, -1)$	2		24. $(-1, 3)$	1
25. $(-5, 4)$	4		26. $(-2, -6)$	5
27. $(-1, -2)$	$\frac{3}{5}$		28. $(-1, 3)$	$\frac{1}{2}$
29. $(2, 0)$	$\frac{3}{4}$		30. $(0, -1)$	$\frac{2}{5}$
31. $(-1, -1)$	$\sqrt{2}$		32. $(3, -4)$	$\sqrt{3}$
33. $(0, 0)$	$\sqrt{3}$		34. $(1, 0)$	$\sqrt{5}$

Find the center and radius of the following circles. Sketch each circle. (See Example 5 and Practice Problem 1.)

35. $x^2 + y^2 = 1$ 36. $x^2 + y^2 = 9$

37. $x^2 + y^2 = 3$ 38. $x^2 + y^2 = 10$

39. $(x - 1)^2 + y^2 = 4$ 40. $(x + 2)^2 + y^2 = 1$

41. $x^2 + (y + 3)^2 = 9$ 42. $x^2 + (y - 2)^2 = 25$

43. $(x - 1)^2 + (y - 3)^2 = 1$ 44. $(x + 2)^2 + (y - 1)^2 = 4$

45. $(x + 3)^2 + (y + 3)^2 = 9$ 46. $(x - 3)^2 + (y - 5)^2 = 4$

47. $x^2 + 2x + y^2 = 0$ 48. $x^2 + 6x + y^2 = 0$

49. $x^2 + y^2 + 2x - 2y = 0$ 50. $x^2 + 8x + y^2 - 6y = 0$

51. $x^2 + y^2 = 2x - 6y + 6$ 52. $x^2 + y^2 = x + y + \frac{1}{2}$

In problems 53 and 54, round the answers to the nearest tenth.

C53. $x^2 + y^2 = 1.4x - 3.6y$ C54. $x^2 + y^2 = 4.2x + 6.2y - 2.7$

Describe the graph of each of the following equations.

*55. $x^2 + y^2 = 0$ *56. $(x - 3)^2 + (y - 3)^2 = 0$

*57. $(x + 2)^2 + (y - 1)^2 = 0$ *58. $(x - 1)^2 + y^2 = 0$

*59. $x^2 + y^2 = -4$ *60. $x^2 + y^2 = -1$

*61. $x^2 + (y - 1)^2 = -3$ *62. $(x - 2)^2 + (y + 5)^2 = -9$

SOLUTION FOR PRACTICE PROBLEM

1. $x^2 + y^2 + 3x + 2y = 1$

$x^2 + 3x + \dfrac{9}{4} + y^2 + 2y + 1 = 1 + \dfrac{9}{4} + 1$

$\left(x + \dfrac{3}{2}\right)^2 + (y + 1)^2 = \dfrac{17}{4}$

Center: $\left(-\dfrac{3}{2}, -1\right)$, radius $= \dfrac{\sqrt{17}}{2}$

Distances can also be used to describe an *ellipse*, which is a football-shaped or oval-shaped curve.

Definition 11-2 An **ellipse** is the set of all points (x, y) such that the sum of the distances of (x, y) to two given points F_1 and F_2 (called **foci**; singular **focus**) is constant.

In Figure 11.13, the sum $d_1 + d_2$ remains constant no matter where (x, y) lies on the ellipse. Figure 11.13(a) shows an ellipse with foci located on the x-axis spaced equally distant from the origin. Figure 11.13(b) shows an ellipse with foci located on the y-axis spaced equally distant from the origin. In each case the center of the ellipse is at the origin, and these are the only kinds of ellipses we examine in this text. The distance formula can be used to derive the equations of ellipses, but we will accept the equations without derivation.

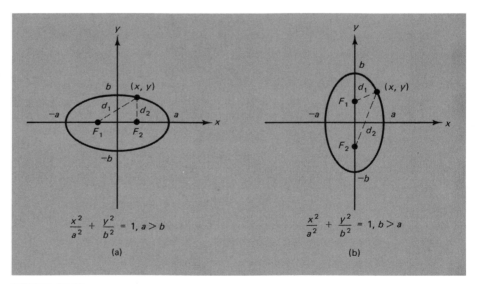

FIGURE 11.13

The points where the ellipse crosses the coordinate axes are called the **vertices** of the ellipse. Because of the symmetric shape of an ellipse, the vertices are the only four points needed to sketch the graph of an ellipse. These four vertices can easily be determined whenever the equation is written in the standard form.

Standard Equation of the Ellipse		
Equation	Vertices on x-axis	Vertices on y-axis
$\dfrac{x^2}{a^2} + \dfrac{y^2}{b^2} = 1$	$(\pm a, 0)$	$(0, \pm b)$

EXAMPLE 1   Sketch the ellipses by locating the vertices.

(a) $x^2 + 4y^2 = 4$
(b) $9x^2 + 4y^2 = 36$

SOLUTION   In each equation, we divide both sides of the equation by the constant and write the equation in standard form.

(a)
$$x^2 + 4y^2 = 4$$

$$\frac{x^2}{4} + y^2 = 1$$

$$\frac{x^2}{2^2} + \frac{y^2}{1^2} = 1$$

Thus $a = 2$, $b = 1$. The vertices are at $(\pm 2, 0)$ and $(0, \pm 1)$. (see Figure 11.14).

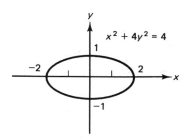

FIGURE 11.14

(b)
$$9x^2 + 4y^2 = 36$$

$$\frac{x^2}{4} + \frac{y^2}{9} = 1$$

$$\frac{x^2}{2^2} + \frac{y^2}{3^2} = 1$$

Thus $a = 2$, $b = 3$. The vertices are $(\pm 2, 0)$ and $(0, \pm 3)$ (see Figure 11.15).

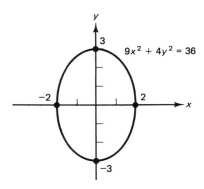

FIGURE 11.15

PRACTICE
PROBLEM 1
(Solution on page 342) Sketch the ellipse by locating the vertices.

$$9x^2 + 36y^2 = 144$$

Distances are also used to describe curves known as hyperbolas.

Definition 11.3 Given two fixed points F_1 and F_2, a **hyperbola** is the set of all points (x, y) such that the absolute value of the difference in the distances from (x, y) to F_1 and from (x, y) to F_2 is a constant. The points F_1 and F_2 are the **foci** (singular, **focus**) of the hyperbola.

Again, the distance formula can be used to derive the equation for a hyperbola, although we omit the derivation in this text. In Figure 11.16, the difference $|d_1 - d_2|$ remains constant no matter where (x, y) is chosen on the hyperbola.

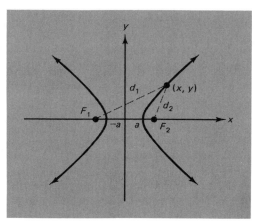

FIGURE 11.16

Figure 11.17 shows a hyperbola with equation $\dfrac{x^2}{a^2} - \dfrac{y^2}{b^2} = 1$

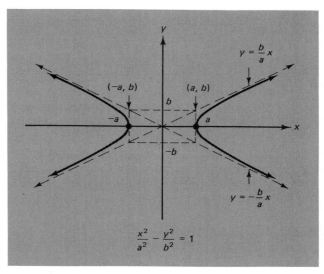

FIGURE 11.17

with foci located on the x-axis spaced equally distant from the origin. The two points where the hyperbola crosses one of the coordinate axes are called the **vertices** of the hyperbola. The two straight lines intersecting at the origin are called the **asymptotes** of the hyperbola. Just as with the foci, the asymptotes are not a part of the graph of the hyperbola. Instead, they are aids in sketching the hyperbola. Hyperbolas centered at the origin are the only types of hyperbolas that we study here. As a point (x, y) on the hyperbola moves farther away from the center of the hyperbola, the point (x, y) becomes closer to one of the asymptotes. Thus the asymptotes of a hyperbola are invaluable in sketching the hyperbola. In fact, the two vertices and the asymptotes are all that is necessary to sketch this hyperbola. Without proof or derivation we state the following.

Facts About the Hyperbola

$$\frac{x^2}{a^2} - \frac{y^2}{b^2} = 1$$

1. The vertices are $(\pm a, 0)$.
2. There are no y-intercepts.
3. The equations of the asymptotes are

$$y = \pm \frac{b}{a}x.$$

The asymptotes are straight lines intersecting at $(0, 0)$, with one passing through (a, b), $(-a, -b)$ and the other going through $(-a, b)$, $(a, -b)$. They can be drawn by first sketching a rectangle going through b and $-b$ on the y-axis and a and $-a$ on the x-axis. Then each asymptote passes through diagonally opposite corners of the rectangle.

EXAMPLE 2   Sketch the hyperbola

$$x^2 - 4y^2 = 16.$$

SOLUTION   We first divide both sides of the equation by 16, so that the constant on the right is 1.

$$\frac{x^2}{16} - \frac{y^2}{4} = 1$$

or, equivalently,

$$\frac{x^2}{4^2} - \frac{y^2}{2^2} = 1.$$

The vertices are $(\pm 4, 0)$. There are no y-intercepts. We sketch the asymptotes by sketching a rectangle going through ± 2 on the y-axis and ± 4 on the x-axis. Then we draw one asymptote through $(4, 2)$, $(0, 0)$, and $(-4, -2)$; and we draw the second asymptote through $(-4, 2)$, $(0, 0)$, and $(4, -2)$. Last, we sketch the hyperbola going through the vertices and approaching each asymptote (see Figure 11.18).

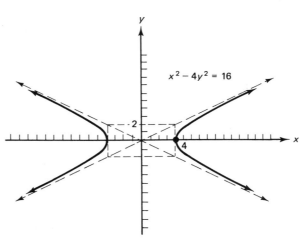

FIGURE 11.18

If the foci F_1 and F_2 lie on the y-axis (see Figure 11.19), the standard equation of the hyperbola is

$$\frac{y^2}{b^2} - \frac{x^2}{a^2} = 1.$$

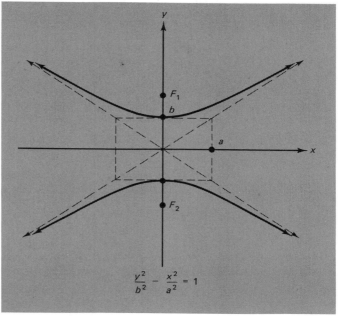

$$\frac{y^2}{b^2} - \frac{x^2}{a^2} = 1$$

FIGURE 11.19

Facts About the Hyperbola

$$\frac{y^2}{b^2} - \frac{x^2}{a^2} = 1$$

1. The vertices are $(0, \pm b)$.
2. There are no x-intercepts.
3. The equations of the asymptotes are

$$y = \pm \frac{b}{a}x.$$

EXAMPLE 3 Sketch the hyperbola

$$y^2 - 4x^2 = 1.$$

SOLUTION   Rewriting into standard form, we have

$$\frac{y^2}{1^2} - \frac{x^2}{(\frac{1}{2})^2} = 1.$$

Thus the vertices are $(0, \pm 1)$. There are no x-intercepts. We draw the asymptotes by sketching a rectangle going through ± 1 on the y-axis and $\pm\frac{1}{2}$ on the x-axis. Finally, we sketch the hyperbola through the vertices and approaching each asymptote (see Figure 11.20).

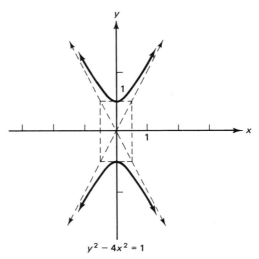

$$y^2 - 4x^2 = 1$$

FIGURE 11.20

PRACTICE   (Solution on page 342) Graph the hyperbola
PROBLEM 2
$$9x^2 - y^2 = 16.$$

EXERCISES 11-3

Graph each ellipse by locating the vertices. (See Example 1 and Practice Problem 1.)

1. $\dfrac{x^2}{9} + \dfrac{y^2}{4} = 1$ 2. $\dfrac{x^2}{25} + \dfrac{y^2}{4} = 1$

3. $\dfrac{x^2}{16} + \dfrac{y^2}{9} = 1$ 4. $\dfrac{x^2}{9} + \dfrac{y^2}{25} = 1$

5. $x^2 + 4y^2 = 16$ 6. $9x^2 + y^2 = 36$

7. $25x^2 + y^2 = 25$ 8. $x^2 + 9y^2 = 9$

9. $4x^2 + 25y^2 = 100$ 10. $16x^2 + 9y^2 = 144$

11. $4x^2 + 9y^2 = 36$

12. $25x^2 + 4y^2 = 100$

13. $4x^2 + y^2 = 1$

14. $16x^2 + y^2 = 1$

15. $x^2 + 9y^2 = 1$

16. $x^2 + 25y^2 = 1$

17. $4x^2 + 9y^2 = 1$

18. $25x^2 + 16y^2 = 1$

19. $4x^2 + y^2 = 9$

20. $x^2 + 16y^2 = 4$

In problems 21 and 22, round the coordinates of the vertices to the nearest hundredth.

C21. $x^2 + 2y^2 = 2.25$

C22. $3x^2 + y^2 = 1.96$

Describe the graph of each of the following.

*23. $\dfrac{x^2}{100} + \dfrac{y^2}{25} = 0$

*24. $\dfrac{x^2}{16} + y^2 = 0$

*25. $x^2 + 4y^2 = -1$

*26. $9x^2 + 16y^2 = -1$

In problems 27–50, graph each hyperbola using the vertices and asymptotes.

(See Example 2 and Practice Problem 2.)

27. $x^2 - y^2 = 1$

28. $x^2 - \dfrac{y^2}{4} = 1$

29. $\dfrac{x^2}{9} - \dfrac{y^2}{4} = 1$

30. $\dfrac{x^2}{25} - \dfrac{y^2}{16} = 1$

31. $9x^2 - 16y^2 = 144$

32. $4x^2 - 9y^2 = 36$

33. $4x^2 - y^2 = 16$

34. $25x^2 - y^2 = 100$

35. $4x^2 - y^2 = 1$

36. $x^2 - 4y^2 = 1$

37. $25x^2 - 16y^2 = 9$

38. $4x^2 - 9y^2 = 25$

In problems 39 and 40, round the coordinates of the vertices to the nearest tenth.

C39. $x^2 - y^2 = 14.2$

C40. $3x^2 - y^2 = 12.7$

(See Example 3.)

41. $y^2 - x^2 = 1$

42. $y^2 - \dfrac{x^2}{4} = 1$

43. $\dfrac{y^2}{36} - \dfrac{x^2}{25} = 1$

44. $\dfrac{y^2}{25} - \dfrac{x^2}{16} = 1$

45. $25y^2 - 4x^2 = 100$

46. $16y^2 - 9x^2 = 144$

47. $y^2 - 16x^2 = 9$

48. $4y^2 - x^2 = 9$

In problems 49 and 50, round the coordinates of the vertices to the nearest tenth.

C49. $4.1y^2 - 2.7x^2 = 23.2$

C50. $11.2y^2 - 4.3x^2 = 37.2$

Graph each of the following.

*51. $x^2 - y^2 = 0$ *52. $9x^2 - y^2 = 0$

*53. $25x^2 - 16y^2 = 0$ *54. $9x^2 - 25y^2 = 0$

SOLUTIONS FOR PRACTICE PROBLEMS

1. $9x^2 + 36y^2 = 144$

   $\dfrac{x^2}{16} + \dfrac{y^2}{4} = 1$

   $\dfrac{x^2}{4^2} + \dfrac{y^2}{2^2} = 1$

   vertices: $\begin{cases}(\pm 4, 0) \\ (0, \pm 2)\end{cases}$

   This ellipse is graphed
   in Figure 11.21.

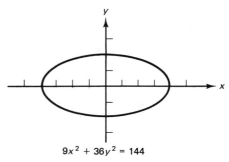

$9x^2 + 36y^2 = 144$

FIGURE 11.21

2. $9x^2 - y^2 = 16$

   $\dfrac{9x^2}{16} - \dfrac{y^2}{16} = 1$

   $\dfrac{x^2}{(\frac{4}{3})^2} - \dfrac{y^2}{4^2} = 1$

   verties: $(\pm \frac{4}{3}, 0)$

   no y-intercepts
   This hyperbola is graphed
   in Figure 11.22.

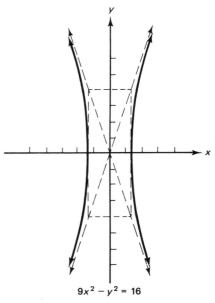

$9x^2 - y^2 = 16$

FIGURE 11.22

The linear and quadratic equations that we have studied so far are included in the following list.

straight line: $ax + by = c$, not both a and b zero

parabola: $\begin{cases} y = ax^2 + bx + c, & a \neq 0 \\ x = ay^2 + by + c, & a \neq 0 \end{cases}$

circle: $\begin{cases} x^2 + y^2 = r^2 \\ (x - h)^2 + (y - k)^2 = r^2 \end{cases}$

ellipse: $\dfrac{x^2}{a^2} + \dfrac{y^2}{b^2} = 1$

hyperbola: $\begin{cases} \dfrac{x^2}{a^2} - \dfrac{y^2}{b^2} = 1 \\ \dfrac{y^2}{b^2} - \dfrac{x^2}{a^2} = 1 \end{cases}$

These types of curves are called the **conic sections**. Each is obtained by intersecting a right circular cone with a plane. The amount of inclination of the plane determines the type of conic section (see Figure 11.23).

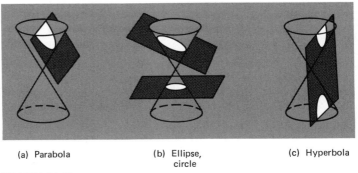

(a) Parabola   (b) Ellipse,   (c) Hyperbola
                          circle

FIGURE 11.23

Any conic section has an equation that can be written in the form

$$Ax^2 + By^2 + Cx + Dy + E = 0.$$

It is essential in the further study of mathematics to be able to recognize by examining the coefficients A, B, C, D, and E, which conic we are dealing with. The table in the next figure lists the conditions the coefficients must meet in order to have each particular conic section as the graph of the equation. Examples of each are also given in Figure 11.24.

The Conic Sections and Their Equations $Ax^2 + By^2 + Cx + Dy + E = 0$		
Conic Section	**Conditions**	**Example**
Straight line	$A = B = 0$ not both C and D zero	$3x + 7y - 2 = 0$
Parabola (opens up/down)	$A \neq 0, B = 0, D \neq 0$	$x^2 - x + 3y - 2 = 0$
Parabola (opens left/right)	$A = 0, B \neq 0, C \neq 0$	$2y^2 + x - 3 = 0$
Circle	$A = B \neq 0$	$2x^2 + 2y^2 - 3x + 5y = 0$
Ellipse	A, B have same sign $C = D = 0$ E has sign opposite A	$4x^2 + 9y^2 - 36 = 0$
Hyperbola	A, B have opposite sign $C = D = 0, E \neq 0$	$25x^2 - 9y^2 + 1 = 0$

FIGURE 11.24

Any system of equations in two variables in which at least one equation is nonlinear is considered to be a **nonlinear system**. Examples include:

$$x^2 + 2x + 3 = y, \qquad x^2 + y^2 = 25, \qquad x^2 + y^2 = 16$$
$$3x + y + 1 = 0 \qquad\quad 3x^2 - y^2 = 7 \qquad\quad 4x^2 + y^2 = 4$$

As with linear systems studied in Chapter 5, the real solutions to a system of nonlinear equations are the points of intersection of the graphs of the equations. In Chapter 5, the *substitution method* and the *elimination method* were used to solve systems of linear equations. These methods can also be used to solve systems of *nonlinear* equations in two variables. The choice of either the substitution or the elimination method depends upon the particular system in question. We first illustrate the *substitution method*.

EXAMPLE 1 Solve the system

$$x^2 + 2x + 3 = y$$
$$3x + y + 1 = 0.$$

SOLUTION   Although it is *not* necessary to look at the graph, we first note that the real
solutions are the points of intersection (see Figure 11.25) of

$$\text{the parabola:} \quad x^2 + 2x + 3 = y$$

$$\text{and the straight line:} \quad 3x + y + 1 = 0.$$

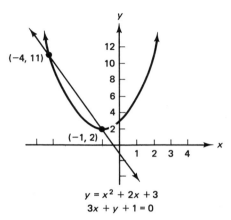

$$y = x^2 + 2x + 3$$
$$3x + y + 1 = 0$$

FIGURE 11.25

Since in the first equation y is expressed in terms of x, we *substitute* this
expression for y into the second equation:

$$3x + (x^2 + 2x + 3) + 1 = 0.$$

Solving for x in this equation, we obtain

$$x^2 + 5x + 4 = 0$$

$$(x + 4)(x + 1) = 0$$

$$x + 4 = 0 \quad \text{or} \quad x + 1 = 0$$

$$x = -4 \qquad \qquad x = -1.$$

To obtain corresponding values of y, we substitute each value of x into
the linear equation. It is *imperative* that we use the equation of lowest
degree. Otherwise, we will obtain an additional point on the parabola
which is *not* on the straight line.

$$x = -4 \qquad\qquad\qquad x = -1$$

$$3(-4) + y + 1 = 0 \qquad 3(-1) + y + 1 = 0$$

$$y - 11 = 0 \qquad\qquad\quad y - 2 = 0$$

$$y = 11 \qquad\qquad\qquad y = 2$$

Thus $(-4, 11)$ and $(-1, 2)$ are points of intersection of the parabola and
the straight line, and the solution set is $\{(-4, 11), (-1, 2)\}$.

PRACTICE PROBLEM 1 (Solution on page 350) Solve

$$xy = 4$$
$$y - 2x = 2.$$

The *elimination method* is illustrated in the next example, involving a circle and a hyperbola.

EXAMPLE 2 Solve

$$x^2 + y^2 = 25$$
$$3x^2 - y^2 = 11.$$

SOLUTION We can eliminate the variable y by adding the two equations together.

$$x^2 + y^2 = 25$$
$$3x^2 - y^2 = 11$$
$$\overline{4x^2 \qquad = 36}$$

This equation involving x only can easily be solved.

$$x^2 = 9$$
$$x = \pm 3$$

The corresponding values of y are found by substituting these values of x into either equation. Here we will use the equation of the circle.

$$(\pm 3)^2 + y^2 = 25$$
$$9 + y^2 = 25$$
$$y^2 = 16$$
$$y = \pm 4$$

The solution set is $\{(3, 4), (-3, 4), (3, -4), (-3, -4)\}$. Again these real solutions can be seen on Figure 11.26 as points of intersection of the circle and hyperbola.

A **system of nonlinear inequalities** is one or more equations or inequalities in which at least one is nonlinear and at least one is an inequality. Some examples of systems of nonlinear inequalities are:

$$\begin{aligned} x^2 + y^2 &< 4 \\ x &< y^2 \end{aligned} , \qquad \text{and} \qquad \begin{aligned} \frac{x^2}{16} + \frac{y^2}{9} &\leq 1 \\ x^2 + y^2 &> 1 \end{aligned} .$$

The solution set for the system is the intersection of the solution sets of the individual statements in the system.

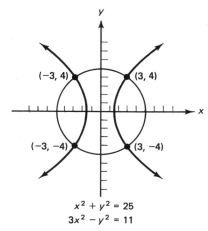

$$x^2 + y^2 = 25$$
$$3x^2 - y^2 = 11$$

FIGURE 11.26

EXAMPLE 3 Graph

$$x^2 + y^2 < 4$$
$$x < y^2.$$

SOLUTION We graph the solution set of each individual inequality on the same coordinate system. The intersection of the two solution sets (indicated in Figure 11.27 by the crosshatching) is the solution set of the system.

Graph: $x^2 + y^2 = 4$ Graph: $x = y^2$
Test $(0, 0)$: $0^2 + 0^2 < 4$ Test $(1, 0)$: $1 \not< 0^2$

Solution set: Solution set:

$$x^2 + y^2 < 4$$
$$x < y^2$$

Solution set: ▨

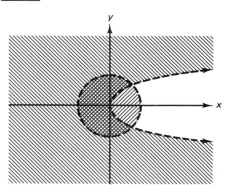

FIGURE 11.27

(Solution on page 350) Graph

$$\frac{x^2}{16} + \frac{y^2}{9} \le 1$$

$$x^2 + y^2 > 1.$$

EXERCISES 11-4

Identify the graph of each of the following equations. (See the examples in Figure 11.24.)

1. $3x + 2y + 7 = 0$

2. $9x + 3y - 5 = 0$

3. $3y^2 + 2x - 4y + 5 = 0$

4. $-9y^2 + x + 3 = 0$

5. $-2x^2 + y - x + 2 = 0$

6. $4x^2 + 2y + 5 = 0$

7. $x^2 + y^2 = 9$

8. $x^2 + y^2 = 16$

9. $x^2 - y^2 = 9$

10. $x^2 - y^2 = 16$

11. $x^2 + 9y^2 = 1$

12. $16x^2 + y^2 = 1$

13. $x^2 - 9y^2 = 1$

14. $16x^2 - y^2 = 1$

15. $x^2 + y^2 + 2x + y = 0$

16. $x^2 + y^2 + 8x - 7y + 1 = 0$

17. $4x^2 + 4y^2 - 8 = 0$

18. $6x^2 + 6y^2 - 2 = 0$

19. $4x^2 + 3y^2 - 12 = 0$

20. $x^2 + 4y^2 - 9 = 0$

21. $x^2 - y^2 - 3 = 0$

22. $-3x^2 + y^2 + 4 = 0$

Solve by using the substitution method (See Example 1 and Practice Problem 1.)

23. $x^2 + y^2 = 9$
    $x = -1$

24. $x^2 + y^2 = 4$
    $y = 1$

25. $y = -x^2 - 2x + 3$
    $x = -1$

26. $y = \frac{1}{2}(x + 1)^2 - 2$
    $y = 1$

27. $y - x = 2$
    $y = x^2$

28. $2x - 3 = y$
    $x = y^2$

29. $x + y = 3$
    $y = x^2 + 1$

30. $3y = 2x + 4$
    $y = x^2 + 2x - 1$

31. $x^2 + y^2 = 25$
    $x + y = 7$

32. $x^2 + y^2 = 25$
    $3x - y = 5$

33. $x^2 + y^2 = 4$
    $\frac{x^2}{4} + \frac{y^2}{25} = 1$

34. $x^2 + y^2 = 1$
    $x^2 + 16y^2 = 16$

C35. $x^2 + y^2 = 6.5$
     $5x - y - 7.8 = 0$

C36. $x^2 - y^2 = -1.8$
     $y = x + 3$

*37. $xy = 6$
$x^2 + y^2 = 13$

*38. $xy = -2$
$2x - 5y = 9$

In problems 39–48, solve by using the elimination method. (See Example 2.)

39. $x^2 + y^2 = 2$
$x^2 - y^2 = 0$

40. $x^2 + y^2 = 53$
$x^2 - y^2 = 45$

41. $x^2 + y^2 = 5$
$2x^2 + 3y^2 = 14$

42. $2y^2 - 3x^2 = 6$
$x^2 + 4y^2 = 40$

43. $2x^2 + 3y^2 = 66$
$3x^2 + 4y^2 = 91$

44. $5x^2 + 2y^2 = 55$
$4x^2 + 3y^2 = 79$

45. $3x^2 - 2y^2 = 97$
$5x^2 - 7y^2 = 70$

46. $8x^2 + 11y^2 = 172$
$3x^2 - 2y^2 = 40$

In problems 47 and 48, round the answers to the nearest tenth.

C47. $y = 3.7 - x^2$
$y = -4.2 + x^2$

C48. $x^2 + y^2 = 43$
$\frac{x^2}{19} + \frac{y^2}{84} = 1$

Graph the solution set for each nonlinear system of inequalities. (See Example 3 and Practice Problem 2.)

49. $y < -x^2 - 2x + 3$
$x < 0$

50. $y > \frac{1}{2}(x + 1)^2 - 2$
$y \leq 1$

51. $y - x < 2$
$y > x^2$

52. $2x - 3 < y$
$x > y^2$

53. $x + y \leq 3$
$y \geq x^2 - 1$

54. $3y \geq 2x + 4$
$y \geq x^2 + 2x - 1$

55. $x^2 + y^2 \leq 25$
$x + y \leq 7$

56. $x^2 + y^2 < 25$
$3x - y \geq 5$

57. $x^2 + y^2 > 4$
$y > 2x^2 - 2$

58. $y \leq x^2 + 2x + 1$
$y^2 \leq 1 - x^2$

59. $x^2 + y^2 > 4$
$\frac{x^2}{4} + \frac{y^2}{25} < 1$

60. $x^2 + y^2 \leq 1$
$x^2 + 16y^2 \leq 1$

61. $\frac{x^2}{9} + \frac{y^2}{49} \leq 1$
$x^2 + y^2 \leq 25$

62. $x^2 + 9y^2 \leq 9$
$9x^2 + y^2 \geq 9$

63. $x^2 + 4y^2 \geq 4$
$x^2 - y^2 \geq 1$

64. $y^2 - x^2 \leq 1$
$\frac{x^2}{9} + \frac{y^2}{16} \leq 1$

65. $y^2 - x^2 \leq 1$
$x^2 - \frac{y^2}{25} \leq 1$

66. $x^2 - y^2 > 1$
$x^2 + y^2 \leq 16$

*1. Solving for y in the first equation and substituting into the second equation yields:

$$y = \frac{4}{x}$$

$$\frac{4}{x} - 2x = 2$$

$$4 - 2x^2 = 2x$$

$$2x^2 + 2x - 4 = 0$$

$$x^2 + x - 2 = 0$$

$$(x + 2)(x - 1) = 0$$

$$x = -2, \quad x = 1.$$

Substituting these values of x into the linear equation to obtain corresponding values of y gives

$$\begin{array}{cc} x = -2 & x = 1 \\ y - 2(-2) = 2 & y - 2(1) = 2 \\ y = -2 & y = 4. \end{array}$$

Solution set $= \{(-2, -2), (1, 4)\}$.

2. Graph: $\dfrac{x^2}{16} + \dfrac{y^2}{9} = 1$ Graph: $x^2 + y^2 = 1$

Test $(0, 0)$: $\dfrac{0^2}{16} + \dfrac{0^2}{9} \leq 1$ Test $(0, 0)$: $0^2 + 0^2 \not> 1$

Solution set: Solution set:

$$\frac{x^2}{16} + \frac{y^2}{9} \leq 1$$
$$x^2 + y^2 > 1$$

Solution set:
See Figure 11.28.

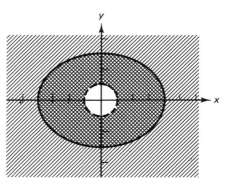

FIGURE 11.28

PRACTICE TEST for Chapter 11

1. Graph the parabolas.
   (a) $y = -2x^2 + 4x + 5$ (b) $y = (x + 4)^2 + 2$

2. Graph the parabolas.
   (a) $x = -y^2 + 4y - 2$ (b) $x = (y + 1)^2 - 3$

3. (a) Find the distance between $(4, -2)$ and $(-5, -3)$.
   (b) Write an equation of the circle with center $(-5, 0)$ and radius 4.

4. (a) Find the center and radius of the circle with equation
   $$x^2 + y^2 = x - 4y - \tfrac{1}{4}.$$
   (b) Sketch the circle in part (a).

5. Sketch the ellipses by locating the vertices.
   (a) $\dfrac{x^2}{16} + \dfrac{y^2}{25} = 1$ (b) $4x^2 + y^2 = 100$

6. Graph each hyperbola by using the vertices and asymptotes.
   (a) $\dfrac{y^2}{4} - \dfrac{x^2}{9} = 1$ (b) $x^2 - 16y^2 = 16$

7. Identify the graphs of each of the following equations.
   (a) $5x^2 + 6y^2 - 12 = 0$ (b) $x^2 - y^2 + 1 = 0$
   (c) $2x + 11y - 15 = 0$ (d) $3x^2 + 2y - x + 11 = 0$
   (e) $x^2 + y^2 - 4 = 0$

8. Solve by using the substitution method.
   $$-y = x^2 + 3x - 1$$
   $$x + 2y = -1$$

9. Solve by using the elimination method.
   $$9x^2 + y^2 = 25$$
   $$2x^2 - 3y^2 = -46$$

10. Graph the solution set for the nonlinear system.
    $$x^2 + y^2 \leq 9$$
    $$x < y$$

Throughout this chapter our attention is confined to variables that represent real numbers. An **ordered pair** of real numbers is a pair (a, b) of real numbers a and b in which a distinction is to be made between positions. That is, (a, b) and (b, a) are to be considered as different pairs if $a \neq b$. It is customary notation to place the ordered pair in parentheses as we have done. The left number a in the ordered pair (a, b) is called the **first entry**, or **first component**, and b is called the **second entry**, or **second component**. **Equality** of ordered pairs is defined by

$$(a, b) = (c, d) \quad \text{if and only if} \quad a = c \text{ and } b = d.$$

Thus $(2, 3) \neq (3, 2)$ and $(2.5, 0.25) = (\frac{5}{2}, \frac{1}{4})$, but $(2.5, 0.25) \neq (\frac{1}{4}, \frac{5}{2})$.

Definition 12-1 A **relation** is a nonempty set of ordered pairs (x, y) of real numbers x and y. The **domain** D of a relation is the set of all numbers x that occur as first components of a pair (x, y) in the relation. The

range R of a relation is the set of all numbers y that occur as second components of a pair (x, y) in the relation.

In other words, the domain is the set of all x-values, and the range is the set of all y-values, for pairs (x, y) in the relation.*

Relations are usually named by letters such as f, g, h, and so on. We reserve D to denote the domain and R to denote the range of a relation. (Recall that $\mathcal{R}$ denotes the set of all real numbers.)

EXAMPLE 1   Write the domain and range of the following relations.

(a) $f = \{(-4, 5), (1, 2), (1, 3), (7, 5)\}$
(b) $g = \{(x, y)\,|\,y = x^2 \text{ and } x \in \mathcal{R}\}$

SOLUTION   (a) The x-values that occur in f are -4, 1, 1, and 7. Even though 1 occurs in two ordered pairs, there is no need to list it more than once, and

$$D = \{-4, 1, 7\}.$$

The range R is the set of all y-values, or second components, of pairs in f, so

$$R = \{3, 2, 5\}.$$

(b) Since the rule that specifies g allows x to be any real number, the domain of g is

$$D = \mathcal{R}.$$

The square of a real number is never negative, so all elements of the range are nonnegative. And since any nonnegative real number has a square root in the real numbers, the range of g includes all nonnegative real numbers. Thus

$$R = \{y\,|\,y \geq 0\}.$$

PRACTICE PROBLEM 1   (Solution on page 360) Find the domain and range of the relation

$$h = \{(x, y)\,|\,y = -\sqrt{x} \text{ and } x \in \mathcal{R}\}.$$

Relations are usually defined by a rule, or equation, which specifies the requirement that must be met by x and y if (x, y) is to be in the relation. We make the following agreement for this sort of situation.

*The variable x in the domain is sometimes called the *independent variable*, and the variable y in the range is called the *dependent variable*.

Unless it is stated otherwise, the domain of a relation defined by a certain rule is the set of all real numbers x that give real numbers as y-values when used in the rule.

EXAMPLE 2 Find the domain and range of the relation

$$p = \left\{ (x, y) \,\middle|\, y = \frac{1}{x - 2} \right\}.$$

SOLUTION If $x - 2 \neq 0$, it has a reciprocal $1/(x - 2)$ in the real numbers. Therefore, the only numbers that are *not* in the domain are those for which $x - 2 = 0$. The only such number is $x = 2$, so

$$D = \{x \,|\, x \neq 2\}.$$

The reciprocal of a number can be any value except 0, and 0 is not the reciprocal of any number. Thus y in the equation $y = 1/(x - 2)$ can take on all nonzero values, and

$$R = \{y \,|\, y \neq 0\}.$$

A graph is frequently useful in finding the domain and range of a relation.

Definition 12-2 The **graph** of a relation is the set of all points in the plane which have coordinates (x, y) that are members of the relation.

EXAMPLE 3 Sketch the graph of the following relations, and state the domain and range of each relation.

(a) $g = \{(x, y) \,|\, y = x^2 - 4\}$

(b) $h = \left\{ (x, y) \,\middle|\, \dfrac{x^2}{25} + \dfrac{y^2}{9} = 1 \right\}$

(c) $r = \{(x, y) \,|\, x = y^2\}$

SOLUTION Whenever a relation is described by a defining equation such as these are, the graph of the relation is the same as the graph of the defining equation.

(a) The relation g has the same graph as the equation $y = x^2 - 4$. This graph is a parabola that opens upward and has vertex at $(0, -4)$, as shown in Figure 12.1. The graph shows that the domain is $D = \Re$, and the range is $R = \{y \,|\, y \geq -4\}$.

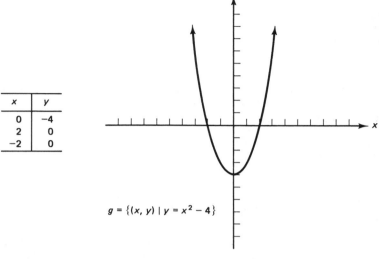

x	y
0	−4
2	0
−2	0

$g = \{(x, y) \mid y = x^2 - 4\}$

FIGURE 12.1

(b) The graph of h is an ellipse with vertices at $(\pm 5, 0)$ and $(0, \pm 3)$. The graph is drawn in Figure 12.2, and it shows that

$$D = \{x \mid -5 \le x \le 5\},$$
$$R = \{y \mid -3 \le y \le 3\}.$$

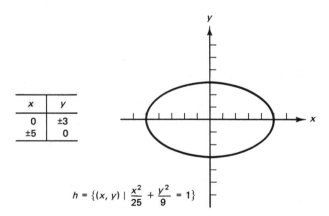

x	y
0	±3
±5	0

$h = \{(x, y) \mid \dfrac{x^2}{25} + \dfrac{y^2}{9} = 1\}$

FIGURE 12.2

(c) As shown in Figure 12.3, the graph of r is a parabola with vertex $(0, 0)$ and opening to the right. From the graph it is clear that

$$D = \{x \mid x \ge 0\},$$
$$R = \Re.$$

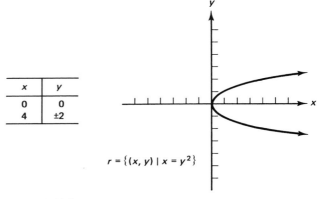

x	y
0	0
4	±2

$r = \{(x, y) \mid x = y^2\}$

FIGURE 12.3

Those relations that have only one value in the range for each element in the domain are the type of relation that is studied in trigonometry and the calculus. They have a special name, given in the following definition.

Definition 12-3 A **function** is a relation which has the property that for each x in the domain, there is one and only one y such that (x, y) is in the relation.

In other words, a function has exactly one y-value for each of its x-values.

EXAMPLE 4 State the domain and range of each of the following relations, and decide whether or not each is a function.

(a) $q = \{(-1, 2), (0, 1), (1, 2), (3, 4)\}$
(b) $s = \{(-3, 6), (1, 4), (-3, 2), (3, -2)\}$
(c) $t = \{(-2, 5), (-1, 5), (1, 5), (2, 5)\}$

SOLUTION

(a) By inspection, q has domain $D = \{-1, 0, 1, 3\}$ and range $R = \{1, 2, 4\}$. There is only one y-value for each $x \in D$ since no two ordered pairs in q have the same first component. [Note that $(-1, 2)$ and $(1, 2)$ have the same y-value, but this does not matter.] Thus q is a function.

(b) The relation s has domain $D = \{-3, 1, 3\}$ and range $R = \{6, 4, 2, -2\}$. The ordered pairs $(-3, 6)$ and $(-3, 2)$ give two different y-values for the same x-value, so s is not a function.

(c) The relation t has $D = \{-2, -1, 1, 2\}$ and $R = \{5\}$. Although all the ordered pairs in t have the same second component, there is only one y-value for each x-value, and t is a function.

By looking at the graph of a relation, it is easy to tell whether or not the relation is a function. This is illustrated in Example 5.

EXAMPLE 5 Use their graphs to determine whether or not each of the following relations is a function.

(a) $g = \{(x, y) \mid y = x^2 - 4\}$

(b) $h = \left\{(x, y) \left| \frac{x^2}{25} + \frac{y^2}{9} = 1 \right. \right\}$

(c) $r = \{(x, y) \mid x = y^2\}$

SOLUTION These are the same relations as in Example 3, and their graphs are reproduced in Figure 12.4.

(a) From the graph of g in Figure 12.4(a), it is clear that, for each particular value of x, there is exactly one point on the graph with that particular value for its x-coordinate. Consequently, there is one y-value paired with that x-value in g. Thus g is a function.

(b) In Figure 12.4(b), we see that for each value of x between -5 and 5, there are two points on the ellipse with that value as x-coordinate. This pictures the fact that there are two distinct pairs (x, y) in h with the same x-value. Therefore, h is not a function.

(c) For each $x > 0$, there are two points on the graph of r in Figure 12.4(c) which have that x-coordinate, so r is not a function.

The dashed lines drawn in Figure 12.4(b) and (c) illustrate that a vertical line intersects the graph of a relation in two places whenever there are two distinct y-values paired with the same x-value in the relation. On the other hand, the dashed lines in Figure 12.4(a) indicate that no vertical line crosses the graph at more than one point. These observations are generalized in the following test.

Vertical Line Test

If any vertical line intersects the graph of a relation at more than one point, the relation is *not* a function. If no vertical line intersects the graph at more than one point, the relation is a function.

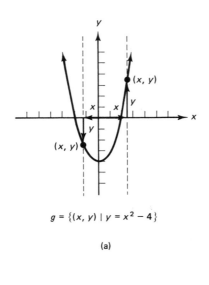

$$g = \{(x, y) \mid y = x^2 - 4\}$$

(a)

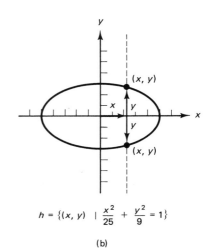

$$h = \left\{(x, y) \ \middle| \ \frac{x^2}{25} + \frac{y^2}{9} = 1\right\}$$

(b)

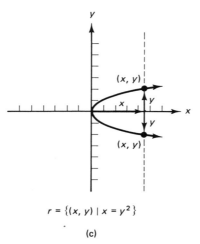

$$r = \{(x, y) \mid x = y^2\}$$

(c)

FIGURE 12.4

In a natural way, any equation in x and y defines the relation that consists of all ordered pairs (x, y) which have components that satisfy the equation. Thinking in this way, we frequently shorten the description of a relation to a simple statement of the defining equation. For example, we would say "the relation $x = y^2$" instead of "the relation $\{(x, y) \mid x = y^2\}$."

EXERCISES 12-1

State the domain D and range R of each of the following relations, and decide which of them are functions. [See Examples 1(a) and 4.]

1. $\{(-2, 5), (0, 1), (2, 5)\}$ 2. $\{(-2, 3), (0, -1), (2, 3)\}$

3. $\{(3, -2), (-1, 0), (3, 2)\}$

4. $\{(5, -2), (1, 0), (5, 2)\}$

5. $\{(1, 2), (3, 4), (5, 6)\}$

6. $\{(-1, 2), (-2, 3), (-3, 4)\}$

7. $\{(-2, 2), (1, -1), (2, -2)\}$

8. $\{(1, -1), (0, 0), (-1, 1)\}$

9. $\{(0, 1), (2, 1), (4, 1), (6, 1)\}$

10. $\{(3, 2), (4, 2), (5, 2), (6, 2)\}$

11. $\{(1, 0), (1, 2), (1, 4), (1, 6)\}$

12. $\{(2, 3), (2, 4), (2, 5), (2, 6)\}$

Find the domain D and the range R of the relation defined by each of the following equations. [See Examples 1(b) and 2, Practice Problem 1, and the remark just before this set of exercises.]

13. $y = x - 2$

14. $y = x + 5$

15. $y = 3x$

16. $y = 2x$

17. $2x - y = 3$

18. $4x - y + 7 = 0$

19. $y = 4x^2$

20. $y = 3x^2$

21. $y = 4x^2 + 1$

22. $y = 3x^2 + 2$

23. $y = \dfrac{1}{x}$

24. $y = \dfrac{1}{x + 1}$

25. $y = \dfrac{1}{2x + 8}$

26. $y = \dfrac{1}{2x - 6}$

27. $y = \sqrt{x}$

28. $y = 1 + \sqrt{x}$

29. $x = y^2 - 1$

30. $x = y^2 + 1$

31. $x = y^3$

32. $y = x^3$

Use the vertical line test to determine whether or not the given graph is the graph of a function. (See Example 5.)

33.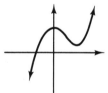

34.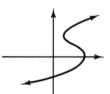

35.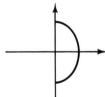

36.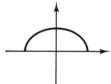

37.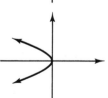

38.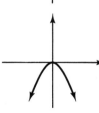

39.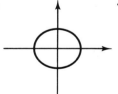

40.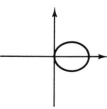

41.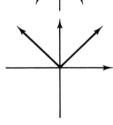

42.   43.   44.

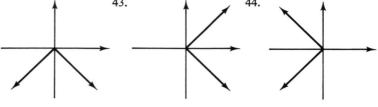

Sketch the graphs of the following relations, and state the domain and range of each relation. (See Example 3.)

45. $y = x^2 - 1$

46. $y = 2x^2 - 2$

47. $x = 2y^2 + 1$

48. $x = y^2 - 4$

49. $(x - 1)^2 + (y + 2)^2 = 4$

50. $(x + 1)^2 + (y - 3)^2 = 9$

51. $x^2 + y^2 + 4x - 6y = 12$

52. $x^2 + y^2 + 4x + 8y = 5$

53. $\dfrac{x^2}{4} + \dfrac{y^2}{9} = 1$

54. $\dfrac{x^2}{16} + \dfrac{y^2}{9} = 1$

55. $4x^2 + 25y^2 = 100$

56. $4x^2 + 9y^2 = 36$

57. $x^2 - y^2 = 1$

58. $y^2 - x^2 = 1$

59. $4y^2 - 9x^2 = 36$

60. $9x^2 - 16y^2 = 144$

61. $x^2 = y$

62. $x^2 = y - 1$

63. $(y - 1)^2 = x + 1$

64. $(y + 2)^2 = x - 1$

65. $y^2 = 16 - x^2$

66. $y^2 = 9 - x^2$

67. $x^2 = 1 + y^2$

68. $x^2 = 1 + y^2$

*69. $y = |x|$

*70. $x = |y|$

*71. $|y| = |x|$

*72. $|y| = |x - 1|$

*73. $y = |2 - x|$

*74. $y = |2 + x|$

*75. $y = 2 - |x|$

*76. $y = 2 + |x|$

SOLUTION FOR PRACTICE PROBLEM

1. Since $\sqrt{x}$ is defined only for $x \geq 0$, $D = \{x \mid x \geq 0\}$. Since $-\sqrt{x} \leq 0$ for all $x \geq 0$, $R = \{y \mid y \leq 0\}$.

12-2
Function
Notation

If a relation f is a function, there is one and only one y-value for each x in the domain. This value is denoted by $f(x)$, where $f(x)$ is read as "f of x" or "f at x." The notation $f(x)$ *does not* represent a product of f and x. We write $y = f(x)$ to indicate that y is the value that is paired with x in f. With this notation, the function

$$g = \{(x, y) \mid y = x^2 - 4\}$$

could be described by the equation

$$g(x) = x^2 - 4.$$

EXAMPLE 1 If $f(x) = 2x^2 - 1$, find the value of each of the following.

(a) $f(-3)$ (b) $f(c)$

(c) $f(x + h)$ (d) $f(x + h) - f(x)$

SOLUTION

(a) $f(-3) = 2(-3)^2 - 1 = 2(9) - 1 = 18 - 1 = 17$

(b) $f(c) = 2c^2 - 1$

(c) $f(x + h) = 2(x + h)^2 - 1$
$$= 2(x^2 + 2hx + h^2) - 1$$
$$= 2x^2 + 4hx + 2h^2 - 1$$

(d) $f(x + h) - f(x) = (2x^2 + 4hx + 2h^2 - 1) - (2x^2 - 1)$
$$= 2x^2 + 4hx + 2h^2 - 1 - 2x^2 + 1$$
$$= 4hx + 2h^2$$

EXAMPLE 2 If $f(x) = x^2 + 2x - 1$ and $g(x) = 2x + 1$, find the value of each of the following.

(a) $f(-2) + g(-2)$ (b) $f(0) + g(3)$

(c) $f(x) - g(x)$ (d) $f(g(x))$

SOLUTION

(a) $f(-2) + g(-2) = [(-2)^2 + 2(-2) - 1] + [2(-2) + 1]$
$$= (4 - 4 - 1) + (-4 + 1)$$
$$= -4$$

(b) $f(0) + g(3) = [0^2 + 2(0) - 1] + [2(3) + 1]$
$$= -1 + 7$$
$$= 6$$

(c) $f(x) - g(x) = (x^2 + 2x - 1) - (2x + 1)$
$$= x^2 - 2$$

(d) $f(g(x)) = [g(x)]^2 + 2g(x) - 1$
$$= (2x + 1)^2 + 2(2x + 1) - 1$$
$$= 4x^2 + 4x + 1 + 4x + 2 - 1$$
$$= 4x^2 + 8x + 2$$

PRACTICE PROBLEM 1 (Solution on page 362) If $f(x) = 2 + \sqrt{x}$ and $g(x) = 3x + 4$, find the value of each of the following.

(a) $f(1) + g(1)$ (b) $f(9) + g(-1)$

(c) $f(g(0))$ (d) $8f(x) - 4g(x)$

(e) $\dfrac{g(x + h) - g(x)}{h}$

If $h(x) = \dfrac{x + 2}{x - 3}$, evaluate each of the following. (See Example 1.) In problems 7 and 8, round the answers to the nearest tenth.

1. $h(0)$ 2. $h(2)$ 3. $h(-2)$ 4. $h(4)$

5. $h(3)$ 6. $h(-3)$ C7. $h(3.18)$ C8. $h(2.82)$

If $f(x) = 4 - x^2$ and $g(x) = 4x - 8$, find each of the following. (See Example 2 and Practice Problem 1.)

9. $f(5)$ 10. $g(5)$

11. $f(-1) + g(-1)$ 12. $f(0) + g(0)$

13. $2f(3)$ 14. $3g(4)$

15. $f(3) + g(1)$ 16. $f(-2) + g(-1)$

17. $f(g(0))$ 18. $g(f(0))$

19. $f(f(1))$ 20. $g(g(1))$

21. $f(a) + f(b)$ 22. $g(a) + g(b)$

23. $f(a + b)$ 24. $g(a + b)$

25. $g(x) - f(x)$ 26. $f(x) - g(x)$

27. $4f(x) + 2g(x)$ 28. $x \cdot g(x) + 4f(x)$

29. $f(x + h) - f(x)$ 30. $g(x + h) - g(x)$

31. $\dfrac{f(3 + h) - f(3)}{h}$ 32. $\dfrac{g(3 + h) - g(3)}{h}$

33. $f(g(x))$ 34. $g(f(x))$

C35. $g(2.316)$ C36. $f(-1.785)$

Find the value of $\dfrac{f(x + h) - f(x)}{h}$ for each of the following functions. (See Practice Problem 1(e).)

37. $f(x) = 3x$ 38. $f(x) = -2x$

39. $f(x) = -2x + 5$ 40. $f(x) = 4x - 3$

41. $f(x) = x^2 + 1$ 42. $f(x) = x^2 - 2$

43. $f(x) = 2x^2 - 7$ 44. $f(x) = 3x^2 + 6$

45. $f(x) = x^2 + 5x - 6$ 46. $f(x) = x^2 - 7x + 2$

47. $f(x) = 3x^2 + 2x - 1$ 48. $f(x) = 2x^2 - 4x + 3$

SOLUTION FOR PRACTICE PROBLEM

1. (a) $f(1) + g(1) = (2 + \sqrt{1}) + (3(1) + 4) = 10$
   (b) $f(9) + g(-1) = (2 + \sqrt{9}) + (3(-1) + 4) = 6$
   (c) $f(g(0)) = f(4) = 2 + \sqrt{4} = 4$

(d) $8f(x) - 4g(x) = 8(2 + \sqrt{x}) - 4(3x + 4)$
$$= 16 + 8\sqrt{x} - 12x - 16$$
$$= 8\sqrt{x} - 12x$$

(e) $\dfrac{g(x + h) - g(x)}{h} = \dfrac{[3(x + h) + 4] - [3x + 4]}{h}$

$$= \frac{3x + 3h + 4 - 3x - 4}{h}$$

$$= \frac{3h}{h}$$

$$= 3$$

12-3
Inverse Relations and Functions

If the components x and y are interchanged in a given relation g, the resulting relation is called the *inverse* of the original relation, and is denoted by g^{-1}.

As an example of this concept, consider the relation

$$g = \{(1, 2), (-5, 7), (0, 3)\}.$$

The inverse of g is given by

$$g^{-1} = \{(2, 1), (7, -5), (3, 0)\}.$$

The inverse of a relation is obtained by interchanging the x-values and y-values of all pairs in the relation. If the relation is described by a defining equation in x and y, the inverse may be found by simply interchanging x and y in the defining equation. For the relation

$$g = \{(x, y) \mid y = 2x - 4\},$$

the inverse of g is the relation

$$g^{-1} = \{(x, y) \mid x = 2y - 4\}.$$

It is common practice to solve for y after the interchange and write

$$g^{-1} = \{(x, y) \mid y = \tfrac{1}{2}x + 2\}.$$

The symbolic definition of the inverse of a relation is given in the following statement.

Definition 12-4 The **inverse** of a given relation g is the relation g^{-1} defined by

$$g^{-1} = \{(b, a) \mid (a, b) \text{ is in } g\}.$$

The symbol g^{-1} is read as "the inverse of g" or as "g-inverse." It *does not* represent the reciprocal $1/g$ of g, and $g^{-1}(x) \neq 1/g(x)$.

It is automatic from the definition that the domain of g^{-1} is the range of g, and the range of g^{-1} is the domain of g.

EXAMPLE 1   Find the inverse of each of the following relations. Decide in each case if the relation or its inverse is a function.

(a) $g = \{(-1, 3), (2, -5), (2, 6), (4, 4)\}$
(b) $r = \{(2, -4), (-7, 8), (3, 9), (0, -5)\}$

SOLUTION   (a) $g^{-1} = \{(3, -1), (-5, 2), (6, 2), (4, 4)\}$. Since both $(2, -5)$ and $(2, 6)$ are in g, g is not a function. But g^{-1} is a function since no two distinct pairs in g^{-1} have the same first component.
(b) $r^{-1} = \{(-4, 2), (8, -7), (9, 3), (-5, 0)\}$. In both r and r^{-1}, no two distinct pairs have the same first component. Hence both r and r^{-1} are functions.

EXAMPLE 2   Find a defining equation for the inverse of each of the following relations, and solve the equation for y. Decide in each case if the relation or its inverse is a function.

(a) $h = \{(x, y) \mid y = 4x - 12\}$
(b) $f = \{(x, y) \mid y = x^2 + 4\}$

SOLUTION   (a) $h^{-1} = \{(x, y) \mid x = 4y - 12\}$
$\qquad = \{(x, y) \mid y = \frac{1}{4}x + 3\}$
Both h and h^{-1} are functions.
(b) $f^{-1} = \{(x, y) \mid x = y^2 + 4\}$
$\qquad = \{(x, y) \mid y = \pm\sqrt{x - 4}\}$
In f, there is exactly one y for each x, so f is a function. However, there are two different values of y for each $x > 4$ in f^{-1}, and f^{-1} is not a function.

The graphs of a relation g and its inverse g^{-1} are related in an interesting way. As an illustration, the graphs of

$$g = \{(x, y) \mid y = 2x - 4\}$$

and

$$g^{-1} = \{(x, y) \mid y = \tfrac{1}{2}x + 2\}$$

are shown in Figure 12.5. In the figure the graph of $y = x$ is drawn as a dashed line. The graphs of g and g^{-1} are two lines that are symmetric about

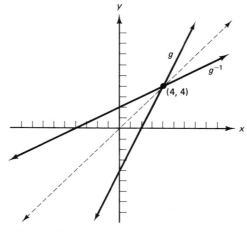

FIGURE 12.5

the line $y = x$. Each one of them is the mirror reflection of the other through the line $y = x$.

The graph of the inverse of a given relation is always the reflection of the graph of the given relation through the line $y = x$. This is true because the points with coordinates (b, a) and (a, b) are located symmetrically† with respect to $y = x$.

EXAMPLE 3 Each of the following equations defines a relation g. Find a defining equation for the inverse relation g^{-1}, and sketch the graphs of g and g^{-1}. Use the vertical line test to decide if the relation or its inverse is a function.

(a) $y^2 = x - 1$

(b) $\dfrac{x^2}{25} + \dfrac{y^2}{9} = 1$

SOLUTION (a) A defining equation for g^{-1} is $x^2 = y - 1$. The graphs of g and g^{-1} are drawn in Figure 12.6. The vertical line test shows that g^{-1} is a function and g is not a function.

(b) A defining equation for g^{-1} is

$$\frac{y^2}{25} + \frac{x^2}{9} = 1.$$

The graphs are drawn in Figure 12.7. Neither g nor g^{-1} is a function.

†It can be shown that the segment joining (b, a) and (a, b) is perpendicular to $y = x$ and has its midpoint located at $\left(\dfrac{b + a}{2}, \dfrac{a + b}{2}\right)$ on the line $y = x$.

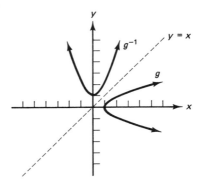

FIGURE 12.6

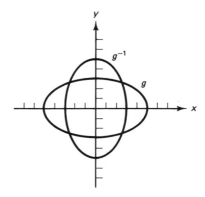

FIGURE 12.7

Example 2(b) shows that the inverse of a function is not always a function. Whenever both a relation f and its inverse f^{-1} are functions, a special type of pairing is made between the elements in the domain D and the range R of f:

(1) for each $a \in D$, there is exactly one $b = f(a)$ in R which is associated with a by f, and

(2) for each $b \in R$, there is exactly one $a = f^{-1}(b)$ in D which has b associated with it by f.

This situation is pictured in Figure 12.8.

FIGURE 12.8

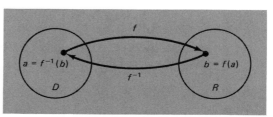

Because of this one-to-one pairing when both f and f^{-1} are functions, f is called a **one-to-one function,** and we say that f sets up a **one-to-one correspondence** between the elements of D and R. Combining the preceding statements (1) and (2), we have

$$f^{-1}(f(x)) = x \text{ for all } x \text{ in the domain of } f$$

and

$$f(f^{-1}(x)) = x \text{ for all } x \text{ in the domain of } f^{-1}.$$

EXAMPLE 4 The equation

$$2x - 3y = 6$$

defines a one-to-one function f. Find expressions for the values of $f(x)$ and $f^{-1}(x)$, and verify that each of the equations $f^{-1}(f(x)) = x$ and $f(f^{-1}(x)) = x$ is true.

SOLUTION To find an expression for $f(x)$, we solve for y in the equation $2x - 3y = 6$.

$$2x - 3y = 6$$
$$2x - 6 = 3y$$
$$\tfrac{2}{3}x - 2 = y$$

Thus

$$f(x) = \tfrac{2}{3}x - 2.$$

To find $f^{-1}(x)$, we interchange x and y in the original equation, and then solve for y.

$$2y - 3x = 6$$
$$2y = 3x + 6$$
$$y = \tfrac{3}{2}x + 3$$

Therefore

$$f^{-1}(x) = \tfrac{3}{2}x + 3.$$

We have

$$f^{-1}(f(x)) = \tfrac{3}{2}f(x) + 3$$
$$= \tfrac{3}{2}(\tfrac{2}{3}x - 2) + 3$$
$$= x - 3 + 3$$
$$= x,$$

so the equation $f^{-1}(f(x)) = x$ is verified. Also,

$$f(f^{-1}(x)) = \tfrac{2}{3}f^{-1}(x) - 2$$
$$= \tfrac{2}{3}(\tfrac{3}{2}x + 3) - 2$$
$$= x + 2 - 2$$
$$= x,$$

and the equation $f(f^{-1}(x)) = x$ is verified.

**PRACTICE
PROBLEM 1**

(Solution on page 369) The equation

$$3x + 4y = 12$$

defines a one-to-one function f. Find expressions for the values of $f(x)$ and $f^{-1}(x)$, and verify each of the equations $f^{-1}(f(x)) = x$ and $f(f^{-1}(x)) = x$.

EXERCISES 12-3

Find the inverse of each of the following relations. Decide in each case if the relation or its inverse is a function. (See Example 1.)

1. $h = \{(-4, 2), (-1, 1), (2, 4), (7, 9)\}$
2. $r = \{(-3, 3), (-1, 1), (0, 0), (2, 5)\}$
3. $g = \{(-1, 0), (1, 3), (5, 3), (6, 8)\}$
4. $f = \{(2, 1), (3, 6), (4, 7), (8, 1)\}$
5. $t = \{(1, 2), (3, 4), (4, 3), (1, 5)\}$
6. $p = \{(1, 0), (2, 0), (3, 7), (4, 9)\}$

Find a defining equation for the inverse of each of the following relations, and solve the equation for y. Decide in each case if the relation or its inverse is a function. (See Example 2.)

7. $f = \{(x, y) \mid y = x + 2\}$ 8. $g = \{(x, y) \mid y = 5 - x\}$
9. $s = \{(x, y) \mid y = 3x - 9\}$ 10. $h = \{(x, y) \mid y = 2x + 10\}$
11. $t = \{(x, y) \mid y = \sqrt{x + 3}\}$ 12. $f = \{(x, y) \mid y = \sqrt{x - 4}\}$
13. $p = \{(x, y) \mid y = 1 - 2\sqrt{x}\}$ 14. $q = \{(x, y) \mid y = -3\sqrt{x}\}$
15. $g = \{(x, y) \mid y = -\sqrt{1 - x^2}\}$ 16. $t = \{(x, y) \mid y = -\sqrt{4 - x^2}\}$
17. $r = \{(x, y) \mid y = \sqrt{16 - 9x^2}\}$ 18. $p = \{(x, y) \mid y = \sqrt{9 - 4x^2}\}$

Each of the following equations defines a relation g. Find a defining equation for the inverse relation g^{-1}, and sketch the graphs of g and g^{-1}. Use the vertical line test to decide if the relation or its inverse is a function. (See Example 3.)

19. $2x + y = 6$ 20. $3x - y = 6$

21. $4x - y = 0$

22. $2x + y = 0$

23. $3x + 2y = 12$

24. $2x - 3y = 12$

25. $x = y^2 + 2$

26. $y = x^2 + 3$

27. $x^2 = 25 - y^2$

28. $x^2 = 16 - y^2$

29. $\dfrac{x^2}{9} + \dfrac{y^2}{16} = 1$

30. $\dfrac{x^2}{16} + \dfrac{y^2}{4} = 1$

31. $4x^2 + 9y^2 = 36$

32. $25x^2 + 4y^2 = 100$

33. $y = (x + 1)^2 + 2$

34. $y = (x + 2)^2 + 1$

*35. $y = 1 + |x|$

*36. $y = |1 + x|$

Each of the following equations defines a one-to-one function f. Find expressions for $f(x)$ and $f^{-1}(x)$, and verify each of the equations $f^{-1}(f(x)) = x$ and $f(f^{-1}(x)) = x$. (See Example 4 and Practice Problem 1.)

37. $3x - y = 9$

38. $4x + y = 8$

39. $x + 2y = 4$

40. $x - 3y = 6$

41. $3x + 5y = 15$

42. $4x - 3y = 12$

43. $4x - 5y = 10$

44. $5x + 4y = 20$

C45. $2.58x - 5.16y = -7.74$

C46. $2.95x + 11.8y = -17.7$

SOLUTION FOR PRACTICE PROBLEM

1. Solving for y in $3x + 4y = 12$, we obtain
$$4y = -3x + 12$$
$$y = -\tfrac{3}{4}x + 3.$$
Thus $f(x) = -\tfrac{3}{4}x + 3$. Interchanging x and y, and then solving for y, we get
$$3y + 4x = 12$$
$$3y = -4x + 12$$
$$y = -\tfrac{4}{3}x + 4.$$
Therefore, $f^{-1}(x) = -\tfrac{4}{3}x + 4$. Verifying the equations, we have
$$f^{-1}(f(x)) = -\tfrac{4}{3}f(x) + 4$$
$$= -\tfrac{4}{3}(-\tfrac{3}{4}x + 3) + 4$$
$$= x - 4 + 4$$
$$= x$$
and
$$f(f^{-1}(x)) = -\tfrac{3}{4}f^{-1}(x) + 3$$
$$= -\tfrac{3}{4}(-\tfrac{4}{3}x + 4) + 3$$
$$= x - 3 + 3$$
$$= x.$$

It is common to find two quantities which are related in such a way that one of them is a constant multiple of the other. A person who is paid by the hour earns pay according to the equation

$$\text{pay} = (\text{hourly rate}) \cdot (\text{number of hours}),$$

where the hourly rate is a constant. If apples sell for $0.49 each, the price P of x apples is given by

$$P = 0.49x.$$

Two familiar examples of similar situations from geometry are the formulas $C = 2\pi r$ and $A = \pi r^2$, where C is the circumference and A is the area of a circle with radius r.

When y is a constant multiple of x, changes in corresponding values of x and y are proportional: y doubles in value when x doubles in value, y triples in value when x triples in value, and so on. For this reason, we say that "y **varies directly** as x" or that "y **is directly proportional** to x." These are two of the very precise phrases in the terminology of variation, which is the subject of this section. In this terminology, certain English phrases translate into very specific types of equations. Our discussion of direct variation can be summarized as follows.

Direct Variation

"y varies directly as x" or "y is directly proportional to x"
means that

$$y = kx \qquad \text{for constant } k$$

EXAMPLE 1 The pressure P exerted by water at a point in the water varies directly as the depth x of the point beneath the surface of the water. If $P = 187.2$ pounds per square foot at a depth of 3 feet, find the pressure at a point 7 feet beneath the surface of the water.

SOLUTION Since P varies directly as x,

$$P = kx,$$

where k is a constant. To find the value of k, we use the given values $P = 187.2$ when $x = 3$.

$$187.2 = k(3)$$

$$k = \frac{187.2}{3} = 62.4$$

The equation relating P and x is given by

$$P = 62.4x.$$

To find the pressure at a depth of 7 feet, we substitute $x = 7$:

$$P = (62.4)(7)$$
$$= 436.8.$$

The pressure at a depth of 7 feet is 436.8 pounds per square foot.

The preceding example is only one of many examples of direct variation in the physical sciences. Another common type of variation in the physical sciences is *inverse variation*. In inverse variation, one of the quantities decreases as the other increases. The translations from a technical English phrase to a specific type of mathematical equation are as follows.

Inverse Variation

"y varies inversely as x" or "y is inversely proportional to x" means that

$$y = \frac{k}{x} \qquad \text{for constant } k$$

EXAMPLE 2   With a constant electromotive force, the current I in a wire varies inversely as the resistance R. If the electromotive force is constant and $I = 5.5$ amps when $R = 20$ ohms, find R when $I = 33$ amps.

SOLUTION   The phrase "I varies inversely as R" translates into the equation

$$I = \frac{k}{R},$$

where k is a constant. Using the given pair of values $I = 5.5$ and $R = 20$, we have

$$5.5 = \frac{k}{20}$$
$$k = (5.5)(20) = 110.$$

Thus

$$I = \frac{110}{R}.$$

Using $I = 33$ in this equation, we obtain

$$33 = \frac{110}{R}$$

$$33R = 110$$

$$R = \frac{110}{33} = \frac{10}{3} = 3\tfrac{1}{3} \text{ ohms.}$$

There are other technical phrases that are used to describe certain situations where the value of one variable depends on two or more other variables. One of these is *joint variation*.

Joint Variation

"y varies jointly as x and z" or "y is jointly proportional to x and z" means that

$$y = kxz \qquad \text{for constant } k$$

EXAMPLE 3   With metric system measure, the amount of work W (in units of joules) done in lifting a mass of m kilograms through a distance of s meters varies jointly as m and s. The work done in raising a mass of 2 kilograms a distance of 5 meters from the ground is 98 joules. How much work is done in lifting 15 kilograms a distance of 4 meters?

SOLUTION   Since W is jointly proportional to m and s,

$$W = kms, \; k \text{ a constant.}$$

Substituting $W = 98$ when $m = 2$ and $s = 5$, we have

$$98 = k(2)(5)$$

$$98 = 10k$$

$$k = 9.8.$$

This gives the equation

$$W = 9.8ms.$$

Using $m = 15$ and $s = 4$ to find W, we get

$$W = 9.8(15)(4)$$

$$= 588 \text{ joules.}$$

The last type of variation that we consider is *combined variation*.

This phrase is used when the value of one variable depends on two or more others in different ways.

> ## Combined Variation
>
> "y varies directly as x and inversely as z"
> or
> "y is directly proportional to x and inversely proportional to z"
> means that
>
> $$y = \frac{kx}{z} \quad \text{for constant } k$$

EXAMPLE 4 The variable r is directly porportional to s and inversely proportional to the square of t. The value of r is 600 when $s = 4$ and $t = 3$. Find the value of r when $s = 8$ and $t = 6$.

SOLUTION The variables r, s, and t are related by

$$r = \frac{ks}{t^2},$$

where k is a constant. We can find k by using $r = 600$ when $s = 4$ and $t = 3$.

$$600 = \frac{k(4)}{3^2}$$

$$150 = \frac{k}{9}$$

$$k = 1350$$

This gives the equation

$$r = \frac{1350s}{t^2}.$$

To find the desired value of r, we let $s = 8$ and $t = 6$. This gives

$$r = \frac{(1350)(8)}{6^2}$$

$$= \frac{\overset{150}{\cancel{(1350)}}(8)}{\underset{4}{\cancel{36}}}$$

$$= 300.$$

The preceding examples illustrate the four main types of variation problems. In each of them, the constant k is called the **constant of varia-**

tion, or the **proportionality constant**. Most variation problems can be worked by using the following steps.

Procedure for Solution of Variation Problems

1. Translate the variation statement to an equation involving a constant of variation k.

2. Use a given set of values to find the value of k, and replace k by this value in the general equation.

3. Substitute another set of known values into the equation, and solve for the corresponding value of the unknown variable.

PRACTICE PROBLEM 1

(Solution on page 376) Assume that p varies jointly as r and s^3, and inversely as $t + 1$. If $p = 40$ when $r = -10$, $s = 2$, and $t = 9$, find p when $r = 4$, $s = -3$, and $t = 11$.

EXERCISES 12-4

Solve the following variation problems. (See Examples 1–4 and Practice Problem 1.)

1. Assume that y varies directly as x. If $y = 14$ when $x = 20$, find y when $x = 50$.

2. Assume that s varies inversely as t, and that $s = 80$ when $t = 5$. Find the value of s when $t = 20$.

3. Suppose that y varies directly as x^2, and that $y = 48$ when $x = 4$. Find y when $x = 5$.

4. It is given that z is proportional to t^3, and that $z = -6$ when $t = 2$. Find z when $t = 4$.

5. Assume that y varies inversely as $x + 9$, and that $y = -15$ when $x = 3$. Find y when $x = 6$.

6. Suppose that w varies jointly as r and p^2. If $w = 30$ when $r = 5$ and $p = 3$, find w when $r = 21$ and $p = 4$.

7. It is given that p is proportional to q^2 and inversely proportional to r, and that $p = 18$ when $q = 6$ and $r = 8$. Find p when $q = 9$ and $r = -12$.

8. The variable w varies directly as $\sqrt{u}$ and inversely as v^2. If $w = 20$ when $u = 25$ and $v = 3$, find w when $u = 36$ and $v = 4$.

9. Suppose that r varies directly as x and inversely as y^2 and z. If $r = 5$ when $x = 6$, $y = 3$, and $z = 2$, find r when $x = 40$, $y = 5$, and $z = -4$.

10. Suppose that v varies jointly as x and y^2, and inversely as $\sqrt{z}$. If

$v = 100$ when $x = 4$, $y = 5$, and $z = 9$, find v when $x = 3$, $y = 6$, and $z = 81$.

11. According to *Hooke's Law*, the force required to stretch a spring x inches beyond its natural length varies directly with x. If a 40-pound force is required to stretch a spring by 2 inches, how much force is required to stretch it by 5 inches?

12. The force required to compress a spring by an amount x is directly proportional to x. A force of 24 pounds compresses a certain spring from its natural length of 12 inches to a length of 10 inches. By how much will a force of 60 pounds compress the spring?

13. At a constant temperature, the volume of a gas varies inversely as the pressure. The pressure of a gas in a 400-cubic-foot container is 48 pounds per square inch. What is the pressure on the container after the gas is allowed to expand to a volume of 600 cubic feet with constant temperature?

14. The intensity of illumination I of a light varies inversely as the square of its distance d from the source of the light. At 15 feet from the light, the intensity is 4 foot-candles. Find the intensity at 10 feet.

15. The distance required to stop a certain car varies directly with the square of its speed. If the car stops in 16 feet at a speed of 24 miles per hour, find the distance required to stop at a speed of 54 miles per hour.

16. The time required for one complete swing of a simple pendulum is directly proportional to the square root of its length. If a pendulum 4 feet long makes one complete swing in 1.1 seconds, how long would it take for a complete swing of a pendulum 1 foot long?

17. The weight of a body above the surface of the earth varies inversely as the square of its distance from the center of the earth. If a person weighs 160 pounds on the surface of the earth, how much would that person weigh at a height of 200 miles above the surface? (Assume 4000 miles as the radius of the earth.)

18. Neglecting air resistance, the distance traveled by a body falling from rest varies directly as the square of the time that it falls. If a body falls 400 feet in 5 seconds, how far will it fall in 10 seconds?

19. The electrical resistance of a wire varies directly as its length and inversely as the square of its diameter. Given that the resistance of a wire that is 20 feet long and has diameter 0.02 inch is 5 ohms, find the resistance of a wire that is 90 feet long and has diameter 0.03 inch.

20. According to *Ohm's Law* for a simple electric circuit, the current I in a wire varies directly as the electromotive force E and inversely as the resistance R. If $I = 10$ amps when $E = 110$ volts and $R = 11$ ohms, find I when $E = 220$ volts and $R = 5$ ohms.

21. The safe load of a rectangular wooden beam varies jointly as the width and the square of the depth. If a beam with width 2 inches and depth 4 inches safely supports a load of 400 pounds, find the safe load for a beam with width 4 inches and depth 6 inches.

22. *Boyle's Law* states that the pressure of a gas varies directly as the absolute temperature and inversely as the volume. If the pressure is 30 pounds per square inch when the volume is 20 cubic feet and the temperature is 280°A, what is the pressure if the volume changes to 40 cubic feet while the temperature increases to 350°A?

SOLUTION FOR PRACTICE PROBLEM

1. Since p varies jointly as r and s^3, and inversely as $t + 1$, we have

$$p = \frac{krs^3}{t + 1}.$$

The values $p = 40$ when $r = -10$, $s = 2$, and $t = 9$ yield

$$40 = \frac{k(-10)(2^3)}{10}$$

$$40 = -8k$$

$$k = -5,$$

and

$$p = \frac{-5rs^3}{t + 1}.$$

When $r = 4$, $s = -3$, and $t = 11$, p has the value

$$p = \frac{-5(4)(-3)^3}{12} = 45.$$

PRACTICE TEST for Chapter 12

1. State the domain and range of the following relation, and decide if the relation is a function.

$$r = \{(-3, 1), (0, 4), (2, 1), (3, 0)\}$$

2. Find the domain D and the range R of the relation defined by the equation

$$y = \sqrt{x - 2}.$$

3. Sketch the graph of the relation defined by the following equation. State the domain and range of the relation, and decide whether or not it is a function.

$$4y^2 = 25 - 4x^2$$

4. If $f(x) = 2x^2 + x$ and $g(x) = 3x - 1$, find each of the following.
   (a) $f(5)$ (b) $g(f(3))$ (c) $f(a) + f(b)$
   (d) $f(a + b)$ (e) $3f(x) - g(x)$

5. If $f(x) = x^2 - 3x$, find the value of $\dfrac{f(x + h) - f(x)}{h}$.

6. Find the inverse of the relation r in problem 1, and decide if r^{-1} is a function.

7. Find a defining equation for the inverse of the following relation g. Sketch the graphs of g and g^{-1}, and decide if g or g^{-1} is a function.

$$g = \{(x, y) \mid y = 1 + x^2\}$$

8. The equation

$$3x - 4y = 24$$

   defines a one-to-one function f. Find expressions for $f(x)$ and $f^{-1}(x)$, and verify each of the equations $f^{-1}(f(x)) = x$ and $f(f^{-1}(x)) = x$.

9. Assume that z varies directly as $u + 1$, and inversely as v^2 and w. If $z = 2$ when $u = 4$, $v = 3$ and $w = 5$, find z when $u = 15$, $v = 2$, and $w = 9$.

10. The pressure on a sail varies jointly as the area of the sail and the square of the wind's speed. There are 2 pounds per square foot of pressure on a sail with area 50 square feet for a wind blowing at 20 miles per hour. Find the pressure produced on the same sail by a wind at 30 miles per hour.

13-1
Exponential
Functions

Two of the most useful types of functions in applications are the exponential and logarithmic functions. The use of exponential functions is necessary in working with epidemics, population growths, radioactive decay, and many other natural processes.

As an example of an exponential function, consider the function f defined by

$$f(x) = 2^x.$$

If x is a rational number, the value of 2^x is defined in Chapter 9. For example, if

$$x = 0.6 = \tfrac{6}{10} = \tfrac{3}{5},$$

then

$$2^{0.6} = 2^{3/5} = \sqrt[5]{2^3} = \sqrt[5]{8} \approx 1.5157,$$

where the decimal approximation to $\sqrt[5]{8}$ is obtained by use of a calculator. For an irrational value of x, we assume that the value of 2^x can be approximated by using a rational approximation to x. If $x = \sqrt{3}$, for instance, the value of x is approximated by

$$\sqrt{3} \approx 1.7$$

and we assume that

$$2^{\sqrt{3}} \approx 2^{1.7} \approx 3.25,$$

where the value of 3.25 for $2^{1.7}$ is obtained using a calculator. Although we make no effort to do so here, this kind of assumption can be justified by rigorous mathematical arguments.

The general definition of an exponential function is as follows.

Definition 13-1 If a is a positive real number and $a \neq 1$, the function f defined by

$$f(x) = a^x$$

is the **exponential function** with base a.

A remark about the restrictions on the base a is in order. First of all, we avoid nonpositive values of a so that, for all real numbers x, a^x will be a real number. [Recall that $(-4)^{1/2} = \sqrt{-4} = 2i$ is not a real number.] We avoid $a = 1$ because $1^x = 1$ defines a constant function.

EXAMPLE 1 Sketch the graph of the exponential function

$$f(x) = 2^x.$$

SOLUTION As indicated in the table in Figure 13.1, we compute some convenient values of f, and plot the corresponding points. We then join these points

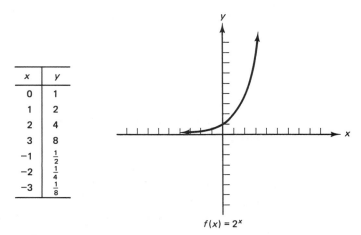

x	y
0	1
1	2
2	4
3	8
-1	$\frac{1}{2}$
-2	$\frac{1}{4}$
-3	$\frac{1}{8}$

$f(x) = 2^x$

FIGURE 13.1

with a smooth curve, as shown in the figure. Drawing a smooth curve like this is consistent with our assumption that the function values are near to each other when the values of x are near to each other.

PRACTICE PROBLEM 1   (Solution on page 384) Sketch the graph of the function g defined by
$$g(x) = 3^{x-1}.$$

EXAMPLE 2   Sketch the graph of the exponential function defined by
$$y = (\tfrac{1}{3})^x.$$

SOLUTION   We note that $(\tfrac{1}{3})^x = 3^{-x}$. Following the same procedure as in Example 1, we tabulate some convenient values of the function. These results and the corresponding graph are shown in Figure 13.2.

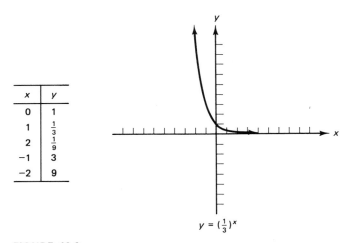

x	y
0	1
1	$\frac{1}{3}$
2	$\frac{1}{9}$
−1	3
−2	9

$$y = (\tfrac{1}{3})^x$$

FIGURE 13.2

The graphs in Figures 13.1 and 13.2 are typical for exponential functions. If $a > 1$, the graph of $y = a^x$ resembles the graph in Figure 13.1. If $0 < a < 1$, the graph of $y = a^x$ resembles the graph in Figure 13.2. This is illustrated in Figure 13.3.

The graphs in Figure 13.3 show that any exponential function has domain $D = \Re$ and range $R = \{y \mid y > 0\}$. If $a > 1$, the values of $f(x) = a^x$ *increase* as x *increases*, and f is called an **increasing function**. If $0 < a < 1$, the values of $f(x) = a^x$ *decrease* as x *increases*, and f is called a **decreasing function**.

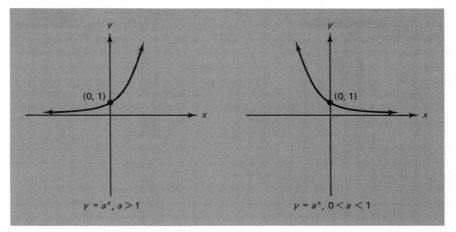

FIGURE 13.3

We note one more important feature from the graphs in Figure 13.3: An exponential function is a one-to-one function, so

> When a is positive and $a \neq 1$,
> $a^u = a^v$ if and only if $u = v$.

This property enables us to solve an equation that has the variable in an exponent, if both sides of the equation can be written as a power of the same base.

EXAMPLE 3 Solve for x in the following equations.

(a) $5^x = 125$ (b) $4^{2x-1} = 32$

SOLUTION (a) We recognize that $5^3 = 125$, so the equation can be written as

$$5^x = 5^3.$$

Therefore, the only solution is $x = 3$.

(b) Since $2^2 = 4$ and $2^5 = 32$, both members of the equation can be expressed as a power of 2.

$$(2^2)^{2x-1} = 2^5$$
$$2^{4x-2} = 2^5$$

Equating exponents, we have

$$4x - 2 = 5$$
$$x = \tfrac{7}{4}.$$

The solution set is $\{\tfrac{7}{4}\}$.

The exponential function $y = 10^x$ is one of the two most useful exponential functions in applications. The other is

$$y = e^x,$$

where e is an irrational number with a decimal approximation given by

$$e \approx 2.71828.$$

The number e is of central importance in calculus and other advanced mathematics courses, and it occurs in many physical situations. As a simple example, a colony of bacteria that starts at a size of 1000 and increases by 10% of its population each day will have population

$$p \approx 1000e^{0.1x}$$

after x days.

EXAMPLE 4   Sketch the graph of the exponential function

$$y = e^x.$$

SOLUTION   Since our space does not permit a great amount of accuracy, we use $e \approx 2.7$. A table of values and the related graph are shown in Figure 13.4. Even after rounding e to the nearest tenth, a calculator is very helpful in computing these values.

x	y
0	1
1	2.7
2	7.3
3	19.7
−1	0.4
−2	0.1

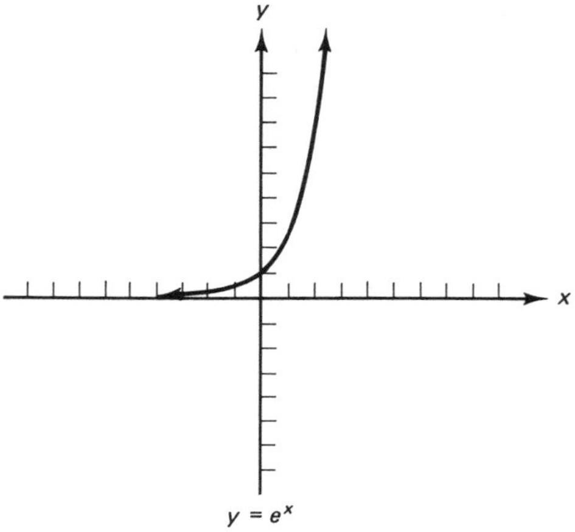

FIGURE 13.4

EXERCISES 13-1

If $f(x) = 3^x$ and $g(x) = (\frac{1}{2})^x$, evaluate each of the following.

1. $f(0)$
2. $g(0)$
3. $f(-2) + g(1)$
4. $f(1) + g(-2)$
5. $f(g(0))$
6. $g(f(0))$

Sketch the graphs of the following functions. (See Examples 1 and 2 and Practice Problem 1.)

7. $y = 3^x$
8. $y = 4^x$
9. $y = (\frac{1}{2})^x$
10. $y = (\frac{1}{4})^x$
11. $y = (\frac{3}{2})^x$
12. $y = 10^x$
13. $y = -2^x$
14. $y = -3^x$
15. $y = 5 \cdot 2^{-x}$
16. $y = 5 \cdot 3^{-x}$
17. $y = 3^{2x+1}$
18. $y = 2^{3x-1}$
19. $y = 2^{1-x}$
20. $y = 3^{2-x}$
21. $y = 3^x + 1$
22. $y = 2^x - 2$

Solve each of the following equations. (See Example 3.)

23. $3^x = 81$
24. $2^x = 16$
25. $2^x = \frac{1}{8}$
26. $3^x = \frac{1}{27}$
27. $5^x = 1$
28. $4^x = 1$
29. $3^{-x} = 9$
30. $5^{-x} = 25$
31. $16^x = 32$
32. $8^x = 16$
33. $4^x = \frac{1}{8}$
34. $9^x = \frac{1}{27}$
35. $16^{2x-1} = \frac{1}{32}$
36. $25^{x-1} = \frac{1}{125}$
37. $(\frac{1}{2})^{2x+1} = 64$
38. $(\frac{1}{3})^{3x-2} = 81$
39. $(125)^{2x+3} = \frac{1}{5}$
40. $(81)^{2x-3} = \frac{1}{9}$

If a suitable calculator is available, sketch the graphs of the following functions. Round the coordinates to the nearest tenth. (See Example 4.)

C41. $y = e^{0.1x}$
C42. $y = e^{0.2x}$
C43. $y = e^{-0.1x}$
C44. $y = e^{-0.2x}$
C45. $y = e^{x^2}$
C46. $y = e^{-x^2}$

In problems 47 and 48, round the answers to the nearest hundredth.

C47. The *half-life* of radium is 1690 years. That is, it takes 1690 years for half of a given amount of radium to decay into another substance. Starting with A_0 milligrams of radium, the amount A that will be left after x years is given by $A = A_0 e^{-0.000411x}$. How much radium would remain after 100 years if 100 milligrams were present at the beginning?

C48. Starting with 80 milligrams of radium, how much would remain after 1000 years? Use the formula in problem 47.

SOLUTION FOR PRACTICE PROBLEM

1. The graph of $g(x) = 3^{x-1}$ is shown in Figure 13.5.

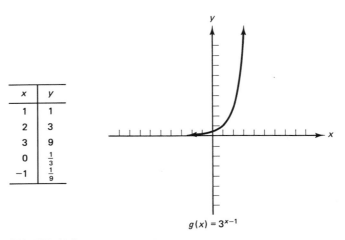

x	y
1	1
2	3
3	9
0	$\frac{1}{3}$
−1	$\frac{1}{9}$

$g(x) = 3^{x-1}$

FIGURE 13.5

13-2
Logarithmic
Functions

For $a > 0$ and $a \neq 1$, the exponential function

$$y = a^x$$

is a one-to-one function with domain $\mathcal{R}$ and range the set of all positive real numbers. This means that

1. any given positive real number N is equal to some power of the base a, and

2. there is only one power of a that equals N.

The exponent L to which the base a must be raised in order to obtain N is called the *logarithm of N to the base a*, abbreviated as $\log_a N$.

Definition 13-2 Let $a > 0$ and $a \neq 1$, and let $N > 0$. The **logarithm of N to the base a** is the number $L = \log_a N$ defined by

$$\boxed{\log_a N = L \quad \text{if and only if} \quad N = a^L.}$$

The statement in Definition 13-2 can be used in the following way to define the **logarithmic function**:

$$y = \log_a x \quad \text{if and only if} \quad x = a^y.$$

Since the equation $x = a^y$ can be obtained by interchanging x and y in the defining equation $y = a^x$ for the exponential function, this means that *the logarithmic function is the inverse of the exponential function.*

Since the logarithmic statement $L = \log_a N$ and the exponential statement $N = a^L$ are equivalent, a statement in either of these forms can be changed to a statement in the other form.

EXAMPLE 1   Change the following statements to logarithmic form.

(a) $81 = 3^4$ (b) $16 = (64)^{2/3}$ (c) $(36)^{-1/2} = \frac{1}{6}$

SOLUTION   (a) $81 = 3^4$ implies that $\log_3 81 = 4$.
(b) $16 = (64)^{2/3}$ implies that $\log_{64} 16 = \frac{2}{3}$.
(c) $(36)^{-1/2} = \frac{1}{6}$ implies that $\log_{36} \frac{1}{6} = -\frac{1}{2}$.

EXAMPLE 2   Change the following statements to exponential form.

(a) $\log_2 32 = 5$ (b) $\log_9 27 = \frac{3}{2}$ (c) $\log_{2/3} \frac{27}{8} = -3$

SOLUTION   (a) $\log_2 32 = 5$ implies that $32 = 2^5$.
(b) $\log_9 27 = \frac{3}{2}$ implies that $27 = 9^{3/2}$.
(c) $\log_{2/3} \frac{27}{8} = -3$ implies that $\frac{27}{8} = \left(\frac{2}{3}\right)^{-3}$.

We have noted that the logarithmic function $y = \log_a x$ is the inverse of the exponential function $y = a^x$. Since the sets for the domain and range are interchanged when we go from a function to its inverse, the *domain* of the logarithmic function is the set of all positive real numbers, and the range of the logarithmic function is the set of all real numbers. It is especially important to notice that **the logarithm of a negative number, or of 0, is undefined.**

If f is a one-to-one function, then $f^{-1}(f(x)) = x$ for all x in the domain of f, and $f(f^{-1}(x)) = x$ for all x in the domain of f^{-1}. Consequently,

$$\log_a a^x = x \qquad \text{for all } x \in \mathcal{R}$$

and

$$a^{\log_a x} = x \qquad \text{for all } x > 0.$$

Two important special cases of $\log_a a^x = x$ are

$$\log_a a = 1$$

and

$$\log_a 1 = 0.$$

EXAMPLE 3   Sketch the graph of

$$y = \log_2 x.$$

SOLUTION   The equality $\log_a a^n = n$ is helpful in obtaining points on the graph. Letting n take on the values 0, 1, 2, 3, -1, and -2 in $\log_2 2^n = n$, we get the points tabulated in Figure 13.6. It is also helpful to note that the

x	y
$1 = 2^0$	0
$2 = 2^1$	1
$4 = 2^2$	2
$8 = 2^3$	3
$\frac{1}{2} = 2^{-1}$	-1
$\frac{1}{4} = 2^{-2}$	-2

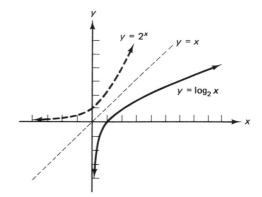

FIGURE 13.6

graph of $y = \log_2 x$ is the reflection of the graph of $y = 2^x$ through the line $y = x$. This is true since $y = \log_2 x$ is the inverse function of $y = 2^x$ (see Section 12-3).

If two of the quantities a, x, and y are known in the equation $y = \log_a x$, the value of the third variable can frequently be found by changing the logarithmic equation to exponential form. This is illustrated in Example 4.

EXAMPLE 4 Solve for the unknown variable.

(a) $y = \log_4 \frac{1}{64}$ (b) $\log_{25} x = -\frac{3}{2}$

(c) $\log_a \frac{27}{64} = -3$

SOLUTION   (a) $y = \log_4 \frac{1}{64}$ is equivalent to $4^y = \frac{1}{64}$. Since $4^3 = 64$,

$$4^y = \frac{1}{4^3}$$

$$4^y = 4^{-3},$$

and therefore $y = -3$.

(b) $\log_{25} x = -\frac{3}{2}$ means that

$$x = (25)^{-3/2} = \frac{1}{(25)^{3/2}} = \frac{1}{(\sqrt{25})^3} = \frac{1}{125}.$$

(c) $\log_a \frac{27}{64} = -3$ means that $a^{-3} = \frac{27}{64}$, or $\frac{1}{a^3} = \frac{27}{64}$. This gives

$$\frac{a^3}{1} = \frac{64}{27}$$

$$a = \sqrt[3]{\frac{64}{27}} = \frac{4}{3}.$$

PRACTICE PROBLEM 1 (Solution on page 388) Solve for the unknown variable.

(a) $y = \log_9 \frac{1}{27}$ (b) $\log_8 x = -\frac{4}{3}$

(c) $\log_a 8 = -\frac{1}{2}$

EXERCISES 13-2

Change the following statements to logarithmic form. (See Example 1.)

1. $2^3 = 8$ 2. $4^3 = 64$ 3. $3^5 = 243$

4. $2^5 = 32$ 5. $2^{-4} = \frac{1}{16}$ 6. $5^{-2} = \frac{1}{25}$

7. $(12)^0 = 1$ 8. $(10)^0 = 1$ 9. $(10)^{-1} = 0.1$

10. $(10)^{-2} = 0.01$ 11. $(9)^{-3/2} = \frac{1}{27}$ 12. $(8)^{-2/3} = \frac{1}{4}$

Change the following statements to exponential form. (See Example 2.)

13. $\log_7 7 = 1$ 14. $\log_6 6 = 1$

15. $\log_4 1 = 0$ 16. $\log_6 1 = 0$

17. $\log_3 27 = 3$ 18. $\log_4 16 = 2$

19. $\log_5 \frac{1}{125} = -3$ 20. $\log_3 \frac{1}{81} = -4$

21. $\log_{3/2} \frac{4}{9} = -2$ 22. $\log_{2/3} \frac{9}{4} = -2$

23. $\log_4 2 = \frac{1}{2}$

24. $\log_{27} 3 = \frac{1}{3}$

25. $\log_{16} \frac{1}{2} = -\frac{1}{4}$

26. $\log_8 \frac{1}{4} = -\frac{2}{3}$

Sketch the graphs of the functions defined by the following equations. (See Example 3.)

27. $y = \log_3 x$

28. $y = \log_4 x$

29. $y = \log_{1/2} x$

30. $y = \log_{1/3} x$

31. $y = \log_2(x + 3)$

32. $y = \log_3(x - 2)$

In problems 33 and 34, round the coordinates to the nearest tenth.

C33. $y = \log_e x$

C34. $y = \log_{3.2} x$

Solve for the unknown variable. (See Example 4 and Practice Problem 1.)

35. $y = \log_2 16$

36. $y = \log_6 36$

37. $y = \log_3 1$

38. $y = \log_7 1$

39. $y = \log_5 5$

40. $y = \log_9 9$

41. $y = \log_{1/2} \frac{1}{4}$

42. $y = \log_{2/3} \frac{4}{9}$

43. $y = \log_{1/9} \frac{1}{3}$

44. $y = \log_{1/4} \frac{1}{2}$

45. $\log_5 x = 3$

46. $\log_3 x = 4$

47. $\log_7 x = 2$

48. $\log_4 x = 3$

49. $\log_9 x = \frac{1}{2}$

50. $\log_8 x = \frac{1}{3}$

51. $\log_8 x = -\frac{1}{3}$

52. $\log_4 x = -\frac{1}{2}$

53. $\log_a 125 = 3$

54. $\log_a 64 = 2$

55. $\log_a 36 = -2$

56. $\log_a 64 = -3$

57. $\log_a 9 = \frac{1}{2}$

58. $\log_a 25 = \frac{1}{2}$

59. $\log_a 8 = -\frac{1}{3}$

60. $\log_a 27 = -\frac{1}{3}$

SOLUTION FOR PRACTICE PROBLEM

1. (a) $y = \log_9 \frac{1}{27}$ implies that $9^y = \frac{1}{27}$.

$$(3^2)^y = \frac{1}{3^3}$$
$$3^{2y} = 3^{-3}$$
$$2y = -3$$
$$y = -\frac{3}{2}$$

(b) $\log_8 x = -\frac{4}{3}$ implies that

$$x = 8^{-4/3} = \frac{1}{8^{4/3}} = \frac{1}{(\sqrt[3]{8})^4} = \frac{1}{2^4} = \frac{1}{16}.$$

(c) $\log_a 8 = -\frac{1}{2}$ implies that $a^{-1/2} = 8$.

$$(a^{-1/2})^{-2} = 8^{-2}$$
$$a = \frac{1}{8^2} = \frac{1}{64}$$

The laws of exponents imply some interesting and useful properties of logarithms. Before the widespread use of calculators, computations with numbers were frequently performed by using these properties and tables of logarithms. Even though they are rarely used in computation now, they are still instrumental in solving logarithmic or exponential equations. The properties that we have in mind are stated in the following theorem.

Theorem 13-3 Let $a > 0$ and $a \neq 1$. If u and v are positive real numbers and r is a real number, then

(a) $\log_a(uv) = \log_a u + \log_a v$

(b) $\log_a\left(\dfrac{u}{v}\right) = \log_a u - \log_a v$

(c) $\log_a u^r = r \log_a u$.

All of these properties are consequences of the laws of exponents. To illustrate, we shall prove part (a). Let $x = \log_a u$ and $y = \log_a v$. Then

$$u = a^x \quad \text{and} \quad v = a^y,$$

so that

$$uv = a^x \cdot a^y = a^{x+y},$$

by the product rule for exponents. But $uv = a^{x+y}$ means that

$$\log_a uv = x + y$$
$$= \log_a u + \log_a v.$$

The properties in Theorem 13-3 are commonly used to either expand a single logarithmic expression into terms with logarithms of simpler expressions, or to write an expanded expression as a single logarithm. These procedures are illustrated in the following examples.

Since a logarithmic function is defined only for positive real numbers, **we assume for the remainder of this section that all variables represent positive real numbers.**

EXAMPLE 1 Express each of the following in terms of the logarithms of x, y, and z.

(a) $\log_a \dfrac{xy^5}{z^7}$

(b) $\log_a\left(\dfrac{x^4}{y^6 z^3}\right)^{2/3}$

(a) $\log_a \dfrac{xy^5}{z^7}$

$$= \log_a(xy^5) - \log_a z^7 \qquad \text{[by Theorem 13-3(b)]}$$
$$= \log_a x + \log_a y^5 - \log_a z^7 \qquad \text{[by Theorem 13-3(a)]}$$
$$= \log_a x + 5 \log_a y - 7 \log_a z \qquad \text{[by Theorem 13-3(c)]}$$

(b) $\log_a \left(\dfrac{x^4}{y^6 z^3} \right)^{2/3}$

$$= \tfrac{2}{3} \log_a \dfrac{x^4}{y^6 z^3} \qquad \text{[by Theorem 13-3(c)]}$$
$$= \tfrac{2}{3}[\log_a x^4 - \log_a(y^6 z^3)] \qquad \text{[by Theorem 13-3(b)]}$$
$$= \tfrac{2}{3}[\log_a x^4 - (\log_a y^6 + \log_a z^3)] \qquad \text{[by Theorem 13-3(a)]}$$
$$= \tfrac{2}{3}[\log_a x^4 - \log_a y^6 - \log_a z^3]$$
$$= \tfrac{2}{3}[4 \log_a x - 6 \log_a y - 3 \log_a z] \qquad \text{[by Theorem 13-3(c)]}$$
$$= \tfrac{8}{3}\log_a x - 4 \log_a y - 2 \log_a z$$

In Example 1, it is interesting to note that the properties of logarithms are used in an order that corresponds to working inward from the outermost symbols of grouping, and this is the *opposite* to what is done in removing symbols of grouping in a computation.

EXAMPLE 2   Express each of the following as a single logarithm.

(a) $2 \log_a x + \tfrac{2}{3} \log_a y - 5 \log_a z$

(b) $3 \log_a y + 4 \log_a 2 + 6 \log_a z - \log_a x$

SOLUTION   (a) $2 \log_a x + \tfrac{2}{3} \log_a y - 5 \log_a z$

$$= \log_a x^2 + \log_a y^{2/3} - \log_a z^5 \qquad \text{[by Theorem 13-3(c)]}$$
$$= \log_a x^2 y^{2/3} - \log_a z^5 \qquad \text{[by Theorem 13-3(a)]}$$
$$= \log_a \dfrac{x^2 y^{2/3}}{z^5} \qquad \text{[by Theorem 13-3(b)]}$$

(b) We first note that part (a) of Theorem 13-3 extends to more than two factors. For example,

$$\log_a(uvw) = \log_a u + \log_a v + \log_a w.$$

$3 \log_a y + 4 \log_a 2 + 6 \log_a z - \log_a x$

$$= \log_a y^3 + \log_a 2^4 + \log_a z^6 - \log_a x \qquad \text{[by Theorem 13-3(c)]}$$
$$= \log_a y^3 + \log_a 16 + \log_a z^6 - \log_a x \qquad \text{(since } 2^4 = 16\text{)}$$
$$= \log_a 16y^3 z^6 - \log_a x \qquad \text{[by Theorem 13-3(a)]}$$
$$= \log_a \dfrac{16y^3 z^6}{x} \qquad \text{[by Theorem 13-3(b)]}$$

PRACTICE PROBLEM 1 (Solution on page 393)

(a) Express $\log_a\sqrt[4]{\dfrac{x^2y^4}{z^6}}$ in terms of the logarithms of x, y, and z.

(b) Write the following expression as a single logarithm.

$$\log_a 12x^2y - 3\log_a 2yz + 2\log_a y^3z$$

Some numerical uses of the properties of logarithms are shown in the next example.

EXAMPLE 3   Given that $\log_{10}3 = 0.4771$ and $\log_{10}5 = 0.6990$, use Theorem 13-3 to find the values of the following logarithms.

(a) $\log_{10}15$ (b) $\log_{10}5^{3/2}$ (c) $\log_{10}20$

SOLUTION   (a) $\log_{10}15 = \log_{10}(3)(5) = \log_{10}3 + \log_{10}5 = 0.4771 + 0.6990$
$= 1.1761$
(b) $\log_{10}5^{3/2} = \tfrac{3}{2}\log_{10}5 = \tfrac{3}{2}(0.6990) = 1.0485$
(c) $\log_{10}20 = \log_{10}\tfrac{100}{5} = \log_{10}100 - \log_{10}5 = 2 - 0.6990 = 1.3010$

A **logarithmic equation** is an equation that contains a logarithmic function. The next example shows how the properties of logarithms are used in solving logarithmic equations. There are two relevant facts about a logarithmic function that are worth mentioning in connection with logarithmic equations. First, $\log_a x$ is a one-to-one function, so

$$\log_a u = \log_a v \quad \text{if and only if} \quad u = v.$$

Second,

> The domain of $\log_a x$ is the set of positive real numbers.

EXAMPLE 4   Solve the following logarithmic equations.

(a) $\log_{10}(x + 2) - \log_{10}5 = \log_{10}x$
(b) $\log_3 x + \log_3(2x + 3) = 2$

SOLUTION   (a) Using the quotient property for logarithms, we have

$$\log_{10}(x + 2) - \log_{10}5 = \log_{10}x$$

$$\log_{10}\frac{x + 2}{5} = \log_{10}x.$$

Since $\log_{10}x$ is one-to-one, this means that

$$\frac{x+2}{5} = x$$

$$x + 2 = 5x$$

$$2 = 4x$$

$$x = \tfrac{1}{2}.$$

(b) Using the product property for logarithms, we have

$$\log_3 x + \log_3(2x + 3) = 2$$

$$\log_3 x(2x + 3) = 2$$

$$\log_3 x(2x + 3) = \log_3 3^2$$

$$x(2x + 3) = 3^2$$

$$2x^2 + 3x - 9 = 0$$

$$(2x - 3)(x + 3) = 0$$

$$2x - 3 = 0 \quad \text{or} \quad x + 3 = 0$$

$$x = \tfrac{3}{2} \qquad\qquad x = -3.$$

The proposed solution $x = -3$ must be rejected since $\log_3(-3)$ is undefined in the original equation. The solution set is $\{\tfrac{3}{2}\}$.

PRACTICE PROBLEM 2   (Solution on page 394) Solve the logarithmic equation.

$$\log_3(4x + 1) - \log_3(x - 1) = 2$$

EXERCISES 13-3

Assume that all variables represent positive real numbers.
Expand each of the following into terms involving the logarithms of x, y, or z. [See Example 1 and Practice Problem 1(a).]

1. $\log_a x^2$

2. $\log_a y^3$

3. $\log_a \sqrt[3]{x}$

4. $\log_a \dfrac{1}{y^2}$

5. $\log_a \sqrt[3]{x^2}$

6. $\log_a \sqrt{x^3}$

7. $\log_a x^2 y^3$

8. $\log_a x^3 y$

9. $\log_a \dfrac{xy}{z}$

10. $\log_a \dfrac{x}{yz}$

11. $\log_a \dfrac{x^2}{zy^3}$

12. $\log_a \dfrac{xy^3}{z^2}$

13. $\log_a \dfrac{x^2}{y\sqrt{z}}$

14. $\log_a \dfrac{x^5}{y^3 \sqrt[4]{z}}$

15. $\log_a \sqrt[3]{x^5 y^3 z^6}$

16. $\log_a \sqrt[4]{xy^4 z^7}$

17. $\log_a \sqrt{\dfrac{xy^3}{z^5}}$

18. $\log_a \dfrac{\sqrt{x^3 y^2}}{\sqrt[3]{z^5}}$

Express each of the following as a single logarithm. [See Example 2 and Practice Problem 1(b).]

19. $3 \log_a x + 2 \log_a y$ 20. $2 \log_a x + 5 \log_a z$

21. $\log_a x + 4 \log_a y + 3 \log_a z$ 22. $4 \log_a x + \log_a y + 2 \log_a z$

23. $2 \log_a x - \frac{4}{3} \log_a z$ 24. $\frac{3}{2} \log_a x - 4 \log_a y$

25. $\frac{1}{2}(2 \log_a x - 3 \log_a y + 4 \log_a z)$ 26. $\frac{1}{2}(\log_a x + 2 \log_a y - 3 \log_a z)$

27. $\log_a 9x^2 y + 2 \log_a 2xy^2 - 3 \log_a 2xy$

28. $2 \log_a 3x^3 + 3 \log_a 2xy^2 - 2 \log_a 3y$

29. $\frac{3}{2} \log_a 4x^2 z^4 - \log_a 2y + \frac{1}{3} \log_a x^3 y^6$

30. $\frac{2}{3} \log_a 27xy^2 z^3 + \frac{1}{2} \log_a 4y^2 z^6 - \frac{1}{3} \log_a x^2 y$

Given that $\log_{10} 2 = 0.3010$ and $\log_{10} 7 = 0.8451$, use Theorem 13-3 to find the values of the following logarithms. (See Example 3.)

31. $\log_{10} 14$ 32. $\log_{10} 28$ 33. $\log_{10} 196$

34. $\log_{10} 56$ 35. $\log_{10} 7^{3/4}$ 36. $\log_{10} 2^{3/5}$

37. $\log_{10} \sqrt[3]{2}$ 38. $\log_{10} \sqrt{7}$ 39. $\log_{10} \frac{2}{7}$

40. $\log_{10} \frac{7}{2}$ 41. $\log_{10} \frac{49}{4}$ 42. $\log_{10} \frac{49}{16}$

Solve the following logarithmic equations. (See Example 4 and Practice Problem 2.)

43. $\log_3 x + \log_3 4 = 2$ 44. $\log_2 x + \log_2 5 = 3$

45. $\log_4 x - \log_4 6 = 1$ 46. $\log_3 x - \log_3 4 = 1$

47. $\log_2 x - \log_2 (2x - 3) = 2$ 48. $\log_3 x - \log_3 (2x - 1) = 2$

49. $\log_2 x + \log_2 (x - 1) = 1$ 50. $\log_4 x + \log_4 (2x - 7) = 1$

51. $\log_{10}(3x + 2) - \log_{10} 4 = \log_{10} x$

52. $\log_{10}(2x + 5) - \log_{10} 3 = \log_{10} x$

53. $\log_{10} x + \log_{10}(3x + 1) = 1$

54. $\log_{10} x + \log_{10}(6x + 1) = 2$

55. $\log_{10} 2x + \log_{10}(3x + 5) = 2$

56. $\log_{10}(3x - 19) + \log_{10}(x - 2) = 1$

SOLUTIONS FOR PRACTICE PROBLEMS

1. (a) $\log_a \sqrt[4]{\dfrac{x^2 y^4}{z^6}} = \log_a \left(\dfrac{x^2 y^4}{z^6}\right)^{1/4}$

$= \frac{1}{4} \log_a \dfrac{x^2 y^4}{z^6}$

$= \frac{1}{4}[\log_a x^2 y^4 - \log_a z^6]$

$= \frac{1}{4}[\log_a x^2 + \log_a y^4 - \log_a z^6]$

$= \frac{1}{4}[2 \log_a x + 4 \log_a y - 6 \log_a z]$

$= \frac{1}{2}\log_a x + \log_a y - \frac{3}{2} \log_a z$

(b) $\log_a 12x^2y - 3\log_a 2yz + 2\log_a y^3z$

$= \log_a 12x^2y - \log_a(2yz)^3 + \log_a(y^3z)^2$

$= \log_a 12x^2y - \log_a 8y^3z^3 + \log_a y^6z^2$

$= \log_a \dfrac{12x^2y}{8y^3z^3} + \log_a y^6z^2$

$= \log_a \dfrac{\overset{3}{(\cancel{12}x^2y)}(\cancel{y^6}z^2)^{\overset{y^3}{}}}{\underset{2}{\cancel{8y^3z^3}}\,{}_z}$

$= \log_a \dfrac{3x^2y^4}{2z}$

2. $\log_3(4x+1) - \log_3(x-1) = 2$

$\log_3 \dfrac{4x+1}{x-1} = \log_3 3^2$

$\dfrac{4x+1}{x-1} = 3^2$

$4x + 1 = 9(x-1)$

$4x + 1 = 9x - 9$

$10 = 5x$

$x = 2$

The solution set is $\{2\}$.

13-4
Common
Logarithms
(Optional)

Since our number system uses the base 10, logarithms to the base 10 are the most suitable for use in computation. Because of their extensive use to perform calculations until 10 or 15 years ago, logarithms to base 10 came to be known as **common logarithms**, and it became conventional to drop the subscript and write log x to indicate $\log_{10} x$. We adopt this convention* for the remainder of this chapter, and use the phrase "logarithm of a number" to mean "logarithm of a number to the base 10."

Many calculators have a "log" button which supplies the logarithm of a positive number to the base 10 when the number is entered and the "log" button is depressed. Values of log x can also be found by use of a table. A table that gives four-place values for logarithms of numbers from 1 to 9.99, at intervals of 0.01, is printed on the back endpapers of this book. A portion of this table is reproduced in Figure 13.7. By "four-place

N	0	1	2	3	4	5	6	7	8	9
5.5	.7404	.7412	.7419	.7427	.7435	.7443	.7451	.7459	.7466	.7474
5.6	.7482	.7409	.7497	.7505	.7513	.7520	.7528	.7536	.7543	.7551
5.7	.7559	.7566	.7574	.7582	.7589	.7597	.7604	.7612	.7619	.7627
5.8	.7634	.7642	.7649	.7657	.7664	.7672	.7679	.7686	.7694	.7701
5.9	.7709	.7716	.7723	.7731	.7738	.7745	.7752	.7760	.7767	.7774

FIGURE 13.7

*The use of this convention is not universal. Some tables books and texts use log x to denote $\log_e x$, which is discussed in Section 13-6.

values" we mean that these values have been rounded to four decimal places, and most of them are not exact. It would be more precise to use "$\approx$" instead of "$=$" with values read from the table, but we shall use "$=$" for convenience. The use of this table is illustrated in Example 1.

EXAMPLE 1 Use the log table to find the value of

$$\log 5.76.$$

SOLUTION In the table, log 5.76 is found in the row that starts with 5.7 under N and in the column that has 6 at the top and bottom. This row and column are shaded in Figure 13.7, with log 5.76 at their intersection:

$$\log 5.76 = 0.7604.$$

Logarithms of three-digit numbers from 1 to 9.99 can be read directly from the table. To find logarithms of other three-digit positive numbers, we first recall from Section 9-2 that any positive number N can be written in *scientific notation* as

$$N = a \times 10^n, \qquad \text{with } 1 \leq a < 10.$$

For example, the number 576 is written in scientific notation as

$$576 = 5.76 \times 10^2.$$

The advantage of writing N in scientific notation becomes apparent when we take the logarithm of both sides of the equation.

$$N = a \times 10^n$$
$$\log N = \log a + \log 10^n$$
$$= (\log a) + n$$

The value of $\log a$ can be read from the table since $1 \leq a < 10$, and $\log N$ can be obtained by adding n. In this sense, $\log N$ comes in two parts, n, and $\log a$. The integral part, n, of the logarithm is called the **characteristic**. The other part, $\log a$, is a nonnegative decimal fraction from the table, and it is called the **mantissa**.

EXAMPLE 2 Use the log table to find the following logarithms.

    (a) log 576
    (b) log 0.000576

SOLUTION   (a) We first write 576 in scientific notation:
$$576 = 5.76 \times 10^2.$$
Then
$$\log 576 = \log 5.76 + \log 10^2$$
$$= 0.7604 + 2$$
$$= 2.7604.$$

The characteristic is 2, and the mantissa is 0.7604.
(b) Writing 0.000576 in scientific notation, we have
$$0.000576 = 5.76 \times 10^{-4}.$$

The characteristic is -4, and the mantissa is $\log 5.76 = 0.7604$. Thus
$$\log 0.000576 = 0.7604 - 4.$$

In numerical computations, a negative characteristic is usually written as a positive integer minus a multiple of 10. With this convention, we would write the result in Example 2(b) as
$$\log 0.000576 = 6.7604 - 10.$$

The reason for this convention will be clear after we have done some computations by using logarithms. However, a calculator combines the characteristic and mantissa, and gives the logarithm as a negative number:
$$\log 0.000576 = -3.2396.$$

In working with logarithms, we also need to be able to find a number N if the value of $\log N$ is given. If a calculator has an "INV" button and a "log" button, N can be obtained by entering the value of $\log N$, depressing the "INV" button, and then depressing the "log" button. The number N can also be found by use of a table, with limitations on the number of digits in N imposed by the table. The table on the back endpapers can be used for numbers with three digits.†

EXAMPLE 3   Find the number N if
$$\log N = 8.6405 - 10.$$

SOLUTION   The characteristic is -2, and the mantissa is 0.6405. This means that
$$N = a \times 10^{-2},$$

†A three-digit number is a number that has three digits when written in scientific notation. Zeros used only to place the decimal are not counted.

where $1 \leq a < 10$ and $\log a = 0.6405$. We can find a by searching for the value 0.6405 in the body of the table. (In this search, we note that the mantissa increases as a increases.) The value 0.6405 is found in the row that starts with 4.3 under N, and in the column that has 7 at the top and bottom. Thus $a = 4.37$ and

$$N = 4.37 \times 10^{-2}$$
$$= 0.0437.$$

The term **antilogarithm** (abbreviated **antilog**) is frequently used to designate the number that has a certain logarithm. The result in Example 3 could be written as

$$\text{antilog } (8.6405 - 10) = 0.0437.$$

There is a possible difficulty that should be mentioned at this point. In using a calculator to solve for N in

$$\log N = 8.6405 - 10,$$

the value used by the calculator is a negative number,

$$\log N = -1.3595,$$

and the "INV log" buttons yield $N = 0.0437$, to three digits. The point we wish to make is this: The decimal part 0.3595 of $\log N$ written as a negative number *does not* give the mantissa that should be found in the table. *To use the table, one must have a positive decimal fraction for the mantissa,* and this mantissa determines the digits of the number N. The characteristic places the decimal in N.

The table on the back endpapers of this book provides logarithms for three-digit numbers, and most mathematical tables books give logarithms for numbers with four or more digits. By using a procedure called **linear interpolation**, our table can be used to provide good approximations for logarithms of numbers with four digits.

We illustrate the procedure by approximating $\log 26.47$. Since

$$26.47 = 2.647 \times 10,$$

the characteristic is 1. The two numbers nearest 26.47 that have mantissas in the table are 26.40 and 26.50. Reading these values from the table, we obtain

$$\log 26.40 = 1.4216$$
$$\log 26.50 = 1.4232.$$

This means that the points $P(26.40, 1.4216)$ and $Q(26.50, 1.4232)$ are on the graph of $y = \log x$. This is pictured in Figure 13.8, where R indicates the point with coordinates $(26.47, \log 26.47)$.

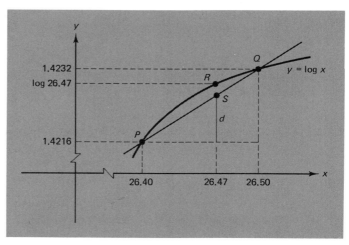

FIGURE 13.8

Linear interpolation uses the straight line through P and Q to approximate the curve $y = \log x$ (hence the name "linear"). The ordinate at S is used as the approximation to the ordinate at R, which is $\log 26.47$. To find the ordinate at S, we add the difference d to the ordinate at P. Since 26.47 is $\frac{7}{10}$ of the way from 26.40 to 26.50, the distance d is $\frac{7}{10}$ of the difference between the ordinates at P and Q. These differences can be set up in the following diagram.

$$10\left[7\left[\begin{matrix}\log 26.40 = 1.4216 \\ \log 26.47 = \underline{\hspace{1.5cm}}\end{matrix}\right]d\middle|0.0016\right.$$
$$\log 26.50 = 1.4232$$

To find d, we set the quotients $d/0.0016$ and $\frac{7}{10}$ equal:

$$\frac{d}{0.0016} = \frac{7}{10}$$

$$d = \frac{7}{10}(0.0016)$$

$$= 0.00112$$

$$\approx 0.0011,$$

where d is rounded to four decimal places to agree with the values in the table. Adding d to the ordinate at P, we get

$$\log 26.47 = 1.4216 + 0.0011$$

$$= 1.4227.$$

A calculator gives log 26.47 = 1.4227539, so our approximation is satisfactory, but not completely accurate.

PRACTICE PROBLEM 1 (Solution on page 401) Use linear interpolation with the log table to find
$$\log 0.2376.$$

EXAMPLE 4 Use interpolation to find N to four digits if
$$\log N = 8.5075 - 10.$$

SOLUTION The characteristic is -2, so $N = a \times 10^{-2}$, where $\log a = 0.5075$. In the table, the mantissas nearest 0.5075 are 0.5065 and 0.5079, corresponding to the digits 321 and 322. We set up our information as follows, where x represents the last digit in N.

$$10\begin{bmatrix} x\begin{bmatrix} \log 0.03210 = 8.5065 - 10 \\ \log N \quad\;\; = 8.5075 - 10 \end{bmatrix}0.0010 \\ \log 0.03220 = 8.5079 - 10 \end{bmatrix}0.0014$$

$$\frac{x}{10} = \frac{10}{14}$$

$$x = \frac{100}{14}$$

$$\approx 7$$

The value of x is rounded to 7 because x represents a digit between 0 and 10. Thus

$$N = 0.03217.$$

Using a calculator and entering the value 8.5075 − 10, the "INV log" buttons yield $N = 0.03217363$, and our approximation agrees to four digits.

PRACTICE PROBLEM 2 (Solution on page 401) Use interpolation to find a four-digit value for N if
$$\log N = 9.2235 - 10.$$

EXERCISES 13-4

Use the log table to find the common logarithms of the following numbers. (See Examples 1 and 2.)

1. 6.53   2. 4.71   3. 4.12×10^3

4. 8.03×10^4 5. 7.88×10^{-2} 6. 6.18×10^{-3}

7. 100   8. 1000   9. 0.1

10. 0.01   11. 24.7   12. 43.9

13. 6180   14. 31,400   15. 0.0448

16. 0.00562   17. 0.000318   18. 0.405

Find the number N that has the given logarithm, using the log table as necessary. (See Example 3.)

19. $\log N = 0.8831$ 20. $\log N = 0.2625$

21. $\log N = 1.6599$ 22. $\log N = 2.9484$

23. $\log N = 3.2355$ 24. $\log N = 3.7993$

25. $\log N = 2.5145$ 26. $\log N = 1.9600$

27. $\log N = 3$ 28. $\log N = -2$

29. $\log N = 9.9930 - 10$ 30. $\log N = 9.1644 - 10$

31. $\log N = 7.7679 - 10$ 32. $\log N = 8.8893 - 10$

Use interpolation with the log table to find the following logarithms. (See Practice Problem 1.)

33. $\log 1.034$ 34. $\log 2.963$

35. $\log 493.7$ 36. $\log 566.8$

37. $\log 0.3632$ 38. $\log 0.7526$

39. $\log 50,750$ 40. $\log 97,130$

41. $\log 0.06891$ 42. $\log 0.008374$

Use interpolation with the log table to find the number N that has the given logarithm. (See Example 4 and Practice Problem 2.)

43. $\log N = 0.7689$ 44. $\log N = 0.2729$

45. $\log N = 2.5017$ 46. $\log N = 1.9515$

47. $\log N = 9.8945 - 10$ 48. $\log N = 9.3171 - 10$

49. $\log N = 4.4651$ 50. $\log N = 4.8020$

51. $\log N = 8.2972 - 10$ 52. $\log N = 7.6941 - 10$

In problems 53–56, use a calculator to find an answer for the indicated exercise.

C53. Problem 35   C54. Problem 36

C55. Problem 47   C56. Problem 48

1. $0.2376 = 2.376 \times 10^{-1}$

$$10\left[{}^{6}\begin{bmatrix}\log 0.2370 = 9.3747 - 10\\ \log 0.2376 = \underline{\hspace{2cm}}\end{bmatrix}d\ \Bigg]0.0019 \\ \log 0.2380 = 9.3766 - 10\right.$$

$$\frac{d}{0.0019} = \frac{6}{10}$$

$$d = \frac{6}{10}(0.0019) = 0.0011$$

$$\log 0.2376 = (9.3747 - 10) + 0.0011$$
$$= 9.3758 - 10$$

2.

$$10\left[{}^{x}\begin{bmatrix}\log 0.1670 = 9.2227 - 10\\ \log N \quad = 9.2235 - 10\end{bmatrix}0.0008\ \Bigg]0.0026 \\ \log 0.1680 = 9.2253 - 10\right.$$

$$\frac{x}{10} = \frac{8}{26}$$

$$x = \frac{80}{26} \approx 3$$

$$N = 0.1673$$

13-5
Computations
with Logarithms
(Optional)

In this section we perform some computations by using logarithms. The properties stated in Theorem 13-3 of Section 13-3 are essential in this work. For simplicity, we avoid interpolations in our examples.

The first example illustrates the computation of a product.

EXAMPLE 1   Use logarithms to compute a three-digit value for the product

$$(28.8)(115).$$

SOLUTION   Let

$$N = (28.8)(115).$$

Then

$$\log N = \log 28.8 + \log 115.$$

Writing each factor in scientific notation, we have

$$28.8 = 2.88 \times 10 \quad \text{and} \quad 115 = 1.15 \times 10^2.$$

The characteristic of 28.8 is 1, and the characteristic of 115 is 2. Using the mantissas from the table and adding, we have

$$\begin{array}{ll}\log 28.8 = 1.4594 \\ \log 115 \;= 2.0607 \\ \hline \log N \quad = 3.5201. \end{array}$$

The characteristic of N is 3 and the mantissa in the table that is nearest 0.5201 is 0.5198, which corresponds to the digits 331. Thus

$$N = 3.31 \times 10^3$$
$$= 3310.$$

The zero in N is not significant, but only places the decimal. The exact value of N is 3312.

The computation of a quotient is demonstrated in our next example.

EXAMPLE 2 Use logarithms to find a three-digit value for

$$\frac{1.68}{73.8}$$

SOLUTION Let

$$N = \frac{1.68}{73.8}.$$

Then

$$\log N = \log 1.68 - \log 73.8.$$

In scientific notation,

$$1.68 = 1.68 \times 10^0 \quad \text{and} \quad 73.8 = 7.38 \times 10.$$

Using the mantissas from the table, we have

$$\log 1.68 = 0.2253$$
$$\log 73.8 = 1.8681.$$

At this point, we *do not* perform the subtraction

$$0.2253 - 1.8681$$

because this would yield a number with a *negative* decimal fraction, and we must keep a *positive* mantissa in order to use the table. To do this, we add and subtract 10 in the logarithm of the numerator, and then subtract the logarithm of the denominator.

$$\begin{array}{ll}\log 1.68 = \;\;\;10.2253 - 10 \\ -\log 73.8 = -1.8681 \\ \hline \log N \quad = \;\;\;\;\;8.3572 - 10 \end{array}$$

The characteristic is -2, and the mantissa in the table nearest 0.3572 is 0.3579, corresponding to the digits 228. Thus

$$N = \text{antilog } (8.3572 - 10)$$
$$= 2.28 \times 10^{-2}$$
$$= 0.0228.$$

Without using logarithms, a calculator gives the value $N = 0.02276423$.

In Example 2, a multiple of 10 was added and subtracted in order to retain a positive decimal fraction in a logarithm. The same sort of procedure is sometimes needed to keep the characteristic in simple form. This is the case in Example 3.

EXAMPLE 3   Use logarithms to find a three-digit value for
$$\sqrt[3]{0.673}.$$

SOLUTION   Let
$$N = \sqrt[3]{0.673} = (0.673)^{1/3}.$$
Then
$$\log N = \tfrac{1}{3} \log 0.673.$$
In scientific notation, $0.673 = 6.73 \times 10^{-1}$, so the characteristic is -1. Reading the mantissa from the table, we have
$$\log N = \tfrac{1}{3} (9.8280 - 10).$$
If both terms inside the parentheses are multiplied by $\tfrac{1}{3}$, we obtain a value for $\log N$ involving two decimal fractions instead of one. To avoid this, we add and subtract 20, making the last term a multiple of 3.
$$\log N = \tfrac{1}{3} (29.8280 - 30)$$
$$= 9.9427 - 10$$
The mantissa nearest 0.9427 in the table is 0.9425, corresponding to the digits 876. Thus
$$N = \text{antilog}(9.9427 - 10)$$
$$= 8.76 \times 10^{-1}$$
$$= 0.876.$$
Without using logarithms, a calculator gives the value $\sqrt[3]{0.673} = 0.87633809$.

The solution for the following practice problem requires the use of all three properties in Theorem 13-3.

PRACTICE PROBLEM 1 (Solution on page 405) Use logarithms to find a three-digit value for

$$\frac{(3.75)(0.0691)^4}{\sqrt[3]{0.00286}}$$

EXERCISES 13-5

Use the log table to compute a three-digit value for each of the following quantities.

(See Example 1.)

1. (41.2)(3.86)
2. (7.05)(6.41)
3. (844)(0.0639)
4. (546)(0.373)
5. (0.688)(0.0294)
6. (36.2)(0.0538)

(See Example 2.)

7. $\dfrac{8.82}{25.1}$
8. $\dfrac{9.54}{0.267}$

9. $\dfrac{232}{0.0551}$
10. $\dfrac{737}{0.658}$

11. $\dfrac{0.215}{0.0486}$
12. $\dfrac{96.3}{0.0388}$

(See Example 3.)

13. $\sqrt{426}$
14. $\sqrt{829}$
15. $\sqrt[3]{0.397}$
16. $\sqrt[3]{0.0523}$
17. $\sqrt[4]{0.0682}$
18. $\sqrt[5]{0.437}$

(See Practice Problem 1.)

19. $\dfrac{(61.4)(0.0235)}{9.51}$
20. $\dfrac{(73.6)(0.187)}{(0.414)}$

21. $\dfrac{(51.4)^3}{168}$
22. $\dfrac{(3.65)^4}{49.8}$

23. $\dfrac{(8.86)^5}{\sqrt{27.9}}$
24. $\dfrac{\sqrt[3]{46.1}}{(13.4)^2}$

25. $\dfrac{(25.3)^2\sqrt[3]{7.53}}{278}$
26. $\dfrac{(3.31)\sqrt[4]{2.69}}{0.493}$

27. $\sqrt{\dfrac{(6.28)^3(0.0531)}{(1.24)^2}}$
28. $\sqrt{\dfrac{(18.4)^2(0.135)^3}{68.3}}$

29. $\dfrac{\sqrt{942}\sqrt[3]{0.0232}}{\sqrt[4]{0.861}}$
30. $\dfrac{\sqrt[3]{19.6}}{\sqrt[4]{0.716}\sqrt{0.0396}}$

Use interpolation with the log table to find a four-digit value for each of the following quantities.

*31. $(0.6319)^2(18.57)^3$

*32. $\dfrac{(0.1934)(8.491)}{(0.07819)}$

*33. $(3.478)^{1.2}$

*34. $(57.95)^{2.1}$

*35. $\dfrac{\sqrt{73.62}}{\sqrt[3]{8.513}(0.3846)^2}$

*36. $\dfrac{(24.61)^3\sqrt[5]{1.368}}{\sqrt[3]{0.5942}}$

Use a calculator to find a value for the quantities in the indicated exercises.

C37. Problem 25

C38. Problem 26

C39. Problem 35

C40. Problem 36

SOLUTION FOR PRACTICE PROBLEM

1.
$$N = \frac{(3.75)(0.0691)^4}{\sqrt[3]{0.00286}}$$

$$\log N = \log 3.75 + 4 \log 0.0691 - \tfrac{1}{3} \log 0.00286$$

In scientific notation,

$$3.75 = 3.75 \times 10^0, \quad 0.0691 = 6.91 \times 10^{-2}, \quad 0.00286 = 2.86 \times 10^{-3}.$$

$$\log 3.75 = 0.5740$$

$$4 \log 0.0691 = 4(8.8395 - 10)$$

$$= 35.3580 - 40$$

$$= 5.3580 - 10$$

$$\tfrac{1}{3} \log 0.00286 = \tfrac{1}{3}(7.4564 - 10)$$

$$= \tfrac{1}{3}(27.4564 - 30)$$

$$= 9.1521 - 10$$

Thus

$$\log N = 0.5740 + (5.3580 - 10) - (9.1521 - 10)$$

$$= (5.9320 - 10) - (9.1521 - 10)$$

$$= (15.9320 - 20) - (9.1521 - 10)$$

$$= 6.7799 - 10.$$

$$N = 6.02 \times 10^{-4} = 0.000602.$$

13-6
Exponential
Equations and
Natural Logarithms

An **exponential equation** is an equation that contains an exponential function. The use of logarithms is frequently necessary in solving an exponential equation.

EXAMPLE 1 Solve

$$3^{2x-1} = 5^{x+2}.$$

SOLUTION   We begin by taking the logarithm of both sides of the equation.

$$\log 3^{2x-1} = \log 5^{x+2}$$
$$(2x-1)\log 3 = (x+2)\log 5$$
$$2x\log 3 - \log 3 = x\log 5 + 2\log 5$$
$$2x\log 3 - x\log 5 = 2\log 5 + \log 3$$
$$(2\log 3 - \log 5)x = 2\log 5 + \log 3$$
$$x = \frac{2\log 5 + \log 3}{2\log 3 - \log 5}$$
$$= \frac{1.8751}{0.2553}$$
$$= 7.345$$

It is sometimes desirable to find a decimal value for the logarithm of a number to a base other than 10. For this reason, we consider changing logarithms from one base to another.

To obtain an equation relating $\log_a N$ and $\log_b N$, let

$$L = \log_b N.$$

Then

$$N = b^L$$

and

$$\log_a N = \log_a b^L$$
$$= L \log_a b.$$

Solving for L, we have

$$L = \frac{\log_a N}{\log_a b}.$$

Substituting $\log_b N$ for L in this equation, we obtain the

Change-of-Base Formula

$$\log_b N = \frac{\log_a N}{\log_a b}$$

As a special case,

$$\log_b N = \frac{\log N}{\log b},$$

and this equation enables us to compute logarithms to any base by using common logarithms.

406

EXAMPLE 2   Find a decimal value for

$$\log_3 87.$$

SOLUTION   From the Change-of-Base Formula, we have

$$\log_3 87 = \frac{\log 87}{\log 3}$$

$$= \frac{1.9395}{0.4771}$$

$$= 4.065,$$

where the division was done with a calculator.

PRACTICE   (Solution on page 410) Find a decimal value for
PROBLEM 1
$$\log_5 64.$$

In Section 13-1, the irrational number e with the decimal approximation

$$e \approx 2.71828$$

was introduced. This number occurs so often in physical situations that it is frequently called "the natural number e," and logarithms to the base e are called "natural logarithms." It is common practice‡ to use "ln x" to denote logarithms to the base e:

$$\boxed{\ln x = \log_e x.}$$

Most mathematical tables books have a table of natural logarithms, and many calculators have a button marked "ln x" which provides the logarithm of a positive number to the base e when the number is entered and the "ln x" button is depressed. The Change-of-Base Formula can be used to derive a conversion formula for obtaining natural logarithms from common logarithms:

$$\ln x = \frac{\log x}{\log e}$$

$$= \frac{1}{\log e} \cdot \log x$$

$$= \frac{1}{0.4343} \cdot \log x$$

$$= 2.303 \log x.$$

‡It should be noted that some texts and tables books use "log x" to denote $\log_e x$.

Thus we have the conversion formula

$$\ln x = 2.303 \log x.$$

EXAMPLE 3   Find the value of

$$\ln 24.7.$$

SOLUTION   Using the conversion formula, we have

$$\ln 24.7 = 2.303 \log 24.7$$
$$= (2.303)(1.3927)$$
$$= 3.21.$$

The next example illustrates the usefulness of natural logarithms in a physical situation. Other illustrations are given in the exercises at the end of this section.

EXAMPLE 4   A colony of bacteria that starts at a size of 1000 and increases by 10% of its population each day will have population P given approximately by

$$P = 1000e^{0.1x}$$

after x days. How long does it take the population to double its initial size?

SOLUTION   We need to find x when $P = 2000$. We have

$$1000e^{0.1x} = 2000$$
$$e^{0.1x} = 2.$$

Taking the natural logarithm of both sides, we get

$$\ln(e^{0.1x}) = \ln 2.$$

Since $\ln e^u = \log_e e^u = u$, this gives

$$0.1x = \ln 2$$

and

$$x = 10 \ln 2$$
$$= 10(2.303)\log 2$$
$$= (23.03)(0.3010)$$
$$= 6.93.$$

The bacteria population will double in slightly less than 7 full days.

Solve the following exponential equations. (See Example 1.)

1. $2^x = 37$

2. $3^x = 15$

3. $6^x = 49$

4. $5^x = 317$

5. $4^{x+1} = 25$

6. $4^{x-1} = 57$

7. $8^{x^2} = 91$

8. $2^{x^2} = 74$

9. $13 = 6 \cdot 2^{x-2}$

10. $9 = 7 \cdot 3^{x+1}$

11. $2^{3x-1} = 5^{x+2}$

12. $3^{2x+1} = 7^{x-2}$

Find a decimal value for each of the following logarithms. (See Example 2 and Practice Problem 1.)

13. $\log_3 7$

14. $\log_2 5$

15. $\log_7 3.8$

16. $\log_6 4.5$

17. $\log_4 19$

18. $\log_3 10$

19. $\log_8 100$

20. $\log_7 1000$

21. $\log_2 31.7$

22. $\log_4 22.6$

23. $\log_5 382$

24. $\log_8 163$

Find a decimal value for the following natural logarithms. (See Example 3.)

25. $\ln 5$

26. $\ln 7$

27. $\ln 41$

28. $\ln 52$

29. $\ln 10$

30. $\ln 100$

31. $\ln 6.38$

32. $\ln 4.09$

33. $\ln 37.6$

34. $\ln 26.3$

35. $\ln 135$

36. $\ln 424$

Use natural logarithms to solve the following exponential equations. (See Example 4.)

C37. $e^x = 3.1$

C38. $e^{-x} = 14$

C39. $e^{x+1} = 154$

C40. $e^{x-1} = 26.2$

C41. $e^{2x} = 61.5$

C42. $e^{2x-1} = 7.24$

C43. The atmospheric pressure P, in inches of mercury, at an altitude of x miles above sea level is given approximately by $P = 30e^{-0.21x}$. What is the altitude of a mountain peak if the pressure there is 17.2 inches of mercury?

C44. Use the formula in problem 43 to determine the altitude at which the atmospheric pressure is equal to one-half of the atmospheric pressure at sea level.

C45. If an investment of P dollars earns interest at an annual interest rate r compounded annually, the value after n years is the amount $A = P(1 + r)^n$. At an annual rate of 10% ($r = 0.10$), how long will it take an investment of \$3000 to accumulate to an amount of at least \$6000?

C46. Work problem 45 using a rate of 14% ($r = 0.14$).

C47. The radioactive carbon atom ^{14}C is used by geologists to estimate the ages of fossils. If a dead organism contains a certain amount A_0 of ^{14}C

at a given time, then the amount A of ^{14}C remaining x years later is given by $A = A_0e^{-0.000124x}$. If a fossil contains 60% of the amount of ^{14}C that was present when it died, what is the approximate age of the fossil? (*Hint:* Put $A = 0.6A_0$.)

C48. Use the formula in problem 47 to determine the age of a fossil which contains 20% of the amount of ^{14}C that was present when it died.

C49. In chemistry, the pH of a solution is defined by $pH = -\log(H_3O^+)$, where (H_3O^+) is the concentration of the hydronium ion measured in moles per liter. Find the hydronium ion concentration (H_3O^+) if the pH is 7.9.

C50. Use the formula in problem 49 to find (H_3O^+) in a solution with a pH of 6.

The formulas in the following exercises are taken from Example 4 and problems 43–50.

51. Solve for x in terms of P if $P = 1000e^{0.1x}$.

52. Solve for x in terms of P if $P = 30e^{-0.21x}$.

53. Solve for n in terms of A if $A = 3000(1.10)^n$.

54. Solve for n in terms of A if $A = 3000(1.14)^n$.

55. Solve for x in terms of A if $A = 50e^{-0.000124x}$.

56. Solve for (H_3O^+) in terms of pH if $pH = -\log(H_3O^+)$.

SOLUTION FOR PRACTICE PROBLEM

1. $\log_5 64 = \dfrac{\log 64}{\log 5} = \dfrac{1.8062}{0.6990} = 2.584$

PRACTICE TEST for Chapter 13

1. Sketch the graph of the function defined by $y = -(\frac{1}{3})^x$.

2. Solve for x:
$$(16)^x = \tfrac{1}{8}.$$

3. Solve for the unknown variable.
   (a) $\log_3 x = -2$ \qquad (b) $\log_a 4 = \tfrac{1}{3}$

4. Sketch the graph of $y = \log_2 x$.

5. (a) Expand $\log_a \dfrac{x^3}{y^4 \sqrt{z}}$ into terms involving the logarithms of x, y, or z.

   (b) Write the following expression as a single logarithm.
$$3 \log_a xy^2 + \log_a 4xz - 2 \log_a 3yz^2$$

6. Solve the following equation.
$$\log x + \log(3x - 1) = 1$$

7. Use interpolation with the log table to find a value for x in each equation.
   (a) $x = \log 39.47$ \qquad (b) $\log x = 9.4719 - 10$

8. Use the log table to compute a three-digit value for
$$\frac{629 \sqrt[3]{0.415}}{(28.3)^2}.$$

9. Solve the equation
$$4^x = 73.$$

10. Find a decimal value for $\log_3 68$.

14

Sequences, Series, and the Binomial Expansion

14-1
Sequences and Series

Most people begin their mathematics "career" by learning to count from 1 to 5:

$$1, 2, 3, 4, 5;$$

later to count "by twos" to 10 and "by tens" to 100:

$$2, 4, 6, 8, 10;$$
$$10, 20, 30, 40, 50, 60, 70, 80, 90, 100.$$

Eventually, we learn the perfect squares:

$$1, 4, 9, 16, 25, 36, \ldots.$$

In each example above, listing the numbers in the correct order was part of the goal to be accomplished in the learning process. Thus in each list of numbers above, we can identify a first element, a second element, a third element, and so on. This leads us to the definition of a sequence.

Definition 14-1 A **finite sequence** is a function whose domain is $\{1, 2, 3, \ldots, k\}$. An **infinite sequence** is a function whose domain is the set of positive integers. The elements in the range are called the **terms** of the sequence.

EXAMPLE 1 Write out the terms of the sequence defined by the function

$$a(n) = 2n - 3, \qquad n \in \{1, 2, 3, 4, 5\}.$$

SOLUTION The first term occurs when $n = 1$, the second term when $n = 2$, and so on. Thus we have

1st term: $n = 1$, $a(1) = 2(1) - 3 = -1$;
2nd term: $n = 2$, $a(2) = 2(2) - 3 = 1$;
3rd term: $n = 3$, $a(3) = 2(3) - 3 = 3$;
4th term: $n = 4$, $a(4) = 2(4) - 3 = 5$;
5th term: $n = 5$, $a(5) = 2(5) - 3 = 7$;

and the five terms are $-1, 1, 3, 5, 7$.

Since the domain of a sequence is always all or part of the positive integers, it is customary to use the following notation:

$$a_n, \qquad n = 1, 2, 3, \ldots, k$$

means

$$a(n), \qquad n \in \{1, 2, 3, \ldots, k\}.$$

If the values of n are not specified, it is customary to assume that $n = 1, 2, 3, \ldots$.

In Example 1, we write

$$a_1 = -1, \quad a_2 = 1, \quad a_3 = 3, \quad a_4 = 5, \quad a_5 = 7$$

and the general term, the nth term, is

$$a_n = 2n - 3, \qquad n = 1, 2, 3, 4, 5.$$

EXAMPLE 2 Find the 9th term and the 40th term of the sequence defined by

$$a_n = (-1)^n \left(\frac{n - 3}{n + 2} \right).$$

SOLUTION   Instead of writing out 40 terms of the sequence, we simply let $n = 9$ and $n = 40$ in

$$a_n = (-1)^n\left(\frac{n-3}{n+2}\right).$$

9th term: $a_9 = (-1)^9\left(\frac{9-3}{9+2}\right) = -\frac{6}{11}$

40th term: $a_{40} = (-1)^{40}\left(\frac{40-3}{40+2}\right) = \frac{37}{42}$

Sometimes the general or nth term is not specified. Instead, enough of the sequence is given so that a pattern becomes obvious and the entire sequence can be determined.

EXAMPLE 3   Write out the next four terms in the sequence whose first four terms are

$$-\tfrac{1}{2},\ \tfrac{2}{3},\ -\tfrac{3}{4},\ \tfrac{4}{5}.$$

Also write the general term.

SOLUTION   By examining the first four terms, we see that

(a) the signs alternate;
(b) each numerator increases by one, and
(c) each denominator increases by one.

Thus the next four terms follow the same pattern and are

$$-\tfrac{5}{6},\ \tfrac{6}{7},\ -\tfrac{7}{8},\ \tfrac{8}{9}.$$

If we let a_n represent the nth term, then

$$a_n = (-1)^n\frac{n}{n+1}.$$

EXAMPLE 4   Write out the first five terms of the sequence defined by

$$a_n = -1.$$

SOLUTION   No matter what integer n assumes, $a_n = -1$. Hence the first five terms are $-1, -1, -1, -1, -1$. This is an example of a **constant sequence**, a sequence in which all the terms are the same.

PRACTICE PROBLEM 1   (Solution on page 419) Find the general term and the 10th term of the sequence whose first four terms are

$$\tfrac{3}{2},\ \tfrac{3}{4},\ \tfrac{3}{6},\ \tfrac{3}{8}.$$

Associated with each sequence is the sum of the first n terms in the sequence. We make the following definition.

Definition 14-2 A **finite series**, denoted by S_n, is the indicated sum of the first n terms of a sequence. An **infinite series**, denoted by S_∞,* is the indicated sum of all the terms in an infinite sequence.

EXAMPLE 5 For the sequence

$$a_n = 2n + 1,$$

write S_6 in expanded form and find the value of the sum.

SOLUTION The series S_6 is given by

$$S_6 = a_1 + a_2 + a_3 + a_4 + a_5 + a_6$$
$$= 3 + 5 + 7 + 9 + 11 + 13,$$

and the value of this sum is 48.

If we know the general term of a sequence, as we did in Example 5, we can use a compact notation, called **sigma notation** or **summation notation,** for writing sums. In Example 5,

$$S_6 = a_1 + a_2 + a_3 + a_4 + a_5 + a_6$$

can be written compactly, using the Greek letter sigma, Σ, as

$$S_6 = \sum_{i=1}^{6} a_i.$$

This notation is read "the sum of terms a_i as i ranges from 1 to 6." The letter i is called the **index of summation** and is a **dummy variable** in the sense that any other variable can be used in its place. Notice that

$$\sum_{i=1}^{6} a_i = \sum_{k=1}^{6} a_k = \sum_{n=1}^{6} a_n = a_1 + a_2 + a_3 + a_4 + a_5 + a_6.$$

EXAMPLE 6 Write each series in expanded form and evaluate.

(a) $\sum_{i=1}^{3} (-1)^i i$

(b) $\sum_{k=4}^{7} (3k + 1)$

*The symbol "∞" is the symbol for infinity.

SOLUTION (a) To obtain the terms in the sum we replace i by 1, 2, and 3 in the expression $(-1)^i i$. Hence the expanded form is

$$\sum_{i=1}^{3} (-1)^i i = \underset{\underset{i=1}{\uparrow}}{(-1)^1 1} + \underset{\underset{i=2}{\uparrow}}{(-1)^2 2} + \underset{\underset{i=3}{\uparrow}}{(-1)^3 3} = -1 + 2 - 3$$

and the value of the series is -2.

(b) We first note that the index of summation does not have to start at 1. This time we replace k by 4, 5, 6, and 7 in the expression $3k + 1$. The expanded form of the series is

$$\sum_{k=4}^{7} (3k + 1) = \underset{\underset{k=4}{\uparrow}}{(3 \cdot 4 + 1)} + \underset{\underset{k=5}{\uparrow}}{(3 \cdot 5 + 1)} + \underset{\underset{k=6}{\uparrow}}{(3 \cdot 6 + 1)} + \underset{\underset{k=7}{\uparrow}}{(3 \cdot 7 + 1)}$$

$$= 13 + 16 + 19 + 22$$

and the value is 70.

EXAMPLE 7 Rewrite the sum using the sigma notation.

$$-\tfrac{7}{2} + \tfrac{7}{3} - \tfrac{7}{4} + \tfrac{7}{5}$$

SOLUTION There is more than one way to rewrite this sum using the summation notation. We can write

$$-\frac{7}{2} + \frac{7}{3} - \frac{7}{4} + \frac{7}{5} = \sum_{k=2}^{5} (-1)^{k+1} \left(\frac{7}{k} \right),$$

or, equivalently,

$$-\frac{7}{2} + \frac{7}{3} - \frac{7}{4} + \frac{7}{5} = \sum_{k=1}^{4} (-1)^k \left(\frac{7}{k+1} \right).$$

PRACTICE PROBLEM 2 (Solution on page 419) Write the series in expanded form and evaluate

$$\sum_{n=4}^{8} (1 - n^2).$$

EXERCISES 14-1

Write out the terms of the sequence defined by each of the following. (See Example 1.)

1. $a_n = n$, $n = 1, 2, 3$ 2. $a_n = n + 2$, $n = 1, 2, 3, 4$

3. $a_n = n^2$, $n = 1, 2, 3, 4$ 4. $a_n = n^3$, $n = 1, 2, 3$

5. $a_k = \dfrac{k+1}{k+2}$, $k = 1, 2, 3, 4, 5$ 6. $a_k = \dfrac{3k}{k+1}$, $k = 1, 2, \ldots, 7$

7. $a_k = (-1)^k \frac{1}{k}, \quad k = 1, 2, \ldots, 7$

8. $a_k = (-1)^k k^{-1}, \quad k = 1, 2, \ldots, 7$

In problems 9 and 10, round the answers to the nearest hundredth.

C9. $a_i = (0.72)^i, \quad i = 1, 2, 3$ C10. $a_i = \frac{i}{1.98}, \quad i = 1, 2, \ldots, 5$

Write out the first five terms of the infinite sequence whose general term is given. (See Example 2.)

11. $a_n = \frac{n}{n+1}$ 12. $a_n = \frac{2}{n+3}$

13. $a_i = \frac{1}{i^2 + 1}$ 14. $a_i = \frac{2i}{i^2 + 1}$

15. $a_k = 1 + \frac{1}{k}$ 16. $a_k = 2 - \frac{1}{k}$

17. $a_n = 4n - 1$ 18. $a_n = 3 - 2n$

19. $a_n = (-1)^n n$ 20. $a_n = (-1)^{n+1} \frac{n}{n+1}$

21. $a_n = (-\frac{1}{2})^n$ 22. $a_n = (-1)^n 2^{n+1}$

Write the next four terms in each sequence. Also give the nth term. (See Example 3 and Practice Problem 1.)

23. $-1, -3, -5, -7$ 24. $2, 4, 6, 8$
25. $10, -20, 30, -40$ 26. $6, -12, 18, -24$
27. $\frac{1}{2}, \frac{2}{2}, \frac{3}{2}, \frac{4}{2}$ 28. $\frac{1}{3}, \frac{2}{3}, \frac{3}{3}, \frac{4}{3}$
29. $\frac{3}{1}, \frac{4}{2}, \frac{5}{3}, \frac{6}{4}$ 30. $\frac{1}{2}, \frac{2}{3}, \frac{3}{4}, \frac{4}{5}$
31. x, x^2, x^3, x^4 32. $x, 2x, 3x, 4x$
33. $2 - x, 2 + 2x, 2 - 3x, 2 + 4x$ 34. $x, -2x^2, 3x^3, -4x^4$

Find the indicated term of the sequence whose general term is given.

(See Example 2 and Practice Problem 1.)

35. $a_9, a_n = \frac{4n}{3}$ 36. $a_{11}, a_n = 7n + 9$

37. $a_2, a_n = 17n^2$ 38. $a_4, a_n = -n^2$

39. $a_{110}, a_i = 4 - i$ 40. $a_{473}, a_i = (-1)^i - i$

41. $a_{11}, a_k = kx + 2$ 42. $a_9, a_k = x^2 - kx$

(See Example 4.)

43. $a_{10}, a_n = -3$ 44. $a_8, a_n = 17$

45. $a_{12}, a_n = x^2$ 46. $a_{93}, a_n = 3x$

Write the first five terms of each sequence.

*47. $a_1 = 3, a_n = -a_{n-1}$ *48. $a_1 = -1, a_n = 2a_{n-1} + 3$

*49. $a_1 = -3, a_2 = 1, a_n = a_{n-1}^2 - a_{n-2}$

*50. $a_1 = 1, a_2 = 1, a_n = a_{n-1} + a_{n-2}$

Write the series in expanded form and evaluate the sum.

(See Example 5.)

51. S_7 where $a_n = \dfrac{n}{n+1}$ 52. S_3 where $a_n = n^4$

53. S_5 where $a_n = (-1)^n n$ 54. S_8 where $a_n = n^2 - n$

55. S_4 where $a_n = 2^n$ 56. S_5 where $a_n = 1 - 2^n$

57. S_3 where $a_n = \dfrac{n^2}{n^2+1}$ 58. S_3 where $a_n = 1 + \dfrac{1}{n^2}$

(See Example 6 and Practice Problem 2.)

59. $\displaystyle\sum_{n=1}^{4} (3n - 2)$ 60. $\displaystyle\sum_{n=1}^{5} n^2$

61. $\displaystyle\sum_{n=2}^{7} n(n - 1)$ 62. $\displaystyle\sum_{n=4}^{8} \left(\dfrac{n}{2} + 1\right)$

63. $\displaystyle\sum_{n=1}^{5} \dfrac{2n - 1}{n + 1}$ 64. $\displaystyle\sum_{n=1}^{8} (-1)^{n+1} n$

65. $\displaystyle\sum_{n=5}^{7} (n^2 - 1)$ 66. $\displaystyle\sum_{n=6}^{8} n(n - 1)(n - 2)$

67. $\displaystyle\sum_{n=4}^{7} 2$ 68. $\displaystyle\sum_{n=8}^{11} (-3)$

In problems 69 and 70, round the answers to the nearest thousandth.

C69. $\displaystyle\sum_{n=2}^{6} \dfrac{1.38n}{1.59 + 2.11n}$ C70. $\displaystyle\sum_{n=3}^{5} 2.37^n$

Write using summation notation. There is more than one correct answer. (See Example 7.)

71. $1 + 4 + 7 + 10$ 72. $1 - 1 + 1 - 1 + 1$

73. $-2 + 4 - 8 + 16 - 32$ 74. $1 - 4 + 9 - 16 + 25 - 36$

75. $x + \dfrac{x^2}{2} + \dfrac{x^3}{3}$ 76. $\dfrac{1-x}{2} + \dfrac{1-x}{3} + \dfrac{1-x}{4} + \dfrac{1-x}{5}$

77. $9 + 9 + 9$ 78. $x + x + x + x + x + x$

1. The terms $\frac{3}{2}, \frac{3}{4}, \frac{3}{6}, \frac{3}{8}$ can be written as $\frac{3}{2(1)}, \frac{3}{2(2)}, \frac{3}{2(3)}, \frac{3}{2(4)}$. Hence the nth term is

$$a_n = \frac{3}{2n},$$

and the 10th term is

$$a_{10} = \frac{3}{2(10)} = \frac{3}{20}.$$

2. The expanded form is

$$\sum_{n=4}^{8} (1 - n^2) = (1 - 4^2) + (1 - 5^2) + (1 - 6^2) + (1 - 7^2) + (1 - 8^2).$$

The value of the sum is

$$\sum_{n=4}^{8} (1 - n^2) = -15 - 24 - 35 - 48 - 63 = -185.$$

14-2 Arithmetic Progressions

The sequence

$$-7, -2, 3, 8, 13, 18$$

has the property that each term is 5 more than the term right before it. Similarly, the sequence

$$4, 1, -2, -5, -8, -11$$

has the property that any term after the first term can be obtained by adding -3 to the term preceding it. Sequences of this special type are called **arithmetic sequences** or **arithmetic progressions**. The constant that is added to each term to get the next term is called the **common difference** and is denoted by d. In any arithmetic sequence, if a_n is the nth term, then a_{n-1} is the term right before it and

$$a_n = a_{n-1} + d,$$

or

$$a_n - a_{n-1} = d.$$

We can also write the nth term strictly in terms of the first term, a_1, the common difference, d, and the number of the term, n. Consider the following:

1st term: a_1

2nd term: $a_2 = a_1 + d$

3rd term: $a_3 = a_2 + d = (a_1 + d) + d = a_1 + 2d$

4th term: $a_4 = a_3 + d = (a_1 + 2d) + d = a_1 + 3d$

$$\vdots \qquad \vdots$$

*n*th term: $a_n = a_1 + (n - 1)d.$

We can use this formula for a_n to find any particular term in an arithmetic progression if the first term and common difference are known.

EXAMPLE 1 Determine whether or not each sequence is an arithmetic progression. If it is, find d and a_n.

(a) 5, 9, 13, 17, 21   (b) 2, 3, 5, 8, 12

SOLUTION In each part we determine the difference d between the first two terms, and then check to see if each term can be found by adding d to the preceding term.

(a) The difference between the first two terms is 4 and this difference is common to each pair of "neighboring" terms. Hence this sequence is an arithmetic progression with $d = 4$ and

$$a_n = 5 + (n - 1)4 = 4n + 1.$$

(b) The difference between the first two terms is 1.

$$a_2 - a_1 = 3 - 2 = 1$$

Adding 1 to the second term does not yield the third term:

$$5 = a_3 \neq a_2 + 1 = 3 + 1 = 4.$$

Hence the sequence

$$2, 3, 5, 8, 12$$

is *not* arithmetic.

EXAMPLE 2 Find the 12th term of the arithmetic progression whose first term is 4 and common difference is -7.

SOLUTION We have

$$a_1 = 4, \qquad d = -7, \qquad n = 12.$$

Using the formula for the *n*th term

$$a_n = a_1 + (n - 1)d,$$

then the 12th term is

$$a_{12} = 4 + (12 - 1)(-7) = 4 - 77 = -73.$$

EXAMPLE 3   Write the first five terms of an arithmetic progression whose 9th term is 11 and common difference is -2.

SOLUTION   Since we know that $d = -2$ and $n = 9$ when $a_n = 11$, we use the formula

$$a_n = a_1 + (n - 1)d$$

to find a_1:

$$11 = a_1 + (9 - 1)(-2)$$
$$11 = a_1 + (-16)$$
$$27 = a_1.$$

Next we add the common difference, -2, to a_1 to obtain a_2, and so on, and find the first five terms to be

$$27, 25, 23, 21, 19.$$

PRACTICE PROBLEM 1   (Solution on page 425) Find the 12th term of the arithmetic progression where $a_2 = 4$ and $a_9 = 67$.

The series, S_n, associated with the n terms, $a_1, a_2, a_3, \ldots, a_n$, of an arithmetic progression appears as

$$S_n = a_1 + a_2 + a_3 + \cdots + a_n.$$

To evaluate this sum, it is usually more efficient computationally to have a formula for the sum of n terms than to add the n terms together. The desired formula is derived by writing S_n in two ways: In the first equation, we form the sum by starting with a_1 and adding d repeatedly $n - 1$ times to obtain n terms. In the second equation, we form the sum in reverse order, starting with a_n and subtracting d repeatedly $n - 1$ times to obtain n terms.

$$S_n = a_1 + (a_1 + d) + (a_1 + 2d) + \cdots + (a_1 + (n - 1)d),$$
$$S_n = a_n + (a_n - d) + (a_n - 2d) + \cdots + (a_n - (n - 1)d).$$

Adding the two equations together and solving for S_n gives

$$2S_n = (a_1 + a_n) + (a_1 + a_n) + (a_1 + a_n) + \cdots + (a_1 + a_n)$$
$$2S_n = n(a_1 + a_n)$$
$$S_n = \frac{n}{2}(a_1 + a_n).$$

Since $a_n = a_1 + (n - 1)d$, we can also write

$$S_n = \frac{n}{2}[a_1 + a_1 + (n - 1)d] = \frac{n}{2}[2a_1 + (n - 1)d].$$

We record our results of this section.

Arithmetic Progression

If a_1 is the first term and d the common difference in an arithmetic progression, then

1. the nth term, a_n, is

$$a_n = a_1 + (n - 1)d,$$

2. the sum, S_n, of the first n terms is

$$S_n = \frac{n}{2}(a_1 + a_n)$$

or

$$S_n = \frac{n}{2}[2a_1 + (n - 1)d].$$

EXAMPLE 4   Find the sum of the first 8 terms of the arithmetic progression where $a_1 = 3$ and $d = -4$.

SOLUTION   Since we know that $a_1 = 3$, $d = -4$, and $n = 8$, we use the formula

$$S_n = \frac{n}{2}[2a_1 + (n - 1)d].$$

Thus

$$S_8 = \frac{8}{2}[2(3) + (8 - 1)(-4)]$$

$$= 4(6 - 28)$$

$$= -88.$$

EXAMPLE 5   Find the sum of the first 11 terms in the arithmetic progression where the general term is

$$a_n = \frac{3}{2}n + 2.$$

SOLUTION   We first find a_1 and a_{11} using

$$a_n = \frac{3}{2}n + 2.$$

$$a_1 = \frac{3}{2}(1) + 2 = \frac{7}{2}$$

$$a_{11} = \frac{3}{2}(11) + 2 = \frac{37}{2}.$$

Then the sum of the first 11 terms is found using

$$S_n = \frac{n}{2}(a_1 + a_n).$$

$$= \frac{11}{2}\left(\frac{7}{2} + \frac{37}{2}\right)$$

$$= \frac{11}{2}\left(\frac{44}{2}\right)$$

$$= 121.$$

PRACTICE   (Solution on page 425) Using one of the formulas for the sum of n terms
PROBLEM 2   in an arithmetic progression, evaluate

$$S_5 = \sum_{n=1}^{5}(3n - 7).$$

EXERCISES 14-2

Determine whether or not each of the following sequences is an arithmetic
progression. If so, find d and a_n. (See Example 1.)

1. 5, 8, 11, 14   2. 41, 48, 55, 62

3. 1, 2, 4, 8   4. $-1, -4, -9, -16, -25$

5. $2, -3, 2, -3$ 6. $1, -2, 3, -4$

7. $\frac{5}{2}, 2, \frac{3}{2}, 1$ 8. $0, \frac{4}{3}, \frac{8}{3}, 4$

Find the indicated term in the given arithmetic progression.

(See Example 2.)

9. $a_1 = 40, d = -7, a_9 = ?$ 10. $a_1 = -7, d = 14, a_8 = ?$

11. $a_1 = \frac{1}{2}, d = -\frac{5}{2}, a_{11} = ?$ 12. $a_1 = -3, d = -\frac{8}{3}, a_{13} = ?$

C13. $a_1 = 1.28, d = -5.71, a_9 = ?$ C14. $a_1 = -17.3, d = 11.2, a_{15} = ?$

(See Example 3.)

15. $a_9 = 8, d = 5, a_1 = ?$ 16. $a_4 = 5, d = 11, a_1 = ?$

423

17. $a_{14} = 48, d = -4, a_1 = ?$ 18. $a_{11} = 93, d = -8, a_1 = ?$

19. $a_2 = 7, d = 8, a_{20} = ?$ 20. $a_5 = 14, d = 4, a_{43} = ?$

21. $a_{26} = 62, d = -3, a_6 = ?$ 22. $a_{43} = -114, d = -7, a_7 = ?$

(See Practice Problem 1.)

23. $a_8 = 3, a_4 = -1, a_1 = ?$ 24. $a_9 = 49, a_4 = -11, a_{10} = ?$

25. $a_{11} = 111, a_4 = 6, a_8 = ?$ 26. $a_7 = 64, a_{11} = 20, a_2 = ?$

Find the value of the sum in the given arithmetic progressions.

(See Example 4.)

27. $a_1 = 5, d = 7, S_6 = ?$ 28. $a_1 = 93, d = -11, S_8 = ?$

29. $a_1 = \frac{9}{2}, d = -\frac{3}{2}, S_{11} = ?$ 30. $a_1 = -\frac{2}{3}, d = \frac{7}{3}, S_6 = ?$

(See Example 5.)

31. $a_n = 9n - 3, S_{20} = ?$ 32. $a_n = 4 + 3n, S_{15} = ?$

33. $a_n = 2 - n, S_{31} = ?$ 34. $a_n = 16 - 2n, S_8 = ?$

*35. $a_4 = 11, d = -2, S_{15} = ?$ *36. $a_{11} = 2, d = 3, S_{10} = ?$

*37. $a_6 = 15, d = \frac{1}{2}, S_{12} = ?$ *38. $a_{40} = 9, d = -1, S_{20} = ?$

C39. $a_{11} = 43.21, a_1 = 92.12, S_{11} = ?$

C40. $a_{53} = -27.01, a_1 = 53.11, S_{53} = ?$

(See Practice Problem 2.)

41. $S_7 = \sum_{n=1}^{7} (2n - 3)$ 42. $S_9 = \sum_{n=1}^{9} (4n + 1)$

43. $S_{50} = \sum_{n=1}^{50} 2n$ 44. $S_{40} = \sum_{n=1}^{40} (1 - n)$

*45. $\sum_{n=3}^{11} (n + 4)$ *46. $\sum_{n=11}^{21} (2n + 5)$

Work each of the following problems using arithmetic progressions.

47. If a child puts 1 penny in her piggy bank one week, 3 pennies the second week, 5 pennies the third week, 7 pennies the fourth week, and so on, how many pennies will she put in her bank on the 20th week?

48. In problem 47, how much money will she have in her bank after she put her money in on the 20th week?

49. Find the sum of the first 100 positive integers.

50. Find the sum of the even integers from 2 to 212, inclusive.

51. A stock boy is to display cans of pork and beans in a triangular-shaped stack with 1 can on the top row, 2 cans on the second row, 3 cans on the

third row, and so on. But since he has to begin stacking from the bottom, how many cans should he place in the bottom row if he must display a total of 45 cans?

52. Work problem 51, if the stock boy must display 66 cans.

SOLUTIONS FOR PRACTICE PROBLEMS

1. We can find a_1 and d by solving the following system.

$$a_9 = a_1 + 8d = 67$$
$$a_2 = a_1 + d = 4$$

Subtracting the second equation from the first gives $7d = 63$ and $d = 9$. Substituting $d = 9$ into the second equation gives $a_1 = -5$. Then the 12th term is

$$a_{12} = a_1 + 11d = -5 + 11(9) = 94.$$

2. The series

$$S_5 = \sum_{n=1}^{5} (3n - 7)$$

is the sum of 5 terms of an arithmetic progression with

$$\text{first term} = a_1 = 3(1) - 7 = -4;$$

and

$$\text{fifth term} = a_5 = 3(5) - 7 = 8.$$

Hence

$$S_5 = \tfrac{5}{2}(a_1 + a_5) = \tfrac{5}{2}(-4 + 8) = 10.$$

14-3
*Geometric
Progressions*

Another special type of sequence, called the **geometric sequence** or **geometric progression**, is one that has the property that any term past the first can be computed by multiplying the term right before it by a nonzero constant r. Two examples of geometric progressions are:

$$5, 10, 20, 40, 80, \text{ with } r = 2;$$
$$1, -\tfrac{1}{3}, \tfrac{1}{9}, -\tfrac{1}{27}, \text{ with } r = -\tfrac{1}{3}.$$

If a_n is the nth term of a geometric progression, then a_{n-1} is the term preceding a_n and

$$a_n = ra_{n-1},$$

or

$$\frac{a_n}{a_{n-1}} = r.$$

The nonzero constant r is called the **common ratio**.

In a geometric progression where a_1 is the first term and r is the common ratio, we have

1st term: $\quad a_1,$

2nd term: $\quad a_2 = a_1 r,$

3rd term: $\quad a_3 = a_2 r = (a_1 r)r = a_1 r^2,$

4th term: $\quad a_4 = a_3 r = (a_1 r^2)r = a_1 r^3,$

$$\begin{matrix} \cdot & & \cdot \\ \cdot & & \cdot \\ \cdot & & \cdot \end{matrix}$$

$$\boxed{n\text{th term:} \quad a_n = a_1 r^{n-1}.}$$

Thus any term can be written in terms of the first term, a_1, and the common ratio, r.

EXAMPLE 1 Determine whether or not each of the following sequences is a geometric progression. If so, state r and a_n.

(a) 16, 8, 4, 2   (b) 1, 2, 4, 6

SOLUTION (a) The sequence 16, 8, 4, 2, is geometric with common ratio $r = \frac{1}{2}$, and nth term

$$a_n = a_1 r^{n-1} = 16\left(\frac{1}{2}\right)^{n-1} = 2^4 \cdot \frac{1}{2^{n-1}} = 2^{5-n}.$$

(b) The sequence 1, 2, 4, 6, is not geometric since there is no common ratio:

$$\frac{a_2}{a_1} = \frac{2}{1} = 2 \quad \text{is not the same as} \quad \frac{a_4}{a_3} = \frac{6}{4} = \frac{3}{2}.$$

EXAMPLE 2 Find the 4th term in the geometric progression where $a_1 = 5$ and $r = -2$.

SOLUTION With $n = 4$, $a_1 = 5$ and $r = -2$, we have

$$a_4 = a_1 r^{4-1} = 5(-2)^3 = 5(-8) = -40.$$

PRACTICE PROBLEM 1 (Solution on page 431) Find the 3rd term in the geometric progression where $a_7 = \left(\frac{1}{4}\right)^3$, $r = \frac{1}{4}$.

A formula for the sum, S_n, of the first n terms of a geometric progression is easily derived by multiplying both sides of

$$S_n = a_1 + a_1 r + a_1 r^2 + \cdots + a_1 r^{n-1}$$

by r, yielding

$$rS_n = a_1 r + a_1 r^2 + a_1 r^3 + \cdots + a_1 r^n.$$

Next we subtract the second equation from the first and solve the resulting equation for S_n.

$$S_n - rS_n = a_1 - a_1 r^n$$

$$(1 - r)S_n = a_1(1 - r^n)$$

$$S_n = a_1 \frac{1 - r^n}{1 - r}, \qquad r \neq 1$$

PRACTICE (Solution on page 431) Evaluate the following sum using the formula for
PROBLEM 2 the sum of the first n terms of a geometric progression.

$$\sum_{i=1}^{5} 7(2)^i.$$

Let us consider the infinite geometric progression

$$2, \tfrac{1}{2}, \tfrac{1}{8}, \tfrac{1}{32}, \ldots$$

where $a_1 = 2$, $r = \tfrac{1}{4}$. The sum, S_n, of the first n terms is given by

$$S_n = 2 \cdot \frac{1 - (\tfrac{1}{4})^n}{1 - \tfrac{1}{4}} = 2 \cdot \frac{1 - (\tfrac{1}{4})^n}{\tfrac{3}{4}} = \frac{8}{3} \cdot \left[1 - \left(\frac{1}{4}\right)^n\right]$$

and we see that the only term in this formula that is affected by n is $(\tfrac{1}{4})^n$. The value of $(\tfrac{1}{4})^n$ and S_n is computed for several values of n in Figure 14.1.

n	1	3	5	8	10
$(\tfrac{1}{4})^n$	0.25	0.015625	0.000977	0.000015	0.000001
S_n	2.00	2.625000	2.664063	2.666626	2.666664

FIGURE 14.1

As n increases without bound, $(\tfrac{1}{4})^n$ becomes closer and closer to zero. We write

$$(\tfrac{1}{4})^n \longrightarrow 0 \qquad \text{as} \qquad n \longrightarrow \infty,$$

which is read as

"$(\tfrac{1}{4})^n$ approaches 0 as n approaches infinity."

At the same time, we have, as $n \longrightarrow \infty$,

$$S_n = 2 \cdot \frac{1 - (\frac{1}{4})^n}{1 - \frac{1}{4}} \longrightarrow 2 \cdot \frac{1 - 0}{1 - \frac{1}{4}} = 2 \cdot \frac{1}{\frac{3}{4}} = \frac{8}{3} = 2.6666\ldots.$$

We say that the sum of all the terms in the infinite geometric sequence is $\frac{8}{3}$,

$$2 + \tfrac{1}{2} + \tfrac{1}{8} + \tfrac{1}{32} + \cdots = \tfrac{8}{3}.$$

Next, suppose that we consider an infinite geometric progression

$$2, 6, 18, 54, \ldots,$$

where $a_1 = 2$ and $r = 3$. The sum S_n of the first n terms is

$$S_n = 2 \cdot \frac{1 - 3^n}{1 - 3} = 2 \cdot \frac{1 - 3^n}{-2} = -(1 - 3^n) = 3^n - 1$$

and these sums increase without bound as n increases (see Figure 14.2).

n	1	3	5	8	10	15
3^n	3	27	243	6561	59049	14348907
S_n	2	26	242	6560	59048	14348906

FIGURE 14.2

Thus we say that the sum of all the terms in the infinite geometric progression does *not* exist,

$$2 + 6 + 18 + 54 + \cdots \text{ does not exist.}$$

With these two examples in mind, we state the following result without formal proof.

Infinite Geometric Series

Let S_∞ represent the sum of an infinite geometric progression with common ratio r and first term a_1. Then

$$S_\infty = \begin{cases} \dfrac{a_1}{1 - r} & \text{if } |r| < 1 \\ \text{does not exist} & \text{if } |r| \geq 1 \end{cases}$$

EXAMPLE 3   Evaluate each sum, if it exists.

(a) $1 + \frac{1}{4} + \frac{1}{16} + \frac{1}{64} + \cdots$

(b) $5 - 10 + 20 - 40 + \cdots$

SOLUTION   (a) The infinite geometric series

$$1 + \frac{1}{4} + \frac{1}{16} + \frac{1}{64} + \cdots$$

has $a_1 = 1$ and $r = \frac{1}{4}$. Since $|r| = |\frac{1}{4}| = \frac{1}{4} < 1$, the sum exists and

$$S_\infty = \frac{a_1}{1 - r} = \frac{1}{1 - \frac{1}{4}} = \frac{1}{\frac{3}{4}} = \frac{4}{3}.$$

(b) The infinite geometric series

$$5 - 10 + 20 - 40 + \cdots$$

has $a_1 = 5$ and $r = -2$. Since $|r| = |-2| = 2 > 1$, the sum does *not* exist.

EXAMPLE 4   If the following sum exists, find its value.

$$S_\infty = \sum_{i=1}^{\infty} \left(-\frac{1}{3}\right)^i$$

SOLUTION   The sum

$$\sum_{i=1}^{\infty} \left(-\frac{1}{3}\right)^i$$

is an infinite geometric series with $a_1 = -\frac{1}{3}$ and $r = -\frac{1}{3}$. Since $|r| = \frac{1}{3} < 1$, the sum exists and is given by

$$\sum_{i=1}^{\infty} \left(-\frac{1}{3}\right)^i = \frac{a_1}{1 - r} = \frac{-\frac{1}{3}}{1 - (-\frac{1}{3})} = \frac{-\frac{1}{3}}{\frac{4}{3}} = -\frac{1}{4}.$$

PRACTICE PROBLEM 3   (Solution on page 431) Use the formula for an infinite geometric series to write the infinite repeating decimal 0.444 . . . as a quotient of integers.

EXERCISES 14-3

Determine whether or not each sequence is a geometric progression. If so, state r and a_n. (See Example 1.)

1. $1, -1, 1, -1, 1, -1$

2. $2, -2, 2, -2$

3. $5, 10, 30, 120$

4. $3, 3, 4, 4, 5, 5$

5. $1.01, 1.02, 1.03, 1.04$

6. $\frac{1}{2}, -\frac{3}{2}, \frac{5}{2}, -\frac{7}{2}$

7. $1.01, (1.01)^2, (1.01)^3, (1.01)^4$ 8. $1, -\frac{5}{2}, \frac{25}{4}, -\frac{125}{8}$

Find the indicated term in each of the following geometric progressions. (See Example 2 and Practice Problem 1.)

9. $a_1 = 7, r = -3, a_4 = ?$ 10. $a_1 = -2, r = -\frac{1}{3}, a_5 = ?$

11. $a_1 = -\frac{4}{9}, r = \frac{2}{3}, a_5 = ?$ 12. $a_1 = 125, r = \frac{1}{5}, a_7 = ?$

13. $a_4 = 16, r = -\frac{1}{4}, a_1 = ?$ 14. $a_3 = 100, r = 10, a_1 = ?$

15. $a_4 = \frac{2}{3}, r = 2, a_1 = ?$ 16. $a_3 = (1.02)^7, r = 1.02, a_1 = ?$

17. $a_5 = 81, r = -\frac{1}{3}, a_3 = ?$ 18. $a_8 = -7, r = -1, a_5 = ?$

19. $a_5 = (1.03)^9, r = 1.03, a_2 = ?$ 20. $a_6 = \frac{81}{5}, r = 3, a_2 = ?$

In problems 21 and 22, round the answers to the nearest hundredth.

C21. $a_1 = 2.93, r = 1.51, a_4 = ?$ C22. $a_1 = 1.07, r = -2.55, a_6 = ?$

Evaluate the sum for each of the following geometric progressions. (See Practice Problem 2.)

23. $a_1 = 4, r = -2, S_6 = ?$ 24. $a_1 = -2, r = 3, S_4 = ?$

25. $a_1 = 1, r = -\frac{2}{3}, S_4 = ?$ 26. $a_1 = -1, r = \frac{3}{2}, S_5 = ?$

27. $a_1 = 7, r = 1, S_{12} = ?$ 28. $a_1 = -3, r = 1, S_{15} = ?$

29. $a_3 = -\frac{1}{2}, r = 1, S_{11} = ?$ 30. $a_9 = 0.7, r = 1, S_{23} = ?$

31. $\sum\limits_{i=1}^{8} 3(-2)^i$ 32. $\sum\limits_{i=1}^{5} 4(-3)^i$

33. $\sum\limits_{i=1}^{4} 2(\frac{1}{3})^i$ 34. $\sum\limits_{i=1}^{4} (-3)(-\frac{1}{3})^i$

*35. $\sum\limits_{i=3}^{6} 4^i$ *36. $\sum\limits_{i=2}^{5} \frac{1}{2}(3)^i$

*37. $\sum\limits_{i=2}^{5} (-\frac{1}{3})^i$ *38. $\sum\limits_{i=5}^{8} (-\frac{1}{2})^i$

If it exists, evaluate each sum. If the sum does not exist, give a reason. (See Example 3.)

39. $1 - \frac{1}{2} + \frac{1}{4} - \frac{1}{8} + \cdots$ 40. $1 - \frac{1}{3} + \frac{1}{9} - \frac{1}{27} + \cdots$

41. $10 + 5 + \frac{5}{2} + \frac{5}{4} + \cdots$ 42. $7 - \frac{7}{3} + \frac{7}{9} - \frac{7}{27} + \cdots$

43. $\frac{1}{16} + \frac{1}{8} + \frac{1}{4} + \frac{1}{2} + \cdots$ 44. $\frac{4}{25} + \frac{4}{5} + 4 + 20 + \cdots$

45. $1 - 1 + 1 - 1 + \cdots$ 46. $10 - 10 + 10 - 10 + \cdots$

(See Example 4.)

47. $\sum\limits_{i=1}^{\infty} (-\frac{2}{3})^i$ 48. $\sum\limits_{i=1}^{\infty} (-\frac{4}{5})^i$

49. $\sum\limits_{i=1}^{\infty} (\tfrac{2}{7})^i$ 50. $\sum\limits_{i=1}^{\infty} (\tfrac{4}{6})^i$

51. $\sum\limits_{i=1}^{\infty} (-3)^i$ 52. $\sum\limits_{i=1}^{\infty} 2^i$

53. $\sum\limits_{i=1}^{\infty} (\tfrac{5}{3})^i$ 54. $\sum\limits_{i=1}^{\infty} (-\tfrac{6}{5})^i$

Write each of the following infinite repeating decimals as a quotient of integers. (See Practice Problem 3.)

*55. 0.333 . . .   *56. 0.777 . . .

*57. 0.555 . . .   *58. 0.111 . . .

*59. 0.212121 . . .   *60. 0.474747 . . .

*61. 0.727272 . . .   *62. 0.595959 . . .

Work each of the following word problems using a geometric progression.

63. Suppose that a ball rebounds $\tfrac{1}{3}$ of the distance it is dropped. If it is dropped from a height of 15 feet, how high will it rebound on the 4th bounce?

64. Suppose that a ball rebounds $\tfrac{2}{3}$ of the distance it is dropped. If it is dropped from a height of 200 feet, how high will it rebound on the 5th bounce?

65. Suppose that a culture of bacteria doubles every 20 minutes. If the culture initially contains 4000 bacteria, how many are present after 1 hour?

66. Sharky, the local lender, computes interest by doubling the amount of interest owed every week. If his favorite customer owes him $50 in interest today, how much interest will he owe at the end of 10 weeks?

SOLUTIONS FOR PRACTICE PROBLEMS

1. We first find a_1 using: $a_7 = a_1 r^6$.
$$a_7 = (\tfrac{1}{4})^3 = a_1(\tfrac{1}{4})^6$$
$$a_1 = 4^3$$

Next we find a_3 using: $a_3 = a_1 r^2$.
$$a_3 = 4^3(\tfrac{1}{4})^2 = 4$$

2. $\sum\limits_{i=1}^{5} 7(2)^i = 7(2) + 7(2)^2 + \cdots + 7(2)^5$

$a_1 = 7 \cdot 2 = 14, \quad r = 2, \quad n = 5$

$S_5 = 14 \cdot \dfrac{1 - 2^5}{1 - 2} = 14 \cdot \dfrac{1 - 32}{-1} = 14 \cdot \dfrac{-31}{-1} = 434$

*3. The infinite repeating decimal 0.444 . . . can be expressed as a sum of an infinite geometric progression with $a_1 = 0.4$ and $r = 0.1$. The sum exists since $|r| < 1$. Thus

$$0.444\ldots = 0.4 + 0.04 + 0.004 + 0.0004 + \cdots$$

$$= \frac{0.4}{1 - 0.1}$$

$$= \frac{0.4}{0.9}$$

$$= \frac{4}{9}.$$

14-4
The Binomial
Expansion

Positive integral powers of the binomial $a + b$ occur frequently in mathematics, especially in the fields of probability and statistics. Direct multiplication can be used to compute

$$(a + b)^n$$

for any positive integer n, but that process is extremely tedious and subject to careless error, especially for large values of n. To expedite the process, we shall first write out the expansions for small values of n and then make a few observations.

$n = 1$: $(a + b)^1 = a + b$

$n = 2$: $(a + b)^2 = a^2 + 2ab + b^2$

$n = 3$: $(a + b)^3 = a^3 + 3a^2b + 3ab^2 + b^3$

$n = 4$: $(a + b)^4 = a^4 + 4a^3b + 6a^2b^2 + 4ab^3 + b^4$

$n = 5$: $(a + b)^5 = a^5 + 5a^4b + 10a^3b^2 + 10a^2b^3 + 5ab^4 + b^5$

The observations about the expansions are included in the following list.

The Expansion of $(a + b)^n$

1. There are $n + 1$ terms.

2. The highest power of a or b is n.

3. In each successive term the power of a decreases and the power of b increases.

4. In each term the sum of the powers of a and b is n.

5. The coefficient in each term can be computed in the following manner:
   (i) the coefficient of the first term is 1; and
   (ii) the coefficient of any term after the first is

$$\frac{\left(\begin{array}{c}\text{coefficient of}\\ \text{preceding term}\end{array}\right) \cdot \left(\begin{array}{c}\text{exponent of } a \text{ in}\\ \text{the preceding term}\end{array}\right)}{\text{number of preceding term}}$$

EXAMPLE 1 Write out the expansion of $(a + b)^6$.

SOLUTION To write out this expansion we adhere to the criteria given above. To begin with we write out the terms without the coefficients:

$$(a + b)^6 = a^6 + \underline{\quad} a^5b + \underline{\quad} a^4b^2 + \underline{\quad} a^3b^3 + \underline{\quad} a^2b^4$$
$$+ \underline{\quad} ab^5 + b^6.$$

Next, we compute the coefficients by multiplying the coefficient of a term by the exponent of a in that term and dividing by the number of the term to obtain the coefficient of the next term.

$$1a^6 \quad + \quad 6a^5b \quad + \quad 15a^4b^2 \quad + \quad 20a^3b^3 \quad + \quad 15a^2b^4 \quad + \quad 6ab^5 \quad + \quad 1b^6$$

$$\frac{1 \times 6}{1} = 6 \quad \frac{6 \times 5}{2} = 15 \quad \frac{15 \times 4}{3} = 20 \quad \frac{20 \times 3}{4} = 15 \quad \frac{15 \times 2}{5} = 6 \quad \frac{6 \times 1}{6} = 1$$

Thus the expansion is

$$(a + b)^6 = a^6 + 6a^5b + 15a^4b^2 + 20a^3b^3 + 15a^2b^4 + 6ab^5 + b^6.$$

In general, the binomial expansion appears as:

$$(a + b)^n = a^n + \frac{n}{1}a^{n-1}b + \frac{n(n-1)}{1 \cdot 2}a^{n-2}b^2 + \frac{n(n-1)(n-2)}{1 \cdot 2 \cdot 3}a^{n-3}b^3$$
$$+ \cdots + \frac{n(n-1)(n-2)\cdots(n-r+1)}{1 \cdot 2 \cdot 3 \cdots r}a^{n-r}b^r + \cdots + b^n.$$

The factorial notation introduced in the following definition is helpful in shortening the appearance of the coefficients in this expansion.

Definition 14-3 Let n be any positive integer. Then **$n!$** (read: "n factorial") is the product of the n integers $n, n - 1, n - 2, \ldots, 2, 1$:

$$n! = n(n - 1)(n - 2) \cdots 2 \cdot 1.$$

Also,

$$0! = 1.$$

EXAMPLE 2 Evaluate each of the following.

(a) 5!   (b) 1!   (c) $\dfrac{5!}{3!}$ (d) $\dfrac{9!}{(9 - 6)!6!}$

SOLUTION (a) $5! = 5 \cdot 4 \cdot 3 \cdot 2 \cdot 1 = 120$
(b) $1! = 1$

(c) $\dfrac{5!}{3!} = \dfrac{5 \cdot 4 \cdot 3 \cdot 2 \cdot 1}{3!} = \dfrac{5 \cdot 4 \cdot 3!}{3!} = 5 \cdot 4 = 20$

(d) $\dfrac{9!}{(9-6)!\,6!} = \dfrac{9!}{3!\,6!} = \dfrac{9 \cdot 8 \cdot 7 \cdot 6!}{3!\,6!} = \dfrac{9 \cdot 8 \cdot 7}{3 \cdot 2 \cdot 1} = 84$

Quotients such as the one in part (d) of Example 2 appear so often in probability and statistics that a special symbol has been devised to represent such quotients.

If n and r are nonnegative integers, then

$$\binom{n}{r} = \frac{n!}{(n-r)!\,r!}, \qquad n \geq r.$$

EXAMPLE 3 Evaluate each of the following.

(a) $\dbinom{4}{2}$ (b) $\dbinom{8}{3}$ (c) $\dbinom{6}{6}$

SOLUTION

(a) $\dbinom{4}{2} = \dfrac{4!}{(4-2)!\,2!} = \dfrac{4!}{2!\,2!} = \dfrac{4 \cdot 3 \cdot 2!}{2 \cdot 1 \cdot 2!} = 6$

(b) $\dbinom{8}{3} = \dfrac{8!}{(8-3)!\,3!} = \dfrac{8!}{5!\,3!} = \dfrac{8 \cdot 7 \cdot 6 \cdot 5!}{5!\,3 \cdot 2 \cdot 1} = 8 \cdot 7 = 56$

(c) $\dbinom{6}{6} = \dfrac{6!}{(6-6)!\,6!} = \dfrac{6!}{0!\,6!} = 1$

For any r such that $1 \leq r \leq n$, we have (see problem 70)

$$\binom{n}{n-r} = \frac{n(n-1)(n-2)\cdots(n-r+1)}{1 \cdot 2 \cdot 3 \cdots r}.$$

Thus the binomial expansion can be restated where the coefficients are expressed using the special symbol, $\dbinom{n}{r}$.

$$(a+b)^n = a^n + \binom{n}{n-1}a^{n-1}b^1 + \binom{n}{n-2}a^{n-2}b^2 + \binom{n}{n-3}a^{n-3}b^3$$

$$+ \cdots + \binom{n}{n-r}a^{n-r}b^r + \cdots + b^n$$

The coefficients $\dbinom{n}{r}$, $1 \leq r \leq n$, are called the **binomial coefficients.**

EXAMPLE 4   Write out and simplify the expansion of

$$(x - 2)^5.$$

SOLUTION   With $a = x$, $b = -2$ and $n = 5$, the expansion is

$$(x - 2)^5 = x^5 + \binom{5}{4}x^4(-2)^1 + \binom{5}{3}x^3(-2)^2 + \binom{5}{2}x^2(-2)^3$$

$$+ \binom{5}{1}x(-2)^4 + (-2)^5$$

$$= x^5 + \frac{5!}{1!\,4!}x^4(-2) + \frac{5!}{2!\,3!}x^3(4) + \frac{5!}{3!\,2!}x^2(-8)$$

$$+ \frac{5!}{4!\,1!}x(16) + (-32)$$

$$= x^5 + 5x^4(-2) + 10x^3(4) + 10(x^2)(-8) + 5x(16) - 32$$

$$= x^5 - 10x^4 + 40x^3 - 80x^2 + 80x - 32.$$

PRACTICE PROBLEM 1   (Solution on page 438) Write the first three terms of the expansion of

$$(x^2 - 1)^{17}.$$

We note that in the binomial expansion of

$$(a + b)^n$$

the exponent of b is always one less than the number of the term containing that particular power of b. Thus in the rth term of the expansion the exponent of b is $r - 1$. Since the sum of the powers of a and b must be n, the exponent of a is $n - (r - 1) = n - r + 1$. Also, the coefficient of the rth term is the binomial coefficient, where the lower number agrees with the exponent of a. Thus we have the following formula.

> The rth term of $(a + b)^n$, $1 \leq r \leq n$, is
>
> $$\binom{n}{n - r + 1}a^{n-r+1}b^{r-1}.$$

EXAMPLE 5   Find the 10th term of $(3x - y)^{11}$.

SOLUTION   We have $a = 3x$, $b = -y$, $n = 11$, $r = 10$, and $n - r + 1 = 11 - 10 + 1 = 2$. Thus the 10th term is

$$\left(n - \frac{n}{r} + 1\right)a^{n-r+1}b^{r-1} = \binom{11}{2}(3x)^2(-y)^9$$

$$= \frac{11!}{9!\,2!}9x^2(-1)y^9$$

$$= \frac{11 \cdot 10 \cdot 9!}{9!\,2 \cdot 1}(-9)x^2y^9$$

$$= 11(5)(-9)x^2y^9$$

$$= -495x^2y^9.$$

***PRACTICE
PROBLEM 2***   (Solution on page 438) Find the 3rd term of $(a - 2b)^{20}$.

EXERCISES 14-4

Evaluate each of the following.

(See Example 2.)

1. $3!$ 2. $4!$

3. $(3 - 2)!$ 4. $(9 - 9)!$

5. $\dfrac{7!}{2!}$ 6. $\dfrac{9!}{6!}$

7. $\dfrac{10!}{9!}$ 8. $\dfrac{15!}{14!}$

9. $\dfrac{5!}{3!\,2!}$ 10. $\dfrac{6!}{4!\,2!}$

11. $\dfrac{7!}{6!\,1!}$ 12. $\dfrac{8!}{2!\,6!}$

13. $\dfrac{4!}{(4-1)!\,1!}$ 14. $\dfrac{7!}{(7-5)!\,5!}$

15. $\dfrac{8!}{(8-3)!\,3!}$ 16. $\dfrac{10!}{(10-2)!\,2!}$

(See Example 3.)

17. $\binom{5}{2}$ 18. $\binom{6}{3}$ 19. $\binom{8}{2}$ 20. $\binom{10}{6}$

21. $\binom{9}{1}$ 22. $\binom{11}{1}$ 23. $\binom{5}{5}$ 24. $\binom{4}{4}$

Expand and simplify. (See Examples 1 and 4.)

25. $(x + 1)^5$

26. $(y + 2)^4$

27. $(x - 2)^4$

28. $(y - 1)^5$

29. $(x + 2y)^3$

30. $(2x - y)^4$

31. $\left(2x - \dfrac{y}{2}\right)^7$

32. $\left(\dfrac{x}{2} - 2y\right)^5$

33. $(4r + 3s)^3$

34. $(5r + 2s)^4$

35. $(2 - 3z)^4$

36. $(3 + 5w)^3$

37. $\left(\dfrac{a}{3} - \dfrac{1}{2}\right)^4$

38. $\left(\dfrac{a}{5} - \dfrac{1}{2}\right)^5$

39. $\left(\dfrac{x}{4} + \dfrac{y}{3}\right)^5$

40. $\left(\dfrac{x}{6} + \dfrac{y}{3}\right)^3$

41. $(a^2 - b^2)^6$

42. $(a^3 - b^3)^4$

43. $(x^4 - y^3)^4$

44. $(x^5 - y^2)^6$

Write the first three terms of each of the following. (See Practice Problem 1.)

45. $(x - y)^9$

46. $(x + z)^9$

47. $(2x - y)^8$

48. $(x - 2y)^8$

49. $(x + 1)^{20}$

50. $(y + x)^{19}$

51. $(z - 2)^{23}$

52. $(t - 1)^{20}$

Find the indicated term in the given expansion. (See Example 5 and Practice Problem 2.)

53. 3rd term of $(x^2 - y)^{10}$

54. 4th term of $(x + 2)^9$

55. 8th term of $(x - y^2)^{10}$

56. 9th term of $(2 + x)^{10}$

57. 12th term of $(x - 1)^{15}$

58. 8th term of $(x - y)^{11}$

59. 13th term of $(x + y)^{13}$

60. 15th term of $(2x + y)^{15}$

61. 20th term of $(9x - y)^{19}$

62. 35th term of $(4x^8 + y)^{34}$

In problems 63 and 64, round the answers to the nearest hundredth.

C63. 4th term of $(x - 1.02)^{17}$ C64. 3rd term of $(x + 2.83)^{15}$

In problems 65–68, approximate the following by using the first four terms in a binomial expansion. Check the accuracy of your results by using a calculator.

C*65. $(1.01)^7 = (1 + 0.01)^7$

C*66. $(2.01)^5 = (2 + 0.01)^5$

C*67. $(0.99)^8 = (1 - 0.01)^8$

C*68. $(0.98)^6 = (1 - 0.02)^6$

*69. Show that $\binom{n}{r} = \binom{n}{n-r}$, $1 \le r \le n$.

*70. Show that $\binom{n}{n-r} = \dfrac{n(n-1)(n-2) \cdots (n-r+1)}{1 \cdot 2 \cdot 3 \cdots r}$, $1 \le r \le n$.

*71. Show that $\binom{n}{r-1} + \binom{n}{r} = \binom{n+1}{r}$, $1 \le r \le n$.

SOLUTIONS FOR PRACTICE PROBLEMS

1. $(x^2 - 1)^{17} = (x^2)^{17} + \binom{17}{16}(x^2)^{16}(-1)^1 + \binom{17}{15}(x^2)^{15}(-1)^2 + \cdots$

$\qquad = x^{34} + \dfrac{17!}{1!16!}x^{32}(-1) + \dfrac{17!}{2!15!}x^{30}(1) + \cdots$

$\qquad = x^{34} + \dfrac{17 \cdot 16!}{16!}(-1)x^{32} + \dfrac{17 \cdot 16 \cdot 15!}{2 \cdot 1 \cdot 15!}x^{30} + \cdots$

$\qquad = x^{34} - 17x^{32} + 136x^{30} + \cdots$

2. $n = 20$, $r = 3$, $n - r + 1 = 20 - 3 + 1 = 18$

The 3rd term of the expansion of $(a - 2b)^{20}$ is

$\binom{20}{18}a^{18}(-2b)^2 = \dfrac{20!}{2!18!}a^{18}4b^2 = \dfrac{20 \cdot 19 \cdot 18!}{2 \cdot 1 \cdot 18!}4a^{18}b^2 = 760a^{18}b^2.$

PRACTICE TEST for Chapter 14

1. Write the terms of the sequence defined by

$$a_n = (-1)^n(n-1), \qquad n = 1, 2, 3, 4.$$

2. Write the series in expanded form and evaluate the sum.

   (a) S_5 where $a_n = (-1)^n n^2$

   (b) $\sum_{n=1}^{6} \frac{2n}{n+1}$

3. Determine whether each of the following sequences is an arithmetic or geometric progression. State d or r, whichever is appropriate, and give an expression for the general term, a_n.

   (a) $-4, -1, 2, 5$

   (b) $-4, -1, -\frac{1}{4}, -\frac{1}{16}$

   (c) $3, -9, 27, -81$

   (d) $3, 9, 15, 21$

4. Find a_6 and S_6 for the arithmetic progression with $a_{12} = 28$ and $d = 3$.

5. Find a_2 and S_4 for the geometric progression with $a_4 = 20$ and $r = -2$.

6. Evaluate each sum by using the fact that each sequence is either an arithmetic or geometric progression.

   (a) $\sum_{i=1}^{12} (2i - 3)$

   (b) $\sum_{i=1}^{4} 3(-\frac{1}{2})^i$

7. Evaluate each sum, if it exists. If the sum does not exist, give a reason.

   (a) $\sum_{i=1}^{\infty} 3(-\frac{1}{2})^i$

   (b) $\sum_{i=1}^{\infty} \frac{1}{2}(3)^i$

8. Evaluate each of the following.

   (a) $0!$

   (b) $6!$

   (c) $\frac{9!}{5!4!}$

   (d) $\binom{7}{4}$

9. Write out and simplify the expansion of

$$(3x - y)^5.$$

10. Find the 11th term of

$$(3x - 1)^{13}.$$

A-1
*Solution
of Linear Systems
in Two Variables
by Determinants*

The solution to the system of linear equations in two variables x and y

$$a_1 x + b_1 y = c_1$$
$$a_2 x + b_2 y = c_2$$

can be determined using the elimination method described in Chapter 5. Suppose that the coefficients a_1, a_2, b_1, and b_2 are such that

$$a_1 b_2 - a_2 b_1 \neq 0.$$

To eliminate y, we multiply the first equation by b_2 and the second equation by $-b_1$, and then add the resulting equations.

$$a_1 x + b_1 y = c_1 \xrightarrow{\text{multiply by } b_2} a_1 b_2 x + b_1 b_2 y = c_1 b_2$$
$$a_2 x + b_2 y = c_2 \xrightarrow{\text{multiply by } -b_1} \underline{-a_2 b_1 x - b_1 b_2 y = -c_2 b_1}$$
$$\text{(adding)} \quad (a_1 b_2 - a_2 b_1)x = c_1 b_2 - c_2 b_1$$

441

Section A-1
Solution of Linear
Systems in Two
Variables by
Determinants

Since $a_1b_2 - a_2b_1 \neq 0$, we can divide by $a_1b_2 - a_2b_1$ to obtain

$$x = \frac{c_1b_2 - c_2b_1}{a_1b_2 - a_2b_1}.$$

Similarly, to eliminate x, we multiply the first equation by $-a_2$ and the second equation by a_1, and add the resulting equations.

$$a_1x + b_1y = c_1 \xrightarrow{\text{multiply by } -a_2} -a_1a_2x - a_2b_1y = -a_2c_1$$

$$a_2x + b_2y = c_2 \xrightarrow{\text{multiply by } a_1} \underline{a_1a_2x + a_1b_2y = a_1c_2}$$

$$\text{(adding)} \qquad (a_1b_2 - a_2b_1)y = a_1c_2 - a_2c_1$$

Again since $a_1b_2 - a_2b_1 \neq 0$, we can divide to obtain

$$y = \frac{a_1c_2 - a_2c_1}{a_1b_2 - a_2b_1}.$$

The two fractions

$$x = \frac{c_1b_2 - c_2b_1}{a_1b_2 - a_2b_1}, \qquad y = \frac{a_1c_2 - a_2c_1}{a_1b_2 - a_2b_1}$$

have the same denominator. The denominator

$$D = a_1b_2 - a_2b_1$$

which is formed using the coefficients a_1, a_2, b_1, and b_2 from the system of equations, is called the **determinant** of the coefficients. A special symbol, | |, is used to denote a determinant:

$$D = \begin{vmatrix} a_1 & b_1 \\ a_2 & b_2 \end{vmatrix} = a_1b_2 - a_2b_1.$$

This determinant is said to be of **order 2** or of **second order** since there are two rows and two columns of entries in the determinant. In general, a **determinant of order** n contains n rows and n columns of entries. Third-order determinants are studied in the next section.

EXAMPLE 1 Evaluate each of the following second-order determinants.

(a) $\begin{vmatrix} 1 & -2 \\ 3 & 2 \end{vmatrix}$ (b) $\begin{vmatrix} 0 & -3 \\ -4 & 2 \end{vmatrix}$ (c) $\begin{vmatrix} -1 & 3 \\ 2 & -6 \end{vmatrix}$

SOLUTION

(a) $\begin{vmatrix} 1 & -2 \\ 3 & 2 \end{vmatrix} = 1(2) - 3(-2) = 2 + 6 = 8$

(b) $\begin{vmatrix} 0 & -3 \\ -4 & 2 \end{vmatrix} = 0(2) - (-4)(-3) = 0 - 12 = -12$

(c) $\begin{vmatrix} -1 & 3 \\ 2 & -6 \end{vmatrix} = (-1)(-6) - (2)(3) = 6 - 6 = 0$

Now the solution to the system

$$a_1 x + b_1 y = c_1$$
$$a_2 x + b_2 y = c_2$$

can be expressed in terms of second-order determinants as long as $a_1 b_2 - a_2 b_1 \neq 0$.

$$x = \frac{c_1 b_2 - c_2 b_1}{a_1 b_2 - a_2 b_1} = \frac{\begin{vmatrix} c_1 & b_1 \\ c_2 & b_2 \end{vmatrix}}{\begin{vmatrix} a_1 & b_1 \\ a_2 & b_2 \end{vmatrix}}$$

determinant of the coefficients with the coefficients of x replaced by the constants

determinant of the coefficients

$$y = \frac{a_1 c_2 - a_2 c_1}{a_1 b_2 - a_2 b_1} = \frac{\begin{vmatrix} a_1 & c_1 \\ a_2 & c_2 \end{vmatrix}}{\begin{vmatrix} a_1 & b_1 \\ a_2 & b_2 \end{vmatrix}}$$

determinant of the coefficients with the coefficients of y replaced by the constants

determinant of the coefficients

The customary notation for each of these determinants is

$$D = \begin{vmatrix} a_1 & b_1 \\ a_2 & b_2 \end{vmatrix}, \qquad D_x = \begin{vmatrix} c_1 & b_1 \\ c_2 & b_2 \end{vmatrix}, \qquad D_y = \begin{vmatrix} a_1 & c_1 \\ a_2 & c_2 \end{vmatrix}.$$

The following, known as *Cramer's Rule*, describes the solution of the system in terms of these determinants. The second and third parts describe the situations when $D = 0$.

Cramer's Rule

for solving the system

$$a_1 x + b_1 y = c_1$$
$$a_2 x + b_2 y = c_2$$

1. If $D \neq 0$, the solution is

$$x = \frac{D_x}{D}, \qquad y = \frac{D_y}{D}.$$

2. If $D = 0$, and either $D_x \neq 0$ or $D_y \neq 0$, there is no solution, and the system is *inconsistent*.

3. If $D = 0$, and both $D_x = 0$ and $D_y = 0$, there are many solutions, and the system is *dependent*.

EXAMPLE 2   Use Cramer's Rule to solve

$$4x + 5y = -7$$
$$-x + 2y = -8.$$

SOLUTION   We first evaluate the three determinants.

$$D = \begin{vmatrix} 4 & 5 \\ -1 & 2 \end{vmatrix} = 4(2) - (-1)(5) = 8 + 5 = 13$$

$$D_x = \begin{vmatrix} -7 & 5 \\ -8 & 2 \end{vmatrix} = -7(2) - (-8)(5) = -14 + 40 = 26$$

$$D_y = \begin{vmatrix} 4 & -7 \\ -1 & -8 \end{vmatrix} = 4(-8) - (-1)(-7) = -32 - 7 = -39$$

Then we form the quotients.

$$x = \frac{D_x}{D} = \frac{26}{13} = 2, \qquad y = \frac{D_y}{D} = \frac{-39}{13} = -3$$

The solution set is $\{(2, -3)\}$.

EXAMPLE 3   Use Cramer's Rule to solve

$$2x - 7y = 3$$
$$4x - 14y = 3.$$

SOLUTION   Since

$$D = \begin{vmatrix} 2 & -7 \\ 4 & -14 \end{vmatrix} = 2(-14) - 4(-7) = -28 + 28 = 0$$

and

$$D_x = \begin{vmatrix} 3 & -7 \\ 3 & -14 \end{vmatrix} = 3(-14) - 3(-7) = -42 + 21 \neq 0,$$

the system is inconsistent. Hence the solution set is $\varnothing$.

EXAMPLE 4   Use Cramer's Rule to solve

$$4x + 10y = 8$$
$$6x + 15y = 12.$$

SOLUTION   Since

$$D = \begin{vmatrix} 4 & 10 \\ 6 & 15 \end{vmatrix} = 4(15) - 6(10) = 60 - 60 = 0$$

and both

$$D_x = \begin{vmatrix} 8 & 10 \\ 12 & 15 \end{vmatrix} = 8(15) - 12(10) = 120 - 120 = 0,$$

$$D_y = \begin{vmatrix} 4 & 8 \\ 6 & 12 \end{vmatrix} = 4(12) - 6(8) = 48 - 48 = 0,$$

the system is dependent. The solution set is

$$\{(x, y) \mid 2x + 5y = 4\}.$$

EXERCISES A-1

Evaluate each of the following determinants. (See Example 1.)

1. $\begin{vmatrix} 2 & 3 \\ 1 & 1 \end{vmatrix}$

2. $\begin{vmatrix} 4 & 7 \\ 2 & 8 \end{vmatrix}$

3. $\begin{vmatrix} -1 & -5 \\ -1 & 2 \end{vmatrix}$

4. $\begin{vmatrix} -3 & -1 \\ 4 & 3 \end{vmatrix}$

5. $\begin{vmatrix} 0 & 0 \\ 4 & 9 \end{vmatrix}$

6. $\begin{vmatrix} -2 & 0 \\ 7 & 0 \end{vmatrix}$

7. $\begin{vmatrix} -1 & 5 \\ 2 & 7 \end{vmatrix}$

8. $\begin{vmatrix} 3 & -9 \\ 2 & 8 \end{vmatrix}$

9. $\begin{vmatrix} -6 & -3 \\ -8 & -4 \end{vmatrix}$

10. $\begin{vmatrix} -5 & 2 \\ 10 & -4 \end{vmatrix}$

11. $\begin{vmatrix} 8 & 9 \\ -4 & 1 \end{vmatrix}$

12. $\begin{vmatrix} -1 & -2 \\ -3 & -4 \end{vmatrix}$

Use Cramer's Rule to find the solution if the determinant of the coefficients is not zero. Otherwise, state if the system is inconsistent or dependent. (See Examples 2–4.)

13. $2x - 5y = 22$
    $7x + y = 3$

14. $-3x + 4y = 6$
    $x - 5y = -2$

15. $3x + 2y = 14$
    $-4x + y = 7$

16. $4x + y = -1$
    $-3x - 2y = 2$

17. $a + 2b = -1$
    $2a + b = -8$

18. $4a - 5b = 1$
    $9a - 12b = 0$

19. $11c - 13d = 0$
    $3c - 2d = 0$

20. $5r - 17s = 0$
    $17r - 5s = 0$

21. $11x + 2y = 12$
    $-3x + y = -11$

22. $3x + 3y = 0$
    $2x - 2y = 4$

23. $2x - 7y = 6$
    $-4x + 3y = -12$

24. $5x - 5y = 0$
    $x + y = 4$

25. $2x - 3y = 3$
    $4x + 7y = 2$

26. $9x - 2y = 1$
    $4x - 3y = 2$

27. $-5x + 7y = 2$
    $-3x - 4y = 8$

28. $x - 2y = 17$
    $4x + 7y = -3$

445

Section A-2
Solution of Linear
Systems in Three
Variables by
Determinants

29. $-2x + 3y = 11$
    $5x - 6y = 9$

30. $x + 2y = 41$
    $-3x - 7y = -102$

31. $6u - 7v = 11$
    $4u + 2v = -7$

32. $9w - 4z = -5$
    $-10w + 7z = -4$

33. $3x - y = 5$
    $-6x + 2y = -5$

34. $4x - 4y = 3$
    $3x - 3y = 4$

35. $x - y = 2$
    $-x + y = 0$

36. $4x + 6y = 8$
    $6x + 9y = 14$

37. $3x + 12y = -5$
    $4x + 16y = -10$

38. $6x + 3y = 5$
    $8x + 4y = 1$

39. $e + f = -3$
    $2e + 2f = -6$

40. $5r + 5s = -25$
    $-3r - 3s = 15$

41. $2x - y = 4$
    $-4x + 2y = -8$

42. $9x - 6y = 18$
    $6x - 4y = 12$

A-2 Solution of Linear Systems in Three Variables by Determinants

Cramer's Rule extends to systems of three linear equations in three unknowns:

$$a_1 x + b_1 y + c_1 z = d_1$$
$$a_2 x + b_2 y + c_2 z = d_2$$
$$a_3 x + b_3 y + c_3 z = d_3.$$

First we must learn to evaluate determinants of order 3. The method used here is called *expansion about the first column*, and is easily described in terms of determinants of order 2.*

Expansion of a Third-Order Determinant about the First Column

$$\begin{vmatrix} a_1 & b_1 & c_1 \\ a_2 & b_2 & c_2 \\ a_3 & b_3 & c_3 \end{vmatrix} = a_1 \begin{vmatrix} b_2 & c_2 \\ b_3 & c_3 \end{vmatrix} - a_2 \begin{vmatrix} b_1 & c_1 \\ b_3 & c_3 \end{vmatrix} + a_3 \begin{vmatrix} b_1 & c_1 \\ b_2 & c_2 \end{vmatrix}$$

The following observations make this awkward expansion easy to remember.

1. Each term in the sum is the product of an element from the first column and a certain second-order determinant, called the **minor** of that element.

*Determinants of any order can be expanded about any row or column. For details of these expansions, see any linear algebra text or see *College Algebra* by Gilbert, Spencer, and Gilbert, Prentice-Hall, 1981.

2. The minor of each of the first, second, and third elements in column 1 is the determinant of the remaining elements after column 1 and rows 1, 2, and 3, respectively, have been deleted.

3. Finally, the sum is formed by alternating the signs of each term beginning with a positive sign.

EXAMPLE 1 Evaluate by expanding about column 1.

$$\begin{vmatrix} -1 & 3 & 7 \\ 3 & 1 & 0 \\ -2 & 0 & -5 \end{vmatrix}$$

SOLUTION We first find the minor of each element in column 1.

Element			*Minor*
-1	Delete row 1 and column 1 in	$\begin{vmatrix} -1 & 3 & 7 \\ 3 & 1 & 0 \\ -2 & 0 & -5 \end{vmatrix}$ to obtain	$\begin{vmatrix} 1 & 0 \\ 0 & -5 \end{vmatrix}.$
3	Delete row 2 and column 1 in	$\begin{vmatrix} -1 & 3 & 7 \\ 3 & 1 & 0 \\ -2 & 0 & -5 \end{vmatrix}$ to obtain	$\begin{vmatrix} 3 & 7 \\ 0 & -5 \end{vmatrix}.$
-2	Delete row 3 and column 1 in	$\begin{vmatrix} -1 & 3 & 7 \\ 3 & 1 & 0 \\ -2 & 0 & -5 \end{vmatrix}$ to obtain	$\begin{vmatrix} 3 & 7 \\ 1 & 0 \end{vmatrix}.$

Then we form the sum of products of each element times its minor, remembering to alternate signs.

$$\begin{vmatrix} -1 & 3 & 7 \\ 3 & 1 & 0 \\ -2 & 0 & -5 \end{vmatrix} = +(-1)\begin{vmatrix} 1 & 0 \\ 0 & -5 \end{vmatrix} - (3)\begin{vmatrix} 3 & 7 \\ 0 & -5 \end{vmatrix} + (-2)\begin{vmatrix} 3 & 7 \\ 1 & 0 \end{vmatrix}$$

alternating signs

$$= (-1)(-5 - 0) - 3(-15 - 0) - 2(0 - 7)$$
$$= (-1)(-5) - 3(-15) - 2(-7)$$
$$= 5 + 45 + 14$$
$$= 64$$

We now can use determinants to solve systems of three linear equations in three unknowns, x, y, and z.

447

Section A-2
Solution of Linear
Systems in Three
Variables by
Determinants

$$a_1 x + b_1 y + c_1 z = d_1$$
$$a_2 x + b_2 y + c_2 z = d_2$$
$$a_3 x + b_3 y + c_3 z = d_3$$

Let D be the determinant of the coefficients.

$$D = \begin{vmatrix} a_1 & b_1 & c_1 \\ a_2 & b_2 & c_2 \\ a_3 & b_3 & c_3 \end{vmatrix}$$

Then D_x is the determinant formed by replacing the first column of D by the column of constants; D_y is the determinant formed by replacing the second column of D by the column of constants; and D_z is the determinant formed by replacing the last column of D by the column of constants.

$$D_x = \begin{vmatrix} d_1 & b_1 & c_1 \\ d_2 & b_2 & c_2 \\ d_3 & b_3 & c_3 \end{vmatrix}, \qquad D_y = \begin{vmatrix} a_1 & d_1 & c_1 \\ a_2 & d_2 & c_2 \\ a_3 & d_3 & c_3 \end{vmatrix}, \qquad D_z = \begin{vmatrix} a_1 & b_1 & d_1 \\ a_2 & b_2 & d_2 \\ a_3 & b_3 & d_3 \end{vmatrix}$$

Cramer's Rule is stated in terms of these determinants.

Cramer's Rule

for solving the system

$$a_1 x + b_1 y + c_1 z = d_1$$
$$a_2 x + b_2 y + c_2 z = d_2$$
$$a_3 x + b_3 y + c_3 z = d_3$$

1. If $D \neq 0$, the solution is given by

$$x = \frac{D_x}{D}, \qquad y = \frac{D_y}{D}, \qquad z = \frac{D_z}{D}.$$

2. If $D \neq 0$ and at least one of $D_x \neq 0$, $D_y \neq 0$, or $D_z \neq 0$, there is no solution and the system is *inconsistent*.

3. If $D = 0$ and all of $D_x = 0$, $D_y = 0$, and $D_z = 0$, then there are many solutions and the system is *dependent*.

EXAMPLE 2   Use Cramer's Rule to solve the system.

$$x + y - z = -1$$
$$2x \quad + 3z = \quad 2$$
$$3y - 2z = -6$$

SOLUTION The determinant of the coefficients is

$$D = \begin{vmatrix} 1 & 1 & -1 \\ 2 & 0 & 3 \\ 0 & 3 & -2 \end{vmatrix} = 1 \begin{vmatrix} 0 & 3 \\ 3 & -2 \end{vmatrix} - 2 \begin{vmatrix} 1 & -1 \\ 3 & -2 \end{vmatrix} + 0 \begin{vmatrix} 1 & -1 \\ 0 & 3 \end{vmatrix}$$

$$= 1(0 - 9) - 2(-2 + 3) + 0(3 - 0)$$

$$= 1(-9) - 2(1) + 0(3)$$

$$= -11.$$

The determinant D_x is formed by replacing the first column of D by the column of constants.

$$D_x = \begin{vmatrix} -1 & 1 & -1 \\ 2 & 0 & 3 \\ -6 & 3 & -2 \end{vmatrix} = -11$$

The determinant D_y is formed by replacing the second column of D by the column of constants.

$$D_y = \begin{vmatrix} 1 & -1 & -1 \\ 2 & 2 & 3 \\ 0 & -6 & -2 \end{vmatrix} = 22$$

The determinant D_z is formed by replacing the third column of D by the column of constants.

$$D_z = \begin{vmatrix} 1 & 1 & -1 \\ 2 & 0 & 2 \\ 0 & 3 & -6 \end{vmatrix} = 0$$

Thus the solution is given by

$$x = \frac{D_x}{D} = \frac{-11}{-11} = 1, \qquad y = \frac{D_y}{D} = \frac{22}{-11} = -2, \qquad z = \frac{D_z}{D} = \frac{0}{11} = 0,$$

and the solution set is $\{(1, -2, 0)\}$.

EXERCISES A-2

Evaluate each of the following determinants by expanding about column 1. (See Example 1.)

1. $\begin{vmatrix} 1 & -2 & 5 \\ 0 & 1 & 7 \\ 1 & 0 & 1 \end{vmatrix}$
2. $\begin{vmatrix} -2 & 0 & 1 \\ 1 & 5 & -1 \\ 1 & 2 & -3 \end{vmatrix}$
3. $\begin{vmatrix} 0 & -2 & -1 \\ -2 & 0 & 3 \\ -1 & 3 & 0 \end{vmatrix}$

4. $\begin{vmatrix} 4 & 2 & 0 \\ -3 & 0 & 1 \\ 0 & 1 & -2 \end{vmatrix}$
5. $\begin{vmatrix} 8 & -3 & 1 \\ 5 & 1 & 1 \\ 1 & 1 & 1 \end{vmatrix}$
6. $\begin{vmatrix} 2 & 7 & 3 \\ -1 & 5 & -2 \\ 1 & 4 & -2 \end{vmatrix}$

449

Section A-2
Solution of Linear
Systems in Three
Variables by
Determinants

7. $\begin{vmatrix} 0 & 1 & 2 \\ 0 & 7 & 9 \\ 0 & 11 & 15 \end{vmatrix}$ 8. $\begin{vmatrix} 1 & -1 & 1 \\ 0 & 0 & 0 \\ 3 & 7 & -11 \end{vmatrix}$ 9. $\begin{vmatrix} 2 & -3 & 4 \\ 1 & -1 & -2 \\ 5 & 3 & -1 \end{vmatrix}$

10. $\begin{vmatrix} 2 & 1 & 5 \\ -3 & -1 & 3 \\ 4 & -2 & -1 \end{vmatrix}$ 11. $\begin{vmatrix} 2 & -3 & 4 \\ 5 & 3 & 1 \\ 1 & -1 & -2 \end{vmatrix}$ 12. $\begin{vmatrix} -3 & 2 & 4 \\ -1 & 1 & -2 \\ 3 & 5 & -1 \end{vmatrix}$

Use Cramer's Rule to find the solution if the determinant of the coefficients is not zero. Otherwise, state if the system is inconsistent or dependent. (See Example 2.)

13. $\begin{aligned} x - y - z &= 0 \\ x + 2y - 4z &= 0 \\ x + y + z &= 4 \end{aligned}$

14. $\begin{aligned} 3x - y + z &= 1 \\ 4x - 2y + z &= 0 \\ -5x + 2y - z &= 0 \end{aligned}$

15. $\begin{aligned} x + y &= 0 \\ y + z &= 0 \\ -x + y - z &= 6 \end{aligned}$

16. $\begin{aligned} x + y + z &= 0 \\ 2x - y &= 0 \\ x - z &= 4 \end{aligned}$

17. $\begin{aligned} -a + 3b + c &= 3 \\ a - 2b - 3c &= -2 \\ 2a - 4b - c &= 1 \end{aligned}$

18. $\begin{aligned} 3a + 7b - c &= 0 \\ 2a - b - c &= 11 \\ a + b + c &= 1 \end{aligned}$

19. $\begin{aligned} 2x + 3y - z &= -1 \\ -x - y + 2z &= 2 \\ 9x + y - z &= -1 \end{aligned}$

20. $\begin{aligned} 2x - 3z &= 0 \\ x - y + z &= 3 \\ y + 2z &= -3 \end{aligned}$

21. $\begin{aligned} x + y + z &= -2 \\ 2x + 3y + 4z &= -8 \\ 5x + 2z &= 3 \end{aligned}$

22. $\begin{aligned} 3x + y &= 3 \\ x + y - z &= -1 \\ 2x + 3y - 2z &= 1 \end{aligned}$

23. $\begin{aligned} r + s + t &= 0 \\ 2r + s &= -8 \\ -3r - t &= 4 \end{aligned}$

24. $\begin{aligned} 2r - s + t &= -1 \\ 3r + s - t &= -9 \\ -r + 2s - 3t &= -11 \end{aligned}$

25. $\begin{aligned} 3x + 2y - z &= 4 \\ x - y + z &= 9 \\ 7x + 3y - z &= 5 \end{aligned}$

26. $\begin{aligned} x - y + 4z &= -2 \\ 3x - 2y + z &= 5 \\ -x + 7z &= 6 \end{aligned}$

27. $\begin{aligned} 2x - 4y - z &= -3 \\ 3x + 5y - 4z &= -3 \\ 5x + y - 5z &= -3 \end{aligned}$

28. $\begin{aligned} 4x + 2y - z &= 0 \\ 2x + 3z &= 1 \\ -2y + 7z &= -1 \end{aligned}$

29. $\begin{aligned} -x + y - z &= 2 \\ 5x - 2y &= 3 \\ 2x + y - 3z &= 9 \end{aligned}$

30. $\begin{aligned} y - 2z &= 0 \\ 3x + 2z &= 5 \\ 3x + 2y - 2z &= 5 \end{aligned}$

31. $\begin{aligned} 2u + 3v &= -5 \\ u + 3v + w &= 6 \\ u - w &= -11 \end{aligned}$

32. $\begin{aligned} -u - v + w &= 2 \\ 3u - v &= 0 \\ 3u - 5v + 3w &= 6 \end{aligned}$

Answers
to Practice Tests

CHAPTER 1 **1.** (a) $\{2, 3\}$ (b) $\{2, 3, 4, 6, 8\}$ (c) $\{1, 2, 3, 4, 6\}$ (d) $\{2, 4, 6\}$
(e) $\{1, 2, 3, 4, 6\}$ **2.** $\{1, 2, 3\}, \{1, 2\}, \{1, 3\}, \{2, 3\}, \{1\}, \{2\}, \{3\}, \varnothing$
3. (a) $1 < x < 4$ or $4 > x > 1$ (b) Not possible

4. 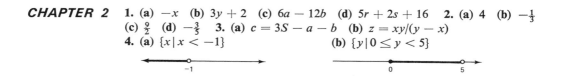   **5.** (a) 3 (b) -5 (c) 0 (d) -6

(e) $2 - \sqrt{2}$ **6.**   **7.** (a) -7 (b) -2

(c) -11 (d) -4 (e) -22 **8.** (a) -3 (b) -15 (c) -3 (d) -3 (e) 5
9. (a) -60 (b) 14 (c) 0 (d) Undefined (e) $\frac{4}{5}$
10. (a) 5 (b) 2 (c) 5 (d) 12 (e) Undefined

CHAPTER 2 **1.** (a) $-x$ (b) $3y + 2$ (c) $6a - 12b$ (d) $5r + 2s + 16$ **2.** (a) 4 (b) $-\frac{1}{3}$
(c) $\frac{9}{2}$ (d) $-\frac{3}{5}$ **3.** (a) $c = 3S - a - b$ (b) $z = xy/(y - x)$
4. (a) $\{x \mid x < -1\}$ (b) $\{y \mid 0 \le y < 5\}$

5. (a) $\{x \mid x \le -1 \text{ or } x > 3\}$ **(b)** $\{z \mid z \le -3\}$

   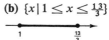

6. (a) $\{-3, 7\}$ **(b)** $\{2, \frac{10}{3}\}$ **7. (a)** $\varnothing$ **(b)** $\{10\}$
8. (a) $\{-7, -3\}$ **(b)** $\{2, -2\}$
9. (a) $\{x \mid -2 < x < 8\}$ **(b)** $\{x \mid 1 \le x \le \frac{13}{3}\}$

10. (a) $\{x \mid x \le -3 \text{ or } x \ge 2\}$ **(b)** $\{x \mid x < -\frac{1}{2} \text{ or } x > 1\}$

CHAPTER 3 **1.** $93, 94, 95$ **2.** Margie's age, 32 years; Barry's age, 11 years.
3. 9 compacts, 4 midsize, 15 pickups   **4.** 14 dimes, 15 nickels, 23 quarters
5. 560 grams   **6.** 9:24 A.M.   **7.** $25\frac{5}{7}$ minutes   **8.** \$161.10   **9.** \$6015
10. \$15,000

CHAPTER 4 **1. (a)**   **(b)**

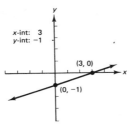   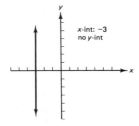

2.   **3.** $m = 2$

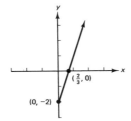   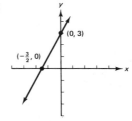

4.   **5.** Neither parallel nor perpendicular

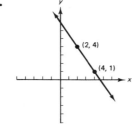

6. Slope $\frac{3}{2}$, y-intercept -6 **7.** $y = \frac{5}{6}x - \frac{4}{3}$ **8.** $x + 2y = 1$

9.

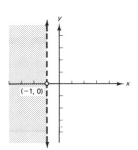

10.

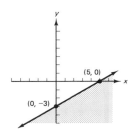

CHAPTER 5   **1.** $\{(-1, -1)\}$ **2.** $\{(2, 1)\}$ **3.** Dependent; $\{(x, y) \mid x - 2y = -3\}$
4. Inconsistent; $\varnothing$ **5.** $\{(2, -1, -3)\}$ **6.** Inconsistent; $\varnothing$

7.

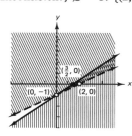

8.

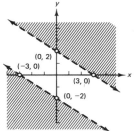

9.

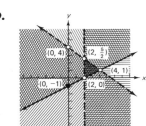

10.

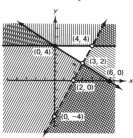

CHAPTER 6   **1.** (a) $36x^3y^4$ (b) $-125x^6y^9$ **2.** (a) $\dfrac{ab^2}{3}$ (b) $4r^7s$ **3.** (a) 5   (b) 12
4. (a) $6x^3 - 2x^2 + 4x - 2$ (b) $-x^4 + x^3 - 6x^2 + 6x - 11$
5. (a) $6x^2 + 5xy - 4y^2$ (b) $x^3 + x^2 - 11x - 15$ **6.** (a) $x^2 - 36$
(b) $4x^2 - 28x + 49$ **7.** (a) $x^3 - 8$ (b) $-x^2 + 7x - 12$ **8.** $-3y^3 + xy^2$
9. $x^2 - 3x - 5 + 5/(2x + 5)$ **10.** $2x^3 - x + \dfrac{2x - 4}{x^2 - 3x + 2}$

CHAPTER 7   **1.** (a) $5xy^2$ (b) $(a + b)^2$ **2.** (a) $5ab(4a - b)$ (b) $2(r + s)^3(9 - 2r - 2s)$
3. (a) $(x - 3)(x + 3)$ (b) $(9a - 8b)(9a + 8b)$ **4.** (a) $(a - 1)^2$
(b) $(x + 7y)^2$ **5.** (a) $(x - 4)(x^2 + 4x + 16)$ (b) $3(a - 1)(a^2 + a + 1)$
6. (a) $(1 + x)(1 - x + x^2)$ (b) $x(x + y)(x^2 - xy + y^2)$
7. (a) $(x + 7y)(x - 5y)$ (b) $(3z - 4)(2z - 1)$
8. (a) $(r - s - 3)(r - s - 2)$ (b) $(x^2 + 3)(x - 1)(x + 1)$
9. $2(x - 1)^2(x + 1)$ **10.** $\{-1, \frac{7}{2}\}$

CHAPTER 8   **1. (a)** $(x + 2)/(x + 5)$ **(b)** $(x + 3)/(7x - 3)$ **2. (a)** $(18y^3z)/(12y^2z^2)$
(b) $(t^2 + 4t + 4)/(t^2 - 3t - 10)$ **3. (a)** $(x^3y^2)/(6z)$ **(b)** $6/(5a)$
4. (a) $m(3m - 1)/(m - 2)$ **(b)** $2/(t + 2)$ **5. (a)** $2(p - 3)(p + 3)$
(b) $3(q - 1)(q - 3)^2$ **6. (a)** $-1/(2z + 1)$ **(b)** $-5/[(r - 1)(r - 6)]$
7. $\{\frac{5}{4}\}$ **8.** $\varnothing$ **9.** $t/(t - 2)$ **10.** $(p - 3)/p$

CHAPTER 9   **1. (a)** xy^4/w^4 **(b)** $x/(y^4z^2)$ **2. (a)** $2.5 \times 10^{-6}, 0.0000025$
(b) $8 \times 10^{-4}, 0.0008$ **3. (a)** $-5pq^3$ **(b)** x^3y^2/z **4. (a)** -16 **(b)** $\frac{1}{4}$
5. (a) $4p^{1/3}q^{1/3}$ **(b)** $(y^3 - x^3)/(x^3y^3)$ **6. (a)** $2x^2\sqrt{15}$ **(b)** $4ab^2\sqrt{3}$
7. (a) $9\sqrt{3}$ **(b)** $7x\sqrt{2xy}$ **8. (a)** $2\sqrt{3xy}/(3y)$ **(b)** $\sqrt[3]{18a^2x^2}/(3xy)$
(c) $5(\sqrt{5} - 1)/2$ **(d)** $(\sqrt{35} - 5)/2$ **9. (a)** $-4 + 4i$ **(b)** $-2 + 5i$
10. (a) 25 **(b)** $-\frac{21}{29} + \frac{20}{29}i$

CHAPTER 10   **1. (a)** $\{2, \frac{5}{2}\}$ **(b)** $\{-12, 2\}$ **2. (a)** $\{-8, 2\}$ **(b)** $\{-2 \pm 2\sqrt{6}\}$
3. (a) $\{0, \frac{9}{4}\}$ **(b)** $\{-1, \frac{5}{3}\}$ **4. (a)** Two unequal real solutions
(b) One real solution   **(c)** Two imaginary solutions
(d) Two unequal real solutions   **5.** $\frac{7}{2}$ seconds   **6. (a)** $\{-1, \frac{5}{2}\}$ **(b)** $\{\pm2, \pm3\}$
7. $\{5\}$ **8.** $\varnothing$
9. $\{x \mid x < -1 \text{ or } x > 3\}$ **10.** $\{x \mid x \leq -2 \text{ or } x > -1\}$

CHAPTER 11   **1. (a)**

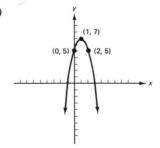

(b)

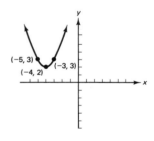

2. (a)

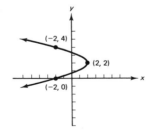

(b)

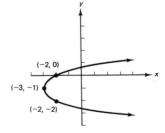

3. (a) $\sqrt{82}$ **(b)** $(x + 5)^2 + y^2 = 16$

4. (a) Center: $(\frac{1}{2}, -2)$
(b) $r = 2$

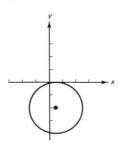

5. (a)

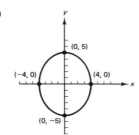

(b)

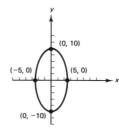

6. (a)

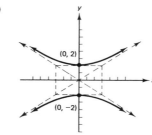

(b)

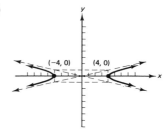

7. (a) Ellipse **(b)** Hyperbola **(c)** Straight Line **(d)** Parabola **(e)** Circle
8. $\{(\frac{1}{2}, -\frac{3}{4}), (-3, 1)\}$ **9.** $\{(1, 4), (1, -4), (-1, 4), (-1, -4)\}$

10.

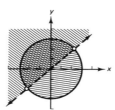

CHAPTER 12 **1.** $D = \{-3, 0, 2, 3\}$, $R = \{0, 1, 4\}$, a function
2. $D = \{x \mid x \geq 2\}$, $R = \{y \mid y \geq 0\}$
3. $D = \{x \mid -\frac{5}{2} \leq x \leq \frac{5}{2}\}$, $R = \{y \mid -\frac{5}{2} \leq y \leq \frac{5}{2}\}$, not a function

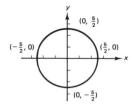

4. (a) 55 **(b)** 62 **(c)** $2a^2 + 2b^2 + a + b$ **(d)** $2a^2 + 4ab + 2b^2 + a + b$
(e) $6x^2 + 1$ **5.** $2x + h - 3$
6. $r^{-1} = \{(1, -3), (4, 0), (1, 2), (0, 3)\}$, r^{-1} is not a function
7. $x = y^2 + 1$, g is a function, g^{-1} is not

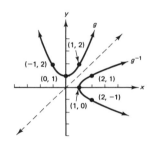

8. $f(x) = \frac{3}{4}x - 6$, $f^{-1}(x) = \frac{4}{3}x + 8$, $f^{-1}(f(x)) = \frac{4}{3}f(x) + 8 =$
$\frac{4}{3}(\frac{3}{4}x - 6) + 8 = x - 8 + 8 = x$, $f(f^{-1}(x)) = \frac{3}{4}f^{-1}(x) - 6 =$
$\frac{3}{4}(\frac{4}{3}x + 8) - 6 = x + 6 - 6 = x$
9. 8 **10.** $\frac{9}{2}$ pounds per square foot

CHAPTER 13 **1.**

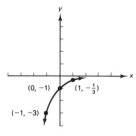

2. $\{-\frac{3}{4}\}$ **3. (a)** $\{\frac{1}{9}\}$ **(b)** $\{64\}$

4.

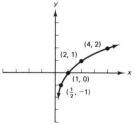

5. (a) $3 \log_a x - 4 \log_a y - \frac{1}{2} \log_a z$
(b) $\log_a(4x^4y^4/9z^3)$

6. $\{2\}$ **7. (a)** 1.5963 **(b)** 0.2964 **8.** 0.586 **9.** $\{3.095\}$ **10.** 3.841

CHAPTER 14 **1.** $0, 1, -2, 3$ **2. (a)** $S_5 = -1 + 4 - 9 + 16 - 25 = -15$
(b) $1 + \frac{4}{3} + \frac{3}{2} + \frac{8}{5} + \frac{5}{3} + \frac{12}{7} = \frac{617}{70}$ **3. (a)** Arithmetic, $d = 3$, $a_n = 3n - 7$
(b) Geometric, $r = \frac{1}{4}$, $a_n = -1(4)^{2-n}$ **(c)** Geometric, $r = -3$, $a_n = 3(-3)^{n-1}$
(d) Arithmetic, $d = 6$, $a_n = 6n - 3$ **4.** $a_6 = 10$, $S_6 = 15$
5. $a_2 = 5$, $S_4 = \frac{25}{2}$ **6. (a)** 120 **(b)** $-\frac{15}{16}$ **7. (a)** -1
(b) Does not exist since $|r| = 3 > 1$ **8. (a)** 1 **(b)** 720 **(c)** 126 **(d)** 35
9. $243x^5 - 405x^4y + 270x^3y^2 - 90x^2y^3 + 15xy^4 - y^5$ **10.** $7722x^3$

Answers to Odd-Numbered Exercises

EXERCISES 1-1,
page 5

1. True **3.** False **5.** False **7.** True **9.** True **11.** $W, I, Q, \mathfrak{R}$
13. $I, Q, \mathfrak{R}$ **15.** $Q, \mathfrak{R}$ **17.** $Q, \mathfrak{R}$ **19.** $\mathfrak{R}, I_r$ **21.** $\{1, 2, 3, 4, 5, 6, 7, 8\}$
23. $\{4, 6, 8\}$ **25.** C **27.** $\{1, 2, 3, 4, 6, 8\}$ **29.** $\{1, 2, 3, 4, 6, 8\}$
31. $\{1, 2, 3, 4, 6, 8\}$ **33.** $\{2, 4\}$ **35.** I **37.** I **39.** O **41.** $\varnothing, \{0\}, \{1\}, \{0, 1\}$
43. P, r, s

EXERCISES 1-2,
page 12

1. 3 **3.** 0 **5.** 4 **7.** y **9.** Transitive Property **11.** Trichotomy Property
13. $<$ **15.** $>$ **17.** $<$ **19.** $>$ **21.** $4 < 6$ **23.** $-3 > -5$
25. $0 \geq -1$ **27.** $1 < 3 < 4$, or $4 > 3 > 1$

29. $1 < x < 3$, or $3 > x > 1$ **31.**

33. **35.** $5 > x > 2$, or $2 < x < 5$

37. $-2 < x < 0$, or $0 > x > -2$ **39.** $2 > x > -1$, or $-1 < x < 2$
41. $0 > x > -3$, or $-3 < x < 0$ **43.** Not possible **45.** Not possible

47. **49.** **51.**

457

53. [number line: shaded from left through −3 (closed dot) to 0 (closed dot)]

55. [number line: open dot at −1, shaded to 4 (closed dot) and beyond]

57. [number line: closed dot at −3, shaded to 0 (open dot)]

59. [number line: closed dot at −3, shaded to 1 (closed dot)]

61. [number line: shaded to −2, open dot at −1, closed dot at 0]

63. [number line: fully shaded through 0]

65. [number line: open dots at 0 and 2, ϕ]

67. [number line: closed dots at −2, 0, 2 and points between]

EXERCISES 1-3,
page 18

1. $b + a$ **3.** $a + (b + c)$ **5.** 1 **7.** $-a$ **9.** xb
11. Multiplication Property of Equality **13.** Multiplicative Identity
15. Closure Property, Multiplication **17.** Multiplicative Inverse
19. Distributive Property **21.** Double Negative Property **23.** $-\frac{4}{3}$
25. -5 **27.** 1 **29.** $|x|$ **31.** xz **33.** 7 **35.** 4 **37.** $\sqrt{3}$ **39.** $\sqrt{5}$
41. 0 **43.** -3 **45.** -9 **47.** $29.13 - \sqrt{817}$ **49.** $\sqrt{72.8} - 8.52$
51. $x - 2$ **53.** $2 - x$ **55.** (b) **57.** (a) **59.** (c)

61. [number line: open dots at −4 and 4, shaded between]

63. [number line: closed dots at −1 and 1, shaded between]

65. [number line: open dots at −3 and 3, shaded between]

67. [number line: closed dots at −2 and 2, shaded between]

EXERCISES 1-4,
page 24

1. -2 **3.** -17 **5.** -8 **7.** -4 **9.** -24 **11.** -14 **13.** -5
15. -12 **17.** 6 **19.** 12 **21.** -6 **23.** 113.88 **25.** 0 **27.** 0 **29.** 10
31. 20 **33.** -37 **35.** -27 **37.** 27 **39.** 15 **41.** -12 **43.** 5
45. -7 **47.** -7 **49.** 5 **51.** 5 **53.** 9 **55.** -8.743 **57.** 3.647
59. 18.219

EXERCISES 1-5,
page 33

1. -42 **3.** -52 **5.** 40 **7.** 0 **9.** 721.44 **11.** -8 **13.** -4 **15.** 13
17. 0 **19.** Undefined **21.** $-\frac{2}{7}$, or $\frac{-2}{7}$ **23.** $\frac{9}{5}$ **25.** $\frac{5}{6}$ **27.** $\frac{4}{9}$
29. $-\frac{5}{2}$, or $\frac{-5}{2}$ **31.** $\frac{5}{17}$ **33.** $\frac{2}{3}$ **35.** $-\frac{1}{12}$ **37.** $-\frac{61}{18}$ **39.** $-\frac{1}{4}$ **41.** $\frac{3}{5}$
43. $\frac{9}{10}$ **45.** $-\frac{14}{9}$ **47.** 17 **49.** 7 **51.** 7 **53.** 3 **55.** 51
57. Not possible **59.** 6 **61.** 18 **63.** 7 **65.** Not possible **67.** -5
69. $\frac{1}{5}$ **71.** 2 **73.** $\frac{4}{11}$ **75.** 19.14 **77.** 74.73

EXERCISES 2-1,
page 42

1. $3x$ **3.** $3x - 2y$ **5.** $-2x + 1$ **7.** $12y$ **9.** $12a + 2$ **11.** $6y - 2x$
13. $12x - 8$ **15.** $52 - 11y$ **17.** $-2 - 6x$ **19.** $a + 4b - 1$ **21.** $12z - 7$
23. $5 - 5a$ **25.** Yes **27.** No **29.** No **31.** Yes **33.** Both are solutions
35. 1 is, -1 is not **37.** $\{4\}$ **39.** $\{\frac{5}{2}\}$ **41.** $\{3\}$ **43.** $\{-4\}$ **45.** $\{10\}$
47. $\{-1\}$ **49.** $\{0\}$ **51.** $\{\frac{1}{2}\}$ **53.** $\{1\}$ **55.** $\{2\frac{5}{9}\}$ **57.** $\{11\}$ **59.** $\{2\}$
61. $\{2\}$ **63.** $\{1\}$ **65.** $\{\frac{1}{2}\}$ **67.** $\{\frac{1}{9}\}$ **69.** $\{-\frac{3}{2}\}$ **71.** $\Re$ **73.** $\Re$ **75.** $\varnothing$
77. $\varnothing$ **79.** $\{2.6\}$ **81.** $\{20.9\}$

1. $q = 7$ inches   **3.** $q = 16$ miles   **5.** F $= 32°$ **7.** C $= 2\frac{2}{9}°$
9. $b = 7$ inches   **11.** $h = 42$ centimeters   **13.** $C = \$27.00$ **15.** $r = 32\%$
17. $A = \$1000$ **19.** $r = 17\%$ **21.** $t = D/r$ **23.** $r = I/(pt)$
25. $y = (c - ax)/b$ **27.** $h = S/(2\pi R)$ **29.** $A = 2(P - 110)$
31. $S = C - nR$ **33.** $n = (i - d)/(di)$ **35.** $d = (D + bc)/a$
37. $P = A/(1 + RT)$ **39.** $M = (6V - hb - hB)/(4h)$
41. $d = 2(S - na)/[n(n - 1)]$ **43.** $d = (100m - 100C + Cp)/m$

1. -7 **3.** 2   **5.** $>$ **7.** $<$ **9.** $\{x \mid x \geq 4\}$ **11.** $\{x \mid x < 1\}$

13. $\{a \mid a \leq 2\}$ **15.** $\{x \mid x \geq 2\}$ **17.** $\{z \mid z \geq 3\}$

19. $\{s \mid s < -\frac{5}{4}\}$ **21.** $\{x \mid x \leq -3\}$ **23.** $\{r \mid r > -3\}$

25. $\{x \mid x \geq 0.71\}$ **27.** $\{x \mid x < 0.16\}$ **29.** $\{y \mid 1 < y < 5\}$

31. $\{x \mid 0 \leq x \leq 5\}$ **33.** $\{x \mid 4 \geq x > -2\}$ **35.** $\{a \mid 7 > a > -5\}$

37. $\{x \mid 1 \leq x < 2\}$ **39.** $\{t \mid 1 \geq t \geq -2\}$ **41.** $\{x \mid -9 < x < -1\}$

43. $\{x \mid 3 \geq x > \frac{3}{2}\}$ **45.** $\{x \mid x > 5\} \cup \{x \mid x \leq -1\}$

47. $\{c \mid c \geq \frac{3}{11}\}$ **49.** $\{y \mid y \leq -4\} \cup \{y \mid y > -1\}$

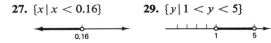

51. $\mathcal{R}$ **53.** $\{x \mid 2 \leq x \leq 3\}$ **55.** $\{x \mid x \leq -4\}$

57. $\{s \mid s \geq 1\}$ **59.** $\varnothing$ **61.** $\{x \mid x < 3\} \cup \{x \mid x > 7\}$

63. $\{x \mid x \neq 1\}$ **65.** $\{2\}$

67. $\{x \mid x < 0\} \cup \{x \mid 1 < x < 5\}$ **69.** $\{a \mid -5 < a \leq -3\} \cup \{a \mid a > 0\}$

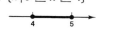   

EXERCISES 2-4, **1.** $\{4, -4\}$ **3.** $\{1, 9\}$ **5.** $\{-1, -\frac{9}{5}\}$ **7.** $\{3\}$ **9.** $\varnothing$ **11.** $\{2, -\frac{8}{9}\}$
page 59 **13.** $\{2, -2\}$ **15.** $\varnothing$ **17.** $\{2, -\frac{16}{5}\}$ **19.** $\{\frac{8}{9}\}$ **21.** $\{8, \frac{8}{5}\}$ **23.** $\{0, -2\}$
25. $\{1, \frac{1}{3}\}$ **27.** $\varnothing$ **29.** $\{1\}$ **31.** $\{4.0, -2.3\}$ **33.** $\{1.8, 2.8\}$

EXERCISES 2-5, **1.** $\{x \mid -3 < x < 3\}$ **3.** $\{x \mid 3 \geq x \geq -1\}$ **5.** $\{x \mid -\frac{1}{5} < x < 1\}$
page 63

7. $\{x \mid -\frac{5}{4} \leq x \leq \frac{7}{4}\}$ **9.** $\{x \mid -1 < x < \frac{11}{3}\}$ **11.** $\{x \mid -\frac{5}{3} \leq x \leq 2\}$

13. $\{x \mid 5 \geq x \geq 4\}$ **15.** $\{x \mid x > 2 \text{ or } x < 0\}$

17. $\{x \mid x < -\frac{1}{3} \text{ or } x > 1\}$ **19.** $\{x \mid x \leq -\frac{7}{5} \text{ or } x \geq -1\}$

21. $\{x \mid x < -\frac{1}{2} \text{ or } x > 3\}$ **23.** $\{x \mid x \leq 0 \text{ or } x \geq \frac{6}{5}\}$

25. $\{x \mid -1.5 < x < 2.8\}$ **27.** $\{x \mid x \geq 18.4 \text{ or } x \leq -81.9\}$

29. $\{x \mid x \neq -7\}$ **31.** $\varnothing$ **33.** $\Re$ **35.** $\{-2\}$ **37.** $\varnothing$ **39.** $\Re$

EXERCISES 3-1, **1.** $\frac{1}{2}r$ **3.** $f + 10$ **5.** $0.03s$ **7.** $s - 5$ **9.** 15 **11.** $46, 47$
page 69 **13.** 5 feet by $5\frac{1}{2}$ feet **15.** 20 cm, 15 cm **17.** 19 years
19. 25 years, 19 years **21.** 2774 children, 5548 adult **23.** 98

EXERCISES 3-2, **1.** 383 adult, 117 children
page 73 **3.** 4 pounds at \$3.10 per pound, 6 pounds at \$1.80 per pound
5. 2 dimes, 7 nickels **7.** 2 pounds corned beef, 2.5 pounds peppered beef
9. 2 liters **11.** 13% **13.** 8 liters **15.** 7500 pounds

EXERCISES 3-3, **1.** 120 miles **3.** 30 kilometers per hour **5.** 36 minutes **7.** 240 tons
page 78 **9.** 100 minutes **11.** 1200 wires per hour
13. Beth: 360 miles, James: 400 miles

460

15. 50 miles per hour, 62 miles per hour
17. $\frac{4}{7}$ miles per hour **19.** 2 miles **21.** 7:55 A.M. **23.** 300 hours
25. $4\frac{2}{17}$ hours $\approx$ 4 hours 7 minutes **27.** $51\frac{3}{7}$ seconds **29.** 8 hours

EXERCISES 3-4,
page 85 **1.** \$0.63, \$16.38 **3.** \$11.16 **5.** \$25.83 **7.** \$153.99 **9.** 12% **11.** 28%
13. \$19.98 **15.** \$45.00 **17.** \$175 **19.** \$285 **21.** \$1350, \$2850
23. \$704, \$1804 **25.** \$1200 at 5%, \$8800 at 8.75% **27.** \$1200
29. \$15,000 at 12%, \$30,000 at 6% **31.** 7.5%

EXERCISES 4-1,
page 99 **1, 3, 5, 7.**

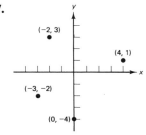

9.

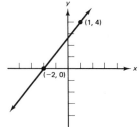

11.

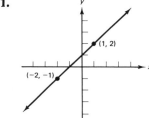

13.

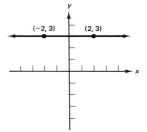

15.

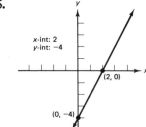

17.

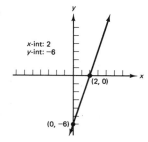

19.

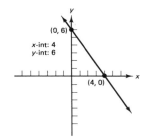

21.

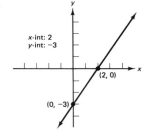

461

23.

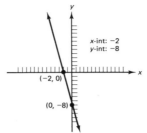

x-int: −2
y-int: −8

(−2, 0)

(0, −8)

25.

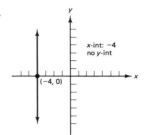

x-int: −4
no *y*-int

(−4, 0)

27.

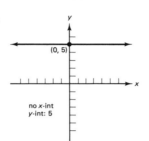

(0, 5)

no *x*-int
y-int: 5

29.

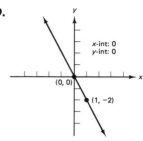

x-int: 0
y-int: 0

(0, 0)

(1, −2)

31.

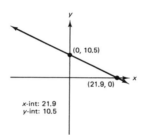

(0, 10.5)

(21.9, 0)

x-int: 21.9
y-int: 10.5

33.

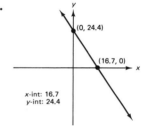

(0, 24.4)

(16.7, 0)

x-int: 16.7
y-int: 24.4

35.

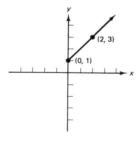

(2, 3)

(0, 1)

37.

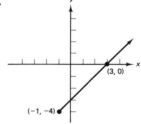

(3, 0)

(−1, −4)

39.

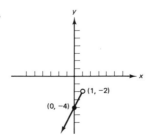

(1, −2)

(0, −4)

41.

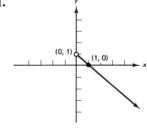

(0, 1)

(1, 0)

43.

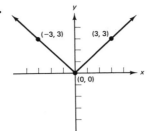

45.

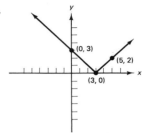

47.

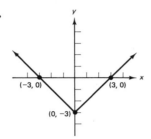

49.

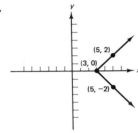

51. (a) $70 **(b)** $130

53. (a) 65 million
 (b) 80 million
 (c) 125 million
 (d) 155 million

EXERCISES 4-2,
page 106
1. $-\frac{3}{4}$ **3.** 1 **5.** 0 **7.** Does not exist **9.** 8.39
11. $m = -\frac{2}{5}$ **13.** $m = \frac{1}{2}$

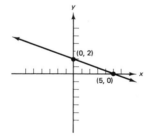

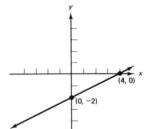

15. $m = 2$

17. $m = 2$

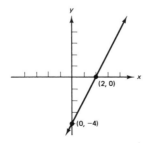

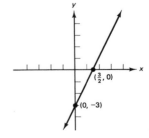

464

Answers to
Odd-Numbered
Exercises

19. $m = -\frac{1}{2}$

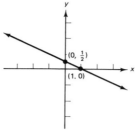

21. $m = \frac{4}{5}$

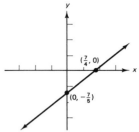

23. m does not exist

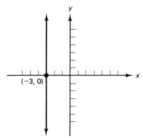

25. $m = 0$

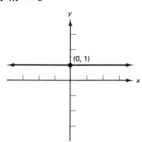

27.

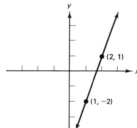

29.

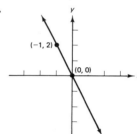

31.

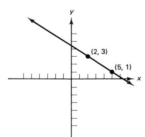

33.

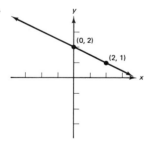

35.

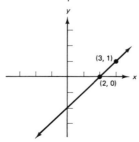

37.

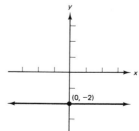

39. Perpendicular   **41.** Perpendicular   **43.** Parallel
45. Perpendicular   **47.** Neither   **49.** −4

51. The side joining $(-3, -2)$ and $(-1, 1)$ has slope $\dfrac{1 + 2}{-1 + 3} = \dfrac{3}{2}$, and the

side joining $(2, 4)$ and $(4, 7)$ has slope $\dfrac{7 - 4}{4 - 2} = \dfrac{3}{2}$, so these two sides are

parallel. The side joining $(-3, -2)$ and $(2, 4)$ has slope $\dfrac{4 + 2}{2 + 3} = \dfrac{6}{5}$, and

the side joining $(-1, 1)$ and $(4, 7)$ has slope $\dfrac{7 - 1}{4 + 1} = \dfrac{6}{5}$, so these two sides

are parallel, and the four points are vertices of a parallelogram.

EXERCISES 4-3,
page 113

1. $m = 2$, y-intercept: -6

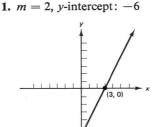

3. $m = \frac{3}{4}$, y-intercept: -3

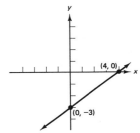

5. $m = -\frac{2}{5}$, y-intercept: 0

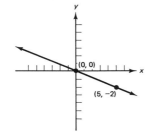

7. m is undefined,
y-intercept does not exist

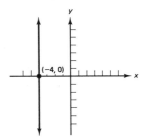

9. $y = 5x - 3$ **11.** $y = -3x + 5$ **13.** $y = 0 \cdot x + 4$ **15.** $y = -2x$
17. $y = \frac{3}{2}x + 3$ **19.** $y = 3x$ **21.** $y = -3x + 2$
23. $x = 4$, slope–intercept form is not possible   **25.** $y = x - 1$
27. $x = 4$, slope–intercept form is not possible   **29.** $3x - y = -5$
31. $3x + 5y = -6$ **33.** $x + 3y = 0$ **35.** $5x - 3y = -10$
37. The line containing $(-3, -2)$ and $(0, 4)$ has slope $m_1 = \dfrac{4 + 2}{0 + 3} = 2$. The

line containing $(0, 4)$ and $(1, 6)$ has slope $m_2 = \dfrac{6 - 4}{1 - 0} = 2$. Since both

lines have slope 2 and both contain $(0, 4)$, they are the same line, and the
given points do lie on the same straight line.
39. (a) \$15   (b) Slope equals the opposite of the monthly decrease.
41. $C = 6x + 78{,}000$

43. $m = -38.5$, y-intercept: 192   **45.** $m = -a/b$

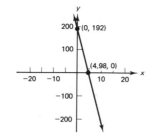

EXERCISES 4-4,
page 119

1.

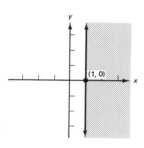

3.

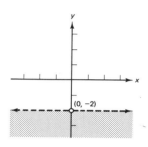

5.

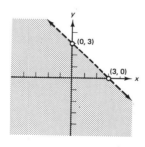

7.

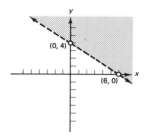

9.

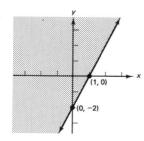

11.

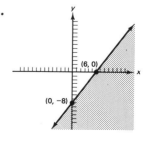

13.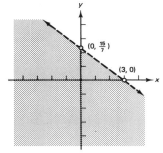

15.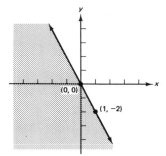

17.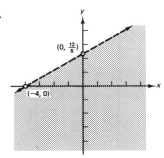

19.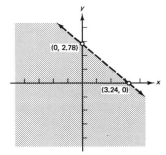

21.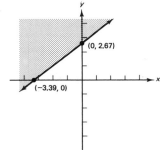

23.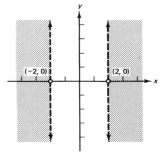

25.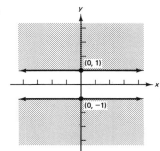

27.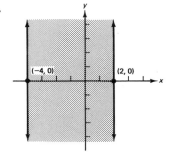

29.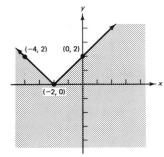

31.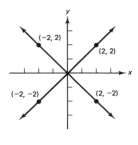

EXERCISES 5-1,
page 129

1. $\{(3, 2)\}$ **3.** $\{(4, 1)\}$ **5.** $\{(1, 1)\}$ **7.** $\{(1, 2)\}$ **9.** $\{(3, 4)\}$ **11.** $\{(3, 2)\}$
13. $\{(x, y) \mid 3x + 2y = 4\}$ **15.** $\{(1, \frac{5}{3})\}$ **17.** $\{(1, -2)\}$ **19.** $\{(-2, 3)\}$
21. $\{(6, -2)\}$ **23.** $\varnothing$ **25.** $\{(\frac{9}{2}, 3)\}$ **27.** $\{(2, -1)\}$ **29.** $\{(4, 3)\}$ **31.** $\varnothing$
33. $\{(4, 15)\}$ **35.** $\{(1, -1)\}$ **37.** $\{(2, -3)\}$ **39.** $\frac{9}{2}$ mph, $\frac{3}{2}$ mph
41. \$33,000 at 8%; \$44,000 at 9%
43. Cheap seats, \$3.50; reserved seats, \$10.50   **45.** 75,000 pounds   **47.** \$20
49. First, 55 kg; second, 275 kg   **51.** 6 hours

EXERCISES 5-2,
page 136

1. $\{(2, 1, -1)\}$ **3.** $\{(1, 3, 2)\}$ **5.** $\{(1, 0, 3)\}$ **7.** $\{(3, 1, -3)\}$
9. $\{(-1, 1, 2)\}$ **11.** $\{(5, 3, 1)\}$ **13.** $\{(3, 0, -1)\}$ **15.** $\{(6, -2, 3)\}$
17. $\{(-4, 1, 6)\}$ **19.** Dependent   **21.** Dependent
23. $a = 3, b = -2, c = 2$ **25.** 14 nickels, 22 dimes, 11 quarters
27. $A = 80°, B = 40°, C = 60°$
29. 24 pounds peanuts, 12 pounds cashews, 10 pounds pecans

EXERCISES 5-3,
page 140

1.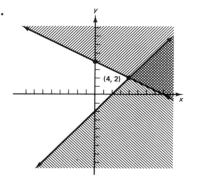

3.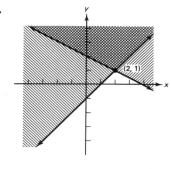

5.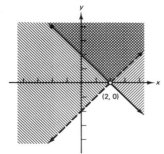

7.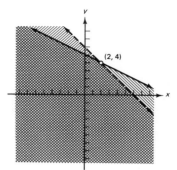

9.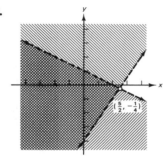

11.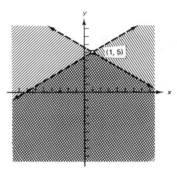

13.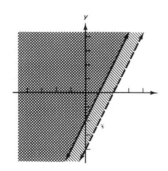

15.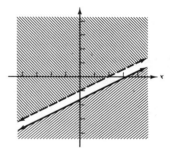

17.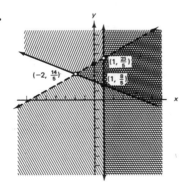

19.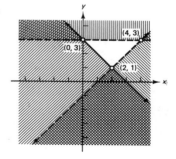

1. $2^5 = 2 \cdot 2 \cdot 2 \cdot 2 \cdot 2$; base: 2; exponent: 5
3. $x^4 = x \cdot x \cdot x \cdot x$; base: x; exponent: 4
5. $(5a)^8 = (5a)(5a)(5a)(5a)(5a)(5a)(5a)(5a)$; base $5a$; exponent: 8
7. $(x - y)^5 = (x - y)(x - y)(x - y)(x - y)(x - y)$; base: $x - y$; exponent: 5
9. $(2z)^4$; base: $2z$; exponent: 4 **11.** $(x + 3)^2$; base: $x + 3$; exponent: 2
13. 81 **15.** -1 **17.** -1 **19.** 729 **21.** 625 **23.** -64 **25.** $\frac{81}{64}$
27. $-\frac{25}{64}$ **29.** 1 **31.** 784 **33.** 16 **35.** 0 **37.** x^{12} **39.** $-12x^4$
41. $-60x^7y^3$ **43.** $(3a - 2)^5$ **45.** x^{10} **47.** a^{14} **49.** $(z + y)^{36}$
51. $-x^2/2$ **53.** $5/y^2$ **55.** $2(x - 7)^3$ **57.** 1
59. 2, if $a \neq 0$ and $b \neq 0$; undefined if either $a = 0$ or $b = 0$ **61.** 1
63. $4x^6y^2$ **65.** $-81a^{17}b^{23}$ **67.** $64/x^6$ **69.** $y^2/(9x^6)$ **71.** $1/z^2$
73. $z^9w^{14}(2x - y)^{19}/27$ **75.** 12.3 **77.** -32.8 **79.** 57.4

1. Monic quadratic binomial **3.** Quadratic trinomial **5.** Linear monomial
7. Monic quadratic binomial **9.** Cubic trinomial
11. Monic linear binomial **13.** 4 **15.** -2 **17.** 2 **19.** 11
21. $5a^3 - a + 2$ **23.** 9 **25.** 100 **27.** 49 **29.** 5.3824 **31.** $8x + 9$
33. $3x^2 + 2x - 3$ **35.** $7x^3 + 5x^2 + x - 5$
37. $-x^5 + x^4 + 3x^3 + 4x - 1$ **39.** $-4x - 3$ **41.** $-4x^2 - 4x + 4$
43. $x^3 + 9x^2 - 21x - 6$ **45.** $6x^4 - 8x^3 + 4x^2 - x + 4$ **47.** $5x$
49. $-9x^2 - x - 3$ **51.** $-x^5 - 3x^4 + 5x^2 - 13x + 32$ **53.** $17x - 11$
55. $-29x + 18$ **57.** $-5x^5 - 6x^3 + 2x - 12$ **59.** $x^2 + x$ **61.** $2x^2$
63. $-12x^2 - 6x - 9$ **65.** $-3x - 5$ **67.** $x^3 + 2x^2 - x$
69. $x^3 - 2x^2 - 3x + 2$ **71.** $5x^2 - 3$ **73.** $3x^3 - 4x^2 - 8x + 5$
75. Neither **77.** Odd **79.** Even **81.** Neither **83.** Odd

1. $32y^3 - 12y^2$ **3.** $-2a^3b^2 + 6a^2b^2$ **5.** $x^{11} - x^5 + 4x^2$
7. $3r^{10}s^2 + 3r^5s^4 - 9r^5s^2$ **9.** $x^2 + 5x + 6$ **11.** $2x^2 + 9x - 5$
13. $15x^2 - 13x + 2$ **15.** $4x^2 - 17x - 77$ **17.** $2x^3 - 5x^2 - 4x + 3$
19. $8y^4 - 4y^3 + 2y^2 - y$ **21.** $4x^4 + 7x^3 - 6x^2 - 7x + 2$
23. $2x^5 + 7x^4 - x^3 + 5x^2 - 10x + 3$ **25.** $x^2 - 9$ **27.** $4a^2 - b^2$
29. $81r^2 - 4s^2$ **31.** $1 - a^2b^2$ **33.** $x^2 + 8x + 16$ **35.** $4y^2 - 4y + 1$
37. $25x^2 - 20x + 4$ **39.** $4y^2 + 28yz + 49z^2$ **41.** $12a^3b - 6a^2b^2$
43. $a^3 - 3a^2b + 3ab^2 - b^3$ **45.** $a^3 + 3a^2b + 3ab^2 + b^3$
47. $27a^3 + 9a^2b - 3ab^2 - b^3$ **49.** $y^3 + 4y^2 - 21y$ **51.** $3 + 3a - b - ab$
53. $ac - ad - bc + bd$ **55.** $16 - 8xy + x^2y^2$ **57.** $4x^2 - 49$
59. $9 - a^2b^4$ **61.** $x^3 - 1$ **63.** $a^3 + b^3$ **65.** $x^4 - x^3 - x^2 + 1$
67. $3x^2 - 10x + 8$ **69.** $3x^4 - 2x^3 - 5x^2 + 5x + 2$ **71.** $6x^3 - 28x^2 + x$
73. $x^2 + 2xy + y^2 - 4$ **75.** $a^2 + 4b^2 + c^2 - 4ab - 2ac + 4bc$
77. $a^2 + b^2 + c^2 + d^2 + 2ab + 2ac + 2ad + 2bc + 2bd + 2cd$

1. $x \neq 0$ **3.** $x \neq 1$ **5.** $y \neq 1$ and $y \neq -2$ **7.** $y \neq \frac{1}{2}$ and $y \neq -3$
9. $a \neq b$ **11.** $8x^2 + 9x + 2$ **13.** $x^2y^4 + 3x^3y^3 - 6x^4y^2$
15. $6x + 3 + (1/x) - (8/x^2)$ **17.** $[1/(8b^4)] + [1/(4ab^3)] - [1/(2a^2b^2)]$
19. $27x^3 - 9x^2$ **21.** $5a - 5b + 2$ **23.** $a^2 + 2ab + b^2 + 8/(a + b)$
25. $x - 2 + 0/(x - 3)$ **27.** $x - 7 + 4/(x + 2)$ **29.** $3x - 1 + 2/(2x + 5)$

31. $x^2 + 5x - 3 + 3/(2x + 3)$ **33.** $y^3 + 7y^2 - 3y - 1 + 0/(4y - 3)$
35. $x^3 + 2x + 1 + 5/(x - 3)$ **37.** $2x^3 - x^2 + 3 - 5/(2x + 1)$
39. $2x^2 - 3x + 1 + 2/(x^2 - 1)$ **41.** $x - 1 - (2x + 2)/(x^2 + 2x - 1)$
43. $x^3 + x + (-5x + 2)/(2x^2 + x)$
45. $x^2 - 2x - 4 + (-9x^2 + 2)/(x^3 - 2x^2)$
47. $2x^3 - 5x^2 + 14x - 35 + 175.5/(2x + 5)$
49. $x^2 - 2x + 4 - 9/(x + 2)$ **51.** $(x/2) + (7/4) + (9/4)/(2x - 3)$
53. $(x^2/2) - (x/4) + (9/8) - (21/4)/(4x + 2)$

EXERCISES 7-1,
page 175

1. 2^3 **3.** $(-1)(2)3^2$ **5.** $(-1)23$ **7.** $2^3(3)(5)$ **9.** 5 **11.** $z^2 y$ **13.** 1
15. $x - y$ **17.** $a(3 - x)$ **19.** $xz^3(9z - 10x)$ **21.** $ax(a + x)$
23. $5x(2x + 3y)$ **25.** $x(x^2 + x + 1)$ **27.** $2xy(4x + 3y - xy)$
29. $(a - 2b)(4 - a)$ **31.** $(y^3 - 4)(2 - y)$
33. $3(a - b)^2[5(a - b) + 3]$
35. $(x - 1)[(x - 1)^2 + (x - 1) + 3] = (x - 1)(x^2 - x + 3)$
37. $(x^2 - 3x + 1)(x - 2)$
39. $(x + 2)[(x - 3) + (2x - 1)] = (x + 2)(3x - 4)$
41. $x^{68}(x^2 - 8)$ **43.** $2a^{20}b^{30}(3a^{33}b^7 - 5a^{15}b^{12} + 4)$ **45.** $x^n(1 - x)$
47. $y^{2n}(y^2 + 2)$ **49.** $x^{4n}(x^{4n} + x^{2n} + 1)$ **51.** $(-1)(y - x)$ **53.** $-a(b + a)$
55. $(-1)(xy + z)$ **57.** $-4(5 + x)$ **59.** $-2x(x - y)$ **61.** $-ab(a - b)$

EXERCISES 7-2,
page 180

1. $(a - b)(a + b)$ **3.** $(4b - a)(4b + a)$ **5.** $(7z - 9w)(7z + 9w)$
7. $(12rs - 1)(12rs + 1)$ **9.** $2(11x - 9y)(11x + 9y)$ **11.** $-3(y - 2)(y + 2)$
13. $(x + 2)^2$ **15.** $(y - 3)^2$ **17.** $(8 - x)^2$ **19.** $-1(9x + 1)^2$
21. $(2x + 3)^2$ **23.** $(2a + 5b)^2$ **25.** $(x - 1)(x^2 + x + 1)$
27. $(x + 2)(x^2 - 2x + 4)$ **29.** $(4a + 1)(16a^2 - 4a + 1)$
31. $(2a - b)(4a^2 + 2ab + b^2)$ **33.** $(2a - 3)(4a^2 + 6a + 9)$
35. $(5x + 2y)(25x^2 - 10xy + 4y^2)$ **37.** $(10 - x)(10 + x)$
39. $(2x - 3y)(2x + 3y)$ **41.** $(x + 5)^2$ **43.** $(2a + 9b)^2$
45. $(5x - 1)(25x^2 + 5x + 1)$ **47.** $-1(1 + 2y)(1 - 2y + 4y^2)$
49. Does not factor   **51.** $-1(y^2 + z^2)$ **53.** $2(4x - 5y)(4x + 5y)$
55. $5s(s + 1)^2$ **57.** $xy(y + 3)^2$ **59.** $xy(x - y)(x + y)$
61. $x^3(y + 1)(y^2 - y + 1)$ **63.** $(a - b - 1)(a - b + 1)$
65. $4(r + s)(2r - s)$ **67.** $(x - y + 2)^2$ **69.** $(abc - 1)^2$ **71.** $2x(x^2 + 3y^2)$
73. $4(3a^2 + 4)$ **75.** $(3x^n - 4)(3x^n + 4)$ **77.** $(3y^{2m} - 2)^2$
79. $(z^r - 2)(z^{2r} + 2z^r + 4)$

EXERCISES 7-3,
page 187

1. $(x + 4)(x + 2)$ **3.** $(x - 3)(x - 1)$ **5.** $(x + 4)(x - 1)$
7. $(x - 7y)(x + 2y)$ **9.** $(a + 3b)(a - b)$ **11.** $(r + 9s)(r - 7s)$
13. $(z - 19w)(z + 10w)$ **15.** $(x + 8y)(x + 9y)$ **17.** $(3x + 1)(2x - 1)$
19. $(4a - 5)(a + 1)$ **21.** $(3x + 2)(x - 7)$ **23.** $(2r - 3)(r - 1)$
25. $(3x + 2y)(3x + y)$ **27.** $(11a - b)(4a - b)$ **29.** $2(2y - 5z)(y - 2z)$
31. $(10x - 11y)(x + 2y)$ **33.** $a(a - 9)(a - 2)$ **35.** $x^3(x - 7)(x + 3)$
37. Does not factor   **39.** Does not factor   **41.** $y^2(x^2 - 3x + 4)$
43. $-1(x - 8)(x - 1)$ **45.** $-2(r + 3s)(r - 2s)$ **47.** $(3 - c)(11 - c)$
49. $3x(2x - 1)(x - 2)$ **51.** $-4x(3x - 4y)(x + 2y)$ **53.** $\{-2, 1\}$

55. $\{-4, 3\}$ **57.** $\{-3, 3\}$ **59.** $\{-\frac{5}{2}, \frac{5}{2}\}$ **61.** $\{-2\}$ **63.** $\{\frac{1}{5}\}$ **65.** $\{0, 3\}$
67. $\{0, \frac{4}{3}\}$ **69.** $\{\frac{3}{2}, 2\}$ **71.** $\{\frac{1}{3}, 1\}$ **73.** $\{-1.0, 1\}$ **75.** $\{-2, 0, 2\}$
77. $\{1, 2, 3, 4\}$

EXERCISES 7-4,
page 191

1. $(x - 1)(x + 1)(x^2 + 1)$ **3.** $(2a - 1)(2a + 1)(4a^2 + 1)$
5. $(x + 2)(x^2 - 2x + 4)(x + 1)(x^2 - x + 1)$ **7.** $(x - 1)^2(x + 1)^2$
9. $(xy - 3)(xy - 1)$ **11.** $(a - 2)^2$ **13.** $x^4(x - y)(x + y)(x^2 + y^2)$
15. $-5x(x - 1)^2$ **17.** $(x + y)(y + z)$ **19.** $(y + 3)(x + 3)$
21. $(r + 1 - s)(r + 1 + s)$ **23.** $(c + 1)(c + 1 + d)$
25. $(x + y)(x - y + 5)$ **27.** $(k - h)(k + h + 4)$ **29.** $(x - 1)(x + 1)(x + 3)$
31. $(x - 2)(x + 2)(2x + 1)$ **33.** $(x^2 + y^2 - xy)(x^2 + y^2 + xy)$
35. $(a^2 + 2 - 2a)(a^2 + 2 + 2a)$ **37.** $4(5 - 3x)(5 + 3x)$
39. $(x - 10)(x^2 + 10x + 100)$ **41.** $(z - 4)(z - 3)$
43. $(3b + 2)(2b + 1)$ **45.** $(2r - 3)^2$ **47.** $2(x - y)^2$ **49.** $4(x^2 + x + 1)$
51. $(ab - cd)(ab + cd)$ **53.** $k(k + 2)(k - 1)$ **55.** $2p(1 - 8p)$
57. $(8r - 3s)(5r + 2s)$ **59.** $(7t + 3)(9t + 2)$ **61.** $x(a + b)^2$
63. $(x - 5)(x + 5)(x + 1)^2$ **65.** $(x - y)^2(x + y)$ **67.** Does not factor
69. Does not factor **71.** $a(a + 5)(a - 4)$ **73.** $2r(r^2 + 3)(r^2 + 2)$
75. $x^{10}(3x^4 + 2)(x^2 + 1)(x + 1)(x - 1)$ **77.** $4(x^p - 5)(x^p + 2)$
79. $(3y^n - 4)(2y^n + 1)$ **81.** $(3z^{2q} - 2)(5z^{2q} + 7)$
83. $(4u^{2p} + v^{2q})(2u^p + v^q)(2u^p - v^q)$

EXERCISES 8-1,
page 201

1. $x \neq \frac{2}{3}$ **3.** $x \neq y/3$ **5.** None **7.** Equal **9.** Not equal **11.** $\frac{3}{7}$
13. -1 **15.** $12y^6/(5x^3)$ **17.** $4a^2b^2c^4/3$ **19.** $7(v - 4)^2/u^3$
21. $6(x + 2)^4/[5x(2x - 1)^2]$ **23.** $(3 + x)/(3x - 5)$ **25.** $-(y + 1)$
27. $-(x + 3)/5$ **29.** $x/(x + 4)$ **31.** $a + b$ **33.** $-(x + 4)/(x + 3)$
35. $(a + 1)/(a - 1)$ **37.** $(y - 3)/(y + 3)$ **39.** $(x - 4)/(x + 4)$
41. $1/(3p + 5q)$ **43.** $(2m - n)/(2m + 3n)$
45. $(2x - 3)(x + 3)/[(2x + 3)(x - 4)]$ **47.** $(y - 3)/(y + 1)$
49. $2/(x^2 + x + 1)$ **51.** $(2x - 3y)/(4x^2 - 6xy + 9y^2)$
53. $-(b + x)/(x + 2b)$ **55.** $12x^3y$ **57.** $15a^3(a + 1)$ **59.** $3z^2 + 10z + 3$
61. $w^2 - 10w - 56$ **63.** $6x^2 - 5x - 6$ **65.** $m^2 - n^2$
67. $2x^2 - 7xz + 3z^2$

EXERCISES 8-2,
page 206

1. $\frac{4}{15}$ **3.** $5b/3$ **5.** $20w^2/(21z)$ **7.** $1/(4xy)$ **9.** $1/(4y^2)$ **11.** $8mn$
13. $y^2/8$ **15.** $2x^6$ **17.** $4a^2/(b^2c^2)$ **19.** $5y^7/(2x^4)$ **21.** $b/3$ **23.** $3mn^2$
25. $(2x - 1)/(2x + 1)$ **27.** $3/(z + 2)$ **29.** $(x - 3)/[6(x - 2)]$
31. $(x - 2)^2/x$ **33.** $1/(x - 4)$ **35.** $\frac{1}{2}$ **37.** $x(2x - 1)/(x - 3)$
39. $(x + 1)/(x - 1)$ **41.** $-(z - 4)^2/(z - 5)^2$
43. $(y^2 + 4y - 4)/(y^2 + 2y - 1)$ **45.** x **47.** $-(2x + 3)/(3x)$
49. $(x^2 + 2x + 4)/x$ **51.** $3(1 - x)/(1 + 2x + 4x^2)$
53. $(w^2 + 1)/[(w - 1)(w + 1)]$ **55.** $(a + p)^2(q - b)/[(a - p)^2(b + q)]$
57. $-y^2(x + y)/(x - y)^2$ **59.** $-(x - y)^2/(x + y)$

EXERCISES 8-3,
page 215

1. 90 **3.** 72 **5.** $6x$ **7.** $18x^2y$ **9.** $10pqr$ **11.** $90r^2s^2t^3$
13. $75x(x-1)^2$ **15.** $3(y-2)(y+2)$ **17.** $(a-1)^2(a+1)$
19. $3w(w-2)$ **21.** $3(x^2-2x+3)(x-2)^2$ **23.** $3x^2(2x-1)(2x+1)$
25. $(2x+5)/7$ **27.** $-2/x$ **29.** 1 **31.** -1 **33.** $1/(x-3)$
35. $2/(a-1)$ **37.** $2(2a+b)/(a-b)$ **39.** $7/[2(x+3)]$
41. $(x^2-2y^2)/(2xy)$ **43.** $(5t-6)/[t(t-2)]$ **45.** $(10a-3)/(6a^2)$
47. $4/(2-x)$ **49.** $3/[(x-1)(x+2)]$ **51.** $(5z-6)/[2z(z-2)]$
53. $3/(1+x)$ **55.** $4(a+1)/(a+2)^2$ **57.** $5(p+1)/[(p-1)(p+2)]$
59. $2/[(t+3)(t+1)]$ **61.** $(2x+3)/[(x+3)(x-2)(x+2)]$
63. $-4/[(w-1)(w+3)]$ **65.** $(-m+6)/[(m-2)(m+2)]$ **67.** $5/(z-3)$
69. $3(x+y)/[(x-2y)(2x-y)]$ **71.** $2(p^2+q^2)/[(p-2q)(p-q)(p+q)]$
73. $1/(r-s)$

EXERCISES 8-4,
page 221

1. $\{-6\}$ **3.** $\{13\}$ **5.** $\{2\}$ **7.** $\{\frac{5}{4}\}$ **9.** $\varnothing$ **11.** $\{2\}$ **13.** $\{-\frac{4}{3}\}$ **15.** $\varnothing$
17. $\{5\}$ **19.** $\{0\}$ **21.** $\{-3\}$ **23.** $\{8\}$ **25.** $\varnothing$ **27.** $\{-2, 2\}$ **29.** $\{-\frac{9}{4}, \frac{9}{4}\}$
31. $\varnothing$ **33.** $\varnothing$ **35.** $\{1\}$ **37.** $\{-\frac{3}{2}\}$ **39.** $\{-9\}$ **41.** $\{3\}$ **43.** $\{\frac{5}{3}\}$
45. $\varnothing$ **47.** $\varnothing$ **49.** $\{\frac{9}{4}\}$ **51.** $\{-2\}$ **53.** $\{3\}$ **55.** $\{-\frac{5}{4}\}$ **57.** $\{\frac{3}{3}\}$
59. $\{7\}$ **61.** $\{0\}$ **63.** 60 mph **65.** 45 mph

EXERCISES 8-5,
page 228

1. $\frac{2}{3}$ **3.** 2 **5.** $\frac{6}{7}$ **7.** $\frac{3}{4}$ **9.** $\frac{15}{8}$ **11.** $1/(2xy)$ **13.** $(2x-1)/(2x+1)$
15. $(1+a)/(1-a)$ **17.** $(y+x)/(y-x)$ **19.** $-1/(ab)$ **21.** $2/(x+y)$
23. $(z+2)/2$ **25.** $1/(x+2)$ **27.** $x+1$ **29.** $(x-1)/(x+1)$
31. $z(2z+1)/(3z+1)$ **33.** $-1/x$ **35.** $(y^2-x+1)/(y^2-x-1)$

EXERCISES 9-1,
page 237

1. $-\frac{1}{9}$ **3.** $\frac{1}{9}$ **5.** $\frac{125}{8}$ **7.** 64 **9.** $\frac{1}{16}$ **11.** 1 **13.** $\frac{1}{64}$ **15.** 64 **17.** 1
19. 32 **21.** 1 **23.** $\frac{1}{64}$ **25.** $1/x^4$ **27.** $1/x^5$ **29.** $1/t^4$ **31.** $-x^8$ **33.** 1
35. x^2 **37.** $1/(32a^5)$ **39.** $1/(25t^2)$ **41.** $-5/t^2$ **43.** $1/(32x^5)$ **45.** $4a^2$
47. s^3/r^3 **49.** x^2/y^5 **51.** $t^3/(8z)$ **53.** $3x^{10}$ **55.** a/b^3 **57.** $-27y^2/x^2$
59. $25r^3/16$ **61.** $9w/8$ **63.** x^6y^{12} **65.** 1 **67.** $1/(m^6n^2)$ **69.** $2xy^6$
71. $2p^2q^5$ **73.** $1/(24p^5q^2)$ **75.** $4/(9x^8y^{12})$ **77.** $x^2/(y^6z^9)$ **79.** $1/(x^4y^4z^4)$
81. $4x^5y^2$ **83.** $\frac{5}{8}$ **85.** $(m+1)/m$ **87.** $(y+x)/(xy)$ **89.** $2x/y$
91. $y+x$ **93.** $-(x-y)^2(x+y)/(x^2y^2)$ **95.** $1/x^n$ **97.** $1/x^{n+1}$ **99.** 0.097
101. -327.784 **103.** 105.807

EXERCISES 9-2,
page 243

1. 430 **3.** 68,100 **5.** 7,920,000 **7.** 0.858 **9.** 0.00533 **11.** 0.000614
13. 5.38×10^2 **15.** 5.781×10^3 **17.** 3.175×10^8 **19.** 4.2×10^{-3}
21. 3.08×10^{-1} **23.** 8×10^{-5} **25.** 2.5×10^{-3}; 0.0025
27. 6×10^{-4}; 0.0006 **29.** 7.5×10^{-3}; 0.0075 **31.** 5×10^4; 50,000
33. 6×10^4; 60,000 **35.** 1.8×10^3; 1800 **37.** 5×10^{-6}; 0.000005
39. 4×10^{-8}; 0.00000004 **41.** 1×10^{-3}; 0.001
43. 2.5×10^{-5}; 0.000025 **45.** 2×10^3; 2000 **47.** 8×10^0; 8
49. 1.005×10^0 **51.** 1.136×10^{-2}

1. 4   **3.** $\frac{1}{3}$ **5.** $\frac{2}{3}$ **7.** $\frac{13}{12}$ **9.** $\frac{8}{7}$ **11.** 0.3   **13.** 0.4   **15.** 1.2   **17.** 0.05
19. 3   **21.** $-\frac{1}{5}$ **23.** $-\frac{1}{3}$ **25.** $\frac{10}{3}$ **27.** 0.3   **29.** -0.7 **31.** -7 **33.** 3
35. -1 **37.** 2   **39.** 0.1   **41.** $-\frac{3}{2}$ **43.** 1   **45.** -1 **47.** 3   **49.** x
51. a **53.** $3z$ **55.** $-3p^3$ **57.** $4x^4$ **59.** ab^3 **61.** a^3b^6 **63.** $-3t$
65. ab **67.** $-2xy^2$ **69.** $2mn^3$ **71.** $-1/x$ **73.** x^2/y^4 **75.** $\frac{2}{3}$ **77.** $2/b^2$
79. ab^3 **81.** x^2 **83.** xy **85.** $-m/n^2$ **87.** $-x^2/(2y^4)$ **89.** x/y^2
91. x/y^2 **93.** uv^3 **95.** $1/(x+y)$ **97.** $-4|m|$ **99.** x^2 **101.** $2/|x+1|$
103. 1.793   **105.** -1.329 **107.** 1.974

1. 12   **3.** -3 **5.** -5 **7.** $\frac{1}{5}$ **9.** $\frac{3}{4}$ **11.** $\frac{3}{2}$ **13.** $\sqrt[5]{x}$
15. $\sqrt[5]{y^3}$ or $(\sqrt[5]{y})^3$ **17.** $z^{1/4}$ **19.** $a^{5/3}$ **21.** r^3 **23.** $(x-y)^{3/5}$
25. $4\sqrt{x^3}$ or $4(\sqrt{x})^3$ **27.** $\sqrt[3]{(xy^2)^2}$ or $(\sqrt[3]{xy^2})^2$
29. $\sqrt[5]{(3m^2n)^2}$ or $(\sqrt[5]{3m^2n})^2$ **31.** 9   **33.** -9 **35.** 9   **37.** $\frac{1}{9}$ **39.** $\frac{1}{9}$
41. x **43.** y^2 **45.** r **47.** x^9 **49.** x^6 **51.** z **53.** $1/p^2$ **55.** $1/x^{1/2}$
57. x^4/y^9 **59.** $128m^{7/6}/9$ **61.** x^2y **63.** q^2/p^3 **65.** m^4/n^2 **67.** $x^{7/3}/y^{1/4}$
69. $-8t^2/(27r)$ **71.** $9p^{1/6}q^{1/3}$ **73.** y^4/x^3 **75.** 1   **77.** $16x^{4/3}/(3y)$
79. $p^{9/4}/(r^5q)$ **81.** $w^2/(48z^{2/3})$ **83.** $z^{1/3}/x^{5/8}$ **85.** $x^2/(y^2z^4)$
87. $y^{1/2}/(x^{1/5}z^3)$ **89.** $x+x^{7/3}$ **91.** $2p-6$ **93.** x^3-y^3
95. $u+2u^{1/2}v^{1/2}+v$ **97.** x^{6n} **99.** x^{n+1} **101.** x^{n-1} **103.** x^{n+6}
105. $\sqrt[6]{x}$ **107.** $\sqrt[8]{x}$ **109.** $\sqrt[10]{x}$

1. $2\sqrt{2}$ **3.** $-10\sqrt{3}$ **5.** $-3\sqrt[3]{3}$ **7.** $2\sqrt[4]{2}$ **9.** $5x\sqrt{2x}$ **11.** $2\sqrt[3]{5}$
13. $3p^2\sqrt[3]{p^2}$ **15.** $-3x\sqrt[3]{4xy^2}$ **17.** $-4(p+q)\sqrt[3]{2(p+q)^2}$
19. $2mn\sqrt[4]{5m^2n^3}$ **21.** $-x^2y\sqrt[5]{x^2y^2}$ **23.** $-2uv\sqrt[5]{u^3v^2}$ **25.** $3\sqrt{10}$
27. $-3\sqrt[3]{2}$ **29.** $(y+z)^2$ **31.** $\sqrt{2}$ **33.** $2y$ **35.** $2bc\sqrt[3]{6a^2c}$ **37.** $\frac{2}{3}\sqrt{\frac{2}{3}}$
39. $\sqrt[3]{y^4}$ **41.** $\sqrt[3]{m^2}$ **43.** $\sqrt{0.3x}$ **45.** $\sqrt[3]{4x^2y^4}$ **47.** $\sqrt[3]{2p^2q}$ **49.** $\sqrt{3}/3$
51. $\sqrt{6}/3$ **53.** $-2\sqrt{3}/3$ **55.** $\sqrt{2x}/2$ **57.** $2\sqrt{x}/x$ **59.** $-\sqrt{2x}/(2x)$
61. $2\sqrt{3rs}/(3s)$ **63.** $\sqrt{6xy}/(2y)$ **65.** $3p\sqrt{3pq}$ **67.** $\sqrt{3rs}/(2s)$ **69.** $\sqrt[3]{2}/2$
71. $\sqrt[4]{2}/2$ **73.** $\sqrt[3]{15}/3$ **75.** $\sqrt[3]{20abc^2}/(2bc)$ **77.** $\sqrt{7xz}/(49z)$
79. $pq\sqrt{q}$ **81.** $\sqrt[3]{21rs^2}/(3s)$ **83.** $\sqrt[4]{27x^2y}/(3x)$ **85.** $\sqrt{2}$ **87.** $2\sqrt{3}/3$
89. $5\sqrt{3}/6$ **91.** $\sqrt{x}$ **93.** $2\sqrt{6x}/(3x^2)$ **95.** $u^3\sqrt[3]{v}/v^2$ **97.** $p^2\sqrt[4]{q}/q^2$
99. $(a+b)\sqrt[3]{a+b}$ **101.** $2uv\sqrt{30vw}/(3w)$ **103.** $3\sqrt[4]{2}/2$
105. $x\sqrt[3]{14x^2y^2}/(7yz)$ **107.** $5y\sqrt[3]{6xyz}/(6z^2)$ **109.** $u\sqrt[4]{14v^2w^3}/(2vw)$
111. $\sqrt[4]{36m^2np^2}/(3np)$ **113.** $\sqrt{6}$ **115.** $\sqrt[3]{2x^2}$ **117.** $r^3\sqrt{r}/s$ **119.** $ab/2$

1. $7\sqrt{3}$ **3.** $8\sqrt{2}$ **5.** $4\sqrt{2}$ **7.** $7\sqrt{3}$ **9.** 0   **11.** $17\sqrt{2}$ **13.** $7\sqrt[3]{x}$
15. $\sqrt{x}+3\sqrt{y}$ **17.** $7\sqrt{5x}$ **19.** $-2y\sqrt{2x}+y\sqrt{x}$ **21.** $-22\sqrt[3]{2z}$
23. $102x\sqrt{2x}$ **25.** $34r\sqrt[3]{2rs}$ **27.** $-3xy\sqrt[3]{3xy^2}$
29. $-19xy\sqrt{3y}-2x\sqrt{2y}$ **31.** $3-\sqrt{3}$ **33.** $5+\sqrt{10}$ **35.** $3\sqrt{x}-2x$
37. -2 **39.** $x-4$ **41.** $x+2\sqrt{x}-15$ **43.** $79+20\sqrt{3}$
45. $-62-23\sqrt{6}$ **47.** $2+19\sqrt{6}$ **49.** $9\sqrt{3}+104\sqrt{2}$
51. $\sqrt{10}-3\sqrt{5}+2\sqrt{2}-6$ **53.** $\sqrt[3]{x^2}-\sqrt[3]{y^2}$ **55.** $x-y$
57. $2(\sqrt{3}-1)$ **59.** $5(\sqrt{5}+\sqrt{3})$ **61.** $10(5+2\sqrt{3})/13$
63. $-(\sqrt{2}+\sqrt{5})/3$ **65.** $(5-2\sqrt{5}-\sqrt{15}+2\sqrt{3})/2$
67. $2(1-\sqrt{x})/(1-x)$ **69.** $2(3x-\sqrt{x})/(9x-1)$

71. $(x - \sqrt{xy})/(x - y)$ **73.** $(6x + 7\sqrt{xy} + 2y)/(9x - 4y)$
75. $(4\sqrt{3} + 3\sqrt{2})/6$ **77.** $5\sqrt{6}/6$ **79.** $(12\sqrt[3]{2} - \sqrt[3]{4})/4$
81. $\sqrt{x+2}/(x+2)$ **83.** $\sqrt{x^2-1}/(x^2-1)$ **85.** $-23/[6(2 - 3\sqrt{3})]$
87. $-6/[5(\sqrt{3} - 3)]$ **89.** $4/[7\sqrt{2}]$

EXERCISES 9-7,
page 279

1. $x = 4, y = -3$ **3.** $x = 2, y = 5$ **5.** $x = -3, y = 1$
7. $x = 1, y = -2$ **9.** $10 - 3i$ **11.** $6 - 4i$ **13.** $-5 - 8i$
15. $-4 - 6i$ **17.** $-2 + 12i$ **19.** $5 + 17i$ **21.** $-31 + 22i$
23. $1 + 10i$ **25.** $2 - 3i$ **27.** $1 - 10i$ **29.** -12 **31.** 10
33. $-10 + 6i$ **35.** $12 + 20i$ **37.** $11 + 2i$ **39.** $17 + i$ **41.** $19 - 13i$
43. 41 **45.** $41i$ **47.** 13 **49.** $-25i$ **51.** $15 + 8i$ **53.** $6 + 8i$ **55.** $4i$
57. $5i\sqrt{2}$ **59.** $-3i\sqrt{5}$ **61.** $\{\pm 8i\}$ **63.** $\{\pm 2i\sqrt{5}\}$ **65.** $\{\pm 4i\sqrt{3}\}$
67. -12 **69.** 4 **71.** $-5\sqrt{3} - 3i\sqrt{5}$ **73.** $3 + 4i$ **75.** $4 - 3i$
77. $\frac{2}{5} - \frac{1}{5}i$ **79.** $\frac{1}{2} + \frac{3}{2}i$ **81.** $\frac{12}{13} + \frac{5}{13}i$ **83.** $\frac{18}{25} + \frac{1}{25}i$
85. $\frac{1}{29} - \frac{17}{29}i$ **87.** $-\frac{1}{5} + \frac{2}{5}i$ **89.** $\frac{21}{29} - \frac{20}{29}i$ **91.** i **93.** $-i$
95. 1 **97.** -1 **99.** $-i$ **101.** i

EXERCISES 10-1,
page 289

1. $\{2, 3\}$ **3.** $\{-5, 1\}$ **5.** $\{-1, \frac{1}{2}\}$ **7.** $\{-\frac{1}{2}, \frac{1}{3}\}$ **9.** $\{\pm 1\}$ **11.** $\{\pm \frac{10}{3}\}$
13. $\{0, 4\}$ **15.** $\{0, \frac{1}{3}\}$ **17.** $\{-2, 4\}$ **19.** $\{-5, \frac{3}{2}\}$ **21.** $\{0, 2\}$ **23.** $\{0, \pm 3\}$
25. $\{\pm 3\}$ **27.** $\{\pm \frac{1}{2}\}$ **29.** $\{-9, 11\}$ **31.** $\{-20, -2\}$ **33.** $\{-1, 2\}$
35. $\{-\frac{5}{3}, 1\}$ **37.** $\{-5, 1\}$ **39.** $\{0, \frac{2}{3}\}$ **41.** $\{\pm \sqrt{2}\}$ **43.** $\{1 \pm \sqrt{3}\}$
45. $\{2 \pm 4i\}$ **47.** $\{-11 \pm i\sqrt{3}\}$ **49.** $\{(1 + i)/2\}$ **51.** $\{-1.37, 4.43\}$
53. $\{-3, 7\}$ **55.** $\{2, 8\}$ **57.** $\{-1, 3\}$ **59.** $\{-2, 1\}$ **61.** $\{(-1 \pm \sqrt{3})/2\}$
63. $\{(-5 \pm 3\sqrt{5})/5\}$ **65.** $\{(1 \pm \sqrt{5})/2\}$ **67.** $\{(3 \pm \sqrt{17})/2\}$
69. $\{1 \pm 2i\}$ **71.** $\{-2 \pm 3i\}$ **73.** $\{(1 \pm i)/2\}$ **75.** $\{(-4 \pm i)/2\}$
77. $\{0, 2a\}$

EXERCISES 10-2,
page 295

1. $\{1, 6\}$ **3.** $\{-2, 3\}$ **5.** $\{\frac{2}{3}, 1\}$ **7.** $\{0, \frac{1}{3}\}$ **9.** $\{1\}$ **11.** $\{2\}$ **13.** $\{-\frac{1}{3}\}$
15. $\{\frac{3}{2}\}$ **17.** $\{1 \pm \sqrt{5}\}$ **19.** $\{(-1 \pm \sqrt{21})/2\}$ **21.** $\{(1 \pm \sqrt{5})/2\}$
23. $\{\pm \sqrt{2}\}$ **25.** $\{(-1 \pm i\sqrt{3})/2\}$ **27.** $\{1 \pm i\sqrt{6}\}$ **29.** $\{\pm i\}$
31. $\{(-1 \pm 2i)/2\}$ **33.** $\{-1, \frac{7}{3}\}$ **35.** $\{-4, 2\}$ **37.** $\{-\frac{5}{3}, -\frac{3}{2}\}$ **39.** $\{-1, 6\}$
41. $\{5\}$ **43.** $\{3\}$ **45.** $\{2, \frac{8}{3}\}$ **47.** $\{-2\}$ **49.** $\{(1 \pm \sqrt{13})/2\}$
51. $\{(-3 \pm \sqrt{21})/2\}$ **53.** $\{(-3 \pm \sqrt{6})/3\}$ **55.** $\{(-5 \pm \sqrt{17})/4\}$
57. $\{\pm 2i\}$ **59.** $\{-3 \pm i\}$ **61.** $\{1 \pm 2i\}$ **63.** $\{-3.04, 1.03\}$
65. $\{1, (-1 \pm i\sqrt{3})/2\}$ **67.** $\{-3, (3 \pm 3i\sqrt{3})/2\}$ **69.** $\{-4, 2 \pm 2i\sqrt{3}\}$
71. $\{2, -1 \pm i\sqrt{3}\}$ **73.** Two unequal real solutions
75. Two unequal real solutions **77.** One real solution **79.** One real solution
81. Two imaginary solutions **83.** Two imaginary solutions

EXERCISES 10-3,
page 298

1. 8 feet high, 10 feet long **3.** 15 feet wide, 20 feet long
5. 8 miles **7.** 44 feet **9.** 30 seconds **11.** 1 second; 2 seconds
13. 10 canoes **15.** 20 lamps **17.** $R = 15,000b - 150b^2$; 20 or 80 boats
19. 100 tons **21.** $4000 or $6000 **23.** $6000

1. $\{\pm 1, \pm 2\}$ **3.** $\{\pm\frac{1}{4}, \pm\frac{1}{2}\}$ **5.** $\{\pm\sqrt{3}, \pm\sqrt{5}\}$ **7.** $\{\pm 1, \pm\sqrt{10}/2\}$
9. $\{\pm 1, \pm i\sqrt{2}\}$ **11.** $\{\pm i, \pm 3i/2\}$ **13.** $\{-2, 6\}$ **15.** $\{-\frac{9}{2}, 2\}$
17. $\{-6, -\frac{1}{2}\}$ **19.** $\{\frac{5}{9}, \frac{5}{6}\}$ **21.** $\{-1\}$ **23.** $\{0\}$ **25.** $\{-\frac{1}{3}, \frac{1}{4}\}$ **27.** $\{-\frac{1}{5}, \frac{1}{7}\}$
29. $\{-3, 2\}$ **31.** $\{\frac{5}{3}, 2\}$ **33.** $\{-\frac{8}{5}, -\frac{1}{2}\}$ **35.** $\{-\frac{8}{49}, -\frac{8}{7}\}$
37. $\{1, -1, (-1 \pm i\sqrt{3})/2, (1 \pm i\sqrt{3})/2\}$
39. $\{-1, 2, -1 \pm i\sqrt{3}, (1 \pm i\sqrt{3})/2\}$
41. $\{\frac{1}{2}, 1, (-1 \pm i\sqrt{3})/2, (-1 \pm i\sqrt{3})/4\}$
43. $\{-\frac{1}{3}, -2, (1 \pm i\sqrt{3})/6, 1 \pm i\sqrt{3}\}$

1. 16 **3.** $\{2\}$ **5.** $\{2\}$ **7.** $\varnothing$ **9.** $\{5\}$ **11.** $\{-1\}$ **13.** $\varnothing$ **15.** $\varnothing$
17. $\{2\}$ **19.** $\{71.2\}$ **21.** $\{1\}$ **23.** $\{\frac{1}{4}\}$ **25.** $\{0, 4\}$ **27.** $\{11\}$ **29.** $\{8\}$
31. $\varnothing$ **33.** $\{-1, 4\}$ **35.** $\varnothing$ **37.** $\varnothing$ **39.** $\{\frac{25}{36}\}$ **41.** $\{1\}$ **43.** $\varnothing$
45. $\{0\}$ **47.** $\{1, 5\}$ **49.** $\{7\}$ **51.** $\{-\frac{8}{9}\}$

1. $\{x \mid -3 < x < 0\}$ **3.** $\{t \mid -1 < t < 5\}$ **5.** $\{x \mid -4 \le x \le -3\}$

7. $\{z \mid 2 \le z \le 4\}$ **9.** $\{x \mid x < -4 \text{ or } x > 2\}$ **11.** $\{y \mid y < -3 \text{ or } y > 1\}$

13. $\{x \mid x \le -5 \text{ or } x \ge -1\}$ **15.** $\{x \mid -2 \le x \le 1\}$ **17.** $\{x \mid 2 < x < 5\}$

19. $\{x \mid x < -5 \text{ or } x > -1\}$ **21.** $\{a \mid -2 \le a \le 2\}$ **23.** $\{x \mid x \le -1 \text{ or } x \ge 1\}$

25. $\{r \mid 0 \le r \le 4\}$ **27.** $\{x \mid x < -\frac{1}{2} \text{ or } x > 0\}$ **29.** $\{x \mid -2 < x < 0\}$

31. $\{z \mid -1 \le z < 3\}$ **33.** $\{t \mid t < -1 \text{ or } t > 1\}$ **35.** $\{y \mid y \le -3 \text{ or } y > 1\}$

37. $\{x \mid -3 < x < 0\}$ **39.** $\{x \mid -1 < x < 1\}$ **41.** $\{x \mid 2 < x < 3\}$

43. $\{x \mid x \le -2 \text{ or } 0 \le x \le 1\}$ **45.** $\{x \mid 0 < x < \frac{1}{2} \text{ or } x > \frac{2}{3}\}$

47. $\{x \mid -3 \le x \le -1 \text{ or } x \ge 1\}$ **49.** $\{x \mid x < -1, x \ne -2\}$

51. $\{r \mid r < -2 \text{ or } 0 < r < 1\}$

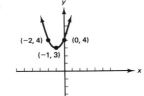

53. $\{y \mid y \le -7 \text{ or } -1 < y < 3\}$

55. $\{x \mid -3 < x < 1\}$

57. $\{p \mid -1 < p < 2\}$

59. $\{x \mid x < 5\}$ **61.** $\{t \mid 1 \le t < 2\}$

63. $\{y \mid y \le -\frac{10}{3} \text{ or } y > -3\}$

65. $\{x \mid 0 \le x < 2 \text{ or } x \ge 3\}$

67. $\{x \mid x < -3 \text{ or } -2 < x < -1\}$

EXERCISES 11-1,
page 324

1.

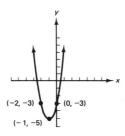

3.

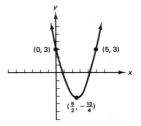

5.

7.

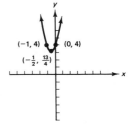

9.

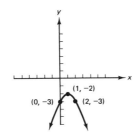

11.

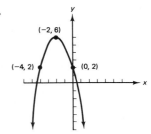

13.

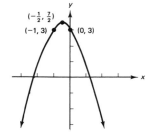

15.

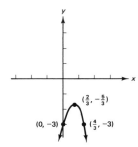

17.

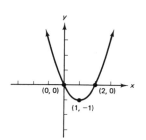

19.

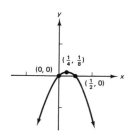

21.

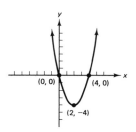

23.

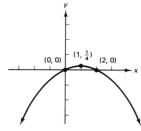

25.

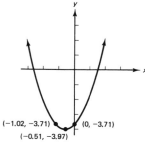

27.

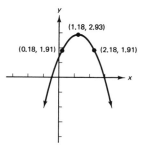

29.

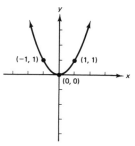

31.

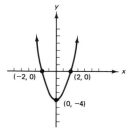

33.

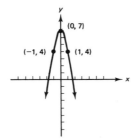

35.

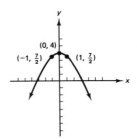

37.

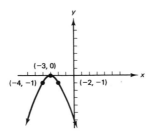

39.

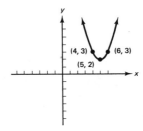

41.

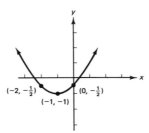

43.

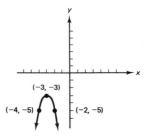

45.

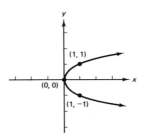

47.

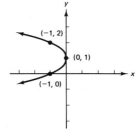

49.

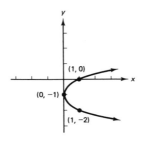

51.

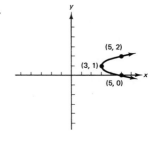

480

53.

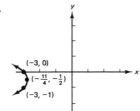

55.

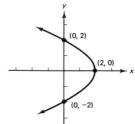

57.

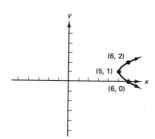

59.

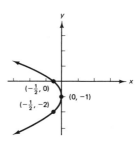

EXERCISES 11-2,
page 332

1. 5 **3.** 6 **5.** 5 **7.** $5\sqrt{2}$ **9.** $10\sqrt{2}$ **11.** 7.3

13.

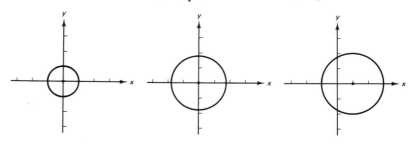

$d_1 = \sqrt{34}$ Since
$d_2 = \sqrt{34}$
$d_3 = \sqrt{68}$ $(d_3)^2 = (d_1)^2 + (d_2)^2,$

then $(1, 3), (-4, 0),$ and $(4, -2)$
are vertices of a right triangle.

15. $3\sqrt{10} + 5\sqrt{2}$ **17.** 46 **19.** $x^2 + y^2 = 9$ **21.** $x^2 + y^2 = \frac{16}{9}$
23. $(x - 2)^2 + (y + 1)^2 = 4$ **25.** $(x + 5)^2 + (y - 4)^2 = 16$
27. $(x + 1)^2 + (y + 2)^2 = \frac{9}{25}$ **29.** $(x - 2)^2 + y^2 = \frac{9}{16}$
31. $(x + 1)^2 + (y + 1)^2 = 2$ **33.** $x^2 + y^2 = 3$
35. Center: $(0, 0);$ **37.** Center: $(0, 0);$ **39.** Center: $(1, 0);$
    $r = 1$ $r = \sqrt{3}$ $r = 2$

41. Center: $(0, -3)$;
$\quad r = 3$

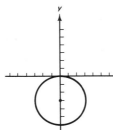

43. Center: $(1, 3)$;
$\quad r = 1$

45. Center: $(-3, -3)$;
$\quad r = 3$

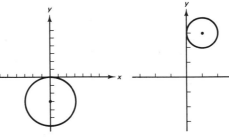

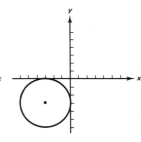

47. Center: $(-1, 0)$;
$\quad r = 1$

49. Center: $(-1, 1)$;
$\quad r = \sqrt{2}$

51. Center: $(1, -3)$;
$\quad r = 4$

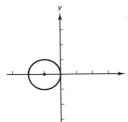

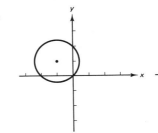

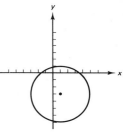

53. Center: $(-0.7, -1.8)$; $r = 1.9$ **55.** $\{(0, 0)\}$ **57.** $\{(-2, 1)\}$

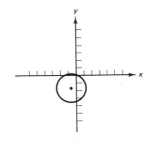

59. $\varnothing$ **61.** $\varnothing$

EXERCISES 11-3,
page 340

1.

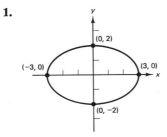

(0, 2)
(−3, 0)   (3, 0)
(0, −2)

3.

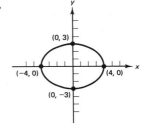

(0, 3)
(−4, 0)   (4, 0)
(0, −3)

5.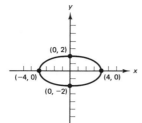

7.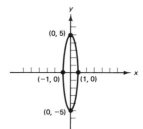

9.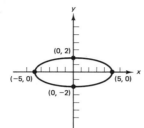

11.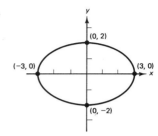

13.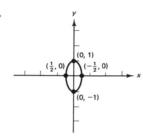

15.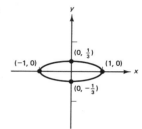

17.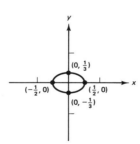

19.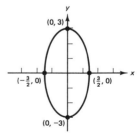

21.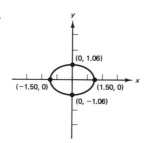

23. $\{(0, 0)\}$ **25.** $\varnothing$

27.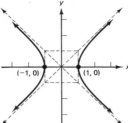

29.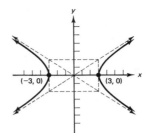

31.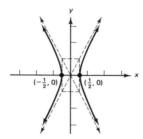

33.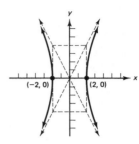

35.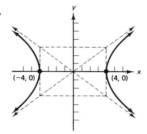

37.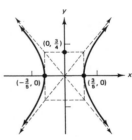

39.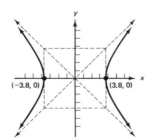

41.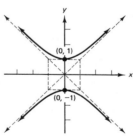

43.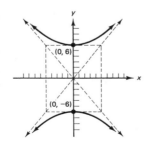

45.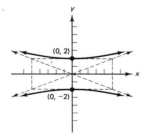

47.

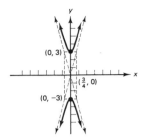

49.

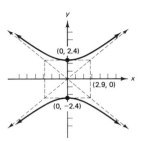

51.

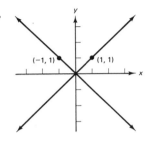

53.

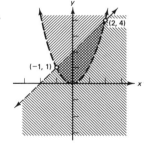

EXERCISES 11-4,
page 348

1. Straight line   **3.** Parabola   **5.** Parabola   **7.** Circle   **9.** Hyperbola
11. Ellipse   **13.** Hyperbola   **15.** Circle   **17.** Circle   **19.** Ellipse
21. Hyperbola   **23.** $\{(-1, 2\sqrt{2}), (-1, -2\sqrt{2})\}$ **25.** $\{(-1, 4)\}$
27. $\{(2, 4), (-1, 1)\}$ **29.** $\{(-2, 5), (1, 2)\}$ **31.** $\{(4, 3), (3, 4)\}$
33. $\{(2, 0), (-2, 0)\}$ **35.** $\{(1.1, -2.3)\}$ **37.** $\{(2, 3), (-2, -3), (3, 2), (-3, -2)\}$
39. $\{(1, 1), (1, -1), (-1, 1), (-1, -1)\}$ **41.** $\{(1, 2), (1, -2), (-1, 2), (-1, -2)\}$
43. $\{(3, 4), (3, -4), (-3, 4), (-3, -4)\}$ **45.** $\{(7, 5), (7, -5), (-7, 5), (-7, -5)\}$
47. $\{(2.0, -0.3), (-2.0, -0.3)\}$

49.

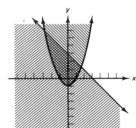

51.

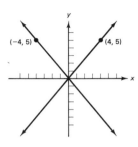

53.

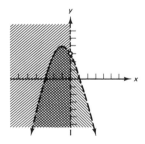

55.

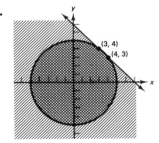

57.

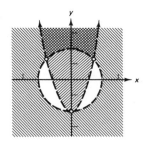

59.

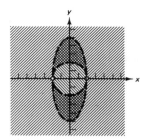

61.

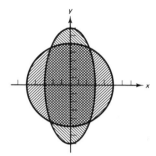

63.

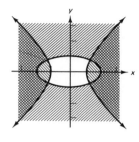

65.

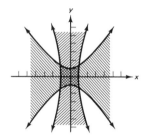

EXERCISES 12-1,
page 358

1. $D = \{-2, 0, 2\}$, $R = \{1, 5\}$, a function
3. $D = \{-1, 3\}$, $R = \{-2, 0, 2\}$, not a function
5. $D = \{1, 3, 5\}$, $R = \{2, 4, 6\}$, a function
7. $D = \{-2, 1, 2\}$, $R = \{2, -1, -2\}$, a function
9. $D = \{0, 2, 4, 6\}$, $R = \{1\}$, a function
11. $D = \{1\}$, $R = \{0, 2, 4, 6\}$, not a function   **13.** $D = \Re$, $R = \Re$
15. $D = \Re$, $R = \Re$ **17.** $D = \Re$, $R = \Re$ **19.** $D = \Re$, $R = \{y \,|\, y \geq 0\}$
21. $D = \Re$, $R = \{y \,|\, y \geq 1\}$ **23.** $D = \{x \,|\, x \neq 0\}$, $R = \{y \,|\, y \neq 0\}$
25. $D = \{x \,|\, x \neq -4\}$, $R = \{y \,|\, y \neq 0\}$ **27.** $D = \{x \,|\, x \geq 0\}$, $R = \{y \,|\, y \geq 0\}$
29. $D = \{x \,|\, x \geq -1\}$, $R = \Re$ **31.** $D = \Re$, $R = \Re$ **33.** Function
35. Not a function   **37.** Not a function   **39.** Not a function   **41.** Function
43. Not a function

45. $D = \Re$, $R = \{y \mid y \geq -1\}$

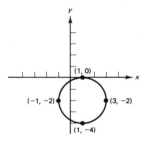

47. $D = \{x \mid x \geq 1\}$, $R = \Re$

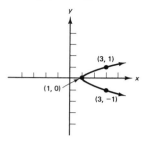

49. $D = \{x \mid -1 \leq x \leq 3\}$
$R = \{y \mid -4 \leq y \leq 0\}$

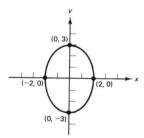

51. $D = \{x \mid -7 \leq x \leq 3\}$
$R = \{y \mid -2 \leq y \leq 8\}$

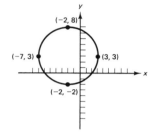

53. $D = \{x \mid -2 \leq x \leq 2\}$
$R = \{y \mid -3 \leq y \leq 3\}$

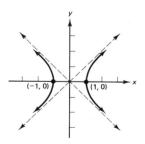

55. $D = \{x \mid -5 \leq x \leq 5\}$
$R = \{y \mid -2 \leq y \leq 2\}$

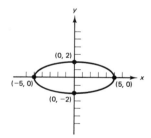

57. $D = \{x \mid x \leq -1 \text{ or } x \geq 1\}$
$R = \Re$

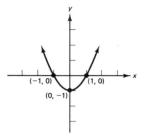

59. $D = \Re$
$R = \{y \mid y \leq -3 \text{ or } y \geq 3\}$

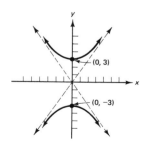

61. $D = \Re$
$R = \{y \mid y \geq 0\}$

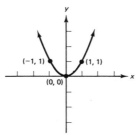

63. $D = \{x \mid x \geq -1\}$
$R = \Re$

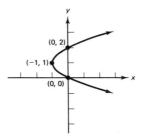

65. $D = \{x \mid -4 \leq x \leq 4\}$
$R = \{y \mid -4 \leq y \leq 4\}$

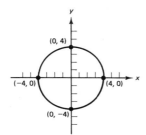

67. $D = \{x \mid x \geq 1 \text{ or } x \leq -1\}$
$R = \Re$

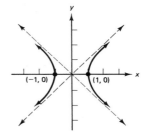

69. $D = \Re$
$R = \{y \mid y \geq 0\}$

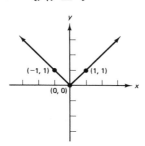

71. $D = \Re, R = \Re$

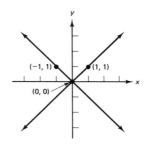

73. $D = \Re, R = \{y \mid y \geq 0\}$

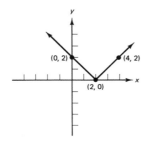

75. $D = \Re, R = \{y \mid y \leq 2\}$

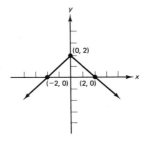

1. $-\frac{2}{3}$ **3.** 0 **5.** Undefined **7.** 28.8 **9.** -21 **11.** -9 **13.** -10
15. -9 **17.** -60 **19.** -5 **21.** $8 - a^2 - b^2$ **23.** $4 - a^2 - 2ab - b^2$
25. $x^2 + 4x - 12$ **27.** $8x - 4x^2$ **29:** $-2hx - h^2$ **31.** $-h - 6$
33. $-16x^2 + 64x - 60$ **35.** 1.264 **37.** 3 **39.** -2 **41.** $2x + h$
43. $4x + 2h$ **45.** $5 + 2x + h$ **47.** $6x + 2 + 3h$

1. $h^{-1} = \{(2, -4), (1, -1), (4, 2), (9, 7)\}$, both h and h^{-1} are functions
3. $g^{-1} = \{(0, -1), (3, 1), (3, 5), (8, 6)\}$, g is a function, g^{-1} is not
5. $t^{-1} = \{(2, 1), (4, 3), (3, 4), (5, 1)\}$, t^{-1} is a function, t is not
7. $y = x - 2$, both f and f^{-1} are functions
9. $y = \frac{1}{3}x + 3$, both s and s^{-1} are functions
11. $y = x^2 - 3$, for $x \geq 0$; both t and t^{-1} are functions
13. $y = (1 - x)^2/4$, for $x \leq 1$; both p and p^{-1} are functions
15. $y = \pm\sqrt{1 - x^2}$, for $-1 \leq x \leq 0$; g is a function, g^{-1} is not
17. $y = \pm\sqrt{16 - x^2}/3$, for $0 \leq x \leq 4$; r is a function, r^{-1} is not
19. $2y + x = 6$, both are functions   **21.** $4y - x = 0$, both are functions

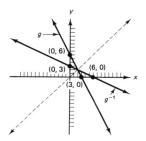

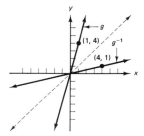

23. $3y + 2x = 12$, both are functions

25. $y = x^2 + 2$, g^{-1} is a function, g is not

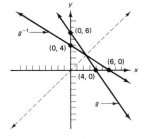

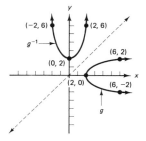

27. $y^2 = 25 - x^2$, neither is a function

29. $y^2/9 + x^2/16 = 1$, neither is a function

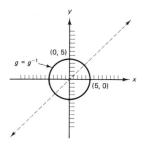

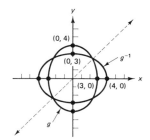

489

31. $4y^2 + 9x^2 = 36$,
neither is a function

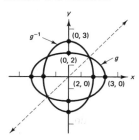

33. $x = (y + 1)^2 + 2$, g is
a function, g^{-1} is not

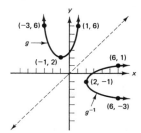

35. $x = 1 + |y|$, g is a
function, g^{-1} is not

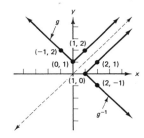

37. $f(x) = 3x - 9$, $f^{-1}(x) = \frac{1}{3}x + 3$,
$f^{-1}(f(x)) = \frac{1}{3}f(x) + 3 = \frac{1}{3}(3x - 9) + 3 = x - 3 + 3 = x$,
$f(f^{-1}(x)) = 3f^{-1}(x) - 9 = 3(\frac{1}{3}x + 3) - 9 = x + 9 - 9 = x$
39. $f(x) = -\frac{1}{2}x + 2$, $f^{-1}(x) = -2x + 4$,
$f^{-1}(f(x)) = -2f(x) + 4 = -2(-\frac{1}{2}x + 2) + 4 = x - 4 + 4 = x$,
$f(f^{-1}(x)) = -\frac{1}{2}f^{-1}(x) + 2 = -\frac{1}{2}(-2x + 4) + 2 = x - 2 + 2 = x$
41. $f(x) = -\frac{3}{5}x + 3$, $f^{-1}(x) = -\frac{5}{3}x + 5$,
$f^{-1}(f(x)) = -\frac{5}{3}f(x) + 5 = -\frac{5}{3}(-\frac{3}{5}x + 3) + 5 = x - 5 + 5 = x$,
$f(f^{-1}(x)) = -\frac{3}{5}f^{-1}(x) + 3 = -\frac{3}{5}(-\frac{5}{3}x + 5) + 3 = x - 3 + 3 = x$
43. $f(x) = \frac{4}{5}x - 2$, $f^{-1}(x) = \frac{5}{4}x + \frac{5}{2}$,
$f^{-1}(f(x)) = \frac{5}{4}f(x) + \frac{5}{2} = \frac{5}{4}(\frac{4}{5}x - 2) + \frac{5}{2} = x - \frac{5}{2} + \frac{5}{2} = x$,
$f(f^{-1}(x)) = \frac{4}{5}f^{-1}(x) - 2 = \frac{4}{5}(\frac{5}{4}x + \frac{5}{2}) - 2 = x + 2 - 2 = x$
45. $f(x) = 0.5x + 1.5$, $f^{-1}(x) = 2x - 3$,
$f^{-1}(f(x)) = 2f(x) - 3 = 2(0.5x + 1.5) - 3 = x + 3 - 3 = x$,
$f(f^{-1}(x)) = 0.5f^{-1}(x) + 1.5 = 0.5(2x - 3) + 1.5 = x - 1.5 + 1.5 = x$

EXERCISES 12-4,
page 374

1. 35　**3.** 75　**5.** −12　**7.** −27　**9.** −6　**11.** 100 pounds
13. 32 pounds per square inch　**15.** 81 feet　**17.** Approximately 145 pounds
19. 10 ohms　**21.** 1800 pounds

1. 1   **3.** $\frac{11}{18}$ **5.** 3

7.

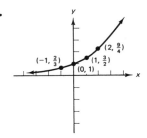

9.

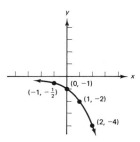

11.

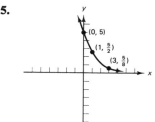

13.

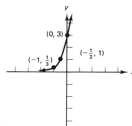

15.

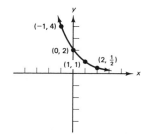

17.

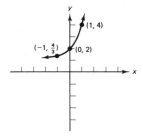

19.

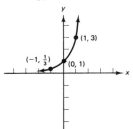

21.

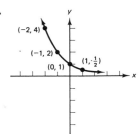

23. $\{4\}$ **25.** $\{-3\}$ **27.** $\{0\}$ **29.** $\{-2\}$ **31.** $\{\frac{5}{4}\}$ **33.** $\{-\frac{3}{2}\}$ **35.** $\{-\frac{1}{8}\}$

37. $\{-\frac{7}{2}\}$ **39.** $\{-\frac{5}{3}\}$ **41.**

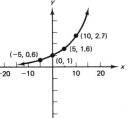

43.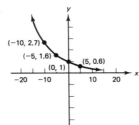

45.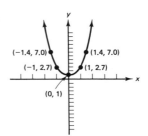

47. 95.97 mg

EXERCISES 13-2,
page 387

1. $\log_2 8 = 3$ **3.** $\log_3 243 = 5$ **5.** $\log_2 \frac{1}{16} = -4$ **7.** $\log_{12} 1 = 0$
9. $\log_{10} 0.1 = -1$ **11.** $\log_9 \frac{1}{27} = -\frac{3}{2}$ **13.** $7 = 7^1$ **15.** $1 = 4^0$
17. $27 = 3^3$ **19.** $\frac{1}{125} = 5^{-3}$ **21.** $\frac{4}{9} = (\frac{3}{2})^{-2}$ **23.** $2 = 4^{1/2}$
25. $\frac{1}{2} = (16)^{-1/4}$

27.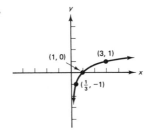

29.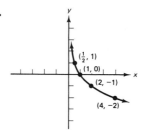

31.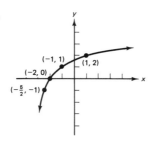

33.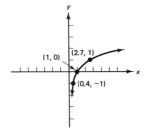

35. $y = 4$ **37.** $y = 0$ **39.** $y = 1$ **41.** $y = 2$ **43.** $y = \frac{1}{2}$ **45.** $x = 125$
47. $x = 49$ **49.** $x = 3$ **51.** $x = \frac{1}{2}$ **53.** $a = 5$ **55.** $a = \frac{1}{6}$ **57.** $a = 81$
59. $a = \frac{1}{512}$

EXERCISES 13-3,
page 392

1. $2 \log_a x$ **3.** $\frac{1}{3} \log_a x$ **5.** $\frac{2}{3} \log_a x$ **7.** $2 \log_a x + 3 \log_a y$
9. $\log_a x + \log_a y - \log_a z$ **11.** $2 \log_a x - \log_a z - 3 \log_a y$
13. $2 \log_a x - \log_a y - \frac{1}{2} \log_a z$ **15.** $\frac{5}{3} \log_a x + \log_a y + 2 \log_a z$
17. $\frac{1}{2} \log_a x + \frac{3}{2} \log_a y - \frac{5}{2} \log_a z$ **19.** $\log_a x^3 y^2$ **21.** $\log_a x y^4 z^3$
23. $\log_a \frac{x^2}{\sqrt[3]{z^4}}$ **25.** $\log_a \sqrt{\frac{x^2 z^4}{y^3}}$ **27.** $\log_a (9xy^2/2)$ **29.** $\log_a 4x^4 yz^6$

31. 1.1461   **33.** 2.2922   **35.** 0.6338   **37.** 0.1003   **39.** -0.5441
41. 1.0882   **43.** $\{\frac{9}{4}\}$ **45.** $\{24\}$ **47.** $\{\frac{12}{7}\}$ **49.** $\{2\}$ **51.** $\{2\}$ **53.** $\{\frac{5}{3}\}$
55. $\{\frac{10}{3}\}$

EXERCISES 13-4,
page 399

1. 0.8149   **3.** 3.6149   **5.** $8.8965 - 10$ **7.** 2   **9.** -1 **11.** 1.3927
13. 3.7910   **15.** $8.6513 - 10$ **17.** $6.5024 - 10$ **19.** 7.64   **21.** 45.7
23. 1720   **25.** 327   **27.** 1000   **29.** 0.984   **31.** 0.00586   **33.** 0.0145
35. 2.6934   **37.** $9.5601 - 10$ **39.** 4.7055   **41.** $8.8383 - 10$ **43.** 5.874
45. 317.5   **47.** 0.7843   **49.** 29,180   **51.** 0.01982   **53.** 2.6934631
55. 0.78433212

EXERCISES 13-5,
page 404

1. 159   **3.** 53.9   **5.** 0.0202   **7.** 0.351   **9.** 4210   **11.** 4.42   **13.** 20.6
15. 0.735   **17.** 0.511   **19.** 0.152   **21.** 809   **23.** 10,300   **25.** 4.51
27. 2.93   **29.** 9.09   **31.** 2556   **33.** 4.463   **35.** 28.41   **37.** 4.5129574
39. 28.408729

EXERCISES 13-6,
page 409

1. $\{5.210\}$ **3.** $\{2.172\}$ **5.** $\{1.322\}$ **7.** $\{\pm 1.473\}$ **9.** $\{3.115\}$ **11.** $\{8.328\}$
13. 1.771   **15.** 0.6861   **17.** 2.124   **19.** 2.215   **21.** 4.987   **23.** 3.694
25. 1.61   **27.** 3.71   **29.** 2.303   **31.** 1.85   **33.** 3.63   **35.** 4.91
37. $\{1.1314021\}$ **39.** $\{4.0369526\}$ **41.** $\{2.0595186\}$
43. 2.65 miles above sea level   **45.** 8 years   **47.** 4,120 years
49. 1.26×10^{-8} mole per liter   **51.** $x = 10(\ln P - \ln 1000)$
53. $n = (\log A - \log 3000)/\log 1.10$ **55.** $x = (\ln 50 - \ln A)/0.000124$

EXERCISES 14-1,
page 416

1. 1, 2, 3   **3.** 1, 4, 9, 16   **5.** $\frac{2}{3}, \frac{3}{4}, \frac{4}{5}, \frac{5}{6}, \frac{6}{7}$ **7.** $-1, \frac{1}{2}, -\frac{1}{3}, \frac{1}{4}, -\frac{1}{5}, \frac{1}{6}, -\frac{1}{7}$
9. 0.72, 0.52, 0.37   **11.** $\frac{1}{2}, \frac{2}{3}, \frac{3}{4}, \frac{4}{5}, \frac{5}{6}$ **13.** $\frac{1}{2}, \frac{1}{5}, \frac{1}{10}, \frac{1}{17}, \frac{1}{26}$ **15.** $2, \frac{3}{2}, \frac{4}{3}, \frac{5}{4}, \frac{6}{5}$
17. 3, 7, 11, 15, 19   **19.** $-1, 2, -3, 4, -5$ **21.** $-\frac{1}{2}, \frac{1}{4}, -\frac{1}{8}, \frac{1}{16}, -\frac{1}{32}$
23. $-9, -11, -13, -15; 1 - 2n$ **25.** $50, -60, 70, -80; (-1)^{n+1}10n$
27. $\frac{5}{2}, \frac{6}{2}, \frac{7}{2}, \frac{8}{2}; n/2$ **29.** $\frac{7}{5}, \frac{8}{6}, \frac{9}{7}, \frac{10}{8}; (n + 2)/n$ **31.** $x^5, x^6, x^7, x^8; x^n$
33. $2 - 5x, 2 + 6x, 2 - 7x, 2 + 8x; 2 + (-1)^n nx$ **35.** 12   **37.** 68
39. -106 **41.** $11x + 2$ **43.** -3 **45.** x^2
47. $3, -3, 3, -3, 3$ **49.** $-3, 1, 4, 15, 221$
51. $S_7 = \frac{1}{2} + \frac{2}{3} + \frac{3}{4} + \frac{4}{5} + \frac{5}{6} + \frac{6}{7} + \frac{7}{8} = \frac{1479}{280}$
53. $S_5 = -1 + 2 - 3 + 4 - 5 = -3$ **55.** $S_4 = 2 + 4 + 8 + 16 = 30$
57. $S_3 = \frac{1}{2} + \frac{4}{5} + \frac{9}{10} = \frac{11}{5}$ **59.** $1 + 4 + 7 + 10 = 22$
61. $2 + 6 + 12 + 20 + 30 + 42 = 112$ **63.** $\frac{1}{2} + 1 + \frac{5}{4} + \frac{7}{5} + \frac{3}{2} = \frac{113}{20}$
65. $24 + 35 + 48 = 107$ **67.** $2 + 2 + 2 + 2 = 8$
69. $0.4750 + 0.5227 + 0.5503 + 0.5684 + 0.5811 = 2.698$
71. $\sum\limits_{n=1}^{4} (3n - 2)$ **73.** $\sum\limits_{n=1}^{5} (-2)^n$ **75.** $\sum\limits_{n=1}^{3} x^n/n$ **77.** $\sum\limits_{n=1}^{3} 9$

EXERCISES 14-2,
page 423

1. Arithmetic, $d = 3$, $a_n = 3n + 2$ **3.** Not arithmetic   **5.** Not arithmetic
7. Arithmetic, $d = -\frac{1}{2}$, $a_n = 3 - \frac{1}{2}n$ **9.** -16 **11.** $-\frac{49}{2}$ **13.** -44.40
15. -32 **17.** 100   **19.** 151   **21.** 122   **23.** -4 **25.** 66   **27.** 135

29. −33 **31.** 1830 **33.** −434 **35.** 45 **37.** 183 **39.** 744.315 **41.** 35
43. 2550 **45.** 99 **47.** 39 **49.** 5050 **51.** 9

EXERCISES 14-3,
page 429

1. Geometric, $r = -1$, $a_n = (-1)^{n+1}$ **3.** Not geometric **5.** Not geometric
7. Geometric, $r = 1.01$, $a_n = (1.01)^n$ **9.** −189 **11.** $-\frac{64}{729}$ **13.** −1024
15. $\frac{1}{20}$ **17.** 729 **19.** $(1.03)^6$ **21.** 10.09 **23.** −84 **25.** $\frac{13}{27}$ **27.** 84
29. $-\frac{11}{2}$ **31.** 510 **33.** $\frac{80}{81}$ **35.** 5440 **37.** $\frac{104}{3125}$ **39.** $\frac{2}{3}$ **41.** 20
43. Does not exist **45.** Does not exist **47.** $-\frac{2}{5}$ **49.** $\frac{2}{5}$
51. Does not exist **53.** Does not exist **55.** $\frac{1}{3}$ **57.** $\frac{5}{9}$ **59.** $\frac{7}{33}$ **61.** $\frac{8}{11}$
63. $\frac{5}{27}$ ft **65.** 32,000

EXERCISES 14-4,
page 436

1. 6 **3.** 1 **5.** 2520 **7.** 10 **9.** 10 **11.** 7 **13.** 4 **15.** 56 **17.** 10
19. 28 **21.** 9 **23.** 1 **25.** $x^5 + 5x^4 + 10x^3 + 10x^2 + 5x + 1$
27. $x^4 - 8x^3 + 24x^2 - 32x + 16$ **29.** $x^3 + 6x^2y + 12xy^2 + 8y^3$
31. $128x^7 - 224x^6y + 168x^5y^2 - 70x^4y^3 + \frac{35}{2}x^3y^4 - \frac{21}{8}x^2y^5 + \frac{7}{32}xy^6$
    $- \frac{1}{128}y^7$
33. $64r^3 + 144r^2s + 108rs^2 + 27s^3$ **35.** $16 - 96z + 216z^2 - 216z^3 + 81z^4$
37. $\frac{1}{81}a^4 - \frac{2}{27}a^3 + \frac{1}{6}a^2 - \frac{1}{6}a + \frac{1}{16}$
39. $\frac{1}{1024}x^5 + \frac{5}{768}x^4y + \frac{5}{288}x^3y^2 + \frac{5}{216}x^2y^3 + \frac{5}{324}xy^4 + \frac{1}{243}y^5$
41. $a^{12} - 6a^{10}b^2 + 15a^8b^4 - 20a^6b^6 + 15a^4b^8 - 6a^2b^{10} + b^{12}$
43. $x^{16} - 4x^{12}y^3 + 6x^8y^6 - 4x^4y^9 + y^{12}$ **45.** $x^9 - 9x^8y + 36x^7y^2$
47. $256x^8 - 1024x^7y + 1792x^6y^2$ **49.** $x^{20} + 20x^{19} + 190x^{18}$
51. $z^{23} - 46z^{22} + 1012z^{21}$ **53.** $45x^{16}y^2$ **55.** $-120x^3y^{14}$ **57.** $-1365x^4$
59. $13xy^{12}$ **61.** $-y^{19}$ **63.** $-721.62x^{14}$ **65.** 1.072135 **67.** 0.922744
69. We have $\binom{n}{r} = \frac{n!}{(n-r)!\,r!}$ and

$$\binom{n}{n-r} = \frac{n!}{(n-(n-r))!\,(n-r)!} = \frac{n!}{r!\,(n-r)!} = \binom{n}{r}$$

71. $\binom{n}{r-1} + \binom{n}{r} = \frac{n!}{(n-r+1)!\,(r-1)!} + \frac{n!}{(n-r)!\,r!}$

$$= \frac{n!}{(n-r+1)(n-r)!\,(r-1)!} + \frac{n!}{(n-r)!\,(r)(r-1)!}$$

$$= \frac{(r)(n!) + (n-r+1)(n!)}{(n-r+1)!\,r!} = \frac{(r+n-r+1)(n!)}{(n+1-r)!\,r!}$$

$$= \frac{(n+1)n!}{(n+1-r)!\,r!} = \frac{(n+1)!}{(n+1-r)!\,r!} = \binom{n+1}{r}$$

EXERCISES A-1,
page 444

1. −1 **3.** −7 **5.** 0 **7.** −17 **9.** 0 **11.** 44 **13.** $\{(1, -4)\}$
15. $\{(0, 7)\}$ **17.** $\{(-5, 2)\}$ **19.** $\{(0, 0)\}$ **21.** $\{(2, -5)\}$ **23.** $\{(3, 0)\}$
25. $\{(\frac{27}{26}, -\frac{4}{13})\}$ **27.** $\{(-\frac{64}{41}, -\frac{34}{41})\}$ **29.** $\{(31, \frac{73}{3})\}$ **31.** $\{(-\frac{27}{40}, -\frac{43}{20})\}$
33. Inconsistent **35.** Inconsistent **37.** Inconsistent **39.** Dependent
41. Dependent

EXERCISES A-2,
page 448

1. −18 **3.** 12 **5.** 16 **7.** 0 **9.** 73 **11.** −75 **13.** $\{(2, 1, 1)\}$
15. $\{(-2, 2, -2)\}$ **17.** $\{(7, 3, 1)\}$ **19.** $\{(0, 0, 1)\}$ **21.** $\{(1, -2, -1)\}$
23. $\{(-3, -2, 5)\}$ **25.** Inconsistent **27.** Inconsistent **29.** Dependent
31. Dependent

Index

495

Components, 352
Compound inequalities, 10, 53
Conic sections, 343, 344
Conjugate:
    of a binomial, 269
    of a complex number, 277
Constant, 5, 37
    term, 37
Constant of variation, 373
Coordinates, 8, 91
Counting numbers, 2
Cramer's Rule, 442, 447

Degree:
    of a polynomial, 152
    of a term, 151
Denominator, 29
Dependent system, 125, 129, 135, 442, 447
Dependent variable, 93
Determinant, 441
    expansion, 445
    order, 441
Difference, 22
    common, 419
    of two cubes, 178
    of two squares, 160, 176
Direct variation, 370
Discriminant, 294
Disjoint sets, 4
Distance formula, 328
Distributive property, 14
Dividend, 29, 166
Division:
    of complex numbers, 278
    of polynomials, 164, 166
    of real numbers, 28
Divisor, 29, 166
Domain:
    of a relation, 352
    of a variable, 5
Double negative property, 16

Element of a set, 1
Elimination method, 126, 134, 346
Ellipse, 334
    foci, 334
    standard equation, 335
    vertices, 334
Empty set, 4
Equality, 7
    of complex numbers, 273
    of fractions, 32
    of ordered pairs, 352
    properties, 7
    of rational expressions, 197
    of sets, 3
Equations, 37
    absolute value, 56

    equivalent, 39
    exponential, 405
    first-degree, 39
    involving radicals, 307
    linear, 39
    literal, 45
    logarithmic, 391
    quadratic, 185
    quadratic in form, 301
Equivalent inequalities, 49
Equivalent systems of equations, 128
Exponent:
    definition, 143, 233, 253
    laws of, 148, 234
Exponential, 143
    equation, 405
    form, 254
    function, 379
Expressions:
    algebraic, 40
    radical, 259
    rational, 195
Extraneous solutions, 220, 304

Factor, 27
Factorial, 433
Factoring by grouping, 190
Field properties, 14
Finite sequence, 413
Finite set, 2
Focus:
    of an ellipse, 334
    of a hyperbola, 336, 339
FOIL method, 159
Fractions:
    complex, 224
    equality of, 32
    in lowest terms, 32, 198
    operations with, 32
    simple, 224
    single, 224
Function, 356
    exponential, 379
    logarithmic, 385
    notation, 360
    one-to-one, 367
Fundamental principle of fractions, 197

Geometric progression, 425
Graph:
    of an equation, 93
    of an inequality, 116
    of a number, 8
    of an ordered pair, 92
    of a relation, 354
    of a system, 139
Graphical method of a solution of a
    linear system, 123

Greater than, 8
Greatest common factor, 172

Half-line, 98
Half-plane, 117
Hierarchy of operations, 30
Horizontal line, 97
Hyperbola, 336
    asymptotes, 337, 339
    foci, 336, 339
    standard equation, 337, 339
    vertices, 337, 339

Identity elements, 14
Imaginary number, 273
Imaginary part of a complex number, 273
Inconsistent system, 125, 129 135, 442, 447
Independent system, 125
Independent variable, 93
Index:
    of a radical, 247
    of summation, 415
Inequalities:
    absolute value, 60
    compound, 10, 53
    equivalent, 49
    linear, 116
    quadratic, 309
Infinite sequence, 413
Infinite set, 2
Integers, 2
Interest:
    compound, 409
    simple, 83
Intersection of sets, 4
Interval:
    closed, 11
    open, 11
Inverse of a relation, 363
Irrational numbers, 2

Joint variation, 372

Laws of exponents, 148, 234
Least common denominator, 213
Least common multiple, 212
Less than, 8
Like sign, 21
Like terms, 38
Linear depreciation, 114
Linear equation, 93
    point-slope form, 111
    slope-intercept form, 110
    standard form, 93

497

Four-Place Common Logarithms (Base 10)

N	0	1	2	3	4	5	6	7	8	9
1.0	.0000	.0043	.0086	.0128	.0170	.0212	.0253	.0294	.0334	.0374
1.1	.0414	.0453	.0492	.0531	.0569	.0607	.0645	.0682	.0719	.0755
1.2	.0792	.0828	.0864	.0899	.0934	.0969	.1004	.1038	.1072	.1106
1.3	.1139	.1173	.1206	.1239	.1271	.1303	.1335	.1367	.1399	.1430
1.4	.1461	.1492	.1523	.1553	.1584	.1614	.1644	.1673	.1703	.1732
1.5	.1761	.1790	.1818	.1847	.1875	.1903	.1931	.1959	.1987	.2014
1.6	.2041	.2068	.2095	.2122	.2148	.2175	.2201	.2227	.2253	.2279
1.7	.2304	.2330	.2355	.2380	.2405	.2430	.2455	.2480	.2504	.2529
1.8	.2553	.2577	.2601	.2625	.2648	.2672	.2695	.2718	.2742	.2765
1.9	.2788	.2810	.2833	.2856	.2878	.2900	.2923	.2945	.2967	.2989
2.0	.3010	.3032	.3054	.3075	.3096	.3118	.3139	.3160	.3181	.3201
2.1	.3222	.3243	.3263	.3284	.3304	.3324	.3345	.3365	.3385	.3404
2.2	.3424	.3444	.3464	.3483	.3502	.3522	.3541	.3560	.3579	.3598
2.3	.3617	.3636	.3655	.3674	.3692	.3711	.3729	.3747	.3766	.3784
2.4	.3802	.3820	.3838	.3856	.3874	.3892	.3909	.3927	.3945	.3962
2.5	.3979	.3997	.4014	.4031	.4048	.4065	.4082	.4099	.4116	.4133
2.6	.4150	.4166	.4183	.4200	.4216	.4232	.4249	.4265	.4281	.4298
2.7	.4314	.4330	.4346	.4362	.4378	.4393	.4409	.4425	.4440	.4456
2.8	.4472	.4487	.4502	.4518	.4533	.4548	.4564	.4579	.4594	.4609
2.9	.4624	.4639	.4654	.4669	.4683	.4698	.4713	.4728	.4742	.4757
3.0	.4771	.4786	.4800	.4814	.4829	.4843	.4857	.4871	.4886	.4900
3.1	.4914	.4928	.4942	.4955	.4969	.4983	.4997	.5011	.5024	.5038
3.2	.5051	.5065	.5079	.5092	.5105	.5119	.5132	.5145	.5159	.5172
3.3	.5185	.5198	.5211	.5224	.5237	.5250	.5263	.5276	.5289	.5302
3.4	.5315	.5328	.5340	.5353	.5366	.5378	.5391	.5403	.5416	.5428
3.5	.5441	.5453	.5465	.5478	.5490	.5502	.5514	.5527	.5539	.5551
3.6	.5563	.5575	.5587	.5599	.5611	.5623	.5635	.5647	.5658	.5670
3.7	.5682	.5694	.5705	.5717	.5729	.5740	.5752	.5763	.5775	.5786
3.8	.5798	.5809	.5821	.5832	.5843	.5855	.5866	.5877	.5888	.5899
3.9	.5911	.5922	.5933	.5944	.5955	.5966	.5977	.5988	.5999	.6010
4.0	.6021	.6031	.6042	.6053	.6064	.6075	.6085	.6096	.6107	.6117
4.1	.6128	.6138	.6149	.6160	.6170	.6180	.6191	.6201	.6212	.6222
4.2	.6232	.6243	.6253	.6263	.6274	.6284	.6294	.6304	.6314	.6325
4.3	.6335	.6345	.6355	.6365	.6375	.6385	.6395	.6405	.6415	.6425
4.4	.6435	.6444	.6454	.6464	.6474	.6484	.6493	.6503	.6513	.6522
4.5	.6532	.6542	.6551	.6561	.6571	.6580	.6590	.6599	.6609	.6618
4.6	.6628	.6637	.6646	.6656	.6665	.6675	.6684	.6693	.6702	.6712
4.7	.6721	.6730	.6739	.6749	.6758	.6767	.6776	.6785	.6794	.6803
4.8	.6812	.6821	.6830	.6839	.6848	.6857	.6866	.6875	.6884	.6893
4.9	.6902	.6911	.6920	.6928	.6937	.6946	.6955	.6964	.6972	.6981
5.0	.6990	.6998	.7007	.7016	.7024	.7033	.7042	.7050	.7059	.7067
5.1	.7076	.7084	.7093	.7101	.7110	.7118	.7126	.7135	.7143	.7152
5.2	.7160	.7168	.7177	.7185	.7193	.7202	.7210	.7218	.7226	.7235
5.3	.7243	.7251	.7259	.7267	.7275	.7284	.7292	.7300	.7308	.7316
5.4	.7324	.7332	.7340	.7348	.7356	.7364	.7372	.7380	.7388	.7396
N	0	1	2	3	4	5	6	7	8	9